A GUIDE TO
RELIGIOUS
MINISTRIES

For Catholic Men and Women

"There are many ministries but one Lord."
- Paul to the Corinthians

Published by
The Catholic News Publishing Company

Cover photo courtesy of the Crosiers

A Guide to Religious Ministries
For Catholic Men and Women

1996 Edition

Publisher: Myles Ridder

Editor: Mari Castrovilla

Associate Editor: Jeanne Marie Healy

Assistant Editor: Janette Aiello

Advertising Manager: Thomas M. White

Assistant Advertising Manager: Virginia Spiridigliozzi

Account Executives: Stephen Brehl
Chris Kristensen
Robert Tennyson
Peter Tirro
Gary Williams

Art Director: Melvin Harris

Production Supervisor: Patricia Korn

Production: Amy Shapiro
Olga Sotire

Circulation: Annette Miserendino
Gloria Nallan

$5.00 per copy

International Standard Book Number (ISBN) Number 0-910635-31-5

For information, write to Catholic News Publishing Company, 210 North Avenue, New Rochelle, NY 10801. (914) 632-1220

PRINTED IN THE UNITED STATES OF AMERICA.

Table of Contents

Section A

Section B

A man can have no greater love
then to lay down his life for his friends.
You are my friends,
if you do what I command you.
I shall not call you servants any more,
because a servant does not know
his master's business;
I call you friends,
because I have made known to you
everything I have learnt from my Father.
You did not choose me,
no, I chose you;
and I commissioned you
to go out and to bear fruit,
fruit that will last;
and then the Father will give you
anything you ask him in my name.
What I command you
is to love one another.

John 15:13-17

The Call to Religious Ministry

The decision to dedicate one's life to the service of God is a much different one than that of choosing a career.

Selecting a career field – in most instances, an occupation – involves decisions about education, personal skills, preferred job characteristics, desired income levels, and often geographic location. The decision impacts on family life, personal interests and long-range goals. A career decision answers the question, "What will I do with my life?"

The more important decision in life is, "What will I be?" Everyone is called to be with God, whether married, single, clergy or religious. Some people are called to be with God as a priest, brother or sister. It is not a calling to do anything, go anywhere, or become something. It is a call to a state of being.

Commitment

Commitment to a religious career often flows from one's whole being. This commitment is rooted in the core of inner being, and it affects and involves the totality of the person. If one is concerned only with external manifestations in a religious career, then that person is making more difficult the acquisition of a deep and inner sense of fulfillment and personal growth to be found in the pursuit of such a career. Religious careers enable persons to express adequately the being they are. External witness touches generally on the demonstrative; it manifests the character of a religious career, but this alone is not enough. When one attempts to justify the rationale and the validity of a religious career in today's society, there is a strong tendency to remain engrossed merely in its circumferential elements such as service to people in need, improvement of the qualitative aspects of human inter-action, and the like. However, there is an important pivotal point from which all other elements spring and in which they are resolved. Some are wont to falsify, more or less seriously, the essence of religious careers and their total ecclesiastical dimension, each time they view an external, visible element as the living core of a religious career. The act of feeding the poor or comforting the sorrowful is not in itself the living core of a religious career. When one makes an external manifestation the essence of a religious career, this essence is simply too shallow to subsist.

What then constitutes the being and validity of religious careers, and makes them relevant today? The same mystery that made religious careers relevant in the past and inspired men and women to dedicate their lives is present today.

At this point one may ask: "What then is the essence of a religious career? What constitutes the state of a religious career choice? What makes it what it is? What gives it its particular identity?' That by which the very being of a religious career as a state of life can be distinguished from another state is very simple; it is a very specific consecration, a consecration often contrary to popular belief. It is not a ritual of a self-gift to the Almighty, nor is it man-made. For it is ultimately the Almighty who consecrates and invests a person in a religious career.

The Need for Prayer

Individuals will be aided in a religious career choice through a life of prayer. The prayerful religious person is able to recognize in other persons their intrinsic worth and potential for good. The religious career person is seeking to make visible what is hidden, and touchable that which is unreachable. Prayer, the great power of grace, will help eliminate a behavior which is contradictory to the great principles upon which moral decisions are made. A person embarking upon his career choice must be personally convinced that prayer and faith give purpose and meaning to this life. In this way, that individual can hope to instill the value of religion in others and manifest this value in him or herself.

The style of religious careers for the years ahead may be determined not so much by those who strive toward this ideal and this goal, as by those others who do not. The audience, the object of activity, the persons whom those in religious careers seek to serve, will determine the mode of relevant activity. The religious is, therefore, challenged to tailor the message to the audience, to communicate on terms which the target group can relate to.

Pursuing a religious career involves a great deal of work. The individual pursuing such a career should pray, seeking to know and gain direction in this regard. The individual should think. The power of the mind may be marshalled to think life through. Reading is important.

Learn about the particular organization or denomination in which you anticipate pursuing a religious career. "Knowledge is power," said Socrates. The more one knows about a subject the better one can handle it. The more an individual knows about the particulars of the specific religious career of interest, the better that individual will be to handle the necessary decisions involved. Talking it over with persons whom we admire and trust, perhaps someone already living a religious career, can be most helpful. If an individual wants to pursue a religious career, then that individual should do the things early that will aid him or her in such a pursuit.

Personal Characteristics Needed

Those pursuing religious careers should possess self-confidence, the ability to make hard decisions, and a willingness to accept criticism and listen to people. They must be tactful, have personal drive and ambition, but yet be tolerant of other's shortcomings. An ability to work under pressure, to live up to moral standards, and ability to get along with others are the ideals to be striven for.

Whatever the denomination or the particular ministry within that denomination, certain predispositions are generally looked for. Good health is desirable as the religious career makes demands upon a person's physical constitution. A good and healthy body aids in the development of a good and healthy mind. A good mind is necessary, as one must be able to combine the spiritual and the intellectual. One must be able to relate meaningfully the theoretical dimensions of religion to the world of practical realities. The well-trained religious career person is thus aided in thinking – deeply – about important things that are necessary parts of the religious career. The supernatural rests upon the natural, and the religious career person must grow naturally and intellectually.

Choosing a life's career can be one of the most exciting, demanding and yet perplexing experiences one is likely to face. The choice made will determine to a large extent the focus of one's energy, attention, and efforts. That career choice offers the possibility of a genuine measure of satisfaction and fulfillment. That career choice will determine the nature of the role and the contribution the individual will make in today's complex and often impersonal world.

A person pursuing a religious career is also a servant, someone doing something, and doing this in a committed way. Giving oneself to the service of others makes that individual a symbol of concern not only in word and deed, but in all of that person's life as a totality of a human person.

Religious career persons are not supermen or wonder women. They are men and women living among men and women – sometimes wounded men and women whose mission is to heal. Often religious career persons are stammering men and women whose mission is to preach; they are often weak persons whose mission is to conquer evil or console.

Surely the religious career offers the reward of full joy and peace for the individual award of the call, honest in service, and giving freely for others. Incomparable happiness realized in deep personal fulfillment is often the reward for those individuals who have pursued a life's career in religion.

People caring about people can be manifested in the pursuit of a religious career. Religious careers offer opportunities, challenges, and lifestyles for a role of influence in molding the outlook and design of tomorrow's world.

Discerning a Vocation

What is a vocation? How does one discover it? Where does it lead? What has it to do with free will?

These are puzzling questions to anyone considering what to do with the rest of his or her life. Ordinarily they are questions facing a person in teen-age or early adult life but many reoccur at other times. Many women face such questions after their family is raised. A married man, his wife and family may very suddenly face the unexpected possibility of a vocation to the permanent diaconate.

Vocation, of course, does not refer exclusively to religious life or priesthood: these, however, are so unusual that frequently in Catholic circles they alone are called "vocations."

The word vocation means "a calling"; it is extremely important to keep this in mind. We are called by the providential arrangement of circumstances, by the realities of life, by our own limitations and potential, by the historical moment, and by our own emotional, intellectual and psychological needs. If one follows the teachings of the Fathers and Doctors of the Church in this regard, one comes to accept that a vocation is found in the providential arrangement of significant aspects of life and also by the grace which we receive to make the best of these situations.

The loss of awareness of this providential aspect of vocation is one of the things that leads to an immense insecurity in modern life. When people forget the divine and providential element in their lives, they try desperately to find a course through life like a man on a raft with neither rudder nor map.

It has been a consistent belief of Christians that the Lord gives each of us something to do, some work to perform that makes us an essential link in the chain of life. Parents pass on life to their children and, by good examples, instruction, encouragement and membership in the Church contribute to their growth in the life of grace.

Single people, including priests and religious, pass on life in a psychological and spiritual way by being a help to those around them. This passing on of life and grace is the ultimate vocation of the Christian. Cardinal Newman sums it up well when he says:

"I am a link in a chain, a bond of connection between persons. God has not created me for nothing. I shall do good; I shall do His work; I shall be an angel of peace, a preacher of truth, in my own place, while not intending it, if I do but keep His commandments."

The idea of God's special purpose in our life is what gives the individual an awareness of his dignity and importance. Among great numbers of people we frequently feel like atoms, little and meaningless. As Newman says, "God has created me to do Him some definite service: He has committed some work to me which He has not committed to another. I have my mission. I may never know it in this life, but I shall be told it in the next."

If one is convinced of being singled out by the Lord for some work in this life, how is that work discovered? First, we quietly discern or observe our potentials and needs and try to fit them into what we can do best. Often in such a process, God leads us by interior inspiration, by an attraction to do this or that work, to follow this person, or to marry that one. We will be attracted by a certain kind of work because it fits our capacity and because it opens to us possibilities of security or fulfillment.

The need for inspiration and divine guidance in any vocation cannot be overstressed. The Lord has led many people in mysterious ways. The only Trappist ever canonized, St. Benedict Joseph Labre, was led to his strange vocation not to be a monk but to be a hobo, by going from one monastery to another, vainly trying to fit in because of psychological difficulties.

St. Catherine of Genoa found herself married to the wrong man as a result of a political alliance of her family. Faced with such a situation, she relied on God and spent the rest of her life working with her husband in the service of the poor and sick.

From such experiences at least two rules emerge for discovering one's vocation. Both come from Holy Scripture: "If today you hear His voice, harden not your heart" (Psalm 95); and Our Lord's own admonition: "He who puts his hand to the plow and looks back is not worthy of the kingdom of heaven."

Apostolic Work

The apostolic works performed by priests, brothers and sisters – also called ministries – encompass a wide range of skills and services. Some religious communities specialize in one or a few types of ministries – health care or teaching, for example – while others have members engaged in many different ministries. The work itself does not constitute a religious "career" but is simply the expression of a religious person's dedication to God.

Some of the most common ministries are:

Parish Work

Home Missions

Child Care

Chaplaincies

Prisons

Hospitals

Military

Education

Administration

Teaching

Coaching

Social Work

Campus Ministry

Foreign Missions

Religious Education

Communications

Film

TV & Radio

Newspapers

Magazines

Books

Health Care

Hospitals

Nursing Homes

Visiting Nursing

Counseling

Students

Families

Adults

Spiritual Direction

Retreats

Inner City Work

The Contemplative Life

The need for contemplation and the hunger for a deeper prayer life are factors in the Church and the world. Contemplative communities do not engage in active ministries. They live in seclusion, apart from the world, their daily lives taken up in prayer and meditation. In order to sustain themselves, members perform such tasks as farming, translation, artistic work, vestment design and production, computer typesetting and publication of a national magazine on prayer.

The Formation Process

There are several stages involved in the process of becoming a
religious priest, brother or sister. Each community has its own rules,
but they generally involve four stages.

The first stage involves the time period when a prospective candidate becomes acquainted with the community, and the community with
the candidate. This may occur as early as high school or college years.
The vocation director is usually the point of contact between the individual and the community. The candidate may spend short
periods of time living with the community in order to become
exposed to the spiritual and community life of the members.

The second stage begins when the candidate is ready for a more formal relationship. This usually involves full-time residency with the
community and gives the candidate the opportunity to experience the
life of the community. During this stage, the candidate may be continuing outside studies or employment. This stage may last one or two
years.

The next stage occurs when the candidate enters the community's
novitiate. This marks the official entry into the community and is a
period of one to two years during which the novice spends time in
prayer and study to learn more about his or her relationship with God,
with the community, and with the decision to make a lifetime commitment to the religious life.

The final stage involves temporary promises. Depending on the community, promises of poverty, celibacy and obedience may be taken for
periods of one to three years at a time, up to nine years. Final vows may
be taken after as few as three years of temporary promises.

Men studying for the priesthood also must complete seminary training in theology before ordination.

The Diocesan Priesthood

A candidate for the diocesan priesthood must complete four years
of high school, four years of college and four and a half years of
graduate study in theology before ordination. A candidate may attend
the college of his choice or a minor seminary to complete studies for his
bachelor's degree. Graduate study is completed in residence at a major
seminary.

Most diocesan priests serve in parishes. Many others serve as
teachers, administrators, military chaplains, hospital chaplains,
prison chaplains, and other ministries.

Educational Requirements

The works performed by members of the religious community usually dictate the amount of education that is required. A bachelor's degree is usually required, and often a master's. Many priests, brothers and sisters earn a doctorate degree, particularly those involved in education.

Most communities prefer candidates to complete their bachelor's degree before entering, although some communities will accept candidates after high school graduation. There are also some high school seminaries for candidates who are prepared to consider a vocation at that age. Some dioceses conduct preparatory seminaries for high school boys who are interested in the priesthood. Generally, the boys live at home while going to school.

Contact A Vocation Director

The people who are in the best position to be helpful to those who are considering a religious career or lay ministry are vocation directors. Their job is to counsel men and women about the requirements for this kind of commitment. They can suggest reading materials, arrange for visitations, answer questions and provide the spiritual guidance candidates need.

Every diocese has a vocation director who can provide information about religious communities for men and women as well as information about the diocesan priesthood. A complete list of diocesan vocation directors is included in one of the following sections in this book.

Most religious communities have one or more members assigned to vocations. Their names, addresses and phone numbers are included in their community's respective listing in the following sections of this book.

RELIGIOUS MINISTRIES

PROFILES

The following pages contain more complete information about the history, charisms, entrance requirements and ministries of many religious communities for men and women.

Use the convenient postcards found in the front of this directory to request additional information.

We are a community of missionaries whose aim is to continue the work of Jesus Christ among the peoples of Africa. We do this in several ways:

- Announcing the Gospel
- Formation of local clergy and lay leaders
- Education
- Caring for refugees and immigrants of African origin

Today we are more than 1,100 members working in 13 countries of Africa. We seek to share the life and history of the people we are sent to evangelize and to assist them in their efforts to build God's kingdom.

Our lifestyle is marked by prayer, sharing, simplicity and hospitality intended to offer joyful and attractive witness to a Gospel centered life.

The needs of evangelization in Africa are immense.

Your presence will make a difference.

SMA

Society of African Missions

Rev. Brendan Darcy, S.M.A.
S.M.A. Fathers
256 North Manor Circle
Takoma Park, MD 20912
Phone: 301-891-2037
FAX NO.: 301-270-6370.

ALEXIAN BROTHERS

A tradition of healing for more than six centuries.

"THE LOVE OF CHRIST COMPELS US" are more than just words. This is the guiding principal which has given strength to all Alexian Brothers.

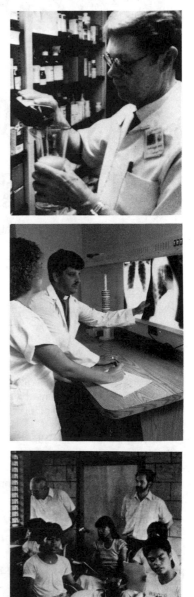

The Alexian Brothers are a Religious Congregation of vowed Catholic laymen, whose tradition reaches back over 650 years to medieval Europe, ministering to the sick, dying, unwanted, and especially known for their care of the dying during the dreaded "Black Plague" which ravished Europe in 1347. Today, the Brothers continue to be guided by Gospel values and witness the Healing Christ in accord with their charism and Mission Statement.

"Strengthened by community, prayer, commitment to the poor and the legacy of our founders, and in partnership with others, we Alexian Brothers witness the Healing Christ by a holistic approach to promoting health, and caring for the sick, dying, aged, and unwanted of all socioeconomic levels, outside as well as within our Health Care Systems."

Brothers are involved in all aspects of health care which may include areas such as: nursing administration, laboratory, x-ray, dietary, physiotherapy, social work, pastoral care, purchasing, and many more. Important is combining the professional expertise and the Alexian tradition of caring for others in the spirit of Christ.

The Alexian Brothers operate general hospitals, life care centers, nursing homes and a residential home for persons with AIDS, as well as a mission in the Philippines. They are also engaged in similar health care activities in Ireland, England, Germany, Belgium and Africa.

In addition to serving mankind in a variety of ways, the priorities of community, prayer and vowed life serves as a source of strength and spiritual development for each Brother.

The Alexian story continues and times and ways may change, but the spirit of love, compassion and sacrifice remains. There is still much to do.

Write for more information to:

DIRECTOR OF VOCATIONS
600 Alexian Way
Elk Grove Village, Illinois 60007
708/981-3625

Send one of the postcards in this book for more information.

The Augustinians

Restless Hearts... Searching Minds... Passionate Lives

It was over 1600 years ago that the man we know as St. Augustine of Hippo wrote in the story of his life "My God, I lost you and was miserable: I found you and was happy, and now I love to praise you. I write this for other sinners like myself, so that they too may find peace."

In 388, Augustine and others who shared his vision and hope established a community where they sought to live the Christian ideal of the Acts of the Apostles.

Today the Order of Saint Augustine continues to search for God through prayer, sharing life intimately with one another in community, and placing ourselves at the service of the needs of the Church whatever they may be, wherever we find ourselves. The uniqueness of Augustinian life is found in the attempt to bring prayer, community, and ministry into such a dynamic balance and harmony that the energy of God's grace is unleashed for the purpose of love.

If you, like Saint Augustine, have a heart restless with a desire to know the Lord, a mind curious enough to join others in a common search for truth and wisdom, and if your life is ready for passionate service of God and all people, then perhaps it is time for you to explore the challenge and opportunity of life as an Augustinian.

For more information contact:

AUGUSTINIAN VOCATION OFFICE
Tolentine Center
20300 Governors Highway
Olympia Fields, IL 60461-1081
(708) 748-9500

Use the convenient Augustinian Friars postcard in this book for more information.

St. Anselm's Abbey
Washington, D.C.

St. Benedict writes that a monk is primarily someone who seeks God. How do we at St. Anselm's do this? First, we seek God by daily communal liturgical prayer, meditation, and spiritual reading.

Also, we seek God through a life together marked by simplicity, celibacy, obedience, stability in this one community, and loving service to one another.

We also seek the Lord in the many kinds of work we do: teaching (at the middle school, high school, or university level), hospitality and retreat work, pastoral assistance in local parishes, spiritual direction, and the numerous tasks necessary for maintaining the abbey's buildings and grounds.

If you would like to learn more about our community, please contact:

The Director of Vocations
St. Anselm's Abbey
4501 South Dakota Ave., N.E.
Washington, D.C. 20017
(202) 269-2300

Send one of the postcards in this book for more information

WHY A MONK AT SAINT LOUIS ABBEY

Our religion is essentially contemplative. It tells us that a man is risen from the dead and living forever with the power of God to transform human life. What is required of us is to pay attention to the spiritual, invisible but real presence of this God-made-man, to focus on him and accept his loving, healing, renewing activity in our lives. This spiritual attention requires a certain letting go of preoccupation with earthly things, and allowing space for his action, a silence, a self-denial, self-emptying, a withdrawal, in which all our powers are submitted to his direction. Energized by his life we return to the world to attempt to love and serve others as we are loved. A monastery is a place set aside for this attentiveness to God with a view to submission to his transforming action in drawing the individual and the world to himself. It is a place for alertness to God, friendship with him, healing for the world. The life of a monk, the witness of a monastery are needed as much as ever in our world where noise, materialism and the frenetic, frantic pursuit of pleasure, are obscuring the call to the simplicity which leads to peace, the call of an infinite person who seeks to dwell with us. It is a happy vocation because in tune with fundamental realities: God, life, joy, the spirit, truth; and it ennobles the lives of others by handing on to them and modeling for them the Good News that offers something to live for, "reasons for living and hoping," a happy, meaningful life. For the laying open of the self to the purifying action of Christ and his Spirit is the introduction into the community of divine and human persons that every human heart was made for and craves. In this way contemplation builds community. Even the sacrifices that the life entails, the crucifixion of self-indulgent desires that Christ and St. Paul speak of, are surrounded by the promise of joy and made endurable by a growing share in the life of Christ.

We seek men who

— seek union with God

— want to learn to live in Christian community

— want to hand on to people of our time values,
  wisdom, and hope.

WRITE FOR INFORMATION:

OR CALL:
800-638-1527

FR. RALPH WRIGHT, OSB
SAINT LOUIS ABBEY
500 SOUTH MASON ROAD
ST. LOUIS, MO 63141

Use our convenient postcard in this book for more information.

Consider the monastic life as a Benedictine monk of St. Procopius Abbey

Do you truly seek God? If the answer is yes, then you have made the first step towards both the sincere practice of Christianity and, perhaps, the particular expression of the Christian life known as Benedictine monasticism.

What is monasticism? It is a response, found in various religions under diverse forms, to the human need to stand apart from the frantic pace of the world and explore instead the ultimate meaning of existence. By clearing away the ephemeral clutter of life, the monk hopes to find God – or, rather, allows God to find him.

What is Benedictine monasticism? Those who follow the monastic way of life as set down in the sixth-century Rule of St. Benedict are called Benedictines. The Benedictine monk engages in the quest for God, under the guidance of an abbot, or spiritual father, in a community of like-minded individuals to whom he makes a permanent commitment and with whom he spends his life in prayer and work.

What is St. Procopius Abbey? We are a Benedictine monastic community, founded in 1885 and located in Lisle, Illinois, nearly thirty miles west of Chicago. Numbering about sixty men, we strive to come closer to God through our prayer and our service to the Church, especially our educational apostolates at Illinois Benedictine College and Benet Academy (a college-preparatory high school).

How does one know whether one has a monastic vocation? St. Benedict begins his Rule with the words, "Listen, my son, to the precepts of the Master; incline the ear of your heart." One discovers one's calling in life by opening oneself to God in prayer and listening for His response; often a priest or other spiritual adviser can be of assistance in discerning God's will. Not everyone has a vocation to the monastic life; if you do, God will offer you the means to recognize it.

If you think God is calling you to the monastic life of St. Procopius Abbey, you can explore the possibility by writing to us. We will be glad to help you in your search.

Please address your inquiries to:
Director of Vocations
St. Procopius Abbey
5601 College Road
Lisle, Illinois 60532
E-Mail guyrj @ eagle.ibc.edu

Send one of the postcards in this book for more information

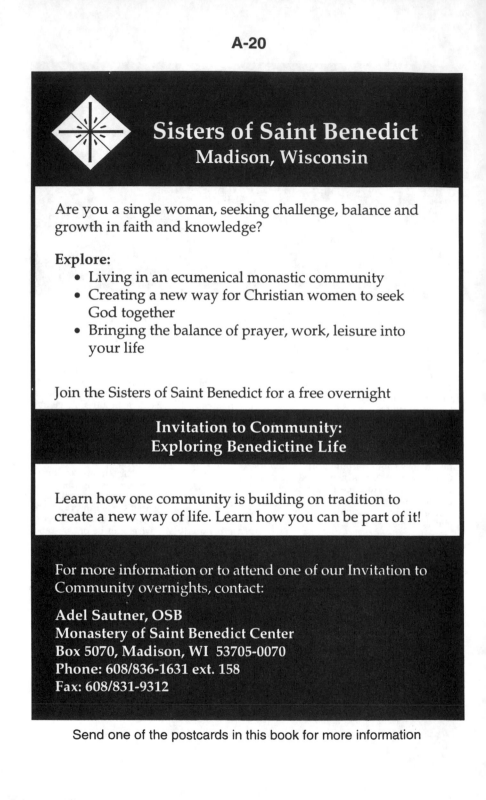

Sisters of Saint Benedict
Madison, Wisconsin

Are you a single woman, seeking challenge, balance and growth in faith and knowledge?

Explore:
- Living in an ecumenical monastic community
- Creating a new way for Christian women to seek God together
- Bringing the balance of prayer, work, leisure into your life

Join the Sisters of Saint Benedict for a free overnight

Invitation to Community:
Exploring Benedictine Life

Learn how one community is building on tradition to create a new way of life. Learn how you can be part of it!

For more information or to attend one of our Invitation to Community overnights, contact:

Adel Sautner, OSB
Monastery of Saint Benedict Center
Box 5070, Madison, WI 53705-0070
Phone: 608/836-1631 ext. 158
Fax: 608/831-9312

Send one of the postcards in this book for more information

The Benedictine Sisters
of Canyon, TX

ARE COMMITTED
TO SEEKING GOD . . .
- in a small monastic community,
- rooted in community and in our area
- with living the monastic life as our primary ministry.

OUR REASON FOR BEING . . .
- is to give glory to God through a life of contemplation and community prayer and work.

WE COMMIT OURSELVES TO
- reverence for one another and the environment,
- and to mutual support.

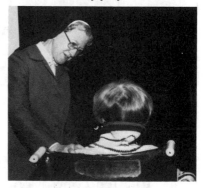

WE SUPPORT OURSELVES
- by any work which fits the talents of the sisters,
- is in harmony with our monastic way of life,
- and serves the needs of the church and society.

If you feel called to the monastic life and desire further information about the Benedictine Sisters of Canyon, Texas, contact:

**Vocation Director,
St. Benedict Monastery
2100 5th Avenue, Canyon, TX 79015
Telephone (806) 655-9317**

Send one of the postcards in this book for more information.

Not Every Woman Who Visits Us Stays. Discernment Is A Door That Opens Both Ways.

To find out more information
about the Ferdinand Benedictines or
to attend one of our Benedictine life weekends,
call Sr. Rose Mary Rexing at 1-800-738-9999.

SISTERS OF ST. BENEDICT
802 E. Tenth Street • Ferdinand, Indiana 47532-9239

BERNARDINE FRANCISCAN SISTERS

Celebrating more than 100 years!

Continuing the Mission in His Name

We, the
Bernardine Franciscan Sisters,
are called by God
to live the Gospel
in the Spirit of Francis of Assisi.
As vowed women of the Church,
we choose to live
simply and poorly.

Rooted in contemplative prayer
and
committed to ongoing conversion,
we strive to create
communities of love and service
wherever we are.

We reach out in compassionate love,
recognizing the dignity
and giftedness
of each person.

Faithful to the Church and to our charism
we seek
justice, peace and reconciliation,
especially as we work with
and in behalf of
the poor.

To carry out the mission of Jesus in today's world we need courageous women who will accept the **Challenge** and **respond to God's call** in their lives. If you are interested in sharing your gifts with others as a **Bernardine Franciscan Sister** please *write or call* the vocation minister.

Contact:

Sister Rosemary Stets, OSF
Vocation Office
460 St. Bernardine St.
Reading, PA 19607
(610) 796-8971

Bernardine Franciscan Sisters
ministering in:

Arizona	New Jersey
California	New Mexico
Connecticut	Puerto Rico
Kentucky	Pennsylvania
Maryland	Texas
Massachusetts	Virginia
Michigan	

Missions in Africa, Brazil, Dominican Republic, Poland, and Romania

Send one of the postcards in this book for more information.

SISTERS OF THE
BLESSED SACRAMENT

This is what God asks of us... that we

Act Justly as prophetic women who bless the bread of life by liberating the UNFREE,

Love Tenderly as compassionate women who break the bread of life by nurturing the UNWELCOMED,

Walk Humbly With God as faithful women who share the bread of life by gathering the UNINVITEDinJUSTICE+UNITY+PEACE.

We are SISTERS OF THE BLESSED SACRAMENT —

a multi-racial, multi-cultural community of Gospel women
— founded by Katharine Drexel —

who are empowered in the Spirit of Christ to
live simply, pray thankfully, and respond joyfully through a variety of ministries

(including education, social work, health care, pastoral and spiritual ministries, etc.)

to the needs of the poor and oppressed,

especially among Native American, African American and Haitian peoples in the USA and Haiti.

COME ACT + LOVE + WALK With Us
that ALL May Be ONE

For More Information write/call:

Sr. Christa McGill, SBS
Vocation Director
1663 Bristol Pike
Bensalem, PA 19020-8502
(215) 638-8482

Send one of the postcards in this book for more information.

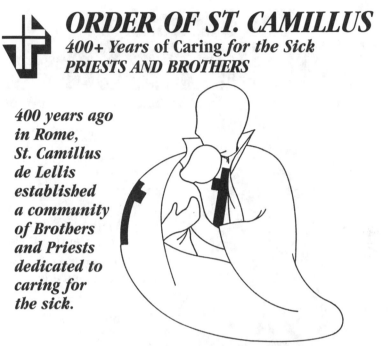

The CARMELITES

"...in the footsteps of Jesus Christ"
- The Rule of Carmel

in PRAYER
in COMMUNITY
in MINISTRY

The Carmelite Way is . . .

1. Prayer:

Prayer is the heart of our Carmelite Rule of life; prayer as continuous conversation with God. Carmelites tackle the most demanding journey of all: the journey inward into the heart to seek God. As part of this journey, we share this experience of God with a world which has lost touch with God's presence. We are contemplatives in action.

2. Community:

Carmelites are called to share our commitment to Christ within a community of priests and brothers. We are called to share everything with our brothers - our time, our income, our wisdom, our talents, our prayer. The Carmelite life of poverty, chastity and obedience gives us complete freedom to serve God's people in total self-giving.

3. Ministry:

Discovering God's presence defines Carmelite ministries. No form of apostolic work is foreign to the Carmelite: preaching the word of God, teaching in schools and universities, serving in parishes, retreats, spiritual direction, outreach to the poor, the sick and the dying, missionary work abroad are among the ways we seek to announce God's presence.

Call or write today:

Fr. Bob Colaresi, O.Carm.
1313 Frontage Road
Darien Illinois 60561
(708) 852-1476

CARMELITE SISTERS OF THE MOST SACRED HEART OF LOS ANGELES

The Carmelite Sisters of the Most Sacred Heart is an active Congregation, joining the spirit of Carmel, prayer and sacrifice with loving service. We enjoy a close Community life praying, dining and recreating together.

The spirit of our Foundress, Mother Maria Luisa Josefa of the Most Blessed Sacrament, forms the core of the spirituality of our Congregation. It is manifested through:

...An intense life of prayer and union with God.

...A deep love for Jesus in the Holy Eucharist.

...A steadfast fidelity to the Magisterium of the Church.

...A constant desire to be of service to the needy poor.

Our apostolates include: caring for the sick in all aspects of health care, caring of the aged, teaching in elementary and high schools, teaching in parish religious education programs, caring for children in day-care centers, and engaging in retreat work.

If you have a desire that persistently recurs to give yourself generously to God and to correspond to His most Holy Will, the Carmelite Sisters of the Most Sacred Heart of Los Angeles invite you to join them in serving Him, His Church and His people.

Contact:

Vocation Directress
Carmelite Sisters
920 East Alhambra Road
Alhambra, California 91801
Tel: (818) 289-1353

Douglas (602) 364-7658 / Cleveland (216) 521-5605
Coral Gables (305) 446-9950 / Miami (305) 663-1704

Send one of the postcards in this book for more information.

Today, women of diverse backgrounds
and experience,
women in business,
in health care
and helping professions,
educators, artists, pastoral ministers,
and many others,

Women with different gifts but the same Spirit are hearing the call to "make Jesus better known and loved" in our time.

We do this through the ministry of retreats, religious education, other forms of pastoral activity whose aim is to awaken and deepen faith.

We are the Religious of the Cenacle.

YOU COULD BE ONE, TOO!

FOR INFORMATION
CONTACT:

PAMELA J. FALKOWSKI, r.c.
312 CENACLE ROAD
LAKE RONKONKOMA, NY
11779
516-737-8491

Send one of the postcards in this book for more information.

SISTERS OF CHARITY OF ST. JOAN ANTIDA

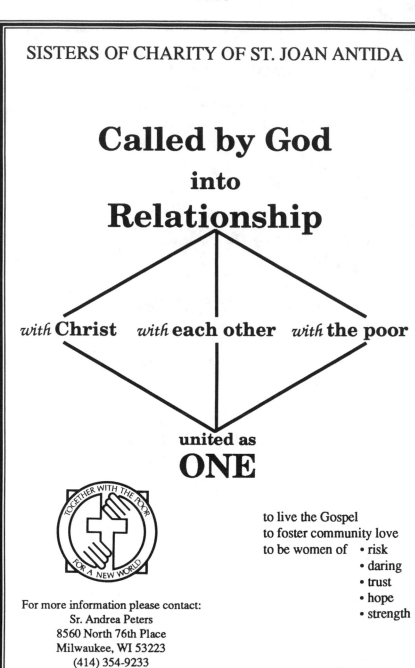

Called by God
into
Relationship

with **Christ**   *with* **each other**   *with* **the poor**

united as
ONE

to live the Gospel
to foster community love
to be women of   • risk
                  • daring
                  • trust
                  • hope
                  • strength

For more information please contact:
Sr. Andrea Peters
8560 North 76th Place
Milwaukee, WI 53223
(414) 354-9233

Send one of the postcards in this book for more information.

THE FUTURE OF RELIGIOUS LIFE IS LOOKING GREAT IF...

You are looking for ...

- *a personal relationship with Jesus.*
- *a community faithful to the Magisterium.*
- *a deeper holiness.*
- *a community-lived profession of the vows.*
- *a common life and common prayer.*

Do you believe ...

- *in witnessing to consecration & poverty through traditional habit?*
- *the role of the superior as fundamental to religious obedience?*

LOOK NO FURTHER
— *COMMUNITY OF TERESIAN CARMELITES* —

For more information contact:

Bro. Daniel-Francis, C.T.C.,   Sr. Susan-Elizabeth, C.T.C   Loretta Carroll, c.t.c.s.
Vocation Director   Vocation Director   Lay Vocation Director

Community of Teresian Carmelites, Box 826, Worcester, MA 01613-0826

(508) 752-5734
Send one of the postcards in this book for more information.

CONSOLATA
MISSIONARIES

Our Lady Of Consolata

Who We Are . . .

We are an international Religious Society born exclusively for the Missions: Priests, Brothers, and Sisters who live a unique family life devoted to spreading the Gospel, especially among the poor.

Following the spirit of their Founder, Blessed Joseph Allamano, the Consolata Missionaries nurture a profound love for Our Blessed Mother and the Blessed Sacrament of the Eucharist, and have a special loyalty to the Pope and the Magisterium of the Church.

Our Call . . .

is to be a source of consolation to all whom we serve in imitation of Mary. We are committed to a lifetime of total consecration to God and the Church. We leave our homeland and respond to the call of being sent wherever the Gospel needs to be proclaimed. JOIN US. With your involvement and God's grace, we will continue to be an effective instrument in His hands, for the salvation of the world.

Where We Are . . .

Africa: Ethiopia, Kenya, Liberia, Lybia, Mozambique, Somalia, South Africa, Tanzania, Uganda, Zaire. **South America:** Argentina, Brazil, Colombia, Equador, Venezuela. **Canada, United States, Europe:** England, Ireland, Italy, Switzerland, Spain, Portugal, Israel. **Asia:** South Korea.

For information contact:
Vocation Director
CONSOLATA MISSIONARIES

7110 Thomas Boulevard	**2669 Islington Avenue**
Pittsburgh, PA 15208 or	**Toronto, Ontario M9V 2X6**
(412) 241-3995	**Canada**
	(416) 743-6864

Send one of the postcards in this book for more information.

DAUGHTERS OF ST. PAUL

■ Our vocation is characterized by a profound Eucharistic spirituality, a dynamic mission of evangelization, and by a warm family spirit. In fifty-three nations throughout the world, we dedicate our time, our energies and our very lives to the Gospel.

■ We have been consecrated for a specific mission in the Church and in the world. Sensitive to today's "urgent need for evangelization," we use all the means of communication – press, video, audio cassettes, compact discs, radio, TV and Christian music – to proclaim the Word of God and the teachings of his Church to everyone.

Consecrated in the Church for evangelization with the communications media.

■ Union with Jesus is the center of our life of consecration. It is nourished daily by participation in the Eucharist, an hour and half of adoration before the Blessed Sacrament, meditation, the Rosary, monthly and annual retreats.

For more information call or write to:

**Vocation Directress
Daughters of St. Paul
50 St. Paul's Avenue
Boston, MA 02130
(617) 522-8911**

Send one of the postcards in this book for more information

The Discalced Carmelite Friars

The **Discalced Carmelite Friars** continue a 400-year tradition initiated by St. Teresa of Jesus and St. John of the Cross. Our **Carmelite Rule** guides our life in community, as we strive to balance a contemplative life of prayer and ministry, approaching the 21st century. We are one of the few orders of men with a woman foundress (see wood-cut above). We are also a Marian order by our devotion to Our Lady of Mount Carmel.

Our **Carmelite** communities support each friar in his commitment for his spiritual life and growth, for the Order, for the Church. These individual commitments form the cornerstone upon which our prayer and ministry find their meaning, challenge and fulfillment.

Our **Carmelite** ministry is rich in diversity: the monastic life, centers of Carmelite Spirituality, retreat ministry, spiritual direction, chaplains to the Secular Order, publications, hermitage solitude, and parish ministry.

Our world yearns for a personal relationship with Jesus in prayer and the vital outreach of evangelization. The **Discalced Carmelite Friars,** inspired by the rich heritage of Saints Teresa and John, both Doctors of the Church, invite candidates for the priesthood and brotherhood to commit themselves to meet that yearning.

The journey is long – it plumbs the very depths of personal prayer – and calls us to climb together with God's people. As **Carmelites,** with Elijah, the Prophet of Carmel, we still cry out: "With zeal have I been zealous for the Lord God of Hosts."

For further information, please contact one of the nearest Vocation Offices listed below.

Fr. Theodore Centala, O.C.D.
Discalced Carmelite Friars
2131 Lincoln Road N.E.
Washington, D.C. 20002-1199

Fr. Steven Sanchez, O.C.D.
Discalced Carmelites
P.O. Box 26127
Oklahoma City, OK 73126

Send one of the postcards in this book for more information

AT DIVINE WORD MISSIONARIES
THE WORLD IS OUR PARISH

Anywhere in the world where there are people who are poor and need God's love you will find the need for a Divine Word Missionary. In Africa, Asia, South and North America and Europe...in over sixty countries...Divine Word Priests and Brothers are making a difference in people's lives everyday. Through extensive education and cross-cultural living environments, Divine Word Missionaries are uniquely prepared to serve people in need throughout the world.

Divine Word is an international Catholic multicultural community of 5,700 men who are committed to making a difference in the world, one person at a time. Choose from one of our five programs in the U.S. to begin your journey into our world of education and service.

Divine Word College Seminary, Epworth, Iowa
is the only four-year college in the U.S. devoted to preparing men for work as missionary Priests or Brothers.

Casa Guadalupe, Los Angeles, California
is a small community of Hispanic college seminarians and brother candidates who attend universities or colleges in the Los Angeles area.

Tolton House of Studies, New Orleans, Louisiana
is a residence for African-American college seminarians and brother candidates. Students attend Xavier University in New Orleans.

Wendelin House of Studies, Washington, D.C.
is a small religious community of brother candidates who attend universities or colleges in the Washington, D.C. area.

Associate Program is a one-year residency program for college graduates who are considering a missionary vocation. Interested men may live in a Divine Word community and have a first-hand experience of ministry.

If you see the world as your parish, please contact Brother Dennis Newton, SVD, Divine Word Missionaries, P.O. Box 380, Epworth, Iowa 52045-0380 or call toll-free at 1-800-553-3321. Together, we can make a difference.

Send one of the postcards in this book for more information

Proclaiming the Savior

Celebrating 100 years of ministry in the United States

Contact:

Sr. Jenada Fanetti, SDS
Sisters of the Divine Savior
4311 North 100th Street
Milwaukee, WI 53222
414-466-0810

Fr. Michael R. Hoffman, SDS
Society of the Divine Savior
1735 Hi-Mount Boulevard
Milwaukee, WI 53208
414-258-1735

Together in Mission

Salvatorians

Our "Salvatorian Family" includes priests, sisters, brothers and lay Salvatorians.

We are committed to spending our time and talents in response to the needs of others so that "all may come to know the Savior."

We are from all walks of life and serve in thirty countries around the world.

We work as chaplains, teachers, pastors, caregivers, secretaries, social workers, foreign missionaries, artists, volunteers, nurses, pastoral ministers, retreat directors — wherever there is a need.

DOMINICAN FATHERS AND BROTHERS

IDENTITY

The Order of Preachers was founded in 1216 by St. Dominic de Guzman in response to a then desperate need for informed preaching - a need that could not be met by the existing resources within the Church. Against a heresy which denied the dignity of our humanity, St. Dominic trained a group of preachers who would serve the Church in its affirmation of the world as the place where Christ was discovered. He adapted the structure of monasticism so that his friars, vowed to poverty, chastity, and obedience, were nevertheless free to move wherever their preaching was needed. He replaced the tradition of manual labor with the sustained reflection on the mystery of Christ. And he began a tradition of spirituality that is rooted in community life, liturgical and choral prayer, and meditation – a spirituality which was meant to bear the fruit of an active apostolate.

SERVICE

We Dominicans continue to draw on our origins and the charism of St. Dominic in order to serve our calling as preachers of the Gospel. While the preaching apostolate remains the chief commitment of the Order, that task is supplemented by numerous other ministries. From the beginning, the Friars sought association with centers of learning and teaching. Presently, a variety of campus ministries continue to be a vital mission for us. Our interests and activities include retreat centers, research, hospitals, preaching teams, numerous parishes, universities, liturgy, art, communications and media, as well as ministries in the area of social justice. Our work extends from the U.S. to our missions in Latin America and Africa.

A call to ordination is not a necessary dimension for a Dominican vocation. A man may feel called to join our preaching community as a cooperator brother. Such men, with a background or interest in the arts, trades and the professional and academic world may find their calling to Christian ministry fulfilled in the Order of Preachers.

INVITATION

Dominic envisioned a family of priests, brothers and sisters proclaiming the message of Jesus. The time of spiritual, academic, pastoral and professional formation seeks to bring to fruition the personal charisms of each friar as he responds to God's call within the Dominican community.

If you are interested in living with the Word of God in a life dedicated to preaching, please contact:

CENTRAL PROVINCE
Promoter of Vocations
7200 W. Division
River Forest, IL 60305-1294
(708) 771-7254

SOUTHERN PROVINCE
Promoter of Vocations
1421 N. Causeway Blvd., Ste. 200
Metairie, LA 70001-4144
(504) 837-2129

EASTERN PROVINCE
Promoter of Vocations
Providence College
Providence, RI 02918-0001
401- 865-2216

WESTERN PROVINCE
Promoter of Vocations
5877 Birch Court
Oakland, CA 94618-1626
(510) 658-8722

Send one of the postcards in this book for more information

MONASTERY OF DOMINICAN NUNS

*Living the **Monastic Life-Style**; withdrawn
from the world to be intensely present
at the vital core of the Church and world.*

Dominican:

Sharing in the Dominican Order's
preaching mission by the witness
of radical Gospel-living and
intercessory prayer.

Women of the Word:

Prayerfully pondering Scripture
in imitation of Mary. Study in
the service of contemplation.

Sacrifice of Praise:

Liturgy of the Hours celebrated
in song at intervals throughout
the day; with Christ, in Christ,
for the Church.

Eucharistic Devotion:

Perpetual Adoration of the
Blessed Sacrament as a way
of entering into Jesus'
unceasing prayer to the Father.

Community Living:

Striving for charity and peace;
unity in welcomed diversity.

Simplicity of Life:

Work as asceticism, open to
prayerful union with God,
in solidarity with the poor.

Interested? Write:
Vocation Directress
Monastery of the Blessed Sacrament
29575 Middlebelt Road
Farmington Hills, Michigan 48334
1-810-626-8321

Send one of the postcards in this book for more information.

THE DOMINICAN SISTERS OF HAWTHORNE

... founded in 1895 by a convert to Catholicism-- Rose Hawthorne, the daughter of the American author Nathaniel Hawthorne.

We nurse incurable cancer patients who cannot afford the care they need. Rose Hawthorne chose this apostolate to demonstrate her love of God and faith in Christ's teachings. In so expressing her love of God, she gave eloquent testimony to God's love of humanity.

GOD AND THE SICK AWAIT US, SIDE BY SIDE.

Over our 95 year history, we have cared for more than 135,000 men, women and children. Middle class or poor, black or white, Christian or Jew -- each finds a home with us where they can pass their precious final days in dignity. We see in each the image of Christ. We minister to each with the same tender care we would give our beloved Savior.

Our community presently has seven free homes in six states: New York, Pennsylvania, Ohio, Massachusetts, Minnesota and Georgia. As our numbers swell, we plan to open new homes in other areas of the Country.

All of our sisters must directly help in the care of the patients, but not all of our sisters are RNs or LPNs. The most important talent, highly prized by us, is the talent for sharing of yourself -- your compassion, your cheerfulness, your faith -- with those who have been made so vulnerable and dependent by this dread disease.

We have a strong community and religious life. Each day, through community and private prayer, reading of the Sacred Scriptures, Liturgy of the Hours, daily Mass and devotion to the Blessed Mother and her Rosary, we seek to perfect our love and devotion.

IS GOD CALLING YOU TO HIS SERVICE?

We would be delighted to answer any questions you may have and to provide you with additional information about our community and prayer life.

Call (914) 769-4794 or write:
Sr. Marie Edward, O.P., Dominican Sisters of Hawthorne, 600 Linda Avenue, Hawthorne, NY 10532

Use the convenient Dominican Sisters of Hawthorne postcard for more information

DOMINICAN SISTERS
Congregation of St. Mary
New Orleans, Louisiana

Today, the women of our Congregation have a strong identity as SISTERS in the worldwide Dominican family, rooted in the spirit handed down by our founding mothers. Our uniqueness is in blending that heritage with the spice, the local color, of our deep south, New Orleans environment. We are close-knit and like to celebrate unity in diversity.

We carry on the tradition of quality education in college, high school, and parochial schools. As preachers proclaiming the Word, we also minister beyond the classroom. Pastoral ministries in the bayous of the deep delta, in urban and suburban parishes, counseling, community organizing, residential living for the elderly, retreat ministry, lecturing, preaching, writing, campus ministry, diocesan administration of schools, programs with handicapped people and hospice ministry are among the variety of ways Dominicans share the Word.

As Dominican women, our mission and charism centers on the Word, Jesus, the Christ.

Called by Jesus and inspired by St. Dominic, we embrace the mission of proclaiming the Word through the ministry of preaching and teaching
— Mission Statement

As we become other Christs for the world, we are enabled to bring His love and truth to others with graciousness.

For more information contact:

Sister Shirley Bodisch, O.P.
Vocation Director
7300 St. Charles Ave, New Orleans. Louisiana 70118
(504) 866-0541

Send one of the postcards in this book for more information.

Preach The Gospel

Teach, Heal, Proclaim The Good News

Live Your Passion
For The Gospel

Sr. Mary Gael Daley, O.P.
Vocation Director
Sacred Heart Convent
1237 West Monroe Street
Springfield, Illinois 62704
(217) 629-8471

**Dominican Sisters
Of Springfield Illinois**

Is There More?

*Yes, there is...
our Eucharistic
Presence to
the world.*

People are hungry. We all long for the deeper realities of life; for meaning, purpose and direction. Our world is also filled with those who have needs — food, shelter, jobs, as well as human love, compassion and a recognition of their dignity and self worth. We are a community that wants to respond to the hunger and need we see around us. We find meaning, purpose and direction in Jesus who became broken bread that others might have life and hope.

We desire to live like Jesus, to break open our lives by responding to those needs we see. We are a community of vowed religious women, volunteers, lay and clergy associates who, through our various ministries and lifestyles, are united in our common vision to bring the broken bread of Christ's life and presence to the world.

For more information write:

Sr. Luisa Derouen O.P.
Vocation Director

Eucharistic Missionaries of St. Dominic
3801 Canal St., Suite 400
New Orleans, Louisiana 70119
(504) 486-0098

Send one of the postcards in this book for more information.

"IN THE CROSS IS VICTORY"

The Congregation of Franciscan Brothers of the Holy Cross were founded in Hausen/Wied, in the Diocese of Trier, Germany, on June 12, 1862, by Brother James Wirth. Brother James left to the community the gift of his particular charism: patience, kindness and love for the poor. Brother James had a deep love for Christ in the Church, in imitation of St. Francis of Assisi. Brother James entrusted himself and his community to the service of the Church. This was expressed in his time to the care of orphans and the sick.

Today, we the Franciscan Brothers of the Holy Cross continue to dedicate ourselves to the Church in various ministries of service to God's people. We, the Franciscan Brothers of the Holy Cross embody and cherish the charism of our founder, Brother James, as expressed in our continued love of Christ and the Church, in the Franciscan Tradition.

We, the Franciscan Brothers of the Holy Cross are an international Congregation of vowed men dedicated to ministries of evangelization, education, pastoral care, and health care.

We, the Franciscan Brothers of the Holy Cross are in the midst of ministry in parishes, schools, hospitals, and long-term care facilities for the developmentally disabled.

Come and join us!

For more information, please contact:
Br. John Francis Tyrrell
Vocation Director
St. Joseph Friary
354 North Willow Avenue
Fayetteville, AR 72701-4365
(501) 442-0890

Send one of the postcards in this book for more information.

Byzantine Franciscans
Custody of St. Mary of the Angels
Order of Friars Minor

We follow
the Gospel life
as priests and brothers
in the footsteps
of Francis of Assisi.

We Live
an active and
contemplative community
life within the Rule of
the Order Friars Minor
and the traditions of
the Byzantine
Ruthenian and
Ukrainian Churches.

We minister
to all types of needs
within the
Byzantine Ruthenian
and Byzantine Ukrainian
Churches in the United
States and other countries

(Saint Francis of Assisi)

To join us, contact:

Fr. William Skurla, O.F.M., Vocation Director
Byzantine Franciscans, P.O. Box 270
Sybertsville, Pennsylvania 18251
(717) 788-1212

Send one of the postcards in this book for more information.

The Franciscans

We are...
people of action
and contemplation.
Somos gente
de acción
y contemplación.

We own nothing...
No tenemos nada...

We are people of
tradition...
Somos gente
de tradición...

Yet we appreciate
everything.
Apreciamos todo.

Yet we embrace
the world of today.
Nos dedicamos al
mundo de hoy.

THE NATIONAL FRANCISCAN VOCATION OFFICE
1-800-234-FRIAR

Western U.S. Provinces

St. Barbara
1500 34th Avenue
Oakland, CA 94601
1-510-536-3722

Our Lady of Guadalupe
Holy Trinity Friary
3100 W. 76th Avenue
Westminister, CO 80030
1-800-944-SEEK

Central U.S. Provinces

Sacred Heart
4860 W. 29th Street
Cicero, IL 60650
1-800-933-4871

St. John The Baptist
10290 Mill Road
Cincinnati, OH 45231
1-800-827-1082

Assumption
5103 S. Ellis Ave.
Chicago, IL 60615
1-800-872-1285

Send one of the postcards in this book for more information.

Order of Friars Minor
Orden de Frailes Menores

We value our common brotherhood...
Valoramos nuestra hermandad común...

And celebrate our differences.
Y celebramos nuestras diferencias.

Founded by St. Francis of Assisi, the Order of Friars Minor is a brotherhood in which the brothers are empowered by the Holy Spirit to follow Jesus Christ more closely. By our profession we are totally consecrated to God whom we love above everything else. We live the gospel in the Church according to the vision that St. Francis lived and taught. As friars we strive to proclaim reconciliation, peace and justice by our works. *(Constitutions - Art.1)*

Eastern U.S. Provinces

Immaculate Conception
147 Thompson Street
New York, NY 10012
1-800-521-5442

Holy Savior Vice-Province
232 S. Home Ave.
Pittsburgh, PA 15202
1-412-761-2550

Holy Name
135 W. 31st Street
New York, NY 10001
1-800-677-7788

St. Mary of the Angels Custody
Byzantine Franciscans
1212 North 5 Sahara
Tucson, AZ 85712-5018
1-602-886-4225

Send one of the postcards in this book for more information.

conventual
franciscan friars
FRANCIS OF ASSISI:
a 13th Century Founder and 21st Century followers

Fr. David Lenz, OFM Conv.
Vocation Office
6901 Dixie Highway
Louisville, KY 40258
(502) 933-4439

Fr. Thomas Blow, OFM Conv.
Office for Vocations
6107 N. Kenmore Avenue
Chicago, IL 60660
(312) 764-8811

Send one of the postcards in this book for more information.

PREACH PENANCE AND PEACE TO ALL THE NATIONS

Beginning from Jerusalem

Faithful to the mission handed on by our founder, St. Francis of Assisi, in 1217, we imitate the life of Jesus Christ through religious, educational and social services to bring Christ to the native and pilgrim peoples, and preserve those shrines which embrace Life, Death, and Resurrection of Our Lord Jesus Christ.

Do you desire to serve God in our Middle East Mission as a brother or priest?

GRM

Vocation Director
Holy Land Franciscans
1400 Quincy Street, NE
Washington, DC 20017
Phone (202) 526-6800

Name _____ Age _____

Address _____

City _____ State ____ Zip _____

Education _____

Phone _____

Send one of the postcards in this book for more information

Third
Order
Regular of
St. Francis

Province of the
Most Sacred
Heart of Jesus

Third Order Regular of St. Francis

(commonly known as Franciscan, T.O.R.), is a religious community of Catholic priests and brothers dedicated to God.

Our beginnings can be found in the Penitents of the Middle Ages: people who were seeking holiness in their daily lives. Francis of Assisi was himself a Penitent, but he gave this movement a new direction and spirit.

• **We follow** a common *Rule of Life* and live in fraternity.

• **We profess** vows of *poverty, chastity and obedience* in the presence of the Church.

• **We continue** the mission of Francis of Assisi through lives of:

CONVERSION • MINORITY
POVERTY • CONTEMPLATION

Fraternal living and praying in community provide the strength for ministry within the Church. The friars of the Third Order Regular endeavor to spend all their energy in advancing the Kingdom of God in the world.

We are:

Educators in High Schools & Colleges
Parish Ministers
Promoters of Church Renewal
Campus Ministers
Advocates of Social Justice
Hospital Chaplains
Foreign and Home Missionaries

For more information about becoming a Franciscan Priest or Brother, return one of the enclosed postcards in this book or write to:

Director of Vocations
Franciscan Friars, T.O.R.
P.O. Box 187
Loretto, PA 15940-0187
Or call (814) 472-9526

Send one of the postcards in this book for more information.

FRANCISCAN SISTERS OF CHRISTIAN CHARITY
MANITOWOC, WISCONSIN

We are a community of apostolic women religious who bring the light of the Gospel to the world in the spirit of St. Francis of Assisi. With Francis and the Blessed Virgin Mary as our models we live a life of...

+ SIMPLICITY BASED ON FAITH IN A LOVING GOD
+ JOYFUL ACCEPTANCE OF POVERTY
+ LOVE FOR THE CHURCH
+ SELFLESS DEDICATION TO THE SERVICE OF OTHERS

Our lives are rooted in prayer. Our prayer is rooted in life. The Eucharist, daily communal prayer, and personal contemplative prayer form the basis of our life in community and of our ministry in the Church. We live out our communal commitments in Catholic education, Catholic health care, and service to our sisters in community in Wisconsin, Michigan, Ohio, Nebraska, Illinois, Arizona, California, Hawaii, and Peru.

If you are a young woman who believes God is calling you to religious life, we invite you to contact us for further information.

Directress of Vocations
Holy Family Convent
2409 S. Alverno Road
Manitowoc, WI 54220-9320
(414) 682-7728

Send one of the postcards in this book for more information.

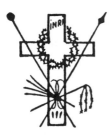

S E A R C H I N G...

... for someone to love?
... for something to do?
... for some way to share?

*We have **good news** for you!!!*

We find joy in giving __and__ receiving!
We work hard __and__ sit still!
We love to talk __and__ to listen!

Write us if you're interested in joining us in community, prayer, and ministry to serve in areas of:

<u>HEALTH CARE</u>: Nursing, Pastoral, Eldercare, AIDS Ministry, Admin
<u>EDUCATION</u>: Teaching, Religious Ed, Parish Ministry, Youth Groups
<u>SERVICE</u>: Retreat Work, Hospitality, Dietary, Diocesan Admin.

*The **good** news is we **found** a treasure.*

Come and seek with us the

FRANCISCAN SISTERS of the SACRED HEART.

Come join us as we too, seek the Reign of God. At the heart of our search is Jesus. We are drawn to be loved through a life of **prayer**. Out of this, love flows into a **ministry** of "works of neighborly love". It is Jesus who bonds us in **community** as Sisters, joyous and poor.

Come..visit us.
Come..work with us.
Come..live with us.

If you're between 18-35 and strongly desire to respond to and live the questions of today...

COME AND SEE...

(815) 469-4895
Sr. Deborah Suddarth, O.S.F.
9201 W. St. Francis Rd
Frankfort, IL 60423

Send one of the postcards in this book for more information.

Franciscan Sisters of St. Paul MN
Living the Gospel simply and plainly among God's people.

Ministries

- Francis Basket Food Shelf
- Clare's Closet Clothing
- Chaplaincy
- Dance for individuals with Handicap
- Beautician
- Day Care Teacher
- Dental Hygienist
- Secretary
- Visit the Homebound
- Prayer

Countries:

- Brazil
- Holland
- Germany
- U.S.A.

Vocation Video Available:

A 12 minute video on the religious life and our community is available for women who may be exploring their religious vocation, or for viewing by Vocation Clubs, College Campuses, CYO, CCD or religion classes. To order a copy of this video, please write our Vocation Director.

Viewing is free of charge if video is returned after use. The purchasing cost of video $8.00.

Vocation Director
1388 Prior Ave., S.
St. Paul MN 55116
(612) 690-1501

Send one of the postcards in this book for more information

Being Franciscan can hardly be put into words!

As Sisters of St. Francis of Assisi,

we listen...we share... we risk... we act on what we believe.

WE BELIEVE WE ARE CALLED TO
- stand in solidarity with minorities and with poor and oppressed persons
- affirm and encourage each person to seek quality of life
- work for the dignity of each person
- commit ourselves to peacemaking and empowering
- live the Gospel
- be faithful to the Rule of the Third Order St. Francis and the Constitutions of the Congregation

WE MINISTER AS
- advocates for women, elderly, disabled, disadvantaged persons
- administrators, teachers, child care workers, counselors
- food service, health care providers
- clerical workers and providers of hospitality
- social workers and parish ministers
- musicians, poets and artists
- pray-ers for all who are in need

We invite you to listen, share, risk and act with us as we move into the twenty-first century!

**Contact: Vocation Director
Sisters of St. Francis of Assisi
3221 South Lake Drive
Milwaukee, Wisconsin 53235-3799 (414)744-1160**

Send one of the postcards in this book for more information

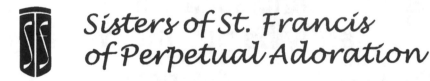

Sisters of St. Francis of Perpetual Adoration

Adoration

Education

Health Care

Other Ecclesial Ministries

"We strive in community to combine the contemplative life with the active through perpetual adoration and the works of mercy. . . " *Mission Statement*

For more information please call or write:

Sr. M. Jacinta, OSF
St. Francis Convent
PO Box 766
Mishawaka, IN
46546-0766

219/ 259-5427

Send one of the postcards in this book for more information

The Sisters of The Third Order of St. Francis

We, the Sisters of the Third Order of St. Francis of East Peoria, Illinois are a Religious Community whose mission it is to serve the people of God, especially the sick and the poor, in the spirit of the Gospel and St. Francis of Assisi.

Because Christ is the center of our lives, a deep prayer life is fostered and is the foundation from which our apostolic works flow. Health related fields are our main apostolate in which there is a variety of positions in which to serve the Lord. Our Sisters work in accounting, administration, education, food service, laboratory, occupational therapy, pharmacy, medical records, nursing, pastoral care, social service, and x-ray technology. We have health care facilities in Illinois, Iowa, and Michigan.

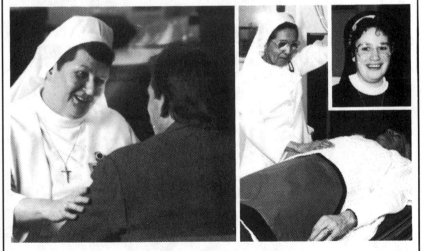

For further information, contact us:
Vocation Director
Mt. Alverno Novitiate
The Sisters of the Third Order of St. Francis
St. Francis Lane, East Peoria, Illinois 61611
(309) 699-9313

Send one of the postcards in this book for more information.

GLENMARY
MISSIONERS TO RURAL AMERICA

WE NEED YOU!
to serve the poor and neglected
in Appalachia, the Deep South & Southwest

*for information
on brotherhood or
priesthood,
contact:*

*Vocation Director
Glenmary Home Missioners
P.O. Box 465618
Cincinnati, OH 45246-5618
513-874-8900*

Send one of the postcards in this book for more information.

Have we got a job for YOU!

Glenmary
Sisters

We're in the business of love. The hours are long, the work is hard and often frustrating, there isn't much of a salary . . . but the benefits are out of this world!

We are **Glenmary Sisters** and **Lay Missioners** who minister to the spiritually and materially impoverished people of the United States. We are women in mission who work in small towns and rural areas of Appalachia and the deep South where Catholics often number less than 1% of the population, and many of the people are completely unchurched.

We place much emphasis on prayer as we strive to bring knowledge of Christ and the Catholic Church to the people, yet we evangelize primarily through our simple presence. We do not own or operate institutions, but work directly with the people in their situations and homes. Our work in extremely poverty-stricken areas often calls for action in social justice issues.

If you feel the need or desire to do something about poverty and injustice here in the United States while bringing knowledge of Christ to spiritually hungry people, then come and spend a few days with us. Find out who we are and what we're about. See the challenge, the excitement, the need.

For further information contact:
Glenmary Sisters, Membership Team
P.O. Box 22264 / Owensboro, KY 42304 / (502) 686-8401

Send one of the postcards in this book for more information.

The Women of Holy Cross

She Stood upright and glorified God . . .

Founded in 1841 by Basil Moreau, the women of Holy Cross have evolved into three distinct congregations, each imbued with the spirit of our founders and responding to the everchanging needs of our church and world.

Come Stand With Us!

MARIANITES OF HOLY CROSS

The two words **community** and **compassion** form the framework for our common response to "be Christ" for and with others. Our mission is to incarnate the love and compassion of Jesus Christ through a responsible presence in an ever-changing world.

Marlene Labbe, M.S.C.
31 Cresci Blvd.
Hazlet, N J 07730
908-264-3553

SISTERS OF HOLY CROSS

The Sisters of Holy Cross seek to identify themselves with Jesus. Drawn together by God, the women who join Holy Cross live in community, encounter their God in daily prayer, faith-sharing, service and celebration, and carry on the work of education in the fullest sense, fulfilling their mission in response to the needs of the young, the poor, the disadvantaged and the emerging Churches.

Anne Hosffler, CSC
106 W. River Dr. Apt. 16
Manchester, NH 03104
603-624-8047

SISTERS OF THE HOLY CROSS

We, Sisters of the Holy Cross throughout the world, are called to participate in the prophetic mission of Jesus to witness God's love for all creation. Compassion moves us to reflect on the signs of the times, discern needs, and respond. We stand in solidarity with the poor and powerless. Our life together enriches and strengthens us to foster community wherever we are.

Rita Slattery, CSC
Bertrand Hall-Saint Mary's
Notre Dame, IN 46556
219-284-5550

Send one of the postcards in this book for more information

SISTERS OF THE GOOD SHEPHERD

Where Faith Meets Courage

We **believe in people** whose lives cry out for healing. We welcome them in the context of their families and communities, and seek to support their courage in reclaiming their lives.

Our ministry and community lifestyles take two forms.

- **The apostolic sisters** – reach out in love to women, families, the abused and addicted, those in prison, the homeless – those seeking meaning and hope.
- **The contemplative sisters** – desire to serve God and our world through hidden lives of prayer with a special commitment to pray for those in need of the care of the Good Shepherd.

We invite women to join us who have a passion for bringing the healing presence of Jesus to those who hunger for love.

 Sisters of the Good Shepherd have locations across the country. For your nearest contact person write or call the Vocation Office 5100 Hodgson Road, St. Paul, MN 55126 **612/ 484-0221**

Send one of the postcards in this book for more information.

CONGREGATION OF HOLY CROSS

HOLY CROSS BROTHERS

THE LIFE OF A BROTHER...

It's not an easy life. In places from Chicago to Bangladesh, you'll serve the poor and rich, the aged and young, the educated and uneducated. The life demands prayer, hard work and vision. The rewards, however, are great...even in this life. You will have the friendship and support of a community. You will continue the work of Christ, share His mission and respond to world needs. There is no joy in this world to compare with that.

By the witness of their personal and communal lives, brothers help to strengthen Christian community.

For more information write or call:
**Vocation Director • Holy Cross Brothers • P.O. Box 460
Notre Dame, IN 46556 • (219) 233-2191**

Send one of the postcards in this book for more information.

CONGREGATION OF HOLY CROSS

HOLY CROSS PRIESTS

The only priest who will always prove necessary to people is the priest who believes profoundly, who professes his faith with caring, who prays fervently, who teaches with deep conviction, who serves, who puts into practice in his own life the Beatitudes, who knows how to love disinterestingly, who is close to everyone and especially to those who are most in need.

—Pope John Paul II

Holy Cross priests serve a variety of ministries: universities and schools, parishes, international missions, service to the poor and others. For information about Holy Cross and the one-year candidate program at Moreau Seminary at the University of Notre Dame contact:

**Vocation Director • Holy Cross Priests • P.O. Box 541
Notre Dame, IN 46556 • (219) 631-6385**

Send one of the postcards in this book for more information.

In faithfulness to our founders and our history,
we give preference to an apostolate that takes us to:

- *those who have not yet heard the gospel message or who have scarcely heard it;*
- *Those oppressed and most disadvantaged, as a group or as individuals;*
- *where the Church has difficulty in finding workers.*

(Spiritan Rule of Life)

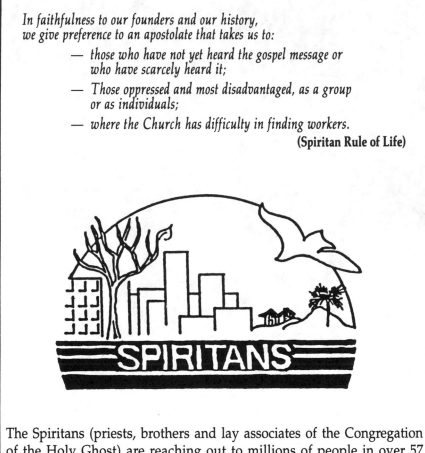

The Spiritans (priests, brothers and lay associates of the Congregation of the Holy Ghost) are reaching out to millions of people in over 57 countries, with vision and hope for a better world.

Share the Vision

write or call:
Spiritan Vocation Office
Duquesne University
Pittsburgh, PA 15282
412-765-0733

Send one of the postcards in this book for more information.

Nothing makes a community stronger than the individual spirit.

Y̶ou are searching. Looking for a place where you are accepted, where spirituality and belief are integrated into all aspects of life. Where you are supported in your personal growth and valued as an individual who contributes to the direction and vision of a community. Women from all walks of life, have found what you are still searching for. They have found a community where tradition and innovation walk hand in hand -- the Sisters of the Holy Redeemer.

- *Daily Eucharist, Morning and Evening Prayer in common*
- *Commitment to a simple, shared lifestyle*

- *Continued tradition of caring for the poor and marginalized founded by Mother Alphonse Maria Eppinger*

- *Focused holistic healthcare ministry along with outreach to homeless mothers and children*

The Sisters of the Holy Redeemer will support you in bringing to light the best of yourself and sharing that part of yourself with others

For more information call:
215-938-0540 *or write.*

Sisters of the Holy Redeemer
521 Moredon Road
Huntingdon Valley, PA 19006

Send one of the postcards in this book for more information.

Sisters of the Holy Spirit and Mary Immaculate

The Holy Spirit speaks words of invitation to each of us ....

Words that gently urge us to generosity in giving of ourselves in joyful service of others. For over 100 years, our sisters have been guided by the power of the Holy Spirit and their love of Mary to proclaim always and in as many ways as they are able the inherent dignity of each person. Following the inspiration of our foundress, Margaret Mary Healy Murphy, we believe that we are called by God to be women of faith and trust who live together in simplicity, humility and love to manifest the compassion of Jesus to the poor, especially those who are denied respect for their human dignity.

For more information write/call

Sr. Mary Fagan, SHSp
Vocation Director
301 Yucca
San Antonio , Texas 78203
(210) 533-5149

Holy Spirit Missionary Sisters

WE ARE an international community of 4,000 women called together to witness to the presence and power of the Holy Spirit through our life and prayer in the community and through our service in the Church.

WE CONTINUE the saving mission of Jesus in thirty-five countries throughout the world: Angola, Argentina, Australia, Austria, Bolivia, Botswana, Brazil, Chile, China, Czech Republic, England, Germany, Ghana, India, Indonesia, Ireland, Italy, Japan, Korea, Mexico, Netherlands, Papua New Guinea, Paraguay, Philippines, Poland, Portugal, Romania, Russia, Slovakia, Spain, Switzerland, Taiwan, Togo, Ukraine and the United States.

WE ARE INVOLVED in the ministries of education, health care, business, parish and social services, fine arts, domestic arts, retreat work, spiritual direction or whatever occupation is needed to be of service to others. "Wherever the work of the Church calls us, our service and our love should lead people to Christ."

WE WELCOME young women between the ages of 20 and 35 who:

● feel called by God to a religious / missionary lifestyle;

● enjoy good physical and mental health;

● have the ability to help others and who are open to personal and professional growth;

● want to share their lives and faith with other women who have similar goals.

For more information, write or phone:

Vocation Minister
Holy Spirit Missionary Sisters
Office of Vocation Ministry

P.O. Box 6026, Techny, Illinois 60082 (708) 272-5930

Use the convenient Holy Spirit Missionary Sisters postcard for more information

INSTITUTE OF CHARITY
(ROSMINIANS)

Founded by Antonio Rosmini, devout priest, philosopher, theologian, educator and spiritual director, at Domodossola, in Italy in 1828.

PURPOSE
To help those who wished to join him, to work out their salvation, by following Christ ever more closely.

MEANS
In addition to the means used by every Christian to follow Christ, members would make the profession of the three vows of Poverty, Chastity and Obedience.

WORK
No specific work. To await in silence the call of God, which would normally come through the invitation of a Bishop of the Church. As a result, though we have remained small in numbers (less than 600 worldwide), we have undertaken a great variety of works. Examples are: Colleges, schools, parishes, home for the blind, for the retarded, and mission work.

WHERE
In Italy, England, Wales, Ireland, New Zealand, Venezuela, Tanzania and the United States of America.

REQUIREMENTS
Applicants must be in good health and over 18 years of age. They must have a desire to follow Christ as closely as possible.

INFORMATION
For further information please write to the

VOCATION DIRECTOR
ROSMINI HOUSE
2327 W. HEADING AVE.
PEORIA, IL 61604

Send one of the postcards in this book for more information.

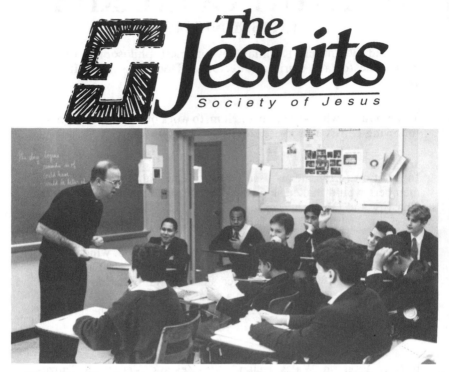

The Jesuits
Society of Jesus

The Jesuit way is deeply engaged with the world, a way of living the values of the Gospel with our companions through learning, teaching, accompanying the lives of others, working for justice alongside the poor, and building a just and believing world that will give greater glory to God.

Come and share the Jesuit vision of the world. Join men committed to being sent on mission, ready to go anywhere and do anything for the greater glory of God.

FOR INFORMATION, CONTACT:
The Jesuits
1424 16th Street, NW
Room 300
Washington, DC 20036
(202) 462-0400

Send one of the postcards in this book for more information.

LORD, *To Whom Shall We Go? And Jesus Said...* COME TO ME!

Josephite Priests and Brothers

- SOCIETY OF ST. JOSEPH OF THE SACRED HEART, an interracial and intercultural community of priests and brothers are known as the JOSEPHITES.

- THE JOSEPHITES, a U.S.A. HOME MISSIONARY SOCIETY, have as their sole apostolate EVANGELIZATION in the AFRICAN AMERICAN COMMUNITY.

Josephite Superior General with Seminarian

- THE JOSEPHITES have served America's NUMBER ONE MISSIONARY RESPONSIBILITY for 100 years.

- THE JOSEPHITE EVANGELIZATION APOSTOLATE is expressed in the parochial, social, and educational ministries in Alabama, California, Louisiana, Maryland, Mississippi, Texas, Virginia, Delaware and Washington, D.C.

VOCATION DIRECTOR   JOSEPHITE PRIESTS AND BROTHERS

1200 Varnum St., N.E., Washington, D.C. 20017

I am interested in the Josephite

☐ Priesthood   ☐ Brotherhood   ☐ Lay Volunteer

Name _____

Address _____

City _____ State _____ Zip _____

Telephone _____

GRMC

SOCIETY OF ST. JOSEPH OF THE SACRED HEART · JOSEPHITES ·

The Josephites: Providing More Than a Century of Service in the Black Community.

Missionaries of Our Lady of La Salette

Celebrating 150 Years of the call to Conversion and Reconciliation

Mary Pleads with us to cooperate and reconcile the world with God

At La Salette She said: *"If my people change..."*
Are you ready? Then call us!

For more information write or call the La Salette Vocation Office nearest you!

Fr. Dennis Meyer, M.S.		Br. Adam Mateja, M.S.
4650 S. Broadway		P.O. Box 777
St. Louis, MO 63111-1398		Twin Lakes, WI 53181-0777
314-353-5000		414-877-3373 ext. 140

Send one of the postcards in this book for more information.

Why wonder about your call when you can find out?

Each month young men from across North America are testing their call. Before deciding on their future, they're willing to give Christ the first shot at their lives. To check out their possible priestly vocation, they're visiting the **Legionaries of Christ.**

Here's why:

A rapidly growing community of priests centered on personal love for Christ, consecrated to Mary, loyal to Peter's successor.

A solid intellectual formation.

A mission that will demand your utmost.

If you are high school or college-age, and you want to conquer the world for Christ, then why put it off? God's time is now.

Call Father Owen Kearns LC today at 203 271-0805
or **write** to him at Legionaries of Christ, Cheshire, Connecticut 06410

Send one of the postcards in this book for more information.

'Who says there is a God...?

We do, and we want to make our God visible to people who are in need... find out about some possibilities with the

Little Brothers of the Good Shepherd

Membership: open to men who wish to become religious Brothers; Permanent Deacons and Priests who desire to serve the poor as Brother Deacons and Brother Priests.

Companion Program: Women and Men who desire to make a yearly commitment and share our life of prayer, community and ministry. (This program is available only in Canada at present.)

Enquire: Vocation Counsellor
Good Shepherd Centre
135 Mary St., P.O. Box 1003
Hamilton, Ontario
L8N 3R1

Telephone: (905) 528-9109

Fax: (905) 546-1743

Send one of the postcards in this book for more information.

Come...Be at Home With Us!

LITTLE SISTERS OF THE ASSUMPTION
AND
VOLUNTEERS

BE AT HOME WITH US ...

In the lives, In the homes, In the neighborhoods of those who are poor.

BE AT HOME WITH US ...

In prayer, In community, In God.

YOUR LIFE WILL NEVER BE THE SAME AGAIN.

Founded in France in 1865 to enhance family life in poverty ridden Paris, a quality of "at-homeness" with those who are oppressed became our lifestyle. We appeal to individuals to embrace a vocation marked by service to others, membership in community, lived in the light of the Gospel. You will be "at home" with the Little Sisters of the Assumption as a professed Sister or a volunteer.

Contact Vocation Directress or Coordinator of Volunteers
Little Sisters of the Assumption, 214 East 30 St., NY, NY 10016.
Phone 212-889-4310 Fax 212-889-7358.

Send one of the postcards in this book for more information.

It is ***Jesus*** *whom we care for in them.*

little sisters of the poor

In 1839, Jeanne Jugan welcomed Christ into her heart and her home in the person of an elderly, blind woman. Today, her daughters continue that humble gesture of love in thirty countries around the world.

It is Jesus...

• **in the elderly poor** to whom we dedicate our lives, as Jeanne Jugan said, "The poor are our Lord."

• **in the heart of fraternal community,** for it is Jesus who has gathered us together so that we may be witnesses of his love in the midst of the world.

• **in the Eucharist,** source of the charity from which our lives of consecrated hospitality flow.

• **in moments of communal and personal prayer,** which consecrate the unfolding of our days and help us to grow in an intimate union with Christ, our Spouse.

It is ***Jesus*** who has called us to live the spirit of the Beatitudes, in the joyful service of hospitality towards the aged poor... *Is* ***Jesus calling you?***

If you feel called to a life of service in the heart of the Church, we would be happy to answer your questions and accompany you in your search. **Contact:**

Sister Mary Richard
St. Ann's Novitiate
110-39 Springfield Blvd.
P.O. Box 280356
Queens Village, NY 11428
(718) 464-4920

Send one of the postcards in this book for more information.

THE MISSIONARIES OF MARIANNHILL

The Congregation of Mariannhill Missionaries was founded in South Africa out of a need, seen by our founder Abbot Francis Pfanner, for missionary work. We now have houses of formation for missionary priests and brothers in Germany, Austria, Holland, Switzerland, the United States and the province of Quebec in Canada. We also have missions and houses of formation in South Africa, Transkei, Brazil, Papua New Guinea, Zambia and Zimbabwe. Our generalate is in Rome, Italy.

In the United States, our vocation/formation center for priest and brother candidates is in Dearborn Heights, Michigan. These candidates would come to our formation center to begin a period of postulancy (pre-novitiate), after which they would enter the novitiate for a period of one year. The novitiate is a time away from academic studies and concentrates mainly on living the religious life and learning about the congregations history, spirituality, founder, prayer, etc. At the end of the novitiate the candidates apply to make a temporary profession of the evangelical vows of chastity, obedience and poverty.

The newly professed religious priest candidates would then attend either the seminary college program or major seminary theology program, depending on what education they have by this time . The brother candidates would further their theological studies as well as complete some degree or technical trade program. After a period of at least three years in temporary vows, but not more than six years, these candidates would apply for permanent profession of their vows.

Those men, who feel called to follow the life and example of our Lord Jesus Christ, working with His people around the world as missionary priests and brothers, are invited to inquiry to our vocation office for more information and assistance in discerning their vocation. Bring your gifts and talents and make them a part of ours!

For more information, write to: **Mariannhill Vocation Office**
23715 Ann Arbor Trail
Dearborn Heights, Michigan 48127

Send one of the postcards in this book for more information.

The Marianists

Communities of Faith

The communities of faith founded by Adele de Trenquelleon and William Joseph Chaminade were inclusive of all social classes and states of life. The Marianist Family includes communities of lay persons, religious women, and religious men. The word "family" is key to understanding the Marianist charism and spirituality. We aim to make family spirit the distinctive mark of our communities as we mirror Mary's faith, humility, simplicity, and hospitality. All are welcomed into these communities; their baptism and their devotion to prayer and the formation of community being their distinction and their unity as the Family of Mary.

The Society of Mary

Founded in 1817, the Society of Mary became the third branch of the Marianist Family. Together with the Daughters of Mary, the religious congregation for women, we make explicit public witness to prayer, community, and the mission of forming faith communities. We take on this task in many different apostolic ministries. For example, you will find Marianists in schools, parishes, universities, retreat centers, working directly with the poor and oppressed, the arts, music, and health care. The Society of Mary today has over 1800 brothers and priests spanning five continents and over 300 countries. We are represented in Canada, Mexico, the United States, and Puerto Rico.

Process Toward Commitment in the Society of Mary

Interested men engage in a process of discernment leading to a commitment to live within one of our communities as an aspirant. During this time the aspirant continues his usual ministry and gradually absorbs the rhythm and demands of community life.

Following aspirancy is the period of novitiate, which is the formal introduction to the history and life of the Society of Mary. Novices participate in formal course work while living in community with other novices and professed religious. The novitiate concludes with the first profession of the vows of poverty, chastity, and obedience.

From novitiate the newly professed is assigned to ministry and community within his Province while continuing study in theology and ministry. Vows are renewed annually until such time as the individual seeks and the community approves the profession of perpetual vows. At that time the brother adds the fourth vow, our vow of stability. Also at this time, he may seek the community's approval to study for ordained ministry.

Light the Way

The Gospel of Jesus announces a new earth;
where darkness does not overcome
where the poor are fed,
the inarticulate find voice
and the stumbling feel uplifted.

Holding high the torch
of Mary's courage and compassion,
Marianist communities live the Gospel
for a new creation.

Help us light the way.
Come walk with the Marianist communities.

✝ⓂThe Marianists

Bro. Dan Klco, S.M.
Marianist Vocation Ministry
Alumni Hall Room 225
University of Dayton
Dayton, OH 45469-0323
513-229-2741

Rev. Jim Schimelpfening, S.M.
Vocation Ministry
St. Mary's University
One Camino Santa Maria
San Antonio, TX 78228-8556
210-431-2193

Use the convenient Marianist postcard in this book for more information

ARE YOU BEING CALLED?

This personal call to live with Jesus is a gift of the Father which is sustained only by honestly cooperating with the Holy Spirit in one's daily life.

THE MARIANS

- Men of good will • Animated by the spirit of Christ • Striving to bring Christ into all things and everywhere
- To renew and revive all things in Christ
- To gain all for Christ
- To attract all to Christ

Marians of the Immaculate Conception

Priests and Brothers • Spanning Three Centuries • Serving on Five Continents

Pope John Paul II gives us a challenge. Very simply put, the Holy Father asked us to join the growing ranks of the new poor and to identify with them --those abandoned, those thirsty for justice, those cast off by society. We Marians want to be there, to open our hearts, to assist them and to comfort them.

Approaching the third Christian millennium, the Marians eagerly continue in their schools, their parishes, missions and printing establishments **for Christ and the Church.**

Marians come from diverse backgrounds and ethnic origins. Some enter at a young age, others after having pursued a first career. Their varied talents, experience, and understanding have blessed our community with tremendous vitality in service of Christ.

If you would like more information about our community, write Fr. Bill Hayward, M.I.C., Congregation of Marians, Thompson, Connecticut 06277 or call (203) 923-2460

If you are being called to be a Marian... *you will find in the Marian Community the lifestyle and commitment that best enables you to become the person God created you to be, using your gifts of personality and talent to their fullest in his service.*

Send one of the postcards in this book for more information.

MARIANS...
Priests and Brothers
MEN WITH A MISSION

"Jesus, I trust in thee."

For more than 300 years the Marians have been serving "CHRIST AND THE CHURCH" in the spirit of Mary Immaculate, the first disciple. She serves as our model of faith, because she "HEARD THE WORD OF GOD AND KEPT IT!" Like her, we strive daily to respond: "YES, LORD, LET IT BE DONE TO ME ACCORDING TO YOUR WORD."

Founded in Poland in the 17th century, the Marians quickly spread to other parts of Eastern Europe. The community suffered greatly from persecutions and suppression by powers hostile to Catholicism and many of our priests and brothers died in concentration camps and in Siberian exile. However, despite great suffering, the Marians could not be destroyed. At the turn of the century, the community was renovated by Blessed George Matulaitis and began to build an underground church in Eastern Europe. We not only survived, we thrived and spread. We now work on five continents and seek to include men of all nations and cultures into our Marian family.

Throughout the centuries, the Marians have discovered that "God makes all things work to the good for those who love him." We have discovered the life-giving power and strength that can be found only in a life of prayer. We seek the happiness and fulfillment that can be found only in service to others. In the words of our Renovator, Blessed George, we are "on the one hand, to be so intent on cultivating a life of prayer and, on the other hand, so dedicated to a life of service and ministry to others, that these two ends come together as one and in no way impede but complement each other!"

In our search to serve the Lord and His people, we Marians exclude no ministry. Rather we strive to read the signs of the times and "to be prophetic bearers of God's merciful love, especially to people in greatest need." We invite you to consider becoming a member of "A PRAYERFUL COMMUNITY OF MEN WORKING TO PROMOTE DEVOTION TO OUR LORD'S DIVINE MERCY AND OUR LADY'S IMMACULATE CONCEPTION."

**IF YOU ARE SEEKING TO DISCOVER THE VOCATION
GOD IS CALLING YOU TO:**

**WRITE
VOCATION DIRECTOR
MARIANS OF THE IMMACULATE CONCEPTION
3885 HAREWOOD ROAD, N.E.
WASHINGTON, DC 20017
(202) 526-8884**

Send one of the postcards in this book for more information.

The Society of Mary
THE MARIST
PRIESTS & BROTHERS

An International
Missionary Community

LIVING THE SPIRIT OF MARY

Marists learn from Mary her singular openness to the Holy Spirit and her distinctive manner of serving the Church.

Thus it is that the Society of Mary is not characterized by any special type of ministry nor by any particular Marian devotion. Rather **it is the vocation of Marists to make the mystery of Mary in the church their constant inspiration.**

The Society of Mary, in **its life of prayer, in its living in community, in its choice of apostolates in the Church,** manifests one concern: to think, to judge, to feel and act in every way as Mary would. **Our communities** are witnesses of a servant church, striving to become its Marian ideal... a Church forever seeking to be Christlike: not Lording, but serving, ready to give up any privileged status provided the LORD be proclaimed.

This Marist Spirit lives on today in the Society bearing the name of Mary. We hope to share our spirit with future generations.

FOR THE GLORY OF GOD AND THE HONOR OF MARY!

For more information about the Society of Mary —

THE MARISTS
Write to:
Fr. Albert Dilanni, S.M.
Marist Vocation Office
518 Pleasant Street
Framingham, MA 01701-2898
508-875-6075 or 508-879-1620

Send one of the postcards in this book for more information.

Overseas *mission!*

Where do you fit in?

Around the world. **Maryknoll Sisters, Brothers, Fathers and Lay Missioners** work together with a **NEW VISION OF CHURCH**. We witness the liberating love of Christ in the struggles of oppressed people for justice, dignity and peace.

JOIN US!

Find out where YOU fit in! Write to:

Director of Vocations
Vocations Office
Maryknoll, NY 10545-0305

Questions? Call us, toll free: 1-800-431-2008.
In New York State: 914-941-7590, ext. 2416

Send one of the postcards in this book for more information.

Sisters
Medical Mission Sisters

We are Medical Mission Sisters. From many countries we are named: Jutta, Belaynesh, Nirmala, Karen, Rosalie, Vijaya, Jane, Kusmilah. We are Sisters! We know that we have been called to be on this journey together and we have entrusted our deepest values to be more together than we can be alone.

In our community we make the choice to live the shared life. We share our vision, our goods, our laughter, our talents and sometimes our tears. We support and we are supported, drawing strength and nourishment for the tasks of healing.

Our multicultural makeup and opportunities to live cross culturally have instilled in us an appreciation for variety while challenging us to live with diversity. For us to be a missionary today means that no matter where we live or what our geography is named, the whole earth is the place of our care and concern. For the whole earth is home.

In mission we choose to link our lives with people who are suffering and dying. We seek ways to address global inequities. We choose to live more deliberately simple. We minister as doctors, nurses, social workers, community organizers. We pray for healing. We advocate for women. We create nurturing ritual. We plant trees, collaborate, teach literacy, do art, recycle paper, boycott products, explore alternative health systems and help others awaken to a view of the whole inhabited earth.

This brings us to the core of what our life in mission is all about. With an authority that comes from our experience of God, of the poor and of community, we give our lives in a wholehearted way to meet need, to establish right relationship, and to be a healing presence.

Do you want to be a "sister" too? Do the tasks of healing and justice resonate with the longings of your heart? Are you seeking an alternative lifestyle? If so, if you have a large capacity for loving, a willingness to change, and the ability to laugh, consider sharing your life with us.

For more information, contact:

Sr. Marie Schmids
8400 Pine Road
Philadelphia, PA 19111
(215) 742-6100

Sr. Teresa Jaramillo
2222 Coronado Ave. #9
San Diego, CA 92154-2037
(619) 424-5502

Send one of the postcards in this book for more information

A challenge to a life of commitment and caring...

Y ou've heard the calling to enter a religious life. Now you're asking yourself, what direction should I take? How can I best serve the Lord?

If you feel a clear purpose to help others and have an earnest compassion for the sick and aging, the Brothers of Mercy may have the answers.

If a sense of belonging and a life of committed service speaks to you, we would like to talk to you.

Brothers of Mercy

"Whatsoever you do for the least of my brothers, that you do unto me"
— Matt.25:40

Although our life is simple, we participate within the community, aiding people who are in need of all kinds of rehabilitation.

Within our institutions and home health care programs, our staff of Brothers receive the very latest training in health care technology to best serve our fellowman.

For more information, contact:
THE VOCATIONS DIRECTOR
4520 Ransom Road
Clarence, NY 14031
(716) 759-6985

Send one of the postcards in this book for more information.

FATHERS OF MERCY

"The Sovereign Pontiff and the Church, inseparable from her visible head, are in our eyes the first authority; it is Jesus Christ Himself transmitting through her to us 'the way, the truth and the life.' The Faith of the Roman Catholic Church is immutably ours." With these words Father John Baptist Rauzan indicated the love and affection the Fathers of Mercy were to entertain for the Holy See, the Magisterium.

In 1808 Cardinal Fesch, Archbishop of Lyons, asked Father Rauzan, a priest of the Diocese of Bordeaux, to gather a group of priests to preach the Word of God throughout France. This was the humble beginning of the Fathers of Mercy. By 1814 the headquarters of the Community was moved to Paris and the Fathers placed in charge of several parishes. Hence, to their task of preaching missions was added parochial work. This work has continued to this day.

Father Rauzan left France in 1830 when religious communities were again forbidden. He lived in Rome where he wrote the Constitutions for his small Community. This work was approved in 1834 by Pope Gregory XVI. It was he who gave the title: "Fathers of Mercy under the title of the Immaculate Conception," to the Congregation.

The year 1839 saw the Fathers introduced to the United States. Since then they have worked and taught in Washington, D.C., Florida, New Jersey, Massachusetts, New York, North Carolina, California, Alabama, Louisiana, Kentucky, Wisconsin, Puerto Rico, Canada. Today, the Community no longer has a house in France. It has become an American Community.

In 1960 the Fathers of Mercy went through a reorganization. The vow of poverty was taken at this time and the task of staffing rural parishes in the United States and foreign lands was emphasized. Again in 1979 the Constitutions were revised in accordance with the decrees of Vatican II.

The members profess the simple vows of poverty, celibacy and obedience. Parishes are staffed in Kentucky. Since our holy founder was a great believer in private devotions, he bound no one to particular devotions. Father Rauzan believed that the best rule is the rule best observed. Therefore, today, as in his day, the rule is free from severity and no one is tempted to violate it.

The habit of the Congregation, received upon entrance to the Novitiate, is a black cassock and matching sash. On the left front side of the cassock the members wear a badge depicting the Prodigal Son being received by his Father. This is the insignia of the Community. The members, therefore, act like the Father in all things: they are "moved by mercy." (LK 15:20)

Today the Fathers of Mercy are looking for men who have completed at least 2 years of college and desire to live and work in a Community dedicated to Mary and holding the Truths taught by Holy Mother Church, as expressed through the person of Our Holy Father and the official Magisterium. They must be willing to bring the Mercy of God to all, especially those in rural areas. This is done through the offering of the Holy Sacrifice of the Mass; the administration of the Sacraments, particularly the Sacrament of Mercy or Reconciliation; preaching; teaching.

Write: Vocation Director
Fathers of Mercy
14480 Bowling Green Road
South Union, KY 42283

Send one of the postcards in this book for more information.

Animated by the Gospel and Catherine McAuley's passion for the poor, we, the **Sisters of Mercy of the Americas**, are impelled to commit our lives and resources to act in solidarity with

> The economically poor of the world, especially women and children

> Women seeking fullness of life and equality in church and society

> One another as we embrace our multicultural and international reality.

This commitment will impel us to

> Develop and act from a multicultural, international perspective

> Speak with a corporate voice

> Work for systemic change

> Act in harmony and interdependence with all creation

> Call ourselves to continual conversion of lifestyle and ministries.

To this end, we invite you to consider the **Institute of the Sisters of Mercy of the Americas**, *Regional Community of Chicago, in one of these ways . . .* **VOWED MEMBERSHIP**

MERCY CORPS VOLUNTEER PROGRAM

ASSOCIATE PROGRAM

For further information, call or write **Carol Mucha, RSM**
Sisters of Mercy of the Americas
10024 S. Central Park Avenue
Chicago, Illinois 60655
Phone 312/779-6011 or FAX 312/779-6094

MILL HILL MISSIONARIES
St. Joseph's Missionary Society

"Touch their world and they will touch yours, and ... the world will never be the same again!"

We are an international fellowship of priests and brothers, especially dedicated to all of God's people who have been hurt most by fate and misfortune.

Come and join us for service in Africa, Asia or South America.

For further information, contact:

Father Emile Frische, M.H.M.
Mill Hill Missionaries
1377 Nepperhan Avenue
Yonkers, NY 10703-1055
914-375-0845

Send one of the postcards in this book for more information

MISSION HELPERS OF THE SACRED HEART

Community Isn't Something You Join, It's Something You Build

WHO ARE THE MISSION HELPERS OF THE SACRED HEART?

We are a missionary community of women religious who try to live so that our shared life is itself ministry, proclaiming more powerfully than words the gospel message that we are called to love one another.
(Community Constitutions)

The Mission Helpers of the Sacred Heart were founded in Baltimore, Maryland in 1890 by Mary Frances Cunningham for the purpose of religious education and evangelization of those not reached by the Catholic school system. In 1902 our Sisters opened our first mission in Puerto Rico and in 1960 we began missionary work in Venezuela. Our charism or founding spirit was to do what wasn't being done by others. We are still women of vision who allow the talents of our members to be used to uncover the Kingdom of God in our world. Because Mission Helpers do not own schools or hospitals, we are free to go where the needs of people are. Mission Helpers can be found on rural roads, city streets or suburban neighborhoods, throughout the United States, in Puerto Rico and Venezuela.

CONSIDER BEING WITH US IN:

Evangelization	Religious Education	Writing, TV, Video Work
Youth Ministry	Hospital Chaplaincy	Peace & Justice Ministry
Campus Ministry	Liturgical Ministry	Ministry to Mentally
Migrant Ministry	Ministry with Elderly	Handicapped & Deaf
Hispanic Ministry	Parish Administrators	Ministry wth Homeless
Pastoral Ministry	African American Ministry	Family Ministry

WE NEED YOUR TALENTS AND PROMISE TO LET YOU USE THEM!

*Necesitamos tus talentos y prometemos
ayudarte a compartirlos y desarrollarlos!*

For more information on these **Ministry Programs,** contact:
Sr. Judy Waldt MHSH
Mission Helpers of the Sacred Heart
1001 W. Joppa Road
Baltimore, MD 21204-3787
(410) 823-8585, Ext. 246

Send one of the postcards in this book for more information

MISSIONARIES OF AFRICA

Christian community at prayer

DESCRIPTION OF PROGRAM: The Missionaries of Africa for more than one hundred years have been offering their service to the Christian communities of the Church in Africa — and to those who have yet to hear the Good News — in the Spirit of fellowship in the Lord Jesus. Jesus' call to share his message with all nations provides the impetus for the Society's international communities, respect for local cultures and methods of team ministry. It serves as a vehicle for Christian men — priests, and brothers – to place their talents at the service of Christ and his people in Africa. Its witness includes sacramental ministry, basic communities, justice and peace development, education, health care, Christian leadership formation, and Islamic apostolate.

GEOGRAPHICAL AREAS OF SERVICE: Twenty-two countries in Africa.

LIFESTYLE:
Internationality . . . Communities are of mixed nationalities. Our intercultural witness is a sign that all nations are one family in the Lord.
Adaptability . . . we adapt as much as possible to the lifestyle and culture of the people we serve in terms of language and customs.
Team Ministry . . . we try to live and work in communities that stress Christian respect, cooperation, mutual planning and support.

MEMBERSHIP:
Life-time Commitment . . . Priesthood and Brotherhood. Requirements include a mature Christianity; 2 years of college or its equivalent; good health and flexibility of character; 20-35 years of age (negotiable).

Contact Person:
Vocation Director
Missionaries of Africa
1624 21st Street, NW
Washington, DC 20009-1055
(202) 232-5154

Use the convenient Missionaries of Africa postcard in this book for more information

THE MISSIONARIES OF THE SACRED HEART OF JESUS

Reaching out into new areas . . . responding to society's changing needs . . . we continue the work of **ST. FRANCES CABRINI** striving to make **CHRIST** the heart of the world as Missionary Sisters, Lay Missioners, Collaborators and Volunteers.

New challenges call for new responses which are creative. In addressing the needs of our times the example of St. Frances Xavier Cabrini serves as a source of encouragement and inspiration to us.

Frances Cabrini was a woman in love with God. Her love overflowed in service to her brothers and sisters in need. The title of our Community, "Missionaries of the Sacred Heart of Jesus", means that each of us is sent to be a bearer of Christ's love to every person we meet.

Mother Cabrini came as a missionary to America to help immigrants. Today, 650 Missionary Sisters, together with our lay missioners, collaborators, and volunteers serve in the United States, Latin America, Europe, Africa, Asia and Australia. Following the example of our foundress we seek to embody Gospel values in our varied works which include: social service, education, health care, counseling, retreat, social justice and pastoral ministries. As Missionary Sisters, our vowed commitment calls us to live simply in faith, pray together in hope, and work with God's people in love.

For further information, call or write:

Sr. Regina Peterson, MSC
Director of Vocation Ministry
610 King of Prussia Rd. Radnor, PA. 19087-3698
610-902-8233

Send one of the postcards in this book for more information.

Missionaries of the Sacred Hearts of Jesus and Mary

"The Word of God becomes like a fire burning in my heart."
(JER 20:10)

CALLED ...

"...to labor selflessly ... to make known to all people the deep and tender love of the Sacred Hearts of Jesus and Mary, and to kindle this love in the hearts of all...."

... TO SERVE

Our Identity

We, the Missionaries of the Sacred Hearts of Jesus and Mary, are a religious community of Priests and Brothers dedicating our lives in the service of God in a particular way through service to our brothers and sisters in the localities of Italy, Argentina, India, the USA and Slovakia. This way is not in the form of a singular, visible apostolate, but an outreach to those in need, whatever those needs may be.

Our Work

Our task is to mission to God's children, helping them to recognize that God's great Love is and has always been present in their lives; then to guide them to a more positive interaction with Him through the deep and tender love of Jesus and Mary in their most Sacred Hearts.

As we relate our own lives to the humanity of Jesus and Mary, we can draw strength and perseverance from their example of selfless love and unconditional surrender to the Father's Will.

Director of Vocations
Missionaries of the Sacred Hearts
832 South 4th Street
Camden, New Jersey   08103-2099
609-541-7618
E-mail: 75602.3234@compuserve.com

Use the convenient Missionaries of the Sacred Hearts of Jesus and Mary
postcard for more information

MISSIONARY OBLATES *of MARY IMMACULATE*

Close to People . . .

We are a community of Catholic priests and brothers who want to be close to people: to share in their hurts, joys, fears, and dreams. Whether in the United States or in the distant reaches of the earth, you will find us there, sent to proclaim the Good News of Jesus Christ.

Write or Call:
**Rev. Louis Studer, O.M.I.
Oblate Vocation Office
5401 S. Cornell Ave.
Chicago, IL 60615
(312) 684-7980 or (800) 358-4394**

Use the convenient Missionary Oblates of Mary Immaculate postcard in this book for more information.

Norbertine Fathers and Brothers

When People of Faith Come Together, Good Things Happen!

In Community
In Prayer
In Ministry

For more information write to:

Vocation Coordinator
St. Norbert Abbey
De Pere, WI 54115-2697
414-337-4300

Send one of the postcards in this book for more information.

ORDER OF THE B.V.M. OF MERCY–
Mercedarian Friars

Setting Captives Free for 778 Years!

Our Community

Friars, both priests and brothers:

– Founded in 1218 by Saint Peter Nolasco.
– Living a fraternal common life based on our Constitutions and the Rule of Saint Augustine.
– Community strengthened by our daily common prayer and centered around the Blessed Virgin Mary, whom we honor as our Mother and Foundress.

Our Life

Shaped by the profession of four vows:

– **Chastity,** freeing us to share our lives and the redeeming love of Christ with all people.
– **Poverty,** witnessed by our simple white habit and the sharing of all things in common.
– **Obedience,** unselfish listening and responding to the needs of the Church and the cries of the captives through our superiors.
– **Redemption,** the vow by which the others are measured. Imitating Christ by surrendering our lives for those whose Faith is endangered by modern captivity.

Our Work

Takes us wherever we see modern captivity eroding and inhibiting the Faith:

– In **parishes,** working with those whose Faith is fragile or broken because of family problems and poverty.
– In **schools,** where peer pressure and the empty values of society threaten the Faith of our young people.
– In **prisons,** where very often the Faith, hopes, and dreams are lost.
– In **hospitals,** where illness may lead to loss of the Faith and despair.
– In **foreign missions,** where social conditions rob the human dignity and the Faith of all people.

Are You Called? If your life is centered around the Holy Eucharist, our Blessed Mother, personal and communal prayer and service, and to the Magisterium, we, the Mercedarian Friars, encourage you to write or call to seek more information. You are invited to share in our life. Become a part of the rich Mercedarian legacy left by our founder to live those words spoken by Jesus the Redeemer: *The Spirit of the Lord is upon me . . . for he has sent me to proclaim liberty to captives . . . and release to those in bondage.*

Make our future – yours. Please contact:

**Mercedarian Friars'
Vocation Director
6398 Drexel Road
Philadelphia, PA 19151-2596
215-877-4858**

Use the convenient Order of the B.V.M. of Mercy postcard for more information

Sisters of Our Lady of Mercy

Mercedarian Sisters

Responding with His Merciful Love for 132 years!

Our Community	– Founded by Venerable Mother Theresa of Jesus Bacq in 1864. – Marian Spirit: Living the life of Jesus in Mary, through Mary, and with Mary, the Mother of Mercy. – International communities in eight nations with nearly six hundred sisters. – Imbued with the Mercedarian mission of redeeming work for the most needy.
Our Life	– **Of vowed living in community:** leaving everything for love, to follow Christ in greater freedom. – **Of prayer:** faithful privileged encounters with the Lord which unite us to His Church through Holy Mass, Liturgy of the Hours, the Rosary, communal - Marian prayer, and meditation. – **Of authentic witness:** signified by our joyful, sisterly communion and the wearing of our simple Mercedarian habit and black veil.
Our Work	– **Is committed** to the freedom of Christ's Merciful Love for all. – **Is accomplished** through teaching children in elementary schools and catechetical programs; caring for the sick and elderly in homes and hospitals; nourishing souls through retreat and evangelization programs. – **Is qualified** by our Promise of Dedication to the spiritual and temporal welfare of all those who are entrusted to our care.
Are you called?	Our foundress learned to follow Christ realistically by discovering the price of that love. Her ideal: *To lose oneself in the abyss of Mary's heart in order to love and glorify Jesus* is still lived out today through us, her daughters. We live as little ones among the little ones of the Lord to carry out our mission of redeeming by responding with His Merciful Love. If you feel called to live completely, simply, and joyfully, please call or write for more information.

Sister M. Celinda, S.O.L.M.
Sisters of Our Lady of Mercy
400 Erial Road
Pine Hill, New Jersey 08021
Telephone: **609/435-2253**

Send the Mercedarian Sisters postcard in this book for more information

P.I.M.E. MISSIONARIES

REACHING THE UNEVANGELIZED

PIME priest and brothers with young people in Philippines.

History and Charism

The Pontifical Institute for Foreign Missions (P.I.M.E.) was founded in Italy in 1850 at the request of Pope Pius IX, exclusively for foreign mission work. In 1947, at the invitation of Edward Cardinal Mooney, Archbishop of Detroit, P.I.M.E. was established in the U.S. From the Detroit Headquarters, American men are recruited and sent to be trained as missionary priests and brothers.

Ministry and Service

The missionary spirit of the Apostles inspires P.I.M.E. communities all over the world. The common bond of love for Jesus Christ and service dedicated to His Church unites all P.I.M.E. missionaries.

P.I.M.E. is concerned with the total needs of the men, women and children served. So the work may range from general pastoral and parish ministry, to social ministry (like organizing agricultural cooperatives), to living a monastic type of life in dialogue with Hindus, Muslims and Buddhists. P.I.M.E. Brothers concentrate on catechetics and involvement with industrial arts training.

P.I.M.E.'s major thrust is among non-Christians in Asia, with other important works in Africa, South America and Oceania. The needs outstrip the available priests and brothers as P.I.M.E. has been invited to extend service to several regions. Mexico has most recently been added to the list of countries P.I.M.E. serves.

Formation Program

P.I.M.E.'s formation program has three distinct phases. In the college program, students live community life in a wing of the headquarters while working toward a liberal arts degree at the University of Detroit Mercy. There is a period of spirituality in an international setting which also includes a mission-exposure trip. At this point a candidate makes an " initial promise" of commitment to P.I.M.E. The final phase is four years of studies in an international theologate. It all results in ordination and assignment to the missions.

CONTACT: Fr. Claudio Corti
PIME Director of Vocations
17330 Quincy St.
Detroit, MI 48221

Phone:
(313) 342- 4066

Use our convenient postcard in this book for more information.

Passionist Nuns
Monastic, Contemplative, Cloistered

Throughout the history of the Church there have always been a few people who were called to leave all, go into the desert and there live a life of prayer and solitude in union with Christ. That call continues in twentieth century affluent America. Today's deserts are small cloistered, contemplative communities such as the Passionist Nuns. Here young women continue to seek the desert solitude and silence of monastic life in order to experience a life of prayer and contemplative knowledge of Jesus for the glory of the Father and the good of others.

Consecrating themselves totally to the mystery of the Passion and death of Jesus, the Passionist Nuns proclaim God's redemptive love for the world by their life of prayer, penance and community. Their message is one of hope — that the Cross of Christ is a testimony of love in a world of suffering.

for information, write or call:

Sister Mary Catherine, C.P.
Passionist Nuns
1151 Donaldson Highway
Erlanger, Kentucky 41018
Phone: 606-371-8568

Send one of the postcards in this book for more information.

SAME TRUTHS.
NEW FORMS!

EVANGELIZATION

...reaching out to those who have yet to experience the joy of the Gospel message.

RECONCILIATION

...bringing peace to Catholics alienated from the Church and responding to the wounds of society, the hunger for peace.

ECUMENISM

...seeking unity with other Christian traditions & fostering understanding with the Jewish People & those of other religions.

THE PAULIST FATHERS
MISSIONARIES TO NORTH AMERICA
MOVING THE CHURCH TOWARD THE 21ST CENTURY

Fr. John B. Ardis, CSP
415 West 59th Street
New York, NY 10019
Toll-free 800.235.3456
In N.Y. 212.757.4260

THE
PAULIST
FATHERS

Use our convenient postcard in this book for more information.

THE PIARISTS

The Piarists is an Order of priests and brothers founded by St. Joseph Calasanctius in 1617 as a Congregation and then an Order in 1621. St. Joseph was a Spaniard who had gone to Rome to better his career but, moved by the squalor and illiteracy of the poor children, found a different kind of success. Today his followers continue his charism throughout the world in Europe, Japan, Senegal, the Cameroons, South and Central America, Cuba, Mexico, Canada and the United States. The Province of the United States, or the American Province, consists of houses in Derby, New York; Devon, Pennsylvania; Washington, DC; and Ft. Lauderdale, Florida. In keeping with the tradition and spirit of its Founder, the American Province also opened a high school in the mountains of Eastern Kentucky for which nominal or no tuition is charged. In the United States we work primarily in secondary schools, but do work in elementary education with seventh and eighth graders or helping in nearby elementary schools. In addition many of the members are involved in various activities such as Boy Scouts, youth retreats, missionary activities to Mexico, etc.

Formation is adapted to each individual's particular educational background. Pre-novitiate, novitiate, and post-novitiate precede final profession and ordination. Members are encouraged to have their Bachelor Degrees in their subject field and are encouraged to acquire a Master's Degree as well. Teacher certification is required according to the demands of the various states in which the member is teaching. Degrees and/or certification are not pre-requisites for acceptance into the Order but a high school diploma is and the age requirement is under 35.

The Piarist is called to impart not only knowledge of the secular science but a knowledge of Christ and his salvific message and their relationship to the world by education in both Piety and Letters in accordance with the Order's mission to imbue its students with Piety and Letters *"Pietas et Litterae."* The ability to relate with young people both in and outside the classroom is a definite asset and part of the charism of the Piarist. Following Christ's command to, *"Go, teach all nations."*, the Piarist cares for the physical, intellectual and spiritual dimensions of youth.

Please call or write:
Rev. Leonard J. Gendernalik, Sch.P.
Piarist Vocational Office
99 Martha's Vineyard
Prestonsburg, KY 41653
(606)285-3950   (606) 874-9594

Send one of the postcards in this book for more information.

POOR CLARE COLETTINE

As enclosed, contemplative nuns we cherish the spirit of our Father St. Francis of Assisi who taught us to follow the Poor and Humble Christ and His Most Holy Mother through our Holy Mother St. Clare. Through her whose very name means light, we catch the fire of loving gratitude to God. She wrote in her Testament: "Among the other favors we have received and daily continue to receive from the Giver of all good gifts and for which we should render all the more thanks, great is the grace of our vocation."

A renewal of this Gospel way of living was given to us by our second mother, Saint Colette, who reformed our order in the fifteenth century. Love marked her entire existence as she strove generously to find practical expression for it within the enclosure.

We also seek to enflesh this rich heritage as we devote ourselves to creating and maintaining an atmosphere of quiet prayer and ready penance. Our prayer is focused on the Holy Mass, Exposition of the Blessed Sacrament and the Liturgy of the Hours. The Hour of Matins, chanted at midnight, is symbolic of the eschatological thrust of our life: an ardent thirst for the coming of the Lord Jesus as we hold precious every soul purchased by His Sacred Blood. Our penance is comprised of our fasting and abstinence, our manual labor and by our going barefoot. Our work consists in supplying altar breads, first Communion veils, spiritual remembrance cards and the care of our monastery and garden.

Our prayer is intensified and our penance lightened by sharing it with our sisters. Within the walls of the monastery we form a true and close family and experience together what it means to be a church in miniature, for we are at the heart of the Church for the needs of the Body of Christ.

CONTACT:
Corpus Christi Monastery
2111 South Main Street
Rockford, IL 61102
Tel: (815) 963-7343

Send one of the postcards in this book for more information

POOR SISTERS OF NAZARETH

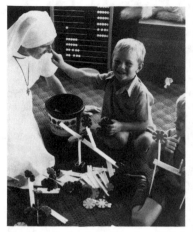

You are warmly invited to 'Come and See' the Poor Sisters of Nazareth. Our Sisters strive to live for God through their vowed consecration, cultivating deep prayer relationships with Christ in warm community living, selfless dedication to their particular apostolate. In imitation of the Holy Family, we aim to give children-in-need a real home and educate them in our own schools. We guarantee our elderly, frail residents loving care in a peace-filled, secure and happy home; while we value every opportunity to care for retired, sick Priests and Brothers.

Besides our five Nazareth Houses in the United States, we have over 50 other mission communities in various parts of Australia, New Zealand, American Samoa, South Africa, Zimbabwe, England, Ireland, Scotland and Wales. Young people today are generous, courageous and love a challenge! Nazareth offers it! So, whatever your capabilities or aptitudes, there is a place for you in our congregation. We have a variety of ministries - a special spot for every helping hand and heart! "Put your gifts at the service of one another, each in the measure you have received."(1 Peter 4:10)

Why not visit or call your nearest Nazareth House and see the realized ideals of our Foundress, Mother St. Basil (Victoire Larmenier), who in London, England in 1854, placed her God-given apostolate under the special protection of Jesus, Mary and Joseph.

Our first American foundation was at Mission San Diego in 1925. Like Blessed Junipero Serra we continue to maintain that mission of love laboring through California and beyond! There is no road more eloquent in service than the El Camino Real; yet this historic road is but the faintest shadow of that Way that leads to Eternal Happiness. Come, journey with us!

To find out how to make your own life more worthwhile please call, phone or write to:

Nazareth House	Nazareth House	Nazareth House
6333 Rancho Mission Rd	P.O. Box 596	245 Nova Albion Way
San Diego, CA 92108	Fatuoaiga Tafuna	San Rafael, CA 94903
(619) 563 0480	Pago Pago	(415) 479 8282
	American Samoa 96799	
	(684) 699 1446	
Nazareth House	Vocation Promoter	Nazareth House
2121 North First Street	Nazareth House	814 Jackson Street
Fresno, CA 93703	3333 Manning Avenue	Stoughton, WI 53589
(209) 237 2257	Los Angeles, CA 90064	(608) 873 6448
	(310) 839 2361	

Please send one of the postcards in this book for more information.

PROVIDENCE
God's call to the world ...

LISTEN

Called by the God of Providence, the Sisters of Providence
of Saint Mary-of-the-Woods listen and respond in ministry
of love, mercy and justice among the people of God.

Are you called too?

Let's talk. Contact the Sisters of Providence,
Saint Mary-of-the-Woods, Indiana 47876 812-535-4193.

Send one of the postcards in this book for more information.

What difference do you make?

What a difference you COULD make!

You CAN make a difference! And we invite you to join with us in making a difference in the world. We are the **Priests of the Sacred Heart** (SCJ), an international religious community of brothers and priests. As men dedicated to the Sacred Heart and nourished by the Eucharist, we live, pray and work together. Our Rule of Life calls us to be, especially among the poor, prophets of love and servants of reconciliation. We can be found in rural and urban settings, in missions at home and abroad, in traditional and new ministries, often working with others as we respond to people's hunger for justice and peace. If you are filled with a spirit of love and compassion, and want to make a difference in the world, we invite you to join us in community and mission.

*FOR MORE INFORMATION ON THE **PRIESTS OF THE SACRED HEART** CONTACT:*
Fr. Jack Kurps, SCJ
P.O. Box 206/GRM
Hales Corners, WI 53130-0206
414/529-4255
e-mail: 75512.1315@compuserve.com

Send one of the postcards in this book for more information.

Sisters of St. Joseph of LaGrange

Our work is as varied as the gifts God gave us.

Serving together, we bring our individual talents and energy to bear on a myriad of personal and social problems:

We heal the sick and listen to the lonely in clinical and pastoral settings.

We serve as hospital chaplains, nurses and as home (and nursing home) visitors. We enrich the practical, social and spiritual lives of the aging through Bethlehem Woods which opened in 1990 to provide retirement living apartments in our area.

We teach to enlighten and bring joy to students of all ages who desire the benefits of our rigorous academic coursework, fine arts training and religious studies.

Nazareth Academy was founded by our congregation in 1900 and is the most visible (though far from only) testament of our teaching ministry.

We support the work of parish communities.

We help coordinate care, direct spirituality programs, and provide outreach services for a number of pressing needs. We are pastoral associates.

We help the newly-arrived acclimate to their adopted American homeland.

We answer their immediate needs for food and housing, then address their need for English literacy as one of a number of tools necessary for successful living in this complex society.

We express our joy and gratitude for life through creative expression.

Our artists and musicians create compositions that touch the hearts of others. We teach fine arts. And we connect ourselves to our earth by celebrating and recognizing our responsibility to the marvelous universe which God has given us.

We strive for better tomorrows by actively promoting social justice in word and deed.

As members of the Illinois Committee for Responsible Investment and other active groups we recognize and work effectively for corporate responsibility based on the Gospel.

Contact: Sister Sue Torgersen, CSJ
Vocation Director
708-354-9200

Sisters of St. Joseph of LaGrange
1515 West Ogden Avenue, La Grange Park, Illinois 60526

"THAT ALL MAY BE ONE"

Send one of the postcards in this book for more information

Society of St. Paul

Pauline Fathers and Brothers

Alba House Publishers
Alba House Communications
Alba House Media

Communicating Christ...

Through book and
magazine publishing.

Through television, radio,
videos and audio tapes.

Through bookstores
and media centers.

Living Christ...

Through prayer and
sacramental life.

Through study and
reflection.

Through vowed life and
community fellowship.

Does this sound like a life for you?
Are you interested in communications ministry?
Write us!

Society of St. Paul Vocation Office

2187 Victory Boulevard
Staten Island, New York 10314-6603
or call (718) 698-3698

Use the convenient Society of St. Paul postcard in this book for more information

Welcome a child... for God's sake!

The words of Jesus: "Anyone who welcomes a child in my name, welcomes me." (Matthew 18:5) Father Lou believes this – believes enough to give it his whole life. So, as a Salesian of Don Bosco, he searches out the young, welcomes them, and in their midst he finds Jesus.

It's a deeply satisfying life for Father Lou and the more than 17,000 other Salesian priests and brothers in 100 countries around the world.

And maybe it's the life for you. To find out, mail in a postcard today to receive information that will help you decide. There's no obligation whatsoever - except, of course, for the one you may feel in your heart.

Write, call or fax us today!

Southern U.S.: Fr. Jonathan Parks, S.D.B.
P.O. Box 1233, Marrero, LA 70073
(504) 341-9109 • Fax (504) 341-9109

Western U.S.: Fr. John Roche, S.D.B.
P.O. Box 8067, Bellflower, CA 90706
(310) 925-0963 • Fax (310) 867-3929

Eastern U.S.: Br. Emil Dube', S.D.B.
Box 9000, West Haverstraw, NY 10993
(914) 429-1457 • E-Mail: salvoc @ aol.com

Send one of the postcards in this book for more information

SERVANTS OF CHARITY

Caring for:
- People with Mental Impairments
- Troubled Youth
- The Aged
- Poor Parishes

The Congregation of the Servants of Charity, often called GUANELLIANS, was founded in the early 1900's by Blessed Louis Guanella.

Father Guanella was one of those who took the Gospel seriously. He was not content to wait for the poor to come to him: he went and looked for the poor wherever he could find them! Under the impulse of the love of Christ, he spent his entire life and all his energies for the needy, those with mental impairments, the orphaned, and the aged. In order to reach out to more of them, Father Guanella sought others to share and continue his work. These are his religious followers–the Priests and Brothers of the Servants of Charity in whom he instilled his ardent spirit, so that more needs could be met, more people could be saved.

Today as yesterday "all the world is the homeland" to the Servants of Charity. They dedicate their lives for the sake of the poor in Italy, Switzerland, Spain, Israel, India, Philippines, United States, Mexico, Columbia, Chile, Paraguay, Brazil, Argentina, and Nigeria. Soon they will be in Poland, Guatemala, Madagascar, Ghana, Mozambique.

For further information, write to:

Fr. Silvio DeNard, S.C.		**Fr. Matthew Weber, S.C.**
Don Guanella Seminary		**St. Louis Center**
1795 Sproul Road	or	**16195 Old US 12**
Springfield, PA 19064		**Chelsea, MI 48118-9646**
or call: (610) 328-3406		**or call: (313) 475-8430**

Use the convenient Servants of Charity postcard in this directory for more information.

Priests and Brothers Helping Other Priests and Brothers. . .

SERVANTS OF THE PARACLETE

A community of men dedicated to ministry to priests and brothers.

Stress, vocational issues, and chemical dependency are some of the problems we are trained to deal with. We are assisted in these programs by professional lay-people.

We live in community according to the Evangelical Counsels. Our spirituality is Eucharistic, and our life is one of liturgical and personal prayer centered around our ministry.

Our work is truly rewarding, although it can be stressful at times. If you are a committed, mature man over twenty-five, with a caring and compassionate personality, we would like to hear from you.

ENQUIRIES SHOULD BE ADDRESSED TO:

REV. BENEDICT LIVINGSTONE s.P.
LOURDES NOVITIATE
SERVANTS OF THE PARACLETE
P.O. BOX 10
JEMEZ SPRINGS, NM 87025

The Helpers

A religious community

A vision,

A style of life

that is

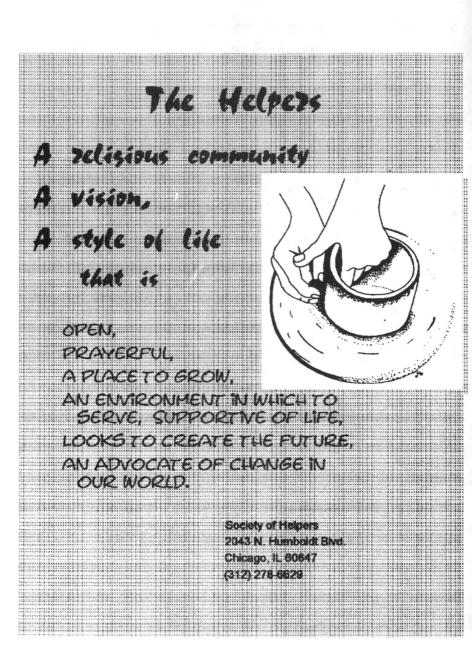

OPEN,
PRAYERFUL,
A PLACE TO GROW,
AN ENVIRONMENT IN WHICH TO
SERVE, SUPPORTIVE OF LIFE,
LOOKS TO CREATE THE FUTURE,
AN ADVOCATE OF CHANGE IN
OUR WORLD.

Society of Helpers
2043 N. Humboldt Blvd.
Chicago, IL 60647
(312) 278-6629

Send one of the postcards in this book for more information.

Somascan Fathers and Brothers

The Order of the Somascans was founded by St. Jerome Aemilian (1486-1537), a layman whom the Church proclaimed "the Father of orphans and Patron Saint of all needy youth".

Our lifestyle combines contemplation and action, within the framework of a joyful communal experience.

THE FOUNDER'S LEGACY

PRAYER
WORK
COMMUNITY

Why The Somascans?

Faithful to their Founder's legacy, through five centuries they have been, and still intend to be a community response to the Church call for helping all underprivileged youth, whether they happen to be affected by poverty, neglect, failure, emotional instability, lack of family support.

What Do The Somascans Do?

EVANGELIZATION
PASTORAL MINISTRIES
RELIGIOUS EDUCATION
YOUTH MINISTRY
ETHNIC MINORITIES APOSTOLATE
MISSION
MINISTRY TO THE POOR

How Do The Somascans Work?

Individual talents and gifts are brought together and shared for mutual support and for the service of the poor.

Where Do The Somascans Work?

USA
MEXICO
EL SALVADOR
HONDURAS
GUATEMALA
COLOMBIA
BRAZIL
PHILIPPINES
SPAIN
POLAND
ITALY
INDIA

Any person wanting to make his life count, might consider the opportunities of life within the Somascan Order.

Contact Somascan Fathers at:
– Pine Haven Boys Center
133 River Road – P.O. Box 162
Allenstown, NH 03275
– Sacred Heart Parish
49 Winthrop St.,
Hartford, CT 06103
– Assumption Church
901 Rose Lane
Houston, TX 77037

Send one of the postcards in this book for more information.

LAY DOWN YOUR NETS AND FOLLOW ME.◆

Nearly 2,000 years ago, His invitation was accepted by ordinary fishermen. Nearly 800 years ago, the same invitation was offered to John DeMatha, founder of the Trinitarians. Now the invitation is extended to you. An invitation to spread the Good News, to bring release to the captive, help to the hopeless, shelter to the homeless and the generosity of Christ to the poor.

Today, you'll find Trinitarians at work in hospitals and schools, prisons and shelters, parishes and missions. Are you ready to lay down your net and join us? Call 1-800-525-3554 or mail the coupon below.

THE TRINITARIANS
ORDER OF THE MOST HOLY TRINITY
A ROMAN CATHOLIC COMMUNITY OF
PRIESTS AND BROTHERS.

- -

PLEASE SEND ME YOUR FREE VOCATIONS BROCHURE.

Name_____

Address_____

City_____ State_____ Zip_____

Age_____ Education _____

Mail to: Fr. Albert Anuszewski, Director of Vocations, The Trinitarians, P.O. Box 5719, Baltimore, MD 21208

Stepping Stones..of Faith

Each day is a new stepping stone in our lives. We can choose to stand still and be "safe"...or listen to the gentle whisper of God and step out in faith.

God speaks to each one of us. Never in a loud voice...only a gentle whisper.

Is God whispering to you?

Take a step of faith. Be a Trinity Missionary. We bring the spirit of hope to the poor, the abandoned, and the neglected throughout the United States, Puerto Rico, Mexico and Costa Rica...one step at a time.

Vocation Director, Trinity Missions
P.O. Box 7130, Silver Spring, MD 20997-0702

Send one of the Trinity Missions Postcards in this book for more information.

The
Spirit
of faith, love, prayer, community, joy, gentleness, service, and sharing.

"Nothing is so strong as gentleness; nothing is so gentle as real strength."

St. Francis de Sales, Founder

Sisters of the Visitation

Live Jesus

You are invited to come, see, and share our way of life.

Contact:
Vocation Director
Monastery of the Visitation
3020 N. Ballas Road
St. Louis, MO 63131
314-432-5353

Send one of the postcards in this book for more information.

Xaverian Brothers

Committed - To the Gospel Message
- To the Poor and Marginalized

We Respond to God's Call:
>   *It is through you*
>   *that God desires to manifest His love*
>   *to the people of the world in these times,*
>   *and to offer them the freedom*
>   *of the children of God.*
>   *(Fundamental Principles of the Xaverian Brothers)*

For More Information, Contact

Xaverian Brothers
704 Brush Hill Road
Milton, MA 02186
(617) 333-0970

Xaverian Brothers
10318B Baltimore Nat'l Pike
Ellicott City, MD 21042
(410) 750-2850

Send one of the postcards in this book for more information

Index of Profiles

3 convenient ways to request vocation information

SPONSORED RETURN POSTCARD

Some religious communities have placed pre-addressed postcards in this guidebook which you can fill out and mail directly to their vocation office.

POSTPAID READER SERVICE CARD

Complete and mail one of these cards in order to receive literature from several religious communities active in your area of interest.

DIRECT RETURN POSTCARD

PLEASE APPLY POSTAGE

These cards are provided for you to fill out and mail directly to religious communities you would like to learn more about.

Vocations in the Catholic Church

"Then He said to His disciples, 'The harvest is ready but the laborers are few. Ask the harvest master to send out laborers to gather his harvest'." Mt. 9:37-38

Many influences come together to bring it about that a woman or a man decides to become more fully involved in the ministerial life of the church. This personal commitment can be temporary or permanent, partial or complete. Whatever form this calling may take, a Catholic believes that the Holy Spirit is the source of every authentic vocation. The instruments, the human means, of His work often include the living example of persons in a given church ministry. There is also the home, the classroom, the hospital, retreat houses, religious experience, reading, friends, prayer...the Bible itself. All of these, and other things also, contribute to a church vocation.

The full and permanent commitment involved in the religious life and priesthood has long had its place in Catholic tradition. Yet these callings are by no means the only vocation: in the best sense all Christians are called to a vocation in the community. Marriage itself, for example, is certainly a vocation. We list here not simply priesthood and religious life but other possibilities for ministry in the Church. And there are others not listed here, such as Third Orders, sodalities, covenant communities, etc. Information about these can be secured from local pastors or chanceries, or from the National Religious Vocation Conference.

It is the Spirit that the Father has sent through Christ that is at the center of a church vocation, just as Christ Himself is the head of the Church. Hence this kind of vocation, while it is certainly a matter of professional guidance and consultation on a "career" level, is also far more than that. Here the assistance of a competent spiritual director is invaluable. The work of the Spirit must be discerned. This discernment means, among other things, evaluating the qualities of a person who wishes to follow such a vocation.

The general qualifications for priesthood and the religious life (and similarly for other church-related occupations) include an appropriate level of spiritual life, emotional and physical health, and a level of intelligence and academic accomplishment consistent with the kind of life one seeks. One may enter some form of training as early as first-year high school or as late as "mid" or even later life. Most commonly, however, a man or woman enters a formation program after high school or college. The length of training varies depending upon when one enters a program, the extent of his or her background, and the specific traditions of a given community or diocese. Generally, for example, it takes the same amount of preparation to become a diocesan priest as for any other professional person: four years after college, or eight years after high school. Formal entrance into a seminary or community is often preceded by participation in an associate or affiliate program.

There is no obligation created by seeking the counsel of a trusted, knowledgeable advisor – and it is most important to do so.

A Catholic might wish to serve the Church, the people of God, in a specific, professional manner. This could be done as a diocesan priest, permanent deacon, religious brother, religious priest, religious sister, as a layman employed in a Church ministry or engaged in volunteer work, as a member of a Secular Institute or Opus Dei, or by participation in any number of Church organizations.

Diocesan Priest

A diocesan priest ordinarily serves the people of God in a given area, a diocese, as a parish priest. And yet diocesan priests are also involved in administration, campus ministry, hospital and prison chaplaincy, teaching and sometimes at foreign missions. Beneath the visible surface of these ministries lies an abiding prayerful relationship with the Lord for whose sake and for whose people he ministers. Information about the diocesan priesthood can be obtained from any diocesan priest, by contacting one or more of the diocesan vocation directors listed in **The Diocesan Priesthood** section of this book or by contacting:

The National Conference of Diocesan Vocation Directors
1603 S. Michigan Avenue–Suite 400
Chicago, IL 60616
(312) 663-5456

Permanent Deacon

Recently the Catholic Church restored the order of permanent dia-conate. A deacon is a man 35 years of age or older, married or single, who serves the people of God in the ordained diaconal ministry. His ministry is liturgical (preaching), sacramental (except the Eucharist and Penance), pastoral and social. Inquiry about deacons' training programs can be made at the local diocesan chancery office or by contacting one of the following:

The Bishop's Committee on the Permanent Diaconate
United States Catholic Conference
3211 Fourth St., N.E.
Washington, DC 20017
(202) 541-3038

National Association of Permanent Diaconate Directors
John Pistone, Deacon, Executive Director
1337 West Ohio St.
Chicago, IL 60622
(312) 226-4033

Religious Brother

As a male religious, a Brother is a lay Christian who commits himself to Christ and the Christian community by vows of poverty, chastity, and obedience. Not only is he in service to the community, he himself lives in a religious community that centers his life. It is from this root and from his own interior life that he is able to meet the needs of the Church in ministries such as teaching, social work, technical occupa-tions, etc. The ministries of religious Brothers are varied and reflect the traditions of a given community.

Flexibility to meet current needs is one of the main characteristics of the Brother's life style.

There are many communities of religious Brothers as well as commu-nities of Priests and Brothers. Often a man applies to a community with which he is familiar. Information about the Brotherhood may be obtained by writing to one or more vocation directors listed in the **Religious Communities for Men** section of this book or by contacting:

The National Religious Vocation Conference
1603 S. Michigan Avenue–Suite 400
Chicago, IL 60616
(312) 663-5454

Religious Priest

Some religious communities are "clerical": they include priests. What was said immediately above about life applies equally to priests living in religious communities. The religious priest takes vows of poverty, chastity, and obedience according to the spirit of his own congregation. Being a priest he is a minister, for the Church, of the sacraments. His work generally depends upon the ministry appropriate to his community and may include teaching, overseas ministry, social work, pastoral ministry, chaplaincy, etc. A person who feels called to this life may contact any member of a community with which he is familiar, by contacting one or more vocation directors listed in the **Religious Communities for Men** section of this book, or by contacting:

The National Religious Vocation Conference
1603 S. Michigan Avenue–Suite 400
Chicago, IL 60616
(312) 663-5454

Women Religious

A woman religious is a lay person who commits herself to Christ and to the Church by vows of poverty, chastity, and obedience. She lives in a religious community that follows a constantly renewed tradition, patterned on the life and teaching of the founder of the community. The work she generally does will depend upon the ministries of that community as influenced by the needs of the Church and its people, in areas such as teaching, social work, administration, technical skills, nursing, etc. The role of women in the Church is constantly developing and expanding. A significant part of that renewal is occuring within the faith communities of women religious. Prayer and work are part of the tradition of all communities but they are primarily contemplative while others are more active. Information about the vocation of a woman religious can be secured by contacting one or more of the vocation directors listed in the Religious Communities for Women section of this book or by contacting:

The National Religious Vocation Conference
1603 S. Michigan Avenue–Suite 400
Chicago, IL 60616
(312) 663-5454

Second Career Vocations
(Older Men and Women)

Second career vocations are not a new trend in the Catholic Church; for instance, all the apostles were men who had previous careers before they answered the calling of Jesus Christ.

Today, people from all walks of life, including retired men and women, leave successful careers as nurses, lawyers, engineers, teachers, secretaries, etc. to join or affiliate themselves with a religious community. They become priests, brothers, sisters or lay ministers with contemplative, evangelical or apostolic communities.

These men and women bring a wealth of talent to religious communities whether it be management know-how, a professional background, technical skill, etc.

Most religious communities listed in this publication have their own age restrictions on accepting second career vocations. There is no set age limit; each community should be contacted to find what age restrictions apply, if any. Generally, age is not a barrier for those men and women who are interested in religious ministry.

This also applies to men who are interested in becoming diocesan priests. All diocesan vocation directors are listed in this publication and should be contacted directly.

Seminary programs structured to meet the needs of the second career priestly candidate provide a unique seminary environment with a supportive peer community and experienced faculty. These seminaries are:

Sacred Heart School of Theology
7335 South Highway 100
P.O. Box 429
Hales Corners, WI 53130
(414) 425-8300

Pope John XXIII National Seminary
558 South Ave.
Weston, MA 02193-2699
(617) 899-5500

Holy Apostles College and Seminary
33 Prospect Hill Rd.
Cromwell, CT 06416
(203) 632-3003

Women who wish to enter the religious life as a second-career vocation should contact the individual congregation in which they are interested. These congregations are listed in the **Religious Communities for Women** section of this book.

Lay Person
(Church-Related Career)

Examples of this vocation would include service as a Director of Religious Education, campus minister, hospital chaplain, prison minister, pastoral associate, pastoral administrator or teacher. Such a person might be married or single. Someone specifically interested in these kinds of ministries should contact the local diocesan chancery and ask for the diocesan official responsible for the given area of interest. One also might contact Catholic colleges or schools of theology where there are graduate programs in ministry.

Lay Person
(Volunteer Service)

Usually this service extends for a year or two in a mission of the Church either in the U.S. or overseas. In this ever expanding group, opportunities are available for people to render service in numerous areas of Church activity. Religious communities affirm that lay extensions actually intensify their charism of service. People representing every type of service are incorporating positions for lay volunteers into the work they give in the Church. Young, old, married and single are responding to this challenge. The benefits include stipend, room and board, health insurance and some travel allotment. The personal rewards for a lay volunteer begin with the immeasurable gratitude expressed by those who are served. The blessings continue in ways bestowed by the Spirit and unique to each person.

Turn now to **The Lay Missionary** section of this book to discover which volunteer mission work holds the most promise for you. And/or, contact:

Catholic Network of Volunteer Service
4121 Harewood Road, N.E.
Washington, DC 20017-1593
(1-800) 543-5046

The St. Vincent Pallotti Center for Apostolic Development
Box 893, Cardinal Station
Washington, DC 20064
(202) 529-3330

Secular Institutes

Over 54,000 Catholic lay men, lay women and secular clergy belong to Secular Institutes throughout the world. The vocation of a consecrated secular is a vocation in, and of, the world. Members take vows of poverty, celibacy and obedience, but do not wear distinctive religious clothing or live in community as do members of religious orders. Generally, members live alone or with their families and hold regular jobs. They come together for periodic meetings, retreats and spiritual renewal. For information about Secular Institutes, contact one or more of the Institutes listed elsewhere in this book or write to:

Dr. Helen St. Denis, President
United States Conference of Secular Institutes
P.O. Box 4556, 12th St., N.E.,
Washington, DC 20017

Opus Dei

Opus Dei is a personal Prelature of the Catholic Church. Its mission is to remind all people that they are called to holiness, especially through work and ordinary life. The principal activity of the Prelature is to provide spiritual assistance to its faithful. While the primary apostolate of Opus Dei is carried out personally by each of its members, some members on their own initiative and responsibility along with others in their communities organize social, charitable or educational activities to meet societal needs. Opus Dei only provides for the spiritual direction of these activities.

Opus Dei
524 North Ave., Ste. 200
New Rochelle, NY 10801
(914) 235-1201

Harvest

Harvest Prayer Association for Vocations wants to bring people to discover prayer as the true solution to the need of vocations in the Church, according to the words of the Gospels: "The Harvest is abundant but the laborers are few. Pray therefore the Lord of the harvest to send out laborers to gather in His harvest." (Mt. 9:37; Lk. 10:2) The goals of the Association are: to make its members aware of their personal Christian vocation in their daily life through prayer and action; to pray every day for numerous and holy vocations to the Church and that those who have accepted God's call may persevere; to offer part of the joys and sufferings of their daily life for vocations and to proclaim, everywhere, the importance of heeding Jesus' command to pray for vocations according to their possibilities. Everyone – religious men and women and lay people – can join Harvest. For information, contact:

Harvest Prayer Association for Vocations
Rogationist Fathers
9815 Columbus Ave.
North Hills, CA 91343
(818) 894-2546

The Diocesan Priesthood

ALABAMA
Diocese of Birmingham
Father Frank Muscolino,
Vicar for Vocations
St. Stephen University Parish
1515 12th Ave.
Birmingham, AL 35205
(205) 933-2500

Archdiocese of Mobile
Rev. Mark Neske,
Vocation Director
2053 Government St.
Mobile, AL 36606
(205) 478-3381

ALASKA
Archdiocese of Anchorage
Rev. Steven Moore,
Vocation Director
2111 Muldoon Rd.
Anchorage, AK 99504
(907) 337-1538

Diocese of Fairbanks
Fr. John Hinsvark,
Vocation Director
St. Joseph's Parish
Box 1010
Nome, AK 99762
(907) 443-5527

Diocese of Juneau
Rev. Michael Nash,
Vocation Director
P.O. Box 508
Petersburg, AK 99833
(907) 772-3257

ARIZONA
Diocese of Phoenix
Rev. R. Clements,
Vocation Office for Diocesan
   Priesthood
400 E. Monroe St.
Phoenix, AZ 85004
(602) 257-0030

Diocese of Tucson
Rev. Patrick M. Crino,
Director of Vocations
P.O. Box 31
192 S. Stone Ave.

Tucson, AZ 85702-0031
(520) 792-3410 (Office)

ARKANSAS
Diocese of Little Rock
Fr. David Le Sieur,
Vocation Director
John Hall,
Associate Director
2500 N. Tyler St.
P.O. Box 7565
Little Rock, AR 72217
(501) 664-0340

CALIFORNIA
Diocese of Fresno
Rev. Roderick Craig,
Vocation Director
1550 N. Fresno St.
Fresno, CA 93703
(209) 488-7400

Archdiocese of Los Angeles
Fr. Richard Martini,
Sr. Kathleen Bryant, R.S.C.,
Vocation Directors
Fr. David M. Velazquez,
Hispanic Vocation Director
1531 W. Ninth St.
Los Angeles, CA 90015
(213) 251-3248

Diocese of Monterey
Rev. Antonio Sanchez,
Vocation Director
680 College St.
Hollister, CA 95023
(408) 637-9212

Diocese of Oakland
Fr. Fernando Cortez,
Director of Vocations
Office of Vocations,
2900 Lakeshore Ave.
Oakland, CA 94610
(510) 893-4711

Diocese of Orange
Rev. Msgr. Daniel J. Murray,
Vocation Director
2811 E. Villa Real Dr.
Orange, CA 92667
(714) 282-3000

Diocese of Sacramento
Rev. James Murphy,
Vocation Director
Rev. Humberto Gomez,
Vocation Director for Hispanics
2110 Broadway, #258,
Sacramento, CA 95818
(916) 733-0258

Diocese of San Bernardino
Vocation Director
1450 N. "D" St.
San Bernardino, CA 92405-4790
(909) 384-8216

Diocese of San Diego
Fr. Jaime Escobedo,
Fr. Cavana Wallace,
Directors for Priestly Vocations
3888 Paducah Drive
P.O. Box 85728
San Diego, CA 92186-5728
(619) 490-8200
Sr. Nancy Kane,
Director, Office for Women
   Religious
P.O. Box 85728
San Diego, CA 92186
(619) 490-8289

Archdiocese of San Francisco
Rev. Jerome P. Foley,
Director of Vocations/Seminarians
445 Church St.
San Francisco, CA 94114-1799
(415) 565-3618

Diocese of San Jose
Rev. Richard J. Garcia,
Vocation Director
900 Lafayette St., Suite 301
Santa Clara, CA 95050
(408) 983-0149

Diocese of Santa Rosa
Rev. Hans Ruygt,
Director of Vocations
P.O. Box 1297
Santa Rosa, CA 95402
(707) 545-7610

Diocese of Stockton
Rev. Bill McDonald, S.T.L.,
Vocation Director

P.O. Box 4237
Stockton, CA 95204
(209) 466-0636

COLORADO
Diocese of Colorado Springs
Fr. George Fagen,
Director of Vocations
29 West Kiowa St.
Colorado Springs, CO 80903
(719) 636-2345

Archdiocese of Denver
Rev. Tom Fryar,
Director of Vocations
Sr. Sharon Ford, RSM,
Associate Director
200 Josephine St.
Denver, CO 80206
(303) 388-4411

Diocese of Pueblo
Rev. David L. Ricken,
Vocations Director
1001 N. Grand Ave.
Pueblo, CO 81003
(719) 544-9861

CONNECTICUT
Diocese of Bridgeport
Fr. Stephen DiGiovanni,
Vocation Director
Saint John Fisher Seminary
    Residence
894 Newfield Ave.
Stamford, CT 06905
(203) 322-5331

Archdiocese of Hartford
Rev. John J. Dietrich,
Vocation Director
467 Bloomfield Ave.
Bloomfield, CT 06002
(203) 286-7670

Diocese of Norwich
Rev. Msgr. Thomas R. Bride, P.A.,
Vocation Director
Box 587 (201 Broadway)
Norwich, CT 06360
(203) 887-9294

DELAWARE
Diocese of Wilmington
Rev. Charles C. Dillingham,
Vocation Director
1925 Delaware Ave.
P.O. Box 2030
Wilmington, DE 19899
(302) 573-3113

DISTRICT OF COLUMBIA
**Archdiocese of Washington/
Suburban Maryland**
Rev. Mark Brennan,
Vocations Director for Men
Archdiocesan Pastoral Center
P.O. Box 29260
Washington, DC 20017-0260
(301) 853-4580

FLORIDA
Archdiocese of Miami
Father Gary F. Wiesmann,
Director of Vocations
9401 Biscayne Blvd.
Miami Shores, FL 33138
(305) 757-6241, ext. 271

Diocese of Orlando
Rev. Richard Trout,
Vocation Director
P.O. Box 1800
Orlando, FL 32802
(407) 425-3556

Diocese of Palm Beach
Rev. Louis Guerin,
Director of Vocations
Sr. John Kevin McNulty, O.S.F.
Assistant Director for Religious
    Vocations
P.O. Box 109650
9995 N. Military Trail
Palm Beach Gardens, FL
    33410-9650
(407) 775-9500

**Diocese of Pensacola-
Tallahassee**
Rev. Joseph P. Callipare,
Vocation Director
P.O. Drawer 17329
Pensacola, FL 32522
(904) 432-1515

Diocese of St. Augustine
Rev. John Tetlow,
Director of Vocations
Catholic Center
P.O. Box 24000
Jacksonville, FL 32241-4000
(904) 262-3200

Diocese of St. Petersburg
Rev. Michael T. O'Brien,
Director of Vocations
Catherine J. Ouellette,
Administrative Assistant
P.O. Box 43022
St. Petersburg, FL 33743
(813) 345-3338, Ext. 348

Diocese of Venice
Fr. Joseph Stearns,
Director of Vocations
St. William's Church
750 Seagate Dr.
Naples, FL 33940
(813) 261-4883

GEORGIA
Archdiocese of Atlanta
Rev. Don Kenny,
Vocation Director
680 W. Peachtree St., N.W.
Atlanta, GA 30308
(404) 888-7802

Diocese of Savannah
Rev. Allan McDonald,
Vocation Director
P.O. Box 2446
Augusta, GA 30903-2446
(706) 722-4944
Rev. Brett Brannen,
Assistant Vocation Director
St. Joseph Church
830 Poplar St.
Macon, GA 31201
(912) 745-1631

HAWAII
Diocese of Honolulu
Office of Clergy/Vocations
Rev. Alan Nagai
St. Stephen Diocesan Center
6301 Pali Hwy.
Kaneohe, HI 96744
(808) 263-8844

IDAHO
Diocese of Boise
Rev. Gerald J. Funke,
Vocation Director
P.O. Box 50899
Idaho Falls, ID 83405
(208) 522-4366

ILLINOIS
Diocese of Belleville
Rev. Kenneth Schaefer,
Vocation Director
2620 Lebanon Ave.
Belleville, IL 62221
(618) 235-9601

Archdiocese of Chicago
Rosy Santiago,
Rev. John Barkemeyer,
Vocation Directors
155 E. Superior St.
Chicago, IL 60611
(312) 751-5240

Diocese of Joliet
Rev. John Regan,
Vocation Director
St. Charles Pastoral Center
402 S. Independence Blvd.
Romeoville, IL 60441
(815) 834-4004

Diocese of Peoria
Rev. David Kipfer,
Vocation Director
607 N.E. Madison Ave.
P.O. Box 1406
Peoria, IL 61655
(309) 671-1568

Diocese of Rockford
Very Rev. Michael Binsfeld,
Vocation Director
1226 N. Church St.
Rockford, IL 61103
(815) 965-5767

Diocese of Springfield
Rev. Michael R. Kuse,
Vocation Director
453 East State St.
Jacksonville, IL 62650
(1-217) 245-6184

INDIANA
Diocese of Evansville
Father Bernard Etienne,
Vocation Director
P.O. Box 4169
4200 N. Kentucky Ave.
Evansville, IN 47724-0169
(812) 424-5536

**Diocese of Fort Wayne-
South Bend**
Rev. Bernard J. Galic,
Vocation Director
114 W. Wayne St.
South Bend, IN 46601
(219) 234-0687

Diocese of Gary
Rev. Stephen G. Gibson,
Vocation Director
822 W. 144th St.
East Chicago, IN 46312
(219) 391-9043

Archdiocese of Indianapolis
Rev. Paul D. Etienne,
Vocation Director
P.O. Box 1410
1400 N. Meridian St.
Indianapolis, IN 46206-1410
(317) 236-1490

Diocese of Lafayette-in-Indiana
Rev. Theodore Rothrock,
Vocation Director
St. Patrick's Church
502 S. Michigan St.
Oxford, IN 47971
(317) 849-9245

IOWA
Diocese of Davenport
Rev. Paul E. Connolly,
Vocation Director
Saint Vincent Center
2706 N. Gaines St.
Davenport, IA 52804-1998
(319) 324-1911

Diocese of Des Moines
Rev. David P. Fleming,
Vocation Director
Sister Eileen Malloy, C.S.C.,
Associate Director
P.O. Box 1816
Des Moines, IA 50306
(515) 243-7653

Archdiocese of Dubuque
Rev. Joseph L. Hauer,
Director of Seminarians
Jennifer Rausch, PBVM,
Director of Vocation Awareness
and Promotion
Rev. Richard Mihm,
Associate Director of Vocations
Archdiocesan Center
1229 Mt. Loretta Ave., Box 479
Dubuque, IA 52004-0479
(319) 556-2580

Diocese of Sioux City
Rev. Daniel Guenther,
Vocation Director
1021 Douglas St.
Sioux City, IA 51105
(712) 252-0573

KANSAS
Diocese of Dodge City
Fr. Brian Hipp,
Vocation Director
St. Mary's
509 St. John St.
Garden City, KS 67846-5294
(316) 275-4204

Archdiocese of Kansas City
Rev. Dennis Schmitz,
Vocation Director
Catholic Church Offices
12615 Parallel Parkway
Kansas City, KS 66109
(913) 721-1570

Diocese of Salina
Father Kevin Weber,
Vocations Coordinator
103 North 9th
Salina, KS 67402
(913) 827-8746

Diocese of Wichita
Rev. Matthew C. McGinness,
Vocation Director
424 N. Broadway
Wichita, KS 67202
(316) 269-3900

KENTUCKY
Diocese of Covington
Rev. Gerald L. Reinersman,
Director Pastoral Ministry
Formation Office
P.O. Box 18548
Covington, KY 41018-0548
(606) 283-6300

Diocese of Lexington
Rev. William Brown,
Director of Vocations
P.O. Box 12350
Lexington, KY 40582-2350
(606) 253-1993

Archdiocese of Louisville
Rev. Stephen Pohl,
Vocation Director
1935 Lewiston Dr.
Louisville, KY 40216-2569
(502) 448-8581

Diocese of Owensboro
Father Brad Whistle,
Vocation Director
St. Romuald Parish
North Main St.
Hardinsburg, KY 40143
(502) 756-2356

LOUISIANA
Diocese of Alexandria
Rev. Daniel O'Connor,
Director of Vocations
P.O. Box 7417
Alexandria, LA 71306-0417
(318) 445-2401

Diocese of Baton Rouge
Rev. M. Jeffery Bayhi,
Vocation Director and Director of
Seminarians
Sister Dianne Heinrich, CDP,
Associate Director of Seminarians
P.O. Box 2028
Baton Rouge, LA 70821
(504) 387-0561

Diocese of Houma-Thibodaux
Rev. Danny Poche,
Vocation Director
P.O. Box 9077
Houma, LA 70361
(504) 868-7720

Diocese of Lafayette
Rev. W. Curtis Mallet,
Vocation Director
1408 Carmel Ave.
Lafayette, LA 70501
(318) 261-5690

Diocese of Lake Charles
Rev. Aubrey V. Guilbeau,
Vocation Director
4029 Ave. G
Lake Charles, LA 70615
(318) 439-7430

Archdiocese of New Orleans
Rev. Henry Bugler,
Director of Vocations
Sr. Marina Aranzabal, STJ,
Associate Director of Vocations
7887 Walmsley Ave.
New Orleans, LA 70125
(504) 861-6298

Diocese of Shreveport
Rev. Rothell Price,
Director of Vocations
Rev. Tim Hurd,
Associate Director of Vocations
2500 Line Ave.
Shreveport, LA 71104
(318) 222-2006

MAINE
Diocese of Portland
Rev. Thomas M. Murphy,
Vocation Director
P.O. Box 11559
Portland, ME 04104-7559
(207) 773-6471

MARYLAND
Archdiocese of Baltimore
Rev. James M. Barker,
Director of Vocations
320 Cathedral St.
Baltimore, MD 21201-4415
(410) 547-5426

MASSACHUSETTS
Archdiocese of Boston
Rev. Robert W. Flagg,
Vocation Director
Archdiocese of Boston
Vocation Office
127 Lake St.
Brighton, MA 02135
(617) 254-2610

Diocese of Fall River
Rev. Msgr. John J. Smith,
Vocation Director
5 Barbara St.
South Yarmouth, MA 02664
(508) 398-2248

Diocese of Springfield
Rev. John J. Bonzagni,
Director of Vocations
625 Carew St.
Springfield, MA 01104-1999
(413) 732-3175

Diocese of Worcester
Rev. Thomas Sullivan,
Vocation Director
49 Elm St.
Worcester, MA 01609
(508) 791-7171

MICHIGAN
Archdiocese of Detroit
Rev. Robert Fisher,
Vocation Director
Sr. Angela Cerna-Plata, IHM,
Associate Vocation Director
305 Michigan Ave.
Detroit, MI 48226
(313) 237-5875

Diocese of Gaylord
Rev. James Hayden,
Director of Priestly Vocations
1665 West M-32
Gaylord, MI 49735
(517) 732-5147

Diocese of Grand Rapids
Rev. Raymond Bruck,
Vocation Director
Holy Family Parish
9669 Craft Road
Caledonia, MI 49316
(616) 891-9259

Diocese of Kalamazoo
Rev. Michael A. Osborn,
Director
Office of Vocations
215 N. Westnedge Ave.
Kalamazoo, MI 49007-3760
(616) 349-7722

Diocese of Lansing
Department of Education and
　　Formation
Rev. Mark Inglot,
Director of Seminarians
Sr. Carla Moeggenborg, O.P.,
Director of Vocation Services
300 W. Ottawa St.
Lansing, MI 48933
(517) 342-2504

Diocese of Marquette, MI
Rev. James Ziminski,
Director of Vocations
444 S. Fourth, P.O. Box 550
Marquette, MI 49855-0550
(906) 228-3302

Diocese of Saginaw
Rev. Thomas Moore, O.S.F.S.,
Director of Seminarians
5800 Weiss St.
Saginaw, MI 48603
(517) 799-7910

MINNESOTA
Diocese of Crookston
Rev. Michael Foltz,
Vocation Director
Rev. Larry Delaney,
Associate Vocation Director
P.O. Box 610
Crookston, MN 56716
(218) 281-4533

Diocese of Duluth
Rev. Steven Daigle,
Director of Vocation Recruitment
Rev. David Tushar,
Director of Seminarians
2830 East 4th St.
Duluth, MN 55812
(218) 724-9111

Diocese of New Ulm
Rev. Joseph A. Steinbeisser,
Vocations Director
Sr. Sue Torgersen, CSJ,
Associate Director
Catholic Pastoral Center
1400 6th St. N.
New Ulm, MN 56073-2099
(507) 359-2966

Diocese of St. Cloud
Deacon Mike Keable,
Director
Offices of Vocations & Diaconate
305 7th Ave. N.
St. Cloud, MN 56303-3633
(612) 251-5001

Diocese of Winona
Rev. Timothy T. Reker,
Vocation Director
Saint Mary's University #43
700 Terrace Heights
Winona, MN 55987-1399
(507) 457-7373

**Archdiocese of St. Paul
& Minneapolis**
Fr. Stan Mader,
Fr. John L. Ubel,
Vocation Directors
2260 Summit Ave.
St. Paul, MN 55105
(612) 962-6890

MISSOURI
Diocese of Jefferson City
Rev. James P. McNally,
Co-Director for Priestly Vocations
245 N. Levering, P.O. Box 858
Hannibal, MO 63401
(314) 221-4330
Sr. Jean Greenwald, SCC,
Co-Director for Religious
　　Vocations
P.O. Box 417
Jefferson City, MO 65102
(314) 635-9127

**Diocese of Kansas City-
St. Joseph**
Rev. Donald Farnan,
Vocation Director
P.O. Box 419037
Kansas City, MO 64141-6037
(816) 756-1850

Diocese of Springfield-Cape Girardeau
Rev. David F. Hulshof,
Vocation Director
Rev. Thomas P. Kiefer,
Associate Vocation Director
601 South Jefferson
Springfield, MO 65806-3143
(417) 866-0841

Archdiocese of St. Louis
Rev. William Kempf,
Rev. Mike Butler,
Sr. Jeanette Hemmer, C.PP.S.,
Vocation Directors
5200 Glennon Dr.
St. Louis, MO 63119
(314) 647-5270

MISSISSIPPI
Diocese of Biloxi
Msgr. James Russell,
Vocation Director
P.O. Box 367
Biloxi, MS 39533
(601) 374-1717

Diocese of Jackson
Rev. Bill Henry,
Director of Vocations
P.O. Box 2248
Jackson, MS 39225-2248
(601) 969-1880; (601) 982-5020

MONTANA
Diocese of Great Falls-Billings
Rev. Dale Yurkovic,
Vocation Director
P.O. Box 646
Livingston, MT 59047
(406) 222-1393

Diocese of Helena
Rev. Thomas O'Donnell,
Vocation Director
Risen Christ Parish
65 West Evergreen Dr.
Kalispell, MT 59901
(406) 752-4219
Rev. Leo Proxell,
Director, Borromeo Pre-Seminary
Program
Carroll College
Helena, MT 59625
(406) 447-4336

NEBRASKA
Diocese of Grand Island
Rev. Bryan Ernest,
Vocation Director
Holy Rosary Church
1104 Cheyenne
Alliance, NE 69301
(308) 762-2009

Diocese of Lincoln
Rev. Msgr. Leonard I. Kalin,
Vocation Director
Fr. Joel Panzer,
Assistant Vocation Director
St. Thomas Aquinas Church
320 N. 16th St.
Lincoln, NE 68508
(402) 474-7914

Archdiocese of Omaha
Rev. Mark D. Filips,
Director of Vocations
James P. Coyle,
Associate Director of Vocations
100 North 62nd Street
Omaha, NE 68132-2702
(402) 558-3100

NEVADA
Diocese of Las Vegas
Fr. Patrick Leary,
Vocation Director
P.O. Box 18316
Las Vegas, NV 89114
(702) 735-9605

Diocese of Reno
Bro. Matthew Cunningham, S.R.,
Vocation Director
P.O. Box 1211
Reno, NV 89504
(702) 329-9274

NEW HAMPSHIRE
Diocese of Manchester
Rev. Anthony R. Frontiero,
Rev. Marc F. Guillemette,
Co-Directors of Vocations
153 Ash St., P.O. Box 310
Manchester, NH 03105
Office (603) 669-3100, ext. 116

NEW JERSEY
Diocese of Camden
Rev. Louis Marucci,
Director of Vocations
Sr. Daniel Marie, D.M.,
Associate Director of Vocations
Camden Diocesan Center
1845 Haddon Ave.
Camden, NJ 08103
(609) 756-7966

Archdiocese of Newark
Rev. James S. Choma,
Vocation Director
Rev. William P. Sheridan,
Assistant Vocation Director
171 Clifton Ave.
Newark, NJ 07104-9500
(201) 497-4365; 4367; 4368

Diocese of Metuchen
Rev. Robert G. Lynam,
Director of Vocations

Neumann House
P.O. Box 48
24 Library Place
Metuchen, NJ 08840
(908) 549-9770

Diocese of Paterson
Rev. Paul Manning,
Chairman, Vocation Board
737 Valley Rd.
Clifton, NJ 07013
(201) 777-2955

Diocese of Trenton
Rev. Robert M. Tynski,
Director of Vocation Recruitment
Rev. Phillip C. Pfleger,
Director of Seminarians
Vocation Centre
701 Lawrenceville Rd.
Trenton, NJ 08648
(609) 882-7125

NEW MEXICO
Diocese of Gallup
Rev. Joaquim Blonski,
Vocation Director
Our Lady of Guadalupe
P.O. Box 250
Holbrook, AZ 86025
(520) 524-3261

Diocese of Las Cruces
Fr. Richard Catanach,
Vocation Director
Charlie Russell,
Program Director
St. Eleanor Parish
P.O. Box S
Ruidoso, NM 88345
(505) 257-2330

Archdiocese of Santa Fe
Fr. John Carney,
Vocation Director
Catholic Center
4000 St. Joseph Pl., N.W.
Albuquerque, NM 87120
(505) 831-8143

NEW YORK
Diocese of Albany
Rev. John Molyn,
Vocation Director
40 N. Main Ave.
Albany, NY 12203
(518) 453-6670

Diocese of Brooklyn
Rev. Robert Whelan,
Director of Vocations
Sr. Regina Wilson, I.H.M.,
Associate Director of Vocations
P.O. Box C
75 Greene Ave.
Brooklyn, NY 11202
(718) 399-5900, ext. 5555

B-13

Diocese of Buffalo
Rev. Msgr. Paul J. E. Burkard,
Assistant to the Bishop for Priestly
Formation and Vocations
Rev. Thomas Doyle,
Associate Vocation Director
Sr. Suzanne M. Kush, C.S.S.F.,
Associate Vocation Director
Catholic Center
795 Main St.
Buffalo, NY 14203
(716) 847-5535

Archdiocese of New York
Rev. Robert F. McKeon,
Vocation Director
St. Joseph's Seminary
Yonkers, NY 10704
(914) 968-1340
Sr. Deanna Sabetta,
Director-Women's Vocations
1011 First Ave.
New York, NY 10022
(212) 371-1000

Diocese of Ogdensburg
Rev. Donald Robinson,
Vocation Director
Wadhams Hall Seminary-College
Ogdensburg, NY 13669
(315) 393-4231

Diocese of Rochester
Rev. John De Socio,
Asst. to the Bishop for Vocations &
Priestly Formation
314 Gregory St.
Rochester, NY 14620
(716) 461-2890

Diocese of Rockville Centre
Rev. William Koenig,
Vocation Director
50 N. Park Ave.
Rockville Centre, NY 11570
(516) 678-5800

Diocese of Syracuse
Rev. Neal E. Quartier,
Director of Seminarians
240 E. Onondaga St.
P.O. Box 511
Syracuse, NY 13201-0511
(315) 470-1452

NORTH CAROLINA
Diocese of Charlotte
Rev. Francis J. O'Rourke,
Vocation Director
1621 Dilworth Rd., E.
Charlotte, NC 28203
(704) 334-2283

Diocese of Raleigh
Rev. John A. Ranalli,
Vocations Director
The Catholic Center
300 Cardinal Gibbons Dr.

Raleigh, NC 27606
(919) 821-9713
(919) 821-9705 Fax

NORTH DAKOTA
Diocese of Bismarck
Rev. Msgr. Gerald J. Walsh,
Vocation Director
P.O. Box 1137
Bismarck, ND 58502
(701) 222-3035

Diocese of Fargo
Rev. Jeffrey L. Wald,
Diocesan Vocation Office
100 35th Ave., N.E.
Fargo, ND 58102-1299
(701) 232-8969

OHIO
Archdiocese of Cincinnati
Rev. Mark T. Watkins,
Vocation Director
100 E. Eighth St.
Cincinnati, OH 45202
(513) 421-3131

Diocese of Cleveland
Sr. Mary Rose Kocab, SIW,
Father Bob Stec,
Co-Directors
1031 Superior Ave., #721
Cleveland, OH 44114
(216) 696-6525, ext. 349

Diocese of Columbus
Rev. Theodore Sill,
Director of Vocations
197 E. Gay St.
Columbus, OH 43215
(614) 221-5565

Diocese of Steubenville
Rev. Kevin Greenwood,
Vocation Director
411 S. Fifth St.
Steubenville, OH 43952
(614) 282-7322

Diocese of Toledo
Rev. William Kubacki,
Vicar for Seminarians
Sr. Joyce Marie Bates, S.N.D.,
Ministry and Adult Formation
P.O. Box 985
Toledo, OH 43697-0985
(419) 244-6711

Diocese of Youngstown
Rev. Kenneth Miller,
Vocation Director
Sr. Dianne Livingstone, MHSH,
Associate Director
144 W. Wood St.
Youngstown, OH 44503
(216) 744-8451

OKLAHOMA
Archdiocese of Oklahoma City
Rev. John R. Metzinger,
Vocations Director
P.O. Box 32180
Oklahoma City, OK 73123
(405) 721-9351

Diocese of Tulsa
Rev. Timothy Davison,
Vocation Director
Catholic Student Center
University of Tulsa
4040 South Florence
Tulsa, OK 74104-2436
(918) 599-0204

OREGON
Diocese of Baker
Rev. Ron Maag,
Vocation Director
St. Peter Church
P.O. Box 41
The Dalles, OR 97058
(503) 296-2026

Archdiocese of Portland
Rev. Liam Cary,
Vocation Director
2838 E. Burnside St.
Portland, OR 97214
(503) 234-5334

PENNSYLVANIA
Diocese of Allentown
Rev. Msgr. Robert J. Wargo,
Vocation Director
202 N. 17th St. (P.O. Box F)
Allentown, PA 18105
(215) 437-0755
Rev. William F. Glosser,
Chairman, Recruitment
Committee
900 W. Market St.
Orwigsburg, PA 17961
(717) 366-1405

Diocese of Altoona-Johnstown
Rev. Robert Kelly,
Director of Vocations
124 Logan Blvd.
Hollidaysburg, PA 16648
(814) 695-5579

Diocese of Erie
Rev. Theodore B. Marconi,
Vocation Director
St. Mark Center
P.O. Box 10397
Erie, PA 16514-0397
(814) 824-1200

Diocese of Greensburg
Rev. Joseph P. Maddalena,
Vocation Director
723 E. Pittsburgh St.
Greensburg, PA 15601
(412) 837-0901

Diocese of Harrisburg
Rev. Thomas J. Rozman,
Vocation Director
4800 Union Deposit Rd.
P.O. Box 2161
Harrisburg, PA 17105-2161
(717) 657-4804

Archdiocese of Philadelphia
Rev. Gregory J. Parlante,
Vocation Director for Diocesan
  Priesthood
St. Charles Borromeo Seminary
1000 East Wynnewood Rd.
Wynnewood, PA 19096-3028
(610) 667-5778

Diocese of Pittsburgh
Rev. Edward J. Burns,
Vocation Director
2900 Noblestown Rd.
Pittsburgh, PA 15205
(412) 928-5836

Diocese of Scranton
Rev. Albert M. Liberatore,
Diocesan Director of Vocations
St. Pius X Seminary
1000 Seminary Rd.
Dalton, PA 18414
(717) 563-1131
Rev. James Paisley,
Dio. Director of Vocation Promotion
St. Maria Goretti Church
42 Redwood Dr.
Laflin, PA 18702
(717) 655-8956
Sr. M. Gabriel Kane, IHM,
Assoc. Dir. of Vocation Promotion
300 Wyoming Ave.
Scranton, PA 18503
(717) 346-8947

RHODE ISLAND
Diocese of Providence
Rev. Francis P. Kayatta,
Vocation Director
485 Pleasant Ave.
Providence, RI 02908
(401) 331-1316
Sr. Georgette Chasse, R.S.M.,
Associate Director
One Cathedral Square
Providence, RI 02903
(401) 278-4633
Rev. Marcel E. Pincince,
Associate Director
485 Mt. Pleasant Ave.
Providence, RI 02908
(401) 831-8011

SOUTH CAROLINA
Diocese of Charleston
Rev. Henry T. Barron,
Vicar for Vocations
The Diocese of Charleston
1662 Ingram Rd.
Charleston, SC 29407
(803) 769-2184

SOUTH DAKOTA
Diocese of Rapid City
Rev. Arnie Kari,
Vocation Director
Box 309
Philip, SD 57567
(605) 859-2664

Diocese of Sioux Falls
Fr. Terry Weber,
Vocation Director
3100 W. 41st St.
Sioux Falls, SD 57105
(605) 333-3372; (605) 333-3371

TENNESSEE
Diocese of Knoxville
Most Rev. Anthony J. O'Connell,
Director of Vocations,
Director of Seminarian Formation
P.O. Box 11127
Knoxville, TN 37939-1127
(615) 584-3307

Diocese of Memphis
Rev. David Graham,
Director of Vocations
1325 Jefferson Ave.
P.O. Box 41679
Memphis, TN 38174-1679
(901) 722-4700

Diocese of Nashville
Rev. Joseph McMahon,
Vocation Director
6401 Harding Rd.
Nashville, TN 37205
(615) 352-2259

TEXAS
Diocese of Amarillo
Rev. Msgr. Norbert G. Kuehler,
Vocation Director
St. John's Church
201 St. John's Rd.
Borger, TX 79007
(806) 274-7064

Diocese of Austin
Rev. Patrick Zurek,
Vocation Director
101 Westlake Dr.
Austin, TX 78746
(512) 328-3220

Diocese of Beaumont
Rev. John DiStefano,
Director, Vocations Office
1010 E. Virginia
P.O. Box 10095, L.U.S.
Beaumont, TX 77710
(409) 835-5037

Diocese of Brownsville
Rev. Heberto "Bert" Diaz,
Director of Vocations and
  Seminarians

P.O. Box 2279
Brownsville, TX 78522-2279
(210) 542-2501

Diocese of Corpus Christi
Rev. Daniel E. Flores,
Episcopal Vicar for Priestly
  Formation and Education
Vocation Office
3036 Saratoga Blvd.
Corpus Christi, TX 78415-5715
(512) 851-0908
Rev. Alejandro Salazar,
Associate Director of Vocations
Holy Family Parish
P.O. Box 1603
Laredo, TX 78041-1603

Diocese of Dallas
Father Greg Kelly,
Vocation Director
Rev. Raul Morales,
Associate Vocation Director
3725 Blackburn
P.O. Box 190507
Dallas, TX 75219
(214) 522-4930

Diocese of El Paso
Rev. Benjamin Flores,
Vocation Director
499 St. Matthews St.
El Paso, TX 79907
(915) 595-5003

Diocese of Fort Worth
Rev. Gonzo Morales,
Vocation Director
800 West Loop 820 South
Fort Worth, TX 76108
(817) 560-3300

Diocese of Galveston-Houston
Rev. Stephen E. Tiemann,
Sr. Rosalie Ann Karstedt, C.D.P.,
Vocation Directors
1700 San Jacinto St.
Houston, TX 77002
(713) 659-5461

Diocese of Lubbock
Father Eugene Driscoll,
Vocation Director
Catholic Center
P.O. Box 98700
Lubbock, TX 79499
(806) 792-3943

Diocese of San Angelo
Rev. Robert Bush,
Vocation Director
Rev. Barry Mc Lean,
Associate Vocation Director
612 East 18th St.
Odessa, TX 79761
(915) 332-5334

Archdiocese of San Antonio
Rev. Carlos Velazquez,
Vocation Director
Sr. Celia Ann Cavazos, MCDP,

Associate Vocation Director
Assumption Seminary
P.O. Box 28240
San Antonio, TX 78284
(210) 735-0553

Diocese of Tyler
Rev. Gavin N. Vaverek, JCL,
Vocation Director
1015 ESE Loop 323
Tyler, TX 75701-9663
(903) 534-1077

Diocese of Victoria
Rev. Gary W. Janak,
Vocation Director
P.O. Box 4070
Victoria, TX 77903
(512) 573-0828

UTAH
Diocese of Salt Lake City
Fr. Gerald P. Lynch,
Vocation Director
St. Marguerite Church
15 S. 7th St.
Tooele, UT 84074
(801) 882-3860
Sr. Jeremia Januschka, O.S.B.,
Assistant Vocation Director
Diocesan Pastoral Center
27 C St.
Salt Lake City, UT 84103
(801) 328-8641

VERMONT
Diocese of Burlington
Rev. Michael W. DeForge,
Vocation Director
The Catholic Center
390 South Prospect St.
Burlington, VT 05401-3534
(802) 658-6110

VIRGINIA
Diocese of Arlington
Rev. James R. Gould,
Vocation Director
200 N. Glebe Rd., Suite 619
Arlington, VA 22203
(703) 841-2514

Diocese of Richmond
Rev. Charles A. Kelly,
Vicar for Priestly Vocation
811 Cathedral Place, Suite B
Richmond, VA 23220-4801
(804) 359-5661
Rev. Michael McCarron,
Vocation Director
Promotion and Recruitment
100 Harpersville Rd.
Newport News, VA 23601
(804) 595-0385
811 Cathedral Place, Suite B
Richmond, VA 23220-4801
(804) 359-5661

WASHINGTON
Archdiocese of Seattle
Richard Shively,
Director of Vocations
910 Marion St.
Seattle, WA 98104
(206) 382-4595

Diocese of Spokane
Rev. Richard A. Root,
Director of Vocations
E. 429 Sharp Ave.
Spokane, WA 99202
(509) 326-3761

Diocese of Yakima
Rev. John Ecker,
Vocation Director
1208 W. Chestnut
Yakima, WA 98902
(509) 575-3713

WEST VIRGINIA
Diocese of Wheeling-Charleston
Rev. John R. Gallagher,
Vocation Director
P.O. Box 230
Wheeling, WV 26003
(304) 233-0880, ext. 242

WISCONSIN
Diocese of Green Bay
Rev. David Pleier,
Vocation Director
P.O. Box 23825
Green Bay, WI 54305
(414) 437-7531

Diocese of La Crosse
Fr. John Parr,
Vocation Director
Box 4004
La Crosse, WI 54602-4004
(608) 788-7700

Diocese of Madison
Rev. Michael C. Richel,
Director of Vocations
3577 S. High Point Rd.
Madison, WI 53719-4999
(608) 833-9043

Archdiocese of Milwaukee
Rev. James E. Kimla,
Director
Sr. Lucille Flores, SSM,
Associate Director
Priestly and Religious Vocations
Office
3257 S. Lake Dr.
St. Francis, WI 53235
(414) 747-6437

Diocese of Superior
Rev. Kevin M. Gordon,
Director of Vocations and
Seminarians

P.O. 969
1201 Hughitt Ave.
Superior, WI 54880
(715) 392-2937

WYOMING
Diocese of Cheyenne
Rev. Carl Gallinger,
Vocation Director
P.O. Box 426
Cheyenne, WY 82003
(307) 638-1530 or (307) 635-9261

TERRITORIAL SEES

AMERICAN SAMOA
Diocese of Samoa-Pago Pago
Rev. Mikaele Falaniko,
Director of Vocations
P.O. Box 596
Pago Pago, American Samoa
96799
011-(684) 699-1402; 622-7516

GUAM
Archdiocese of Agana
Rev. Adrian Cristobal,
Director of Vocations
Cuesta San Ramon,
Agana, Guam 96910
011-(671) 472-6116 or 6573

MARIANA ISLANDS
Diocese of Chalan Kanoa
Rev. Roger P.T. Tenorio,
Director of Vocations
P.O. Box 745
Saipan, MP 96950
011-(670) 234-3000

CAROLINE-MARSHALL ISLANDS
Diocese of the Carolines
Most Rev. Amando Samo,
Director of Vocations
P.O. Box 250
Chuuk, Caroline Islands,
FM 96942
011-(691) 330-2399

PUERTO RICO
Archdiocese of San Juan
Rev. Msgr. Fernando Felices,
Promoter of Vocations
Santa Maria de los Angeles
Seminary
P.O. Box 11,714,
Caparra Heights Sta.,
Rio Piedras, PR 00922
(809) 781-6166; 783-1919

Diocese of Arecibo
Rev. Miguel Mercado,
Vocation Director
Apdo. 2164
Arecibo, PR 00613
(809) 878-1528

Diocese of Caguas
Rev. Feliciano Rodriquez,
Vocation Director
Urb. Santa Elvira
Calle Santa Rita H-13
Caguas, PR 00725

Diocese of Mayaguez
Rev. Fr. Edwin Lugo Silva,
Vocation Director
Ntra. Sra. de Fatima Church
Parcelas Castillo C-2
Mayaguez, PR 00680
(809) 833-0794

Diocese of Ponce
Rev. Eduardo Torres,
Vocation Director
Rev. Jesus R. Diez,
Rector of Seminarians,
Rev. Alfredo Alvarez,
Spiritual Director
P.O. Box 110, Sta. 6
Ponce, PR 00732-2110
(809) 848-4380

VIRGIN ISLANDS
**Diocese of St. Thomas in the
Virgin Islands**
Rev. George Franklin,
Director of Vocations
Sr. Germaine Convery, O.S.F.,
Assistant Director
P.O. Box 1160
Kingshill, St. Croix 00851-1160
(809) 778-0484

EASTERN RITE DIOCESES

**Byzantine Catholic Eparchy of
Van Nuys**
Rev. Robert Pipta,
Director of Vocations
8131 North 16th
Phoenix, AZ 85020
(602) 861-9778

**Eparchy of Newton (Melkite-
Greek Catholic)**
Rev. George Gallaro,
Vocation Director
233 Grant Ave.
Newton Centre, MA 02159
(617) 965-9862

**Ukrainian Catholic Diocese of
Stamford**
Rev. Miroslaw Trojanowski,
Vocation Director
161 Glenbrook Rd.
Stamford, CT 06902
(203) 324-7698

**Diocese of St. Nicholas in
Chicago for Ukrainians**
Vocation Office
2245 W. Rice
Chicago, IL 60622
(312) 276-5080

**Byzantine Catholic Diocese of
Passaic**
Rev. Edward Cimbala,
Vocation Director
St. Therese Church
4265 13th Ave. N.
St. Petersburg, FL 33713
(813) 323-4022

**Byzantine Catholic Eparchy of
Parma**
Rev. Dennis M. Hrubiak,
Vocation Director

5500 W. 54th St.
Parma, OH 44129-2274
(216) 884-8452

**Ukrainian Catholic Diocese of
St. Josaphat in Parma**
Very Rev. Protopresbyter
Father James E. Poorman,
Vocation Director
St. Mary's Annunciation Ukrainian
Catholic Church
P.O. Box 205
Ramey, PA 16671
(814) 378-7688

**Archeparchy of Pittsburgh
(Byzantine-Ruthenian Rite)**
Rt. Rev. Msgr. Russell A. Duker,
S.T.D.,
Vocation Director
3605 Perrysville Ave.
Pittsburgh, PA 15214-2297
(412) 321-7550

**Metropolitan Archdiocese of
Philadelphia-Ukrainian**
Rev. Msgr. Ronald Popivchak,
Director of Vocations
Chancery Office
827 N. Franklin St.
Philadelphia, PA 19123
(215) 627-0143

**Eparchy of Our Lady of Lebanon
of Los Angeles**
Fr. Sharbel Maroun,
Director of Vocations
219 6th Ave. N.E.
Minneapolis, MN 55413

**Eparchy of St. Maron of
Brooklyn**
Msgr. David M. George,
Director of Vocations
P.O. Box 2567
Brockton, MA 02405-2567
(508) 586-1428

Archdiocese for the Military Services

The Archdiocese for the Military Services is one American diocese that is almost worldwide. Its two million people and one thousand priests are to be found wherever military personnel or diplomatic personnel serving overseas are assigned. They are located in the Arctic Circle in Greenland and Alaska, at Antarctica, in Asia, Europe, Africa, the Far East, the Mideast, South America, and in almost every state. Its priests are loaned to the Archdiocese from almost every American diocese and from many religious institutes. The most recent program, begun in 1986, sponsors young men who wish to serve as priests in the military.

For more information write or call:

Most Reverend John J. Glynn
Vocations Office
Archdiocese for the Military Services
United States of America
962 Wayne Avenue
Silver Spring, Maryland 20910-4433
(301) 495-4100

Serving Catholics in the Army, Navy, Air Force, Marine Corps, Coast Guard, Veterans Administration and Government Service Overseas.

Religious Communities for Men

ADORNO FATHERS (CRM)
(Clerics Regular Minor)
575 Darlington Ave., Ramsey, NJ 07446.

Conduct: 2 parishes, 1 seminary.

Apostolic Work: Parish work, retreats, teaching, missions and chaplaincies.

Represented in the Archdiocese of Newark and in the Diocese of Charleston, SC. Also in Italy, Germany, Zaire (Africa) and India.

Vocation Director: Fr. Michael Marotta, CRM, St. Michael's Seminary, Adorno Fathers, 575 Darlington Ave., Ramsey, NJ 07446. (201) 327-7375.

SOCIETY OF AFRICAN MISSIONS (S.M.A.)
A community of priests and lay missionaries in the service of Africa and the African American community.

Provincialate: 23 Bliss Ave., Tenafly, NJ 07670. (201) 567-0450

Conduct: Pastoral work, education, health care, formation of local clergy and lay leaders, social and agricultural development, Justice & Peace ministry, care for refugees.

Represented in the Archdioceses of Los Angeles, Boston, Washington, DC and Newark. Missions in Benin, Central African Republic, Egypt, Ghana, Ivory Coast, Kenya, Liberia, Niger, Nigeria, South Africa, Tanzania, Togo, Zaire, Zambia.

Vocation Director: Rev. Brendan Darcy, S.M.A. Fathers,256 North Manor Circle, Takoma Park, MD 20912. (301) 891-2037.

ALEXIAN BROTHERS (C.F.A.)
(Immaculate Conception Province) 600 Alexian Way, Elk Grove Village, IL 60007.

70 Brothers

Conduct: 3 general hospitals, 2 life care centers, 3 nursing homes, a 30-bed residential home for people with AIDS, 2 novitiates (Chicago, IL and in the Philippines.)

Apostolic Work: All aspects of the health care field, such as nursing, pastoral care, clerical and mechanical.

Represented in the Archdioceses of Chicago, St. Louis and Milwaukee and in the Dioceses of San Jose, Knoxville, and Davao, Philippines.

Vocation Director: Brother Andrew Thome, 600 Alexian Way, Elk Grove Village, IL 60007. (708) 981-3625.

ASSUMPTIONISTS (A.A.)
(Augustinians of the Assumption)
U.S. Provincial House: 330 Market St., Brighton, MA 02135. (617) 783-0400

69 Priests, 20 Brothers

Conduct: 5 parishes, 3 shrines, 1 house of studies, 2 hospital chaplaincies, 2 missions, 3 formation centers, 1 university.

Apostolic Work: Teaching: college & high school, parishes, Hispanic apostolate, ecumenical work, foreign missions, retreats, chaplaincies, campus ministry, journalism, preaching, youth work and administration.

Represented in the Archdioceses of New York and Boston and in the Dioceses of Worcester and Knoxville. Also in Canada, Kenya, Mexico, Moscow, Jerusalem and Rome.

Vocation Director: Fr. David Gallo, A.A., 512 Salisbury St., Worcester, MA 01609. (508) 767-7529.

ATONEMENT FRIARS (SA)
(Franciscan Friars of the Atonement)
Graymoor, P.O. Box 300, Garrison, NY 10524-0300. (914) 424-3671

108 Friar-Priests, 57 Friar-Brothers, 2 Novices, 2 Postulants, 1 Tertiary, 11 Associates.

Conduct: 5 U.S. and 4 Canadian parishes; 1 retreat and conference center; 1 shelter for homeless and needy men; 1 alcohol rehabilitation center; 2 libraries (Rome and London); 3 ecumenical centers (New York, Rome, and London); 1 house of formation; 1 novitiate.

Apostlic Work: Ecumenical ministry (annual Week of Prayer for Christian Unity; ecumenical centers in U.S. and Rome; ecumenical agency staffing: U.S., Rome and London; ecumenical publications); alcohol rehabilitation; parishes at home and overseas (Japan and England); institutional chaplaincies (hospitals and prisons); AIDS ministries.

Represented in the Archdioceses of Boston, Los Angeles, New York, and Washington, DC, and in the Dioceses of Arlington (VA), Charlotte (NC), Oakland (CA), Ogdensburg (NY), Raleigh (NC); and Stockton (CA); and in Canada, Great Britain, Italy and Japan.

Vocation Director: Rev. Joseph Cavoto, SA, Graymoor, P.O. Box 300, Garrison, NY 10524-0300. (914) 424-3671.

AUGUSTINIANS (O.S.A.)
(Province of St. Augustine) 1605 28th St., San Diego, CA 92102. (619) 235-0247

30 Priests, 7 Brothers

Conduct: High schools, parishes, retreat house, housing ministry, missions (in Peru), chaplaincies to hospitals, charismatic renewal.

Represented in the Archdioceses of Los Angeles and Portland, OR and in the Dioceses of Oakland and San Diego. Also in Chulucanas, Peru.

Vocation Director: Fr. Jim Mott, O.S.A., 1605 28th St., San Diego, CA 92102. (619) 235-0247.

AUGUSTINIAN FRIARS (O.S.A.) (Order of St. Augustine)

(Province of St. Thomas of Villanova) P.O. Box 338, Villanova, PA 19085-0338

280 Priests and Brothers

Conduct: 43 friaries, 33 parishes, 1 university, 1 college, 3 high schools, 2 foreign missions.

Apostolic Work: Friars work as active contemplatives in preaching and teaching, parish ministry and renewal, spiritual direction, counseling and liturgical arts. In education: Theological research and the arts and sciences; secondary, college, graduate levels in teaching and administration. In-service to the poor, youth, Hispanic and Black apostolates and other chaplaincies. Foreign missions in Japan and Peru; Formation–Pre-Novitiate: Washington, DC; Novitiate: Racine, WI; Theological Studies: Washington, DC.

Represented in the Archdioceses of Boston, New York, Milwaukee, Philadelphia, Washington, DC, Miami and Tokyo and Nagasaki, Japan; and in the Dioceses of Albany, Brooklyn, Camden, Ogdensburg, Orlando, Venice, FL, Nagoya and Fukuoka, in Japan, and Piura, in Peru.

Vocation Director: Vocation Team, St. Augustine Friary, P.O. Box 338, Villanova, PA 19085-0338. (610) 525-7890.

AUGUSTINIANS (O.S.A.)

(Province of St. Joseph in North America)

Motherhouse: The Augustinian Monastery at Marylake, P.O. Box 333, King City, Ontario, Canada. LOG 1KO. (905) 833-5368.

25 Priests, 26 Brothers, 4 Seminarians

Apostolate: Parish work, retreats.

Represented in the Archdiocese of New York.

Vocation Director: Fr. Larry Clark, O.S.A., 114 Madison Ave., Toronto, Canada. M5R 2F5 (416) 920-5814.

AUGUSTINIANS (O.S.A.)

(Province of Our Mother of Good Counsel) Tolentine Center, 20300 Governors Hwy., Olympia Fields, IL 60461. (708) 748-9500

110 Priests, 25 Brothers

Apostolic Work: Secondary education, parochial ministry, foreign missions, retreat work, adult education, hospital chaplaincies.

Represented in the Archdioceses of Chicago, Detroit, Milwaukee and St. Louis and in the Dioceses of Ft. Worth, Hamilton, Joliet, Kalamazoo and Tulsa, with missionaries in Japan and Peru.

Vocation Director: Rev. Tim Cuny, O.S.A., 20300 Governors Hwy., Olympia Fields, IL 60461. (708) 748-9500.

AUGUSTINIAN RECOLLECTS (O.A.R.)

(Province of St. Augustine) Provincial Residence: Monastery of St. Cloud, 29 Ridgeway Ave., West Orange, NJ 07052. (201) 731-0616

44 Priests, 11 Brothers, 13 Professed Students

Conduct: 2 pre-novitiates, 1 philosophy and a residence for theological students, 8 parishes, 1 Cursillo center.

Apostolic Work: Dedicated to working with the Hispanics in the U.S. (main apostolate), pastoral ministry, retreats, charismatic renewal, Cursillos, hospital chaplaincies, neo-catechumenate movement and working with youths.

Represented in the Archdioceses of New York, Newark, Los Angeles, Kansas City (KS), Omaha and Mexico City and in the Diocese of Orange.

Vocation Directors: Fr. Francisco Legarra, O.A.R., Fr. Jose Luis Martinez, O.A.R., St. Augustine Priory, 400 W. Sherwood Way, Oxnard, CA 93033. (805) 486-9651; Fr. John Oldfield, O.A.R., Fr. Ulises Feliciano, O.A.R., Tagaste Monastery, 220 Lafayette Ave., Suffern, NY 10901. (914) 357-0067.

AUGUSTINIAN RECOLLECT FATHERS (OAR)

(Province of St. Nicholas of Tolentine – NY Delegation) 2800 Schurz Ave., Bronx, NY 10465. (718) 823-0460

10 Priests

Conduct: 5 parishes.

Represented in the Archdiocese of New York.

Vocation Director: 2800 Schurz Ave., Bronx, NY 10465. (718) 823-0460.

BARNABITE FATHERS AND BROTHERS (C.R.S.P.) (Clerics Regular of St. Paul)

(North American Province) 1023 Swann Rd., Youngstown, NY 14174. (716) 754-7489

19 Priests, 1 Postulant, 1 Student

Conduct: 1 novitiate, 1 house of studies, 5 parishes, a Marian Shrine-Basilica, open year round; National Shrine as of Mar. '94.

Apostolic Work: Working with youth and young adults, teaching, retreats, parishes, hospital chaplaincies, directing of Our Lady of Fatima Shrine, Youngstown, NY, publishing of "The North American Voice of Fatima". Also in Afghanistan, Argentina, Belgium, Brazil, Chili, France, Italy, Philippines, Poland, Rwanda, Spain and Zaire.

Represented in the Dioceses of Allentown, Buffalo, San Diego and Hamilton, Ontario, Canada.

Vocation Director: Fr. Anthony M. Bianco, CRSP, Barnabite Spiritual Center, 4301 Hecktown Rd., Bethlehem, PA 18017. (215) 691-8648; (716) 754-7489.

BASILIAN FATHERS OF MARIA POCH

See Eastern Catholic Religious Communities for Men.

BASILIAN ORDER OF ST. JOSAPHAT

See Eastern Catholic Religious Communities for Men.

BASILIAN SALVATORIAN FATHERS

See Eastern Catholic Religious Communities for Men.

BASILIAN FATHERS (C.S.B.) (Congregation of St. Basil)

Motherhouse: Cardinal Flahiff Basilian Centre, 95 St. Joseph St., Toronto, Ont. M5S 3C2 Canada. (416) 921-6674.

Conduct: In the U.S.: 1 college, 1 university, 4 campus ministries, 6 high schools, 10 parishes. In Canada: 3 colleges, 2 universities, 8 campus ministries, 5 high schools, 12 parishes. In Mexico: 1 novitiate, 4 mission parishes. In Colombia: 1 novitiate, 1 school, 1 mission parish.

Apostolates: The service of the Church in any priestly capacity but have centered their work on education and evangelization.

Represented in the U.S. Dioceses of Rochester, Detroit, Gary, Galveston-Houston, Las Cruces, Santa Fe, Phoenix and Oakland. In the Canadian Dioceses of Toronto, Hamilton, London, Sault Ste. Marie, Saskatoon, Edmonton, Calgary, Nelson and Vancouver.

Vocation Director: Rev. James O'Neill, C.S.B., Cardinal Flahiff Basilian Centre, 95 St. Joseph St., Toronto, ON M5S 3C2 Canada. (416) 506-0250.

BENEDICTINE MONKS (O.S.B.) (Sylvestrine Congregation O.S.B.)

St. Benedict Monastery, 2711 E. Drahner Rd., Oxford, MI 48370-2815.

Community of Priests and Lay Brothers

Apostolic Work: Teaching, parish work and catechetical work in addition to monastic, community life and youth retreat ministry.

Represented in the Archdiocese of Detroit and in the Diocese of Paterson, NJ.

Vocation Director: Rev. Daniel Homan, O.S.B.

BENEDICTINE MONKS (O.S.B.)

St. Anselm Abbey, 100 St. Anselm Dr., Manchester, NH 03102-1310. (603) 641-7000

45 Monks

Conduct: 1 parish, 1 college, 1 dependent priory.

Apostolic Work: Education and related activities.

Represented in the Diocese of Manchester and in the Archdiocese of San Francisco.

Vocation Director: Rev. Mathias Durette, O.S.B.

BENEDICTINE MONKS (O.S.B.)

St. Leo Abbey, Saint Leo, FL 33574.

24 Fathers, 39 Brothers

Conduct: 6 parishes, 1 mission.

Apostolic Work: Pilgrim Center Retreat House, college administration, teaching, health care, parishes, mission, chaplain work.

Represented in the (Arch)dioceses of Saint Petersburg, FL, Rockville Centre, NY, Erie, PA, Phoenix, AZ, Pensacola/Tallahassee, FL and Miami, FL.

Vocation Director: Rev. David Draim, O.S.B., P.O. Box 2081, St. Leo Abbey, Saint Leo, FL 33574. (904) 588-2881.

BENEDICTINE MONKS (O.S.B.)

St. Gregory's Abbey, Shawnee, OK 74801. (405) 878-5490

42 Monks

Apostolic Work: The monastic community maintains its daily prayer and common life, and the monks, both priests and brothers, serve principally in the following areas: St. Gregory's College, early child development, parishes in Oklahoma and southern California, retreat work and hospitality, and manual labor.

Represented in the Archdioceses of Los Angeles and Oklahoma City and in the Diocese of Tulsa.

Contact: Rev. Martin Lugo, O.S.B., St. Gregory's Abbey, Shawnee, OK 74801. (405) 878-5100.

BENEDICTINE MONKS (O.S.B.)

Assumption Abbey, P.O. Box A, Richardton, ND 58652. (701) 974-3315

34 Priests, 26 Brothers

Apostolic Work: Farm, print shop, parish work, hospitality, teaching. Mission community and school in Bogota, Columbia, South America.

Represented in the Diocese of Bismarck.

Vocation Director: Assumption Abbey, P.O. Box A, Richardton, ND 58652. (701) 974-3315.

BENEDICTINE MONKS (O.S.B.)

Saint Martin's Abbey, 5300 Pacific Ave. S.E., Lacey, WA 98503. (206) 491-4700

45 Monks

Conduct: 1 college, 2 parishes, 5 chaplaincies.

Apostolic Work: Daily prayer and common life; St. Martin's College, parishes and hospital chaplaincies.

Represented in the Archdioceses of Seattle and Portland.

Vocation Director: Abbot Neal Roth, O.S.B., Saint Martin's Abbey, 5300 Pacific Ave. S.E., Lacey, WA 98503. (360) 491-4700.

BENEDICTINE MONKS (O.S.B.)

Holy Cross Abbey, P.O. Box 1510, Canon City, CO 81215-8631. (719) 275-8631

19 Priests, 6 Brothers, 2 Oblates

Works: The monks are dedicated

to community life and prayer as well as to parish work and chaplaincies.

Represented in the Archdiocese of Denver and in the Dioceses of Cheyenne, Pueblo and Colorado Springs.

Vocation Director: Holy Cross Abbey, P.O. Box 1510, Canon City, CO 81215-1510. (719) 275-8631.

BENEDICTINE MONKS (O.S.B.)

Woodside Priory, 302 Portola Rd., Portola Valley, CA 94028. (415) 851-8220.

8 Priests, 4 Brothers

Conduct: 1 preparatory school (grades 7-12).

Apostolic Work: Education and related activities.

Represented in the Archdiocese of San Francisco.

Vocation Director: Very Rev. William Sullivan, O.S.B.

BENEDICTINE MONKS (O.S.B.)

Mt. Michael Abbey, 22520 Mount Michael Rd., Elkhorn, NE 68022-3400. (402) 289-2541

17 Priests, 9 Brothers

Apostolic Work: College preparatory high school.

Represented in the Archdiocese of Omaha, NE, and in the Dioceses of Pueblo and Sioux City.

Vocation Director: Rev. Daniel Lenz, Mt. Michael Abbey, 22520 Mount Michael Rd., Elkhorn, NE 68022-3400. (402) 289-2541.

BENEDICTINE MONKS (O.S.B.)

Subiaco Abbey, Subiaco, AR 72865. (501) 934-4295

44 Priests, 31 Brothers

Conduct: 13 parishes, 1 high school, 1 foreign mission. Usual works involved in maintaining an abbey.

Represented in the Dioceses of Fort Worth and Little Rock and in Belize City, Belize, Central America.

BENEDICTINE MONKS (O.S.B.)

Mt. Angel Abbey, 1 Abbey Dr., St. Benedict, OR 97373. (503) 845-3030

90 Monks

Conduct: 1 seminary, 1 retreat house, 3 parishes.

Represented in the Archdiocese of Portland, OR and in the Dioceses of Boise, ID and Cuernavaca, Mexico.

Vocation Director: Fr. Paul Thomas, O.S.B., Mount Angel Abbey, 1 Abbey Dr., St. Benedict, OR 97373. (503) 845-3030.

BENEDICTINE MONKS (O.S.B.)
St. Benedict's Abbey, Benet Lake, WI 53102. (414) 396-4311
30 Monks: 14 Priests, 12 Brothers, 2 Novices, 2 Postulants
Conduct: 1 abbey, 1 dependent priory, 1 parish
Represented in the Archdiocese of Milwaukee and Morelia, Mexico.
Vocation Director: Abbot Leo Ryska, OSB.

BENEDICTINE MONKS (O.S.B.)
Blue Cloud Abbey, P.O. Box 98, Marvin, SD 57251. (605) 432-5528
29 Priests, 17 Brothers
Apostolic Work: Divine Office & common life; retreat work at Abbey; chaplaincies; pastoral work in North and South Dakota and Guatemala, including among Native Americans.
Represented in the Dioceses of Sioux Falls, SD; Fargo, ND; Coban, Guatemala.
Vocation Promoter: Br. Chris Wesely, O.S.B., Blue Cloud Abbey, P.O. Box 98, Marvin, SD 57251.

BENEDICTINE MONKS (O.S.B.)
Corpus Christi Abbey, HCR #2, Box 6300, Sandia, TX 78383.
9 Priests, 12 Brothers
Ministries: Retreats at the monastery, weekend pastoral work.
Represented in the Diocese of Corpus Christi.
Vocation Director: Father Gregory Yockey, O.S.B., (512) 547-3257.

BENEDICTINE MONKS (O.S.B.)
Prince of Peace Abbey, 650 Benet Hill, Oceanside, CA 92054. (619) 430-1305
11 Priests, 15 Brothers
Conduct: A retreat house at the monastery. Parish assistance. A semi-contemplative order of monks with an emphasis on liturgy and prayer.
Represented in the Diocese of San Diego.
Vocation Director: Rev. Stephanos Pedrano, O.S.B.

BENEDICTINE MONKS (O.S.B.) (Congregation of the Annunciation)
St. Andrew's Abbey, Valyermo, CA 93563. (805) 944-2178

26 Monks
Apostolic Work: Retreat house, youth center, missions.
Represented in the Archdiocese of Los Angeles.
Vocation Director: Fr. Isaac Kalina, O.S.B.

BENEDICTINE MONKS (O.S.B.)
Mount Saviour Monastery (Elmira), 231 Monastery Rd., Pine City, NY 14871. (607) 734-1688
14 Monks
Represented in the Diocese of Rochester.
Vocation Director: Very Rev. Martin Boler, Prior.

BENEDICTINE MONKS (O.S.B.)
Weston Priory, 58 Priory Hill Rd., Weston, VT 05161. (802) 824-5409
14 Monks
Represented in the Diocese of Burlington.
Vocation Director: Brother Philip, O.S.B.

BENEDICTINE MONKS (O.S.B.) (Olivetan Benedictines)
Holy Trinity Monastery, P.O. Box 298, St. David, AZ 85630. (602) 720-4642
7 Priests, 7 Monks, 4 Postulants
Represented in the Dioceses of Phoenix and Tucson.
Vocation Director: Fr. Henri Capdeville, O.S.B.

BENEDICTINE MONKS (O.S.B.)
St. Mary's Abbey, 230 Mendham Rd., Morristown, NJ 07960.
60 Monks
Conduct: 3 parishes, 1 preparatory school, 1 summer camp, 1 retreat house.
Apostolic Work: Teaching, parish work, campus ministry, ministry to the aged, adult education, hospital ministry, retreats.
Represented in the Dioceses of Paterson, Trenton and Wilmington, DE and in the Archdiocese of Newark.
Vocation Director: Br. Paul Diveny, O.S.B., (201) 538-3231.

BENEDICTINE MONKS (O.S.B.) (Congregation of St. Ottilien for Foreign Missions)
St. Paul's Abbey, Newton, NJ 07860.
12 Monks

Conduct: 1 novitiate, retreat house, monastic experience program.
Apostolic Work: Foreign missions, teaching, retreats.
Represented in the Diocese of Paterson. Also, in East and South Africa.
Vocation Director: Father Basil, O.S.B., (201) 383-2470.

BENEDICTINE MONKS (O.S.B.) (Congregation of St. Ottilien for Foreign Missions)
Christ The King Priory–Benedictine Mission House, P.O. Box 528, Schuyler, NE 68661.
4 Priests, 8 Brothers
Conduct: U.S. Headquarters for the financial support for the Benedictine Missions in Africa, Asia, Philippines and South America. Parish assistance and retreats.
Vocation Director: Father Adam Patras, O.S.B. (402) 352-2177.

BENEDICTINE MONKS (O.S.B.)
Saint Vincent Archabbey, Fraser Purchase Rd., Latrobe, PA 15650. (412) 532-6600.
208 Monks
Conduct: 1 archabbey, 3 dependent priories, 31 parishes, 5 chaplaincies, 1 seminary, 1 college, 1 high school.
Apostolic Work: Education, foreign missions, parochial ministry and chaplaincies.
Represented in the Archdiocese of Baltimore and in the Dioceses of Altoona-Johnstown, Erie, Greensburg, Pittsburgh, Richmond and Savannah. Foreign Missions in Taiwan and Brazil.
Vocation Director: Fr. Richard Ulam, O.S.B., Saint Vincent Archabbey, Fraser Purchase Rd., Latrobe, PA 15650. (412) 532-6655.

BENEDICTINE MONKS (O.S.B.)
Saint John's Abbey, Collegeville, MN 56321-2015.
225 Monks
Apostolic Work: University, seminary and preparatory school education; parochial and hospital ministry; publishing house; campus ministry, carpentry, retreats, counseling, plumbing, writing, gardening, forestry.
Represented in the Diocese of Saint Cloud. Dependent priories in the Bahamas and Japan.
Contact: Fr. Robert Pierson, O.S.B., Saint John's Abbey, Box 2015, Collegeville, MN 56321-2015. (612) 363-2548.

BENEDICTINE MONKS (O.S.B.)
St. Benedict's Abbey

57 Priests, 17 Brothers

Apostolic Work: Teaching on the secondary and college level. Serving parishes, hospitals, and schools as chaplains. Performing professional skills and trades: carpenter, printer, plumber, etc.

Represented in the Archdioceses of Detroit and Kansas City (KS). Also in Brazil.

Vocation Director: Rev. Meinard Miller, O.S.B., St. Benedict's Abbey, Atchison, KS 66002. (913) 367-5340, ext. 2885.

BENEDICTINE MONKS (O.S.B.)
Newark Abbey, 520 Dr. Martin Luther King Jr. Blvd., Newark, NJ 07102.

19 Priests, 6 Brothers

Conduct: 1 abbey, 2 parishes, 1 preparatory high school

Represented in the Archdiocese of Newark.

Vocation Director: Rev. Luke Edelen, O.S.B., Director of Vocations, Newark Abbey, 520 Dr. Martin Luther King Jr. Blvd., Newark, NJ 07102. (201) 643-4800.

BENEDICTINE MONKS (O.S.B.)
Belmont Abbey, Belmont, NC 28012.

21 Monks

Apostolic Work: Teaching on the college level, liturgical and pastoral ministry, common prayer.

Represented in the Diocese of Charlotte.

Vocation Director: Rev. Placid Solari, O.S.B., (704) 825-6702.

BENEDICTINE MONKS (O.S.B.)
Mary Mother of the Church Abbey, 12617 River Rd., Richmond, VA 23233. (804) 784-3508.

Apostolic Work: Celebration of the Eucharist and common prayer, teaching in high school, parochial and hospital ministry, chaplaincies and retreats.

Represented in the Diocese of Richmond.

Contact: Vocation Director Bro. David Owen, O.S.B., (804) 784-3508.

BENEDICTINE MONKS (O.S.B.)
St. Bernard Abbey, Cullman, AL 35055.

38 Monks

Conduct: 5 parishes; co-ed prep school; ecumenical retreat house; parish weekend assistance; farming.

Represented in the Dioceses of Birmingham and Mobile.

Vocation Director: Br. Leo Borelli, O.S.B., Saint Bernard Abbey, Cullman, AL 35055. (205) 734-8291.

BENEDICTINE MONKS (O.S.B.)
St. Procopius Abbey, 5601 College Rd., Lisle, IL 60532. (708) 969-6410

60 Monks

Conduct: Praising God through the Celebration of the Eucharist and the Liturgy of the Hours; serving the Church by teaching in Illinois Benedictine College and Benet Academy, by parish work, and foreign missions in Taiwan.

Vocation Director: Bro. Guy Jelinek, O.S.B., St. Procopius Abbey, 5601 College Rd., Lisle, IL 60532. (708) 969-6410, FAX (708) 969-6426, e-mail guyrj@eagle.lbc.edu.

BENEDICTINE MONKS (O.S.B.)
St. Bede Abbey, Peru, IL 61354.

30 Priests, 4 Brothers, 2 Juniors, 2 Novices

Conduct: 6 parishes, 1 mission, 1 high school.

Represented in the Archdioceses of Chicago and in the Diocese of Peoria.

Vocation Director: Fr. Placid Hatfield, O.S.B., St. Thomas More, 302 Chestnut, Dalzell, IL 61320. (815) 663-6201.

BENEDICTINE MONKS (O.S.B.)
St. Andrew Abbey, 10510 Buckeye Rd., Cleveland, OH 44104. (216) 721-5300

47 Monks

Conduct: Contemplative life of liturgy and lectio; apostolic works of hospitality, secondary education, parochial and pastoral services.

Represented in the Dioceses of Cleveland and Great Falls-Billings.

Vocation Director: Rev. Albert Marflak, O.S.B., St. Andrew Abbey, 10510 Buckeye Rd., Cleveland, OH 44104. (216) 721-5300.

BENEDICTINE MONKS (O.S.B.)
St. Maur Monastery, 4615 N. Michigan Rd., Indianapolis, IN 46208.

3 Priests, 4 Brothers

Apostolic Work: Prayer and hospitality.

Vocation Director: Rev. Robert McElaney, O.S.B. (317) 925-9095.

BENEDICTINE MONKS–
Byzantine Rite (Holy Trinity Monastery)
See Eastern Catholic Religious Communities for Men.

BENEDICTINE MONKS (O.S.B.)
Benedictine Priory, 6502 Seawright Dr., P.O. Box 13577, Savannah, GA 31416. (912) 356-3520

6 Priests, 4 Brothers

Conduct: 1 high school.

Represented in the Diocese of Savannah.

Vocation Director: Br. Timothy Brown, O.S.B.

BENEDICTINE MONKS (O.S.B.)
St. Meinrad Archabbey, St. Meinrad, IN 47577.

91 Priests, 36 Brothers, 3 Novices

Conduct: An interdiocesan seminary (college, school of theology), various trades and crafts in a monastic context of recollection, spiritual reading, and common prayer.

Vocation Directors: Fr. Kurt Stasiak, O.S.B., Br. Raben Bivins, O.S.B., St. Meinrad Archabbey, St. Meinrad, IN 47577-1010. (812) 357-6302.

BENEDICTINE MONKS (O.S.B.)
Conception Abbey, P.O. Box 501, Conception, MO 64433. (816) 944-2211

80 Monks (Priests & Brothers)

Apostolic Work: College seminary for students from many Midwestern dioceses, publish Christian cards and art through the Printery House, staff some parishes in the Midwest, and work in various trades and crafts.

Vocation Director: Fr. Martin De Meulenaere, O.S.B.

BENEDICTINE MONKS (O.S.B.)
Marmion Abbey, Butterfield Rd., Aurora, IL 60504.

38 Priests, 8 Brothers

Conduct: Marmion Academy and San Jose Seminary in Guatemala (Primary work is teaching).

Represented in Rockford Diocese in IL and in Quetzaltenango Diocese in Guatemala.

Contact: Vocation Director, Marmion Abbey, Butterfield Rd., Aurora, IL 60504. (708) 897-7215.

BENEDICTINE MONKS (O.S.B.)
Glastonbury Abbey, Order of St. Benedict, 16 Hull St., Hingham, MA 02043. (617) 749-2155

10 Monks (Priests and Brothers)

Conduct: Monastery and retreat center.

Represented in the Archdiocese of Boston.

Contact Person: Fr. Thomas.

BENEDICTINE MONKS (O.S.B.)
St. Anselm's Abbey, 4501 S. Dakota Ave., Washington, DC 20017.

24 Monks, including Priests and Brothers

Conduct: Centers on prayer, both liturgical and private; on living together in fraternal community; and on work, especially in high-school and university-level education, spiritual guidance, and hospitality.

Vocation Director: Fr. Hilary Hayden, O.S.B., St. Anselm's Abbey, Washington, DC 20017. (202) 269-2300.

BENEDICTINE MONKS (O.S.B.)
Abbey of St. Gregory the Great, Cory's Ln., Portsmouth, RI 02871.

20 Monks

Apostolate: Boarding secondary school for boys and girls (Portsmouth Abbey School).

Vocation Director: Fr. Ambrose, O.S.B., Abbey of St. Gregory the Great, Cory's Ln., Portsmouth, RI 02871. (401) 683-2000.

BENEDICTINE MONKS (O.S.B.)
Saint Louis Abbey, 500 S. Mason Rd., St. Louis, MO 63141 (800) 638-1527

11 Priests, 7 Brothers, 1 Oblate

Conduct: Own, operate and teach in boys' college prep 7-12 grade school; parish and retreat work and convent chaplaincies.

Vocation Director: Rev. Ralph Wright, O.S.B.

BENEDICTINE MONKS (O.S.B.) (Benedictines, Subiaco Congregation)
Monastery of Christ in the Desert, Abiquiu, NM 87510. (505) 470-4515

24 Monks

Represented in the Archdiocese of Santa Fe. Also in Mexico.

BENEDICTINE MONKS (O.S.B.)
St. Joseph Abbey, St. Benedict, LA 70457. (504) 892-1800

52 Monks (Priests and Brothers)

Apostolate: College seminary, retreat house, summer camp for children, staffs several parishes.

Represented in the Archdiocese of New Orleans.

Vocation Director: Father Thomas Perrier, O.S.B.

BENEDICTINE MONKS (O.S.B.)
St. Benedict Abbey, Box 67, Still River, MA 01467. (508) 456-3221

6 Priests, 17 Brothers

Apostolic Works: Monastic life, centered on contemplative prayer and the celebration of Mass and the Divine Office in Latin to Gregorian chant, and flowing over into the dissemination of Catholic doctrine through publishing and guest apostolates.

Represented in the Diocese of Worcester.

Vocation Director: Rev. Basil Rechenberg, O.S.B.

BETHLEHEM FATHERS
See Society of Bethlehem Missionaries.

THE BLESSED SACRAMENT FATHERS AND BROTHERS (S.S.S.)
(United States Province of St. Ann)

Provincial Offices: 5384 Wilson Mills Rd., Cleveland, OH 44143. (216) 442-6311

86 Priests, Deacons and Brothers.

Conduct: novitiate, 10 parishes, specialized ministries.

Apostolic Work: Eucharistic worship, prayer and ministry: parishes; retreats; writing; teaching; hospital chaplaincy and missions.

Represented in the Archdioceses of Chicago, New York, San Antonio and Santa Fe and in the Dioceses of Albany, Cleveland, Green Bay, Houston and Salt Lake City.

Vocation Director: Rev. Ed Stapleton, S.S.S., 5384 Wilson Mills Rd., Cleveland, OH 44143. (216) 442-7243.

BRIGITTINE MONKS (O.Ss.S.) (Order of the Most Holy Savior)
Monastery of Our Lady of Consolation, 23300 Walker Ln., Amity, OR 97101. (503) 835-8080

13 Monks, 1 Novice, 1 Postulant

Apostolic Work: Contemplative.

Represented in the Archdiocese of Portland.

Contact: Bro. Benedict Kirby, O.Ss.S., Prior.

BROTHERS OF THE ANNUNCIATION
See Eastern Catholic Religious Communities for Men.

BROTHERS OF THE CHRISTIAN SCHOOLS
See De La Salle Christian Brothers.

BROTHERS OF THE POOR OF ST. FRANCIS
See Poor of St. Francis, Brothers of.

CALASANZIAN FATHERS
See Piarists.

CAMALDOLESE HERMITS OF MONTE CORONA
Holy Family Hermitage, Rt. 2, Box 36, Bloomingdale, OH 43910.

3 Priests, 1 Brother

Contemplative, no exterior ministry.

Represented in Italy, Poland, Spain, and Colombia.

CAMALDOLESE MONKS (O.S.B.Cam.)
New Camaldoli Hermitage, Big Sur, CA 93920. (408) 667-2456

30 Monks in U.S.

Contemplative monastic life combining community and solitude with emphasis on prayer.

Represented in the Dioceses of Monterey, Oakland and Manchester and in Italy, Brazil and India.

Vocation Director: Very Rev. Robert Hale, O.S.B.Cam., Prior, Big Sur, CA 93920. (408) 667-2456.

CAMILLIANS (O.S.Cam.) (Servants of the Sick)
Camillian Provincialate of North American Province: St. Camillus Community, 10100 W. Blue Mound Rd., Milwaukee, WI 53226.

12 Priests, 8 Brothers

Conduct: 4 religious houses, 2 health centers, 2 retirement centers, 1 home health agency, 1 retreat center for inner healing, 2 parishes and are on staff at several public and private health care institutions.

Apostolic Work: Known throughout the world as Camillians, an Order founded by St. Camillus de Lellis in 1582 – caring for the sick as chaplains, counselors, nurses, doctors, psychologists, physical therapists, ethicists, health care administrators, and serving in all the fields of health care, medicine and rehabilitation.

Represented in the Archdiocese of Milwaukee and in the Dioceses of Madison and Worcester. Also in 26 other countries throughout the world.

Director of Vocations: Fr. Louis Lussier, O.S.Cam., 3661 S. Kinnickinnic Ave., St. Francis, WI 53235.

CANONS REGULAR OF PRE-MONTRE

See Norbertines.

CAPUCHIN FRANCISCAN FRIARS (OFM Cap.)

(Province of the Stigmata of St. Francis – New Jersey and Eastern coast)

80 Friars

Provincialate: Our Lady of Guadalupe Friary, P.O. 789, Union City, NJ 07087-0789. (201) 865-6107.

Apostolic Work: Parish ministries, hospital chaplaincies, retreat centers, preaching apostolate, social ministry with destitute men and women, communications, military, Secular Franciscans, foreign missions, Hispanic ministry, formation on college and post college levels, AIDS ministry, marriage tribunal.

Represented in the Archdioceses of Newark and New York and in the Dioceses of Paterson, Metuchen, Wilmington, Arlington, Charlotte, St. Petersburg and Zambia, Africa.

Vocation Coordinator: Bro. Thomas Crangle, O.F.M. Cap., Box 789, Union City, NJ 07087-0789. (201)865-6721.

CAPUCHIN FRANCISCAN FRIARS (O.F.M. Cap.)

(Province of St. Mary of New York and New England).

Provincialate: 30 Gedney Park Dr., White Plains, NY 10605. (914) 761-3008

206 Perpetually Professed Friars

Conduct: 21 friaries, 12 parishes, 1 parish high school, 5 parish grammar schools, 3 houses of formation, 1 youth and family ministries center.

Apostolic Work: Pastoral couselling, hospital, home for aged, military, prison chaplaincies; parish ministries; work with the disabled;

preaching apostolate; marriage and teenage encounters; teaching in high school, college and seminary.

Represented in the Archdiocese of New York and in the Dioceses of Brooklyn, Rockville Centre, Rochester, Norwich and Bridgeport, Springfield, Manchester and Portland. Also in the Marianas Islands, Japan and Central America.

Vocation Director: Robert Abbatiello, O.F.M. Cap., St. Francis Friary, Box 191, Garrison, NY 10524. (914) 424-3295.

CAPUCHIN FRANCISCAN FRIARS (O.F.M.Cap.)

(Our Lady of the Angels-Western American Province), 1345 Cortez Ave., Burlingame, CA 94010. (415) 342-3839.

62 Friars (Brothers and Priests)

Apostolic Works: Parish ministries, chaplaincies, high school and collegiate education, campus ministries, retreat and renewal ministries, social justice and peace, and similar ministries of prayer and service.

Represented in the Archdioceses of Los Angeles, San Francisco and Portland and in the Dioceses of Fresno, Oakland, Baker and Obregon, Mexico.

Vocation Director: Bro. Bernard Mc Allister, O.F.M. Cap., San Buenaventura Friary, 750 Anza St., San Francisco, CA 94118. (415) 221-7921.

CAPUCHIN FRANCISCAN FRIARS (O.F.M. Cap.)

(Capuchin Viceprovince of Texas), 2601 Singleton Blvd., Dallas, TX 75212. (214) 631-9627

15 Priests, 2 Lay Brothers

Apostolic Work: Parish, renewal movements, jail ministry, hospitals, schools, preaching.

Represented in the (Arch)dioceses of Dallas, Fort Worth and San Antonio.

Vocation Director: Fr. Juan Cruz Gaston, O.F.M. Cap., 2601 Singleton Blvd., Dallas, TX 75212. (214) 631-9627.

CAPUCHIN FRANCISCAN FRIARS (O.F.M. Cap.)

(Province of St. Augustine)

Provincialate: 220-37th St., Pittsburgh, PA 15201. (412) 682-6011

150 Friars (Brothers and Priests)

Conduct: 18 friaries, 30 parishes,

1 novitiate, 2 houses of study, hermitage, 2 foreign missions.

Apostolic Work: Parishes, chaplaincies, inner city ministry, work with the poor, Hispanic ministry, justice and peace ministry, Appalachian ministry, youth ministry, preaching, teaching, foreign missions.

Represented in the States of DC, IN, KY, MD, OH, PA, WV as well as in Puerto Rico and Papua, New Guinea.

Capuchin Vocation Office: 220 37th St., Pittsburgh, PA 15201. (412) 682-7974, FAX (412) 682-0506.

CAPUCHIN FRANCISCAN FRIARS (ofm Cap)

(Province of St. Joseph), 1740 Mt. Elliott Ave., Detroit, MI 48207.

240 members (Brothers and Priests)

Provincial: Anthony Scannell, O.F.M.Cap.

Apostolic Work: Parochial, seminary teaching, preaching, retreat work, campus ministry, social justice, peace and ecology, Black, Hispanic, Native American ministry, social work and similiar types of ministry. Foreign missions in Central America.

Represented in WI: Milwaukee, Green Bay, La Crosse, Madison, MI: Detroit, Saginaw, Marquette; IL: Chicago; IN: Fort Wayne/South Bend; MN: St. Paul; MT: Great Falls, and in Central America: Nicaragua, Honduras, Costa Rica, Panama.

Vocation Directors: Ken Casper, ofm Cap, David Schwab, ofm Cap, Capuchin Vocation Office, 301 Church St., Mt. Calvary, WI 53057. (414) 753-2702; FAX: (414) 753-2907.

CAPUCHIN FRANCISCAN FRIARS (O.F.M. Cap.)

(Province of St. Conrad) St. Francis of Assisi Friary, 3553 Wyandot St., Denver, CO 80211.

70 Friars (Priests and Brothers)

Conduct: All types of service in the Church: teaching, parish work, chaplaincies, missions in Papua New Guinea and Puerto Rico, social work, evangelization, etc.

Represented in the Archdioceses of Denver, Saint Louis and Kansas City (KS) and in the Dioceses of Salina, Mendi (Papua New Guinea) and several in Puerto Rico.

Vocation Director: Fr. William Kraus, O.F.M. Cap., St. Joseph Friary, 215 W. 13th St., Hays, KS 67601. (913) 628-2482.

CARMELITES (O. CARM.)

(Province of the Most Pure Heart of Mary)

Provincial House: 1313 Frontage Rd., Darien, IL 60561

276 Priests, 21 Brothers

Seminaries: Pre-Novitiate House in Washington, DC. Novitiate in Middletown, NY. Theology at Washington Theological Union, with residence at Whitefriars Hall, Washington, DC.

Apostolates: Community, Contemplative Prayer and Prophetic Ministry are the Carmelite Charism. Priests and brothers minister at 4 retreat houses, 35 parishes, 6 high schools and various ministries in 16 dioceses throughout the United States and Canada, with missions in Peru.

Represented in the Archdioceses of Boston, Newark, Chicago, Kansas City, Los Angeles, Louisville and Washington, DC. Ministry in the Dioceses of Houston, Joliet, Phoenix, Stockton and Tucson. Also in Ontario, Canada, with missions in Peru.

Provincial Vocation Directors: Rev. Robert Colaresi, O.Carm., Provincial Office, 1313 Frontage Rd., Darien, IL 60561. (708) 852-1476; East: Rev. John Lord, O.Carm., 158 Prospect St., Englewood, NJ 07631. (201) 569-8234; Midwest/West: Rev. Peter McGarry, O. Carm., 1313 Frontage Rd., Darien, IL 60561. (708) 852-4536; Hispanic: Marco H. Pardo, 6725 Reed Rd., Houston, TX 77087. (713) 649-6955.

CARMELITE FRIARS (O.Carm.)

(Province of St. Elias-Eastern Region) P.O. Box 3079, Carmelite Dr., Middletown, NY 10940. (914) 344-2225, FAX (914) 344-2210

78 Carmelites in the Province

Apostolic Ministry: 11 parishes, 4 elementary schools, retreats and renewal work (including youth ministry, Cursillo, charismatic renewal, sisters renewal, directed retreats, preached retreats, etc.), lay Carmelites, social work, counseling, campus ministry, teaching (all levels: elementary, high school, college), hospital chaplaincy (Veterans Administration) and other specialized ministries.

Represented by 14 Carmelite residences in the Archdioceses of New York and Washington, DC and in the Dioceses of Albany, Brooklyn, Rochester (NY), Springfield (MA), Greenburg (PA) and Palm Beach (FL).

Vocation Director: Fr. Michael Kissane, O.Carm., Carmelite Vocation Office, P.O. Box 3079, Carmelite Dr., Middletown, NY 10940. (914) 344-2225, FAX (914) 344-2210.

ORDER OF CARMELITES (O. Carm.)

Mt. Carmel Hermitage, Pineland, R.D. 3, Box 36, New Florence, PA 15944. (412) 235-2157

2 Priests

Contemplative, semi-eremitical life.

Represented in the Diocese of Greensburg.

Vocation Director: Fr. Bede Mulligan, O.Carm.

CARMELITES OF MARY IMMACULATE (C.M.I.)

North American Headquarters: 21 Nassau Ave., Brooklyn, NY 11222. (718) 388-5145

Generalate: P.B. No. 1056 Ernakulam, Cochin 682 011, Kerala, India

41 Priests in U.S. and Canada

Apostolic Work: Ministry to parishes, hospitals, universities, prisons, mission to Syro-Malabar Catholics.

Represented in the Archdioceses of New York and Philadelphia and in the Dioceses of Bridgeport, Brooklyn, Joliet, Lafayette, Lake Charles, Syracuse and Toledo. Also in Canada.

CARMELITES (TERESIAN)

See "C" section - Community of Teresian Carmelites.

ORDER OF CARTHUSIANS (Cart.)

Charterhouse of the Transfiguration, RR2, Box 2411, Arlington, VT 05250. (802) 362-2550

13 Choir Religious, 9 Brothers

A purely contemplative semi-eremitic order.

Represented in the Diocese of Burlington. There are 23 monasteries (of which 5 for nuns) in 8 countries in Europe. One foundation in Brazil.

Vocation Directors: Fr. Philip Dahl, Fr. Joseph Kim.

THE BROTHERS OF CHARITY (F.C.)

American District: Brothers of Charity.

Apostolic Work: Elementary and secondary education, special education, social work and foreign missions.

Represented in the Archdiocese of Philadelphia and 19 other countries.

Vocation Director: Director of Vocations, P.O. Box 27278, Philadelphia, PA 19118. (215) 887-6361.

CHRISTIAN BROTHERS (F.S.C.)

See De La Salle Christian Brothers.

CONGREGATION OF CHRISTIAN BROTHERS (C.F.C.)

(Eastern American Province), 21 Pryer Terrace, New Rochelle, NY 10804. (914) 636-6194

240 Brothers

Conduct: 1 college, 15 high schools, 4 grammar schools, 1 home of prayer, 1 St. Joseph's Care Center. Missions in Peru and Bonita Springs.

Apostolic Work: Specialize in the education of young people. Special interest in education of poor and underprivileged.

Represented in the Archdioceses of Boston, Miami, Newark and New York and in the Dioceses of Albany, Providence, Rochester, Metuchen, Tampa and Venice (FL) as well as in the missionary areas of Peru.

Vocation Director: Br. R. Kenneth Grondin, C.F.C., 21 Pryer Terrace, New Rochelle, NY 10804.

CONGREGATION OF CHRISTIAN BROTHERS (C.F.C.)

(Western American Province), Brother Rice Provincialate, 958 Western Ave., Joliet, IL 60435. (815) 723-5464

105 Brothers

Conduct: Secondary schools.

Apostolic Work: Specialize in the education of young people. Special interest in education of poor and underprivileged.

Represented in the Archdioceses of Chicago, Detroit and Seattle and in the Dioceses of Honolulu, Joliet and Monterey. Also in Peru and West Africa.

Vocation Director: Br. G.T. Smyth, C.F.C., 9757 S. Seeley Ave., Chicago, IL 60643. (312) 445-4988.

BROTHERS OF CHRISTIAN INSTRUCTION (F.I.C.)

(Notre Dame Province), Alfred, ME 04002. (207) 324-0067

56 Members in the Province

Apostolic Work: Education (secondary and college), home and foreign missions, youth and pastoral ministers (school and parish settings), ministers to the poor, catechists, retreat and spiritual directors.

Represented in the (Arch)dioceses of Fall River, Fairbanks, Indianapolis, Ogdensburg, Portland and Youngstown, (25 countries in the 5 major continents) Foreign Missions: Japan, Kenya, Seychelles Islands, Tanzania, Uganda, Philippines.

Vocation Director: P.O. Box 159, Alfred, ME 04002. (207) 324-0067.

CISTERCIAN FATHERS (O.C.)

Cistercian Monastery, 564 Walton Ave., Mt. Laurel, NJ 08054. (609) 235-1330

3 Priests in U.S.

Conduct: Teaching, missions, parish work, retreats.

Vocation Director: Superior of Monastery, Cistercian Monastery, 564 Walton Ave., Mt. Laurel, NJ 08054. (609) 235-1330.

CISTERCIAN FATHERS (O. Cist.)

Cistercian Monastery of Our Lady of Dallas, One Cistercian Rd., Irving, TX 75039. (214) 438-2044

27 Priests, 1 in Temporary Vows, 1 Novice

Ministries: Teaching and pastoral work both in college and in secondary school, parish assistance.

Represented in the Dioceses of Dallas and Fort Worth.

Vocation Director: Rev. Roch Kereszty, O. Cist., One Cistercian Rd., Irving, TX 75039. (214) 438-2044.

CISTERCIAN ORDER (O. Cist.)

St. Mary's Cistercian Priory, R.D. 1, Box 206, New Ringgold, PA (717) 943-2645

3 Priests

Conduct: A contemplative community, with intramural ecumenical activity.

Vocation Director: Rev. Hugh Montague, O. Cist., St. Mary's Cistercian Priory, New Ringgold, PA 17960. (717) 943-2645.

CISTERCIAN ORDER (O. Cist.)

Cistercian Abbey of Our Lady of Spring Bank

4 Priests, 1 in Solemn Vows, 2 in Temporary Vows

Conduct: Contemplation, retreats.

Vocation Director: Rev. Gregory Norman, O. Cist., Cistercian Abbey, Rt. 3, Box 211, Sparta, WI 54656. (608) 269-8138.

THE CLARETIANS (C.M.F.) (Missionary Sons of the Immaculate Heart of Mary)

126 Fathers, 9 Students, 12 Brothers, 3 Novices

Conduct: 2 provinces, formation houses, parishes, Hispanic ministry-Casa Claret, youth ministry, Claretian Publications (U.S. Catholic, SALT), Claret Center for Resources in Spirituality, hospital ministry, prison ministry, work among the poor, elderly, hungry and marginated, campus ministry.

Apostolic Work: Men, women and couples, vowed religious and laity, seek to respond to the most urgent needs of evangelization, especially in favor of the poor. Claretian missionaries, Lay Claretians and Claretian volunteers each seek to live out this call according to their own charism.

Represented in the Archdioceses of Atlanta, Chicago, Los Angeles, San Antonio and Seattle and in the Dioceses of Austin, Baker, El Paso, Fort Worth, Fresno, Metuchen, Oakland, Phoenix, Portland, Santa Rosa, Springfield-Cape Girardeau, Trenton, Izabal (Guatemala) and Owerriand Ikot Ekpene (Nigeria).

Vocation Director: Eastern Province: Sr. Ellen Kalenberg, Associate Director of Vocations, 205 W. Monroe St., 10th Fl., Como Office, Chicago, IL 60606. (312) 236-7846. Western Province: Fr. Robert Billett, C.M.F., 1119 Westchester Pl., Los Angeles, CA 90019. (213) 733-7712.

CLERICS OF ST. VIATOR (C.S.V.) (Viatorians)

(Chicago Province), 1212 E. Euclid St., Arlington Heights, IL 60004.

130 Brothers and Priests

Apostolic Work: Education, parish ministry, chaplaincies, social ministry, community administration.

Represented in the Archdioceses of Chicago and Kansas City (KS) and in the Dioceses of Joliet, Springfield-in-Illinois, Rockford, Peoria, Reno-Las Vegas, San Diego, San Jose, Monterey and Tucson. Foundation in Bogota,

Colombia (South America). Mission in Taiwan.

Vocation Director: Fr. Christopher Glancy, C.S.V., 1212 E. Euclid St., Arlington Heights, IL 60004. (708) 398-1354.

CLERICS REGULAR OF ST. PAUL

See Barnabite Fathers and Brothers.

COLUMBAN FATHERS (S.S.C.) (St. Columban's Foreign Mission Society)

St. Columban's, NE 68056.

680 Priests engaged exclusively in foreign mission work.

Conduct: 1 theologate, 1 pre-theology house, 1 spiritual year.

Represented in the (Arch)dioceses of Boston, Providence, New York, Philadelphia, Chicago, Omaha, San Francisco, Los Angeles and Dallas.

Foreign Missions: Belize, Brazil, Chile, Fiji/Vanuatu, Jamaica, Japan, Korea, Pakistan, Peru, Philippines and Taiwan.

Vocation Director: (National) Fr. Mark Mengel, St. Columban's, 5722 S. Drexel, Chicago, IL 60637. (312) 955-5044.

COMBONI MISSIONARIES (M.C.C.J.)

Comboni Mission Center, 8108 Beechmont Ave., Cincinnati, OH 45255.

An international order of Priests and Brothers, working for the most part in 22 countries of Africa and Latin America. They come from 15 different countries around the world.

Apostolic Work: Evangelization, social development and promotion of mission awareness. Work among the poorest and most disadvantaged people in the world. Involved in pastoral ministry among minority groups, and conduct formation programs for college-level and graduate candidates.

Represented in North America in the (Arch)dioceses of Newark, Cincinnati, Detroit, Chicago, Los Angeles and Hamilton (Ontario).

Vocation Director: Father Lorenzo Schiavon, M.C.C.J., 8108 Beechmont Ave., Cincinnati, OH 45255. (513) 474-4997.

COMMUNITY OF TERESIAN CARMELITES (C.T.C.)

(A semi-cloistered community of Nuns, Friars and Third Order Members), Box 826, Worcester, MA 01613-0826. (508) 752-5734

Religious: 6 Solemn Professed, 1 Simple Professed, 1 Novice; Lay: 7 Final Professed Members, 4 Simple Professed

Apostolic Work: Contemplatives, spiritual life center, evangelization, music ministry, pilgrimages.

Represented in the Diocese of Worcester.

Vocation Directors: Religious Vocations: Sister Susan-Elizabeth, C.T.C., or Brother Daniel-Francis, C.T.C.; Lay Vocations: Loretta M. Carroll, c.t.c.s., Community of Teresian Carmelites, Box 826, Worcester, MA 01613-0826. (508) 752-5734.

CONGREGATION OF CHRISTIAN BROTHERS
See Christian Brothers, Congregation of.

CONGREGATION OF HOLY CROSS
See Holy Cross Priests & Brothers.

CONGREGATION OF THE IMMACULATE HEART OF MARY
See Missionhurst.

CONGREGATION OF JESUS AND MARY
See Eudist Fathers and Brothers.

CONGREGATION OF THE MISSION
See Vincentians.

CONGREGATION OF MISSIONARIES OF THE BLOOD OF CHRIST
See Society of the Precious Blood.

CONGREGATION OF THE PASSION
See Passionists.

CONGREGATION OF THE SACRED HEARTS OF JESUS AND MARY
See Sacred Hearts Community.

CONGREGATION OF ST. JOSEPH
See St. Joseph, Congregation of.

CONSOLATA MISSIONARIES (I.M.C.)
2301 Highway 27, P.O. Box 5550, Somerset, NJ 08875. (908) 297-9191

1,000 Priests and Brothers; 31 in U.S. and Canada

Conduct: 6 mission centers, 1 formation program.

Apostolic Work: foreign missions. Present in Argentina, Brazil, Colombia, Equador, Venezuela, Ethiopia, Kenya, Liberia, Libya, Mozambique, Somalia, Tanzania, South Africa, Uganda and Zaire, Europe (Italy, Portugal, England, Ireland, Spain, Switzerland), Canada, Israel, South Korea and in the United States.

Vocation Director: Fr. Alex Moreschi, I.M.C., Consolata Missionaries, 7110 Thomas Blvd., Pittsburgh, PA 15208. (412) 241-3995.

THE CROSIERS (O.S.C.) (Canons Regular of the Order of the Holy Cross)
3510 Vivian Ave. St. Paul, MN 55126. (612) 486-7456

The Crosiers are an international Order of Catholic priests and brothers. As canons regular, there are three pillars on which our life is built: 1) living in COMMUNITY; 2) praying the LITURGY of the Church together; and 3) serving the needs of the Church through our MINISTRY. As pastoral leaders we are involved in parish and campus ministry, missionary activity in Indonesia and Zaire, education, retreat work, Hispanic ministry and ministry with, and among, the poor.

Represented in the Archdioceses of St. Paul-Minneapolis, MN, New York, NY, Chicago, IL, and Detroit, MI and in the Dioceses of St. Cloud, MN, Duluth, MN, Lincoln, NE, Phoenix, AZ and Agats, Irian Jaya, Indonesia.

Vocation Director: Rev. Dale Ehrman, OSC, 3510 Vivian Ave., St. Paul, MN 55126. (612) 486-7456.

DE LA SALLE CHRISTIAN BROTHERS (F.S.C.) (Brothers of the Christian Schools) (Christian Brothers)
Regional Office for the United States and Toronto, Canada: Brother John Linhardt, FSC, Director of Vocations and Formation, 4351 Garden City Dr., Suite 200, Landover, MD 20785. (301) 459-9410; (800) 433-7593.

1,100 Brothers in the U.S.A./ Toronto Region: 7,800 Brothers worldwide, 9 Provinces in the U.S.A./Toronto Region

Apostolic Work: An International Institute of Brothers involved in all forms of EDUCATION on the elementary, secondary, collegiate, literacy and GED levels. The Brothers are teachers, social workers, religious educators, human service providers, counselors, spiritual directors, youth ministers, campus ministers, educational administrators and foreign missionaries.

DE LA SALLE CHRISTIAN BROTHERS (F.S.C.) (Brothers of the Christian Schools) (Christian Brothers)
Baltimore Province: Provincialate, P.O. Box 29, Adamstown, MD 21710

230 Brothers

Conduct: 1 house of studies, 10 high schools, 3 child care institutions for court adjudicated youth, La Salle University, 1 retreat center, 2 middle schools, 5 campus ministries.

Represented in the (Arch)dioceses of Pittsburgh, Philadelphia, Baltimore, Washington, DC and Newark. Also in the Philippines, Kenya, Guatemala, Costa Rica and Sri Lanka.

Vocation Director: Brother Patrick Cassidy, FSC, Vocation Office, P.O. Box 7315, Audubon, PA 19407. (610) 666-7267.

DE LA SALLE CHRISTIAN BROTHERS (F.S.C.) (Brothers of the Christian Schools) (Christian Brothers)
Mid-West Province: Provincialate, 200 S. Frontage Rd., Ste. 300, Burr Ridge, IL 60521-6953. (708) 323-3725.

266 Brothers

Conduct: Provincialate, 17 high schools, 4 retreat centers, Lewis University, Saint Mary's College of Minnesota, Christian Brothers University, 1 counseling center, 1 adolescent boys' home, 1 Catholic worker house, 1 educational computer center, 1 development office, 1 socially conscious investment service, 26 community houses, Saint Mary's Press.

Represented in the (Arch)dioceses of Chicago, Cincinnati, Dubuque, Green Bay, Jackson, Jefferson City, Joliet, Kansas City-St. Joseph, La Crosse, Memphis, Omaha, St. Cloud, St. Louis, St. Paul/Minneapolis, Tulsa and Winona. Also in Bethlehem, Central America, Kenya, Pakistan, the Philippines, Sri Lanka, the West Indies.

Vocation Director: Brother Thomas Sullivan, FSC, 200 S. Frontage Rd., Ste. 300, Burr Ridge, IL 60521-6953. (708) 323-3725.

DE LA SALLE CHRISTIAN BROTHERS (F.S.C.) (Brothers of the Christian Schools) (Christian Brothers)

Long Island-New England Province: Provincialate, 635 Ocean Rd., Narragansett, RI 02882-1314

115 Brothers

Conduct: 3 high schools, 1 boarding school, 1 urban parish school, 1 special inner-city middle school, 1 special education center and related group residence, 1 school for adjudicated youth and related residences, 1 at-risk youth and family counseling program, 11 mission educational centers, 10 community houses.

Represented in the (Arch)dioceses of Brooklyn, Providence and Rockville Centre. Also in Rome, Kenya, Ethiopia and Eritrea.

Vocation Director: Brother Robert Hazard, FSC, 635 Ocean Rd., Narragansett, RI 02882-1314. (401) 789-0244.

DE LA SALLE CHRISTIAN BROTHERS (F.S.C.) (Brothers of the Christian Schools) (Christian Brothers)

New Orleans-Santa Fe Province: Provincialate, 1522 Carmel Dr., Lafayette, LA 70501. (318) 234-1973

137 Brothers

Apostolic Work: Elementary, high school and college education, campus ministry, social work, foreign missions.

Conduct: 1 college, 6 high schools, 3 elementary schools, 14 community houses.

Represented in the (Arch)dioceses of Santa Fe, Lafayette, Denver, El Paso and New Orleans. Also in Africa, the Philippines, Central America.

Vocation Directors: Bro. Tim Coldwell, FSC, St. Paul's School, P.O. Box 928, Covington, LA 70434; Bro. John Fairfax, FSC, P.O. Box 663, Metairie, LA 70004; Bro. Jim Brown, FSC, College of Santa Fe, Box 301, Santa Fe, NM 87501.

DE LA SALLE CHRISTIAN BROTHERS (F.S.C.) (Brothers of the Christian Schools) (De La Salle Christian Brothers)

New York Province: Provincialate, 800 Newman Springs Rd., Lincroft, NJ 07738. (908) 842-7420

213 Brothers

Conduct: 1 novitiate, 3 elementary schools, 5 middle schools, 10 urban and suburban high schools,

Manhattan College, 1 special education school for delinquent and neglected adolescents, 1 urban community based adult education center, 1 day-care program, 1 hospital chaplaincy, 9 campus ministries, 17 community houses, 1 nursing and retirement community.

Represented in the (Arch)dioceses of New York, Newark, Trenton, Metuchen, Albany, Syracuse, Buffalo and Detroit. Also in Central America, Africa, West Indies, the Holy Land, the Philippines.

Vocation Directors: Brother Robert Carnaghi, FSC, Christian Brothers Center, Manhattan College, Bronx, NY 10471. (718) 920-0178, Brother Patrick McNally, FSC, 845 Kenmore Ave., Buffalo, NY 14223. (716) 877-1616.

DE LA SALLE CHRISTIAN BROTHERS (F.S.C.) (Brothers of the Christian Schools) (Christian Brothers)

San Francisco Province: Provincialate, Box 3720, Napa, CA 94558-0372. (707) 252-0222

169 Brothers

Conduct: St. Mary's College, 9 high schools, 15 community houses, 1 house of studies, 1 novitiate, 1 Newman center, 1 educational group home, 2 inner city educational centers, 1 educational center in Tijuana, Mexico.

Represented in the (Arch)dioceses of Fresno, Monterey, Oakland, Sacramento, San Jose, Santa Rosa, Los Angeles, Portland and San Francisco.

Vocation Directors: Brother James Meegan, FSC; Brother Norman Cook, FSC; Brother Gary Hough, FSC, De La Salle Institute, Box 3720, Napa, CA 94558-0372. (707) 252-0222.

DE LA SALLE CHRISTIAN BROTHERS (F.S.C.) (Brothers of the Christian Schools) (Christian Brothers)

Toronto Province

66 Brothers

Conduct: 1 retreat house, 2 high schools, 1 refugee center, 1 institution for youthful offenders, 7 community houses.

Represented in the (Arch)diocese of Toronto. Also in St. Vincents, the West Indies and Nigeria.

Vocation Director: Brother Walter Farrell, FSC, 5 Avonwick Gate, Don Mills, Ontario, M3A 2M5. (416) 444-4479.

DISCALCED CARMELITE FATHERS (O.C.D.)

(Polish Province of the Holy Spirit) Our Lady of Mt. Carmel Monastery/Shrine, 1628 Ridge Rd., Munster, IN 46321. (219) 838-7111

8 Priests, 1 Oblate

Represented in the Diocese of Gary.

Vocation Director: Fr. Michael Veneklase, OCD.

DISCALCED CARMELITE FATHERS AND BROTHERS (O.C.D.)

(Oklahoma Province of St. Therese of the Child Jesus)

Provincial House: 555 Marylake Dr., Little Rock, AK 72206. (501) 888-3052

21 Priests, 3 Solemnly Professed Brothers, 6 Students in Vows, 2 Novices, 5 Postulants

Conduct: 1 contemplative monastery, 1 center of adult spirituality, 3 parishes, 1 student house.

Represented in the Archdioceses of New Orleans, San Antonio and Oklahoma City and in the Dioceses of Dallas and Little Rock.

Vocation Director: Fr. Steven Sanchez, O.C.D., Monastery of Our Lady of Mt. Carmel and St. Therese, P.O. Box 26127, Oklahoma City, OK 73126. (405) 235-2037.

DISCALCED CARMELITE FRIARS (O.C.D.)

(Province of St. Joseph of the Western U.S.), Provincial House: El Carmelo Retreat House, P.O. Box 2178, Redlands, CA 92373. (909) 793-0424

32 Priests, 2 Brothers in Solemn Vows, 1 Brother in Simple Vows, 1 Student, 3 Novices, 1 Secular Order Brother to the Common Life

Conduct: 4 parishes, 1 retreat house, 1 institute of spirituality, 1 house of prayer, 1 novitiate, 1 house of studies.

Represented in the Archdioceses of Los Angeles and Seattle and in the Dioceses of Oakland, San Bernardino, San Jose, Santa Rosa and Tucson.

Vocation Director: Mt. St. Joseph, P.O. Box 3420, San Jose, CA 95156.

DISCALCED CARMELITE FRIARS (O.C.D.)

(Province of the Immaculate Heart of Mary) Discalced Carmelite Friars, 1233 So. 45th St., W. Milwaukee, WI 53214. (414) 672-7212

64 Priests, 13 Brothers, 11 Students, 1 Novice, 1 Postulant

Conduct: 1 Marian shrine, 2 retreat houses, 2 parishes, 1 hermitage community, 3 formation communities, 1 international publication, 1 publishing house.

Apostolates: Retreats, spiritual direction, parishes, translation, publication, teaching, secular order, chaplaincies, in-house ministries: cook, tailor, maintenance, formation, administration. Overseas missions in the Philippines and Kenya.

Represented in the Archdioceses of Boston, Milwaukee and Washington, DC and in the Diocese of Manchester.

Vocation Director: Fr. Theodore Centala, OCD, 2131 Lincoln Rd. N.E., Washington, DC 20002. (202) 832-6622; Fr. Michael Dodd, OCD, 166 Foster St., Brighton, MA 02135. (617) 787-5056.

SONS OF DIVINE PROVIDENCE (FDP) (Don Orione Fathers)

Don Orione Home, 111 Orient Ave., East Boston, MA 02128. (617) 569-2100

11 Priests in U.S.

Conduct: 1 Marian Shrine, 1 nursing home, 1 home for retarded men, 1 vocation center, 1 parish.

Apostolic Work: Multiple.

Represented in the Archdioceses of Boston and New York and in the Diocese of Evansville.

Vocation Director: Fr. John Kilmartin, FDP, 150 Orient Ave., East Boston, MA 02128. (617) 569-2100, ext. 274.

SOCIETY OF THE DIVINE SAVIOR, (S.D.S.) (The Salvatorians)

Salvatorian Provincial Residence, 1735 Hi-Mount Blvd., Milwaukee, WI 53208.

129 Priests, 65 Brothers, 70 Lay Salvatorians

Apostolic Work: Founded to use "any means which the Love of Christ inspires" to bring the Gospel to the world. Involved in parishes, home and foreign missions, education, hospital and military chaplaincies, youth ministry, communications, counselling, campus ministry, specialized ministries.

Represented in the Archdioceses of Baltimore, Louisville, Milwaukee, New York, San Francisco and Washington and in the Dioceses of Bismarck, Birmingham, Camden, Green Bay, Kalamazoo, Knoxville, La Crosse, Mobile, Nashville, Oakland, Orlando, Phoenix, Sacramento, Santa Rosa, Savannah, Tucson and Wilmington. American Salvatorians are also serving in Tanzania, East Africa.

Vocation Director: Fr. Michael R. Hoffman, S.D.S., 1735 Hi-Mount Blvd., Milwaukee, WI 53208. (414) 258-1735.

DIVINE WORD MISSIONARIES (S.V.D.)

Society of the Divine Word, Vocation Office, P.O. Box 380, Epworth, IA 52045-0380.

Over 5,700 members worldwide; 350 priests and brothers in 3 U.S. Provinces.

Apostolic Work: An international missionary community of Brothers and Priests working in 59 countries. Also involved in African-American, Latino, Appalachian and multicultural apostolates in the U.S.

FORMATION PROGRAMS:
*Divine Word College Seminary, Epworth, IA: a four-year, fully accredited college seminary with degrees in philosophy and cross-cultural studies.
*Wendelin House, Washington, DC: a community for Brother candidates pursuing studies at various colleges and universities in Washington.
*Tolton House of Studies, New Orleans, LA: a house of formation for African-American candidates who study at Xavier University.
*Divine Word Theologate, Chicago, IL: seminarians who have completed their undergraduate degree and who meet the admissions requirements at Catholic Theological Union in Chicago may begin pre-novitiate formation at Divine Word Theologate.

Vocation Director: Bro. Dennis Newton, SVD, Divine Word Missionaries, P.O. Box 380, Epworth, IA 52045-0380. (800) 553-3321 or (319) 876-3353 (after 5 p.m. CST).

DOMINICANS (O.P.) (Order of Preachers)

(Eastern Province) 141 E. 65 St., New York, NY 10021-6607. (212) 737-5757

288 Priests, 17 Brothers, 3 Deacons, 20 Clerical Students, 5 Novices

Conduct: 19 parishes, 1 college, 1 house of study, 1 novitiate, 2 foreign missions, 8 campus ministries.

Apostolic Work: Preaching, teaching, parishes, foreign missions, campus ministry, hospital and prison chaplaincies, spiritual renewal center.

Represented in the Archdioceses of Boston, Cincinnati, Detroit, Hartford, Louisville, Newark, New York, Philadelphia and Washington and in the Dioceses of Albany, Camden, Buffalo, Providence, Richmond and Youngstown. Foreign missions in Pakistan and Peru.

Promoter of Vocations: Father John J. Reid, O.P., Providence College, Providence, RI 02918-0001. (401) 865-2216.

DOMINICANS (O.P.)

(Province of St. Dominic) 5353 Notre Dame de Grace Ave., Montreal H4A 1L2, Canada. (514) 481-5603, 0115

19 Fathers, 7 Brothers in U.S.; 179 worldwide

Represented in the Dioceses of Fall River, MA and Portland, ME.

DOMINICANS (O.P.) (Order of Preachers)

(Central Province), 1909 S. Ashland Ave., Chicago, IL 60608-2994.

212 Priests, 4 Novices, 26 Brothers

Apostolic Work: Preaching, teaching, research and writing, campus and parish ministry, social justice.

Represented in the (Arch)dioceses of Cheyenne, Chicago, Des Moines, Denver, Detroit, Grand Rapids, Madison, Milwaukee, Peoria, St. Cloud, St. Louis, St. Paul/ Minneapolis, Santa Fe and Sioux Falls. Foreign missions in Bolivia, Honduras, Jerusalem, Kenya and Nigeria.

Vocation Director: Father Jesse Cox, O.P., 7200 W. Division, River Forest, IL 60305. (708) 771-7254.

DOMINICANS (O.P.) (Order of Preachers)

(Province of the Holy Name-Western Province) 5877 Birch Court, Oakland, CA 94618.

130 Priests, 16 Brothers, 24 Student Brothers, 5 Novices

Conduct: 12 parishes, 8 campus ministries, 1 house of study and 1 novitiate.

Represented in the Archdioceses of Anchorage, Los Angeles, Portland, San Francisco and Seattle. Also in the Dioceses of Oakland, Phoenix, Sacramento, Salt Lake City, San Bernardino, and Tucson.

Also represented in missions in Mexical (Baja, Mexico).

Vocation Director: Fr. Martin de Porres Walsh, O.P., 5877 Birch Court, Oakland, CA 94618-1626. (510) 658-8722; FAX: (510) 658-1061.

DOMINICANS (O.P.)
(Order of Preachers)

Southern Dominican Province (Province of St. Martin de Porres) 1421 N. Causeway Blvd., Ste. 200, Metairie, LA 70001-4144. (504) 837-2129

145 Friars (Priests and Brothers)

Apostolic Work: Preaching, teaching, chaplaincies, parish and campus ministry. Missionaries; Peru, Honduras, Kenya.

Province covers 11 southern states.

Promoter of Vocations: Fr. Henry Groover, O.P., 1421 N. Causeway Blvd., Ste. 200, Metairie, LA 70001-4144. (504) 837-2129.

EDMUNDITES (S.S.E.)
(Society of St. Edmund)

Edmundite Generalate, 270 Winooski Park, Colchester, VT 05439. (802) 654-3400

65 Priests & Brothers

Apostolic Work: Evangelization of those who are spiritually and materially poor in a variety of pastoral, missionary and educational apostolates.

Represented in AL, VT, CT, LA, MI and Venezuela.

Vocation Director: Fr. Stephen Hornat, S.S.E., Office of Vocation Ministries, 1419 Broad St., Selma, AL 36701. (334) 874-3798.

EUDISTS (C.J.M.)
(Congregation of Jesus and Mary)

71 Burke Dr., Buffalo, NY 14215.

128 Priests, Deacons and Laymen in North American Province

Apostolic Work: Parishes, young adult ministry, youth ministry, campus and Newman Center ministries, counseling, teaching, ministry formation.

Represented in the Dioceses of Buffalo and San Diego and also in Rome; France; Ivory Coast, Benin and Central Africa; Canada; Brazil, Columbia, Equador and Venezuela; Cuba, Dominican Republic and Mexico.

Vocation Director: The Eudist Community, 71 Burke Dr., Buffalo, NY 14215. (716) 832-9464.

FRANCISCAN BROTHERS
(The Congregation of the Religious Brothers of the Third Order Regular of St. Francis)

Franciscan Brothers Generalate: 135 Remsen St., Brooklyn, NY 11201.

125 Brothers

Conduct: 4 high schools, 2 elementary schools, 1 college, 1 summer camp, 1 novitiate, 1 prenovitiate community and retreat center.

Apostolic Work: Education on all levels and in every aspect of its work (special education, elementary, secondary, and college levels, administration), parish Religious Education coordinators, Catholic Charities, health careers, pilgrims in apostolic life, campus ministry, youth ministry, prison ministry, counselling, parish ministry, retreat work.

Represented in the Dioceses of Brooklyn and Rockville Centre (NY), Greenville (NC) and Bridgeport (CT).

Vocation Director: Jeffery Pedersen, O.S.F., 135 Remsen St., Brooklyn, NY 11201. (718) 858-8217.

FRANCISCAN BROTHERS OF CHRIST THE KING (O.S.F.)

General Motherhouse: 3737 N. Marybelle Ave., Peoria, IL 61615. (309) 688-0093; 0094

4 Brothers, 2 Novices

Conduct: Religious ed program, 1 elementary school, 1 home for the aged, 1 hospitality center.

Represented in the Diocese of Peoria.

Vocation Director: Bro. Francis A. Skube, O.S.F.

FRANCISCAN BROTHERS OF THE HOLY CROSS (F.F.S.C.)

2500 St. James Rd., Springfield, IL 62707. (217) 544-4876

15 Brothers

Apostolic Work: Work with mentally handicapped children and adults; elementary education.

Represented in the Dioceses of Little Rock, Madison and Springfield, IL.

Vocation Director: Br. John Francis Tyrrell, Vocation Director, St. Joseph Friary, 354 North Willow Ave., Fayetteville, AR 72701-4365. (501) 442-0890.

FRANCISCAN FRIARS (O.F.M.)
(Croatian Franciscan Custody of the Holy Family)

4848 S. Ellis Ave., Chicago, IL 60615. (312) 373-3463

41 Friars

Conduct: 16 parishes, 2 friaries, 1 printery.

Apostolic Work: Pastoral ministry among Croatians in the U.S. and Canada; Croatian Franciscan Press (Chicago).

Represented in the U.S. (Arch) dioceses of Chicago, New York, Milwaukee, Detroit, St. Louis, Allentown, Erie and Canadian (Arch)dioceses of Montreal, London, Hamilton and Sault Ste. Marie.

Vocation Director: Fr. Stephen Bedenikovic, O.F.M., Sacred Heart Church, 917 N. 49th St., Milwaukee, WI 53208. (414) 774-9418.

FRANCISCAN FRIARS (O.F.M.)
(Province of the Assumption of the B.V.M.), Assumption Friary, Pulaski, WI 54162.

173 Priests, 89 Brothers, 6 Students in Formation

Conduct: 23 parishes, 19 friaries, 1 novitiate, 2 retreat houses, 1 diocesan high school, 1 printery, publishing house and 2 social justice centers.

Apostolic Work: Parish work, social service, retreats, teaching, institutional chaplaincies, foreign missions, home missions, publication, world peace and justice, special education, inner city apostolate.

Represented in the Archdioceses of Boston, Chicago, Milwaukee and Philadelphia and in the Dioceses of Fort Wayne-South Bend, Gary, Gaylord, Grand Rapids, Green Bay, Joliet, Natchez-Jackson, Pittsburgh, Rochester, Rockford, Saginaw and Toledo. Also in the Philippines, Africa, New Guinea, Mexico and Thailand.

Vocation Director: Fr. John Wojtowicz, O.F.M., Vocation Office, Assumption B.V.M. Province, Holy Name Friary, 5103 South Ellis Ave., Chicago, IL 60615. (312) 947-9147, (312) 667-9113.

FRANCISCAN FRIARS (O.F.M.)
(Viceprovince of St. Casimir), Franciscan Friary, P.O. Box 980, Kennebunkport, ME 04046.

1 Bishop, 28 Priests, 2 Brothers, 1 Seminarian

Conduct: 6 friaries, 4 parishes.

B-31

Apostolic Work: Parish work, retreats, missions, printed word apostolate.

Represented in Portland, ME; Brooklyn, NY; St. Petersburg, FL; Toronto, Ont., St. Catharines, Ont., Hamilton, Ont.

Vocation Director: Fr. John Bacevicius, O.F.M., Franciscan Friary, P.O. Box 980, Kennebunkport, ME 04046. (207) 967-2011.

FRANCISCAN FRIARS (O.F.M.)
(Custody of the Holy Cross)
St. Mary's Friary, 14246 Main St., Box 608, Lemont, IL 60439. (708) 257-2494

6 Fathers, 1 Brother

Conduct: 4 parishes and missions, 1 monastery, 1 retreat house, college training, monthly magazine, minister to European immigrants in Australia and Canada.

Represented in the Archdioceses of Chicago and New York and in the Dioceses of Altoona-Johnstown and Joliet.

Vocation Director: Fr. Bernard Karmanocky, 536 Decker Ave., Johnstown, PA 15906. (814) 539-7633.

FRANCISCAN FRIARS (O.F.M.)
(Province of the Most Holy Name) Holy Name Provinciate, 58 W. 88th St., New York, NY 10024-2502. (212) 721-1600.

5 Bishops, 451 Priests, 80 Brothers

Conduct: 5 large service churches in city apostolates, 3 inner-city apostolates, 1 university, 1 college, 1 novitiate, member of Washington Theological Union. 24 parishes in East, 11 southern parishes, pilgrimages, 5 publications, house of prayer.

Apostolic Work: Social work, counseling, teaching, parishes, home missions, foreign missions (Peru, Brazil, Bolivia, Jamaica, Hong Kong, Japan, Kenya), retreats, Newman Centers, inner-city, specialize in working with God's poor.

Represented Eastern Coastal States from Maine to Florida, the Caribbean, South America, Asia and Africa.

Vocation Director: Franciscan Vocation Office, 135 W. 31st St., New York, NY 10001. (212) 629-5868; 1-800-677-7788.

FRANCISCAN FRIARS (O.F.M.)
(Vice-Province of the Holy Savior) Provincial House: Holy Family Friary, 232 S. Home Ave., Pittsburgh, PA 15202. (412) 761-2550

24 Priests, 5 Brothers, 2 Friars in Formation

Conduct: 4 friaries, 4 parishes, 1 shrine, 1 retreat house, 1 publication.

Apostolic Work: Parish ministry, retreat ministry, preaching missions, retreats, counseling, secular Franciscan ministry, hospital chaplaincies, assisting parishes on weekends, work with the poor, nursing homes, education, spiritual direction, pilgrimages, some ministry in the Byzantine-Rite.

Represented in the Dioceses of Allentown, Gary, Greensburg, Paterson, Pittsburgh and Joliet.

Vocation Director: Friar David Moczulski, O.F.M., Franciscan Friars, Holy Family Friary, 232 S. Home Ave., Pittsburgh, PA 15202. (412) 761-2550.

FRANCISCAN FATHERS
(BYZANTINE FRANCISCANS)
See Eastern Catholic Religious Communities for Men.

FRANCISCAN FRIARS (O.F.M.)
(Province of the Immaculate Conception), 147 Thompson St., New York, NY 10012. (212) 674-4388

221 Friars

Conduct: 27 parishes, 1 novitiate, 4 retreat houses, 2 formation residences, 2 high schools.

Apostolic Work: Teaching, colleges, high school, campus ministry, hospital and school chaplaincies, pastoral counseling, parishes, ecumenical work, retreats, renewals, and Christian Formation, foreign and home missions, inner-city projects, tutorial programs, Spanish and Italian speaking apostolates, special services, pilgrimages, development programs, formation and vocation apostolates, experimental communities, medical and clerical work, CCD apostolates, teenage apostolates with prisoners, mentally retarded, addicts, alcoholics, caring for the aged, Secular Franciscan apostolates, summer camps, working with the poor, the Apostolate of Prayer.

Represented in the Archdioceses of Boston, Hartford and New York and in the Dioceses of Albany, Fall River, Brooklyn, Manchester, Metuchen, Pittsburgh, Portland, Trenton, Wheeling and Youngstown. Also, in the Diocese of Toronto, Canada and in Honduras, Guatemala and El Salvador.

Vocation Director: Fr. Mario F. Julian, O.F.M., Franciscan Vocation Office, 147 Thompson St., New York, NY 10012. (800) 521-5442; (212) 995-9164.

FRANCISCAN FRIARS (O.F.M.)
(Province of Our Lady of Guadalupe), 1350 Lakeview Rd. S.W., Albuquerque, NM 87105. (505) 877-5425

99 Friars, 18 Brothers, 73 Priests, 3 Professed Students

Conduct: Parishes and missions among the culturally rich American Indian, Hispanic, and Anglo Communities, hospital chaplaincies, retreats, social work, renewal preaching.

Represented in the Archdioceses of Santa Fe and Denver and in the Dioceses of Gallup and Las Cruces. Also in the Dioceses of Juarez and Chihuahua, Mexico.

Vocation Director: Fr. Larry Schreiber, O.F.M., Holy Trinity Friary, 3100 W. 76th Ave., Westminster, CO 80030. (303) 428-1693; 1-800-944-SEEK.

FRANCISCAN FRIARS (O.F.M.)
(Province of St. John the Baptist), 1615 Vine St., Cincinnati, OH 45210. (513) 721-4700

237 Friars: 67 Brothers, 170 Priests.

Ministries: In the vision and the Rule of St. Francis of Assisi, one of the primary ministries of the friars is to live the Gospel life in a community of brothers.Community itself is a ministry and a witness to the world of the Reign of God coming among us. From their community lives, the friars of St. John the Baptist Province serve the poor and the middle class, various cultural heritages, farmers, inner city folk, suburbanites and Secular Franciscans. They minister in homes and on the streets and in the friaries; in parishes, schools, retreats, hospitals and mission lands.

Represented in 14 states from Michigan to Texas. Also in Africa and the Philippines.

Vocation Directors: Fr. Rock Travnikar, O.F.M., Fr. Bruno Kremp, O.F.M., 10290 Mill Rd., Cincinnati, OH 45231. (513) 825-1082.

FRANCISCAN FRIARS (ofm)
(Province of St. Barbara) 1500 34th Ave., Oakland, CA 94601. (510) 536-3722

300 Friars

Ministries: "All honest work can be Franciscan Ministry." Parishes, retreat houses, Native American and foreign missions, education, social work, social justice, hospital chaplains.

Represented in the Archdioceses of Los Angeles, Portland (OR) and San Francisco and in the Dioceses of Fresno, Monterey, Oakland, Orange, Phoenix, Sacramento, Salt Lake City, San Diego, Spokane, Stockton and Tucson.

Vocation Directors: Rev. Miguel Obregon, ofm, Br. Angelo Cardinalli, ofm.

FRANCISCAN FRIARS (O.F.M.)

(Province of the Holy Gospel) Roger Bacon College, 2400 Marr St., El Paso, TX 79903. (915) 565-2921.

3 Priests, 1 Brother

Represented in the Diocese of El Paso.

FRANCISCAN FRIARS (O.F.M.)

(Province of Saints Francis and James of Jalisco, Mexico), 504 E. Santa Clara St., Hebbronville, TX 78361. (512) 527-3865

Motherhouse: Basilica de Zapopan, Zapopan, Jal 45000, Mexico

2 Priests, 2 Brothers

Apostolic Work: Mission with Indians in Mexico and Africa, poor parishes, schools.

Represented in the Dioceses of Corpus Christi and Hebbronville. Also represented in the country of Mexico.

Vocation Director: Belen 220, 44290 Guadalajara Jal, Mexico.

FRANCISCAN FRIARS (O.F.M.)

(Sacred Heart Province), Motherhouse: St. Anthony Friary, 3140 Meramec St., St. Louis, MO 63118. (314) 353-7470

365 Priests and Brothers, 4 Novices

Apostolic Work: Work is determined by the talents and interests of the members. 75 parishes, 1 university, 2 high schools, 3 foreign missions, and work with minorities (Mexicans, Blacks, Native Americans) at home. Many engaged in special ministries; nursing care, chaplains at a variety of institutions (hospitals, jails, etc.), teachers at other colleges and high schools, military chaplains, Social Justice issues, youth ministry, etc.

Vocation Director: Fr. Henry V. Willenborg, O.F.M., 4860 W. 29th St., Cicero, IL 60650. 1-800-933-4871.

FRANCISCAN FRIARS OF THE ATONEMENT

See Atonement Friars.

FRANCISCAN FRIARS (O.F.M.) (Custody of the Holy Land)

U.S. Foundation: 1400 Quincy St., N.E., Washington, DC 20017. (202) 526-6800

97 Priests, 44 Brothers, 55 Students in Formation, 7 Novices, 35 Candidates in U.S. and Holy Land.

Apostolic Work: All areas of Church service in Washington, DC, in the Holy Land and Middle East

Vocation Director: Bro. Callistus, O.F.M., 1400 Quincy St. N.E., Washington, DC 20017. (202) 526-6800.

FRANCISCAN FRIARS OF THE RENEWAL (COMMUNITY OF) (C.F.R.)

St. Crispin Friary, 420 E. 156th St., Bronx, NY 10455. (718) 665-2441

23 Friars, 3 Novices, 6 Postulants, 3 Friaries

Apostolate: Spiritual and corporal works of mercy extended toward the poor and homeless; evangelization in all forms.

Conduct: The Padre Pio Shelter and The Saint Anthony Residence – short and long-term housing for men in the South Bronx; retreats, days/evenings of recollection, parish missions, conferences, street evangelization, youth prayer festivals.

Represented in the Archdiocese of New York.

Vocation Director: Rev. Glenn Sudano, C.F.R., Our Lady of Guadalupe Friary, 3537 Bainbridge Ave., Bronx, NY 10467. (718) 547-9840.

FRANCISCAN FRIARS (O.F.M. Conv.) (Order of Friars Minor Conventual)

(Immaculate Conception Province)

Provincial Office: Immaculate Conception Friary, 517 Washington, Box 629, Rennselaer, NY 12144. (518) 472-1000

207 Priests and Brothers, 21 Student Friars, 3 Novices, 6 Pre-Novitiate Students

Apostolate Work: Active-contemplative men involved in parish ministry, education (secondary, college, graduate level teaching and administration), campus ministry, youth ministry, hospital chaplaincies, counseling, retreats, secular Franciscan Order, social work, health care, manual labor, service to the poor, special education. Special ministries in Covenant House/Under 21, Black and Spanish speaking apostolates and a Hermitage, missions in Costa Rica and Brazil. Pre-novitiate house: Holyoke, MA; Novitiate: Staten Island, NY; Major Theological Seminary, WTU, Forestville, MD.

Represented in the Archdioceses of New York and Newark and in the Dioceses of Albany, Syracuse, Ogdensburg, Trenton, Camden, Charlotte, Raleigh, and St. Augustine.

Vocation Director: Bro. Mike Snyder, O.F.M. Conv., P.O. Box 629, Rensselaer, NY 12144. (518) 465-7460.

FRANCISCAN FRIARS (O.F.M. Conv.) (Order of Friars Minor Conventual)

(St. Anthony of Padua Province), Ellicott City, MD.

260 Priests & Brothers, 20 Student Friars, 4 Novices, 7 Candidates

Apostolic Work: Parish ministry, secondary education, campus ministry, counselling, foreign missions in Amami Oshima, Japan and Ghana, West Africa, retreats, nursing. College seminary at Granby, MA; novitiate at Staten Island, NY.

Represented in the Archdioceses of Baltimore and Boston and in the Dioceses of Altoona-Johnstown, Bridgeport, Hartford, Brooklyn, Buffalo, Erie, Fall River, Harrisburg, Birmingham, Norwich, Ogdensburg, Paterson, Portland, ME, Rochester, Springfield, MA, Trenton, Atlanta, GA and W. Palm Beach, FL.

Vocation Director: Fr. Gerry Waterman, O.F.M. Conv., Vocation Office, 66 School St., Granby, MA 01033. (413) 467-9195.

FRANCISCAN FRIARS (O.F.M. Conv.)(Order of Friars Minor Conventual)

(St. Bonaventure Province), 6107 N. Kenmore Ave., Chicago, IL 60660.

70 Friars, 41 Friar Priests, 29 Nonordained Friars (Brothers), 7 Students

Conduct: 12 friaries, 7 parishes, 3 residences, 2 missions in Mexico.

Apostolic Work: Parish, education, counseling, catechectics, publications, nursing and health care, retreats, skilled trades, institutional chaplaincies, foreign missions, Marian and Eucharistic Apostolate.

Represented in the Archdioceses of Chicago, Detroit and Milwaukee and in the Dioceses of Rockford, Peoria, Guerrero State Diocese of Acapulco in Mexico.

Vocation Director: Office for Vocations, 6107 N. Kenmore Ave., Chicago, IL 60660. (312) 764-8811.

FRANCISCAN FRIARS (O.F.M. Conv.) (Order of Friars Minor Conventual)

(Province of Our Lady of Consolation), Mount Saint Francis, IN 47146

38 Brothers, 163 Priests, 8 Students

Apostolic Work: Parish, retreats, education, campus, youth, counseling, chaplaincies, teaching. Missions in Zambia, Africa; Central America and Denmark.

Represented in the Archdioceses of Minneapolis-Saint Paul, MN, Dubuque, IA, Milwaukee, WI, Washington, DC, Indianapolis, IN, Louisville, KY, St. Louis, MO and San Antonio, TX and in the Dioceses of Cleveland and Toledo, OH, El Paso, TX, Grand Rapids and Lansing, MI, Fort Wayne, IN, Las Cruces, NM and Savannah, GA.

Vocation Directors: Fr. Jim Kent, OFM Conv., Conventual Franciscans, 6901 Dixie Hwy., Louisville, KY 40258. (502) 933-4439 or (502) 935-1223; Fr. Miguel Briseno, San Damiano Friary, 1104 Kentucky Ave., San Antonio, TX 78201. (201) 734-4962.

FRANCISCAN FRIARS (O.F.M. Conv.) (Order of Friars Minor Conventual)

(St. Joseph Cupertino Province), P.O. Box 820, Arroyo Grande, CA 93421-0820. (805) 489-1012

38 Priests, 11 Brothers, 8 Friar Seminarians, 4 Novices

Conduct: 7 parishes, 1 high school, 1 mission, 3 hospital chaplaincies, 1 prison chaplaincy, 2 houses of formation, 11 friaries, 1 renewal center.

Represented in the Archdiocese of Los Angeles and in the Dioceses of Fresno, Monterey, Oakland, San Bernardino, San Diego, Reno and Acapulco (Mexico).

Vocation Director: Fr. Charles Shelton, O.F.M. Conv., P.O. Box 820, Arroyo Grande, CA 93421-0820. (805) 489-1012.

FRANCISCANS, THIRD ORDER REGULAR (T.O.R.)

(Province of The Most Sacred Heart of Jesus), Loretto, PA 15940.

2 Bishops, 120 Priests, 30 Brothers, 12 Friars in Formation

Apostolic Work: Parishes, colleges, high schools, houses of formation, Church renewal, campus ministries, social justice, hospital chaplaincies and foreign missions in Brazil (South America).

Represented in the Archdioceses of Philadelphia, Washington and Manaus (Brazil) and in the Dioceses of Altoona-Johnstown, Arlington, Borba (Brazil), Erie, Fort Worth, Pittsburgh, St. Petersburg, Sioux Falls, Steubenville and Wheeling-Charleston.

Vocation Director: Father Bernard Tickerhoof, T.O.R., Franciscan Vocation Office, P.O. Box 187, Loretto, PA 15940-0187. (814) 472-9526.

FRANCISCAN FRIARS, THIRD ORDER REGULAR (T.O.R.)

(Province of the Immaculate Conception) P.O. Box 29655, Brookland Sta., Washington, DC 20017. (202) 526-3332

62 Friars in Province (Priests and Brothers)

Apostolic Work: Parish ministry, elementary and high school teaching, social work, health care, Newman chaplaincies, retreats.

Represented in the Archdioceses of Dubuque, Miami, Minneapolis-St. Paul and Washington and in the Dioceses of Altoona-Johnstown, Orlando, Owensboro and Wheeling-Charleston.

FRANCISCAN FRIARS, THIRD ORDER REGULAR (T.O.R.)

Third Order of St. Francis, 301 Jefferson Ave., Waco, TX 76701. (817) 752-8434

Represented in the Archdioceses of Newark and New York and the Diocese of Austin.

Vocation Director: Fr. Amando Trojillo, T.O.R.

FRANCISCAN MISSIONARY BROTHERS OF THE SACRED HEART OF JESUS (O.S.F.)

Our Lady of the Angels Monastery, Eureka, MO 63025.

15 Brothers

Apostolic Work: Geriatric nursing.

Vocation Director: Brother Bernardo, O.S.F., Franciscan Missionary Brothers, Our Lady of the Angels Monastery, Eureka, MO 63025. (314) 938-5361.

GLENMARY HOME MISSIONERS

Box 465618, Cincinnati, OH 45246-5618. (513) 874-8900

67 Priests, 20 Brothers

Apostolic Work: Mission work with the poor, unchurched, and Catholic minority in the U.S.; Appalachia, Deep South, and Southwest.

Conduct: 83 mission locations. Novitiate in Washington, DC, Candidacy Program in Hartford, KY. Theology at Washington Theological Union, Washington, DC

Represented in the Archdioceses of Atlanta, GA; Cincinnati, OH; and Washington, DC; and the Dioceses of Birmingham, AL; Little Rock, AR; Savannah, GA; Owensboro, KY; Covington, KY; Lexington, KY; Jackson, MS; Charlotte, NC; Tulsa, OK; Nashville, TN; Tyler, TX; Richmond, VA and Wheeling-Charleston, WV.

Vocation Contacts: Bro.Virgil Siefker, Fr. Steve Pawelk, Bro. Bob Hoffman.

GUANELLIANS

See Servants of Charity.

HERMITS OF OUR LADY OF MOUNT CARMEL (H.O. Carm)

Mount Carmel Hermitage, P.O. Box 337, Christoval, TX 76935

3 Hermits

Apostolic Work: Contemplative - following eremitical, Carmelite rule (no active ministry).

Represented in the Diocese of San Angelo.

Vocation Contact: Vocation Director, Mount Carmel Hermitage, P.O. 337, Christoval, TX 76935.

HOLY APOSTLES, MISSIONARY SOCIETY OF THE

See Missionary Society of the Holy Apostles.

HOLY CROSS BROTHERS (C.S.C.)

(Eastern Province)

146 Brothers

Conduct: 4 high schools, 1 middle school, 1 social service agency, 1 spiritual life center and missions in

Kenya and Uganda.

Apostolic Works: Education, campus ministry, spiritual direction/ retreats, parish and social ministry, health care, ministries to the chemically dependent, foreign missions.

Represented in the Archdioceses of Hartford, New York and Washington, DC and in the Dioceses of Albany, Brooklyn, Fall River, Savannah and Wilmington.

Vocation Director: Bro. Paul Bednarczyk, C.S.C., 85 Overlook Circle, New Rochelle, NY 10804. (914) 632-4468.

HOLY CROSS BROTHERS (C.S.C.)

(Midwest Province) Provincial House, Box 460, Notre Dame, IN 46556.

300 Brothers, 4 Novices

Apostolic Work: Brothers are engaged in education, campus and youth ministry, retreat ministry, parish and social work, health care, work with the poor and elderly, in trades and other areas of service in the United States and overseas in Bangladesh, South America, Ghana and Liberia.

Represented in the Archdioceses of Anchorage, Chicago, Detroit, Louisville, Milwaukee, Los Angeles and Miami and in the Dioceses of Cleveland, Evansville, Venice, Portland, OR, Fort Wayne-South Bend and Gary. Also in Bangladesh, Ghana and Liberia.

Vocation Director: Brother Raymond Papenfuss, CSC, Box 460, Notre Dame, IN 46556. (219) 233-2191.

HOLY CROSS BROTHERS (C.S.C.)

(South-West Province), Provincial Office: St. Edward's University, Austin, TX 78704-6489. (512) 442-7856.

140 Brothers, 7 in Initial Formation

Apostolic Work: Primary, secondary and university education; hospital chaplain; health care; music; liturgy; care of the elderly; research; law; social work: work with migrants, feeding, clothing and sheltering the poor, abandoned mothers and children, delinquent youth; maintenance; art and theater; parish administration; counseling; campus ministry; youth ministry; administration; foreign missions.

Represented in the Archdioceses of Los Angeles, New Orleans and San Antonio and in the Dioceses

of Austin, Beaumont, Cheyenne, Knoxville, Lake Charles, Oakland, Portland, San Jose and Savannah. Also in Bangladesh, Brazil and Chile.

Vocation Director: Bro. Joseph Tomei, C.S.C., St. Edward's University #1046, 3001 S. Congress Ave., Austin, TX 78704-6489. (512) 442-7856.

CONGREGATION OF HOLY CROSS EASTERN PROVINCE OF PRIESTS AND BROTHERS (C.S.C.)

Provincial House: 835 Clinton Ave., Bridgeport, CT 06604. (203) 367-7252

145 Priests, 15 Brothers, 14 Men in Formation

Conduct: 2 colleges, 2 retreat houses, Family Rosary and Family Theater, administer or assist in 24 parishes.

Apostolic Work: Teaching - university and secondary education, chaplaincies - hospital, military; campus ministry, retreats and renewals, parishes, pastoral counseling, youth, elderly, urban and migrant ministry and foreign missions.

Represented in Northeastern U.S., Florida and Peru in the Archdioceses of Boston, Hartford, Los Angeles, Newark, New York and Washington, DC and in the Dioceses of Albany, Austin, Brooklyn, Bridgeport, Burlington, Fall River, Fort Wayne-South Bend, Orlando, Portland (ME), Rochester, Scranton and Wilmington, DE. Foreign missions in Africa, Asia and South America.

Admissions: College and post-college programs.

Vocation Director: Rev. James T. Preskenis, C.S.C.; Associate Vocation Director: Rev. John P. Phalen, C.S.C., Congregation of Holy Cross, P.O. Box 557, North Easton, MA 02356. (508) 238-5810.

HOLY CROSS PRIESTS (C.S.C.)

(Indiana Province) Provincial House: 1304 E. Jefferson Blvd., South Bend, IN 46617.

331 Priests, 23 Brothers, 80 Seminarians

Apostolic work: University and secondary education, retreat preaching, parishes, hospital chaplains, military chaplains, scholars, authors, publishers, social work, minorities, counseling, psychology, music, liturgy, inner-city, elderly, marriage encounter, catechetical, seminary formation, spiritual directors, youth ministry

and administration. Foreign missionaries in Chile, South America; Kenya and Uganda, Africa; and Bangladesh.

Represented in Archdioceses of Austin, Boston, Cleveland, Chicago, Colorado Springs, Los Angeles, New Orleans, Portland OR, San Francisco and Washington and in the Dioceses of Fall River, Fort Wayne-South Bend, Fort Worth, Fresno, Kansas City-St. Joseph, La Crosse, Lafayette IN, Madison, Oakland, Phoenix, San Diego, San Francisco, San Jose, San Bernardino, Santa Rosa, Scranton, Stockton, and Tucson.

Contact: Reverend John Conley, C.S.C., Director of Vocations, P.O. Box 541, Moreau Seminary, Notre Dame, IN 46556. (219) 631-6385.

HOLY CROSS FATHERS AND BROTHERS (C.S.C.)

(Southern Province), Provincial House: 2111 Brackenridge St., Austin, TX 78704. (512) 443-3886.

33 Fathers, 2 Brothers, 15 Initial Formation

Apostolic Work: Parishes, ministry to Hispanics, youth work, campus ministry, retreats, renewals, and foreign missions (Africa, Asia, Central and South America). Southern Province includes the Gulf States and the row of states above the Gulf States.

Represented in the Archdioceses of New Orleans, St. Louis and San Antonio and in the Dioceses of Austin, Baton Rouge, Fort Wayne-South Bend, Lafayette (LA) and Las Cruces.

Vocation Director: Rev. Leonard Collins, C.S.C., 2111 Brackenridge St., Austin, TX 78704. (512) 443-3886.

BROTHERS OF HOLY EUCHARIST (F.S.E.)

General Motherhouse: P.O. Box 25, Plaucheville, LA 71362. (318) 922-3630; 922-3401

Conduct: 2 houses, 3 schools, 1 high school, 1 nursing home, 1 novitiate.

Represented in the Diocese of Alexandria.

Vocation Director: Bro. Andre M. Lucia, F.S.E., Superior General.

CONGREGATION OF THE MISSIONARIES OF THE HOLY FAMILY

See Missionaries of the Holy Family.

SONS OF THE HOLY FAMILY (S.F.)

(North American Vice Province) 401 Randolph Rd., P.O. Box 4138, Silver Spring, MD 20904. (301) 622-1184

Generalate: Barcelona, Spain.

North American Vice Province: 14 Priests, 2 Men in Formation

Apostolic Work: Teaching, social work, parishes, retreats, Hispanic ministry.

Represented in East and Southwest U.S., Spain, Italy, Argentina, Columbia, Brazil, Venezuela and Mexico.

Vocation Director: Fr. Ron Carrillo, S.F., P.O. Box 1228, Santa Cruz, NM 87567. (505) 753-3345.

HOLY GHOST FATHERS OF IRELAND (C.S.Sp.)

48-49 37th St., Long Island City, NY 11101. (718) 729-5273

65 Fathers

Represented in the Archdioceses of Miami, New Orleans, New York and San Francisco and in the Dioceses of Brooklyn, Fargo, Metuchen, St. Augustine and West Palm Beach.

Vocation Director: Fr. Norman Beevan, St. Mary Magdalene, 8426 S. Marquette Ave., Chicago, IL 60617. (312) 768-1700.

HOLY GHOST FATHERS AND BROTHERS (C.S.Sp.) (Spiritans)

Priests, Brothers, Lay Associates

(Province of the United States East) 6230 Brush Run Rd., Bethel Park, PA 15102. (412) 831-0302

(Province of the United States West)919 Briarcliff, San Antonio, TX 78213. (210) 349-6349

200 Priests and Brothers

Conduct: 1 university, 3 university chaplaincies, 2 novitiates, hospital chaplaincies, 2 renewal centers, 1 home for homeless boys, 1 high school, 37 parishes, foreign missions in the Archdiocese of Arecibo, Caguas and Ponce, Puerto Rico. Missions also in the Diocese of Cuidad Valles, Mexico, as well as Arusha and Moshi, Tanzania. Direct Pontifical Association of the Holy Childhood in the U.S. and Puerto Rico. Algeria; Amazon Brazil and South Africa.

Apostolic Work: Foreign missions, education and parishes.

Represented in the Archdioceses of Chicago, Cincinnati, Detroit, New Orleans, New York, Philadelphia, San Antonio and Washing-ton, DC and in the Dioceses of Alexandria, Arlington, Charleston, Charlotte, Erie, Little Rock, Houston, Pittsburgh, Providence and San Bernardino.

Vocation Offices: Spiritan Vocation Office, Duquesne University, Pittsburgh, PA 15282. (412) 765-0733; Spiritan Vocation Office, 4410 Yoakum Blvd., Houston, TX 77006. (713) 529-4236.

BROTHERS OF THE HOLY ROSARY (Congregation of Our Lady of the Rosary)

Motherhouse: 1725 S. McCarran Blvd., Reno, NV 89502.

Apostolic Work: A small diocesan community serving the needs of the Diocese of Reno with emphasis on educational apostolate in elementary and secondary schools. Brothers staff 1 elementary school and 1 high school. Also work in the areas of CCD, adult education and parish ministry.

Represented in the Diocese of Reno.

Vocation Director: Bro. Philip Napolitano, F.S.R., 1725 S. McCarran Blvd., Reno, NV 89502. (702) 358-6806.

HOSPITALLER BROTHERS OF ST. JOHN OF GOD (O.H.)

(Our Lady Queen of Angels Province) U.S. Provincial House: 2425 S. Western Ave., Los Angeles, CA 90018.

2 Priests, 30 Brothers, 1 Novice

Conduct: 3 health facilities: 2 geriatric centers, 1 novitiate, I Christian community.

Apostolic Work: Called daily to witness Christ's healing love through a community of prayer and service to God's suffering people.

Represented in the Archdiocese of Los Angeles and in the Diocese of San Bernardino, CA. International Headquarters of Order's 225 hospitals and schools at Tiber Island, Rome. Missions in Africa, South America, Korea, Japan, Vietnam, India, Philippines and the Holy Land.

Vocation Director: Bro. Fidelis Knight, O.H., Brothers of St. John of God, 2035 W. Adams Blvd., Los Angeles, CA 90018. (213) 734-6624.

HOSPITALLER BROTHERS OF ST. JOHN OF GOD (O.H.)

Immaculate Conception Province (Ireland), 532 Delsea Dr., Westville Grove, NJ 08093.

3 Brothers, 1 Postulant

Apostolic Work: School and vocational center for children and adults with special needs. Outreach program and pastoral counselling for the underprivileged. A worldwide order of Brothers founded by St. John of God at Granada, Spain in 1539. A Community of Brothers sharing love, hope and respect with those who need it most. Headquarters of the Order in Rome.

Represented in the Diocese of Camden.

Vocation Director: Bro. Derek O'Connell, O.H., 532 Delsea Dr., Westville Grove, NJ 08093. (609) 848-4700; (609) 848-4141 (after 4:30 PM).

BROTHERS OF THE IMMACULATE HEART OF MARY (I.H.M.)

609 N. 7th St., Steubenville, OH 43952.

8 Brothers in Apostolic Works

Apostolic Work: Parishes, CCD teachers, chancery office and Bishop's Residence.

Represented in the Diocese of Steubenville.

Contact Vocation Director: Rev. Patrick Geary, 609 N. 7th St., Steubenville, OH 43952. (614) 283-2462.

INSTITUTE OF CHARITY (I.C.) (The Rosminian Priests and Brothers)

U.S.: 18 Priests; worldwide: 450 members – priests and brothers.

Apostolic Work: Founded to accept ANY and ALL works of charity. At present, our members are involved in teaching the handicapped, parish work, and missionary activity throughout the world.

Represented in the Dioceses of Peoria, Venice and St. Petersburg.

Vocation Director: Fr. Bruce King, P.O. Box 589, Galesburg, IL 61402-0589. (309) 343-9874.

JESUITS (S.J.) (Society of Jesus)

(Maryland Province), 5704 Roland Ave., Baltimore, MD 21210.

460 Priests, 63 Scholastics, 34 Brothers

Conduct: 3 universities, 2 colleges, 5 high schools, 12 parishes, 3 houses of retreat, 1 spiritual center, 1 novitiate, 11 residences.

Apostolic Work: Teaching higher

and secondary education, parishes, retreats, chaplaincies, spiritual direction, social ministries, foreign missions.

Represented in the (Arch)dioceses of Allentown, Altoona-Johnstown, Arlington, Baltimore, Camden, Charlotte, Erie, Greensburg, Harrisburg, Metuchen, Philadelphia, Pittsburgh, Raleigh, Richmond, Scranton, Trenton, Washington, Wheeling-Charleston and Wilmington. Also in Chile, England, Germany, Ghana, Honduras, Italy, Japan, Kenya, Mexico, Micronesia, Nicaragua, Nigeria, Taiwan and Thailand.

Vocation Director: Rev. Joseph Costantino, S.J., 39 E. 83 St., New York, NY 10028. (212) 774-5500.

JESUITS (S.J.)
(Society of Jesus)

(Chicago Province), 2050 N. Clark St., Chicago, IL 60614. (312) 975-6363.

249 Priests, 28 Scholastics, 20 Brothers

Conduct: 4 parishes, 2 universities, 4 high schools, 1 house of study, 2 retreat houses, 6 residences, 1 house of writers, 1 center for action/research.

Represented in the Archdioceses of Chicago, Cincinnati and Indianapolis and in the Dioceses of Gary, IN, Covington and Lexington, KY. Also in Nepal, Patna, India, Peru and East Africa.

Vocation Director: Rev. Brian G. Paulson, S.J., 2050 N. Clark St., Chicago, IL 60614. (312) 975-6363.

JESUITS (S.J.)
(Society of Jesus)

(Detroit Province), 7303 W. Seven Mile Rd., Detroit, MI 48221-2198. (313) 861-7500

186 Fathers, 26 Scholastics, 29 Brothers

Conduct: 6 parishes, 2 universities, 5 high schools, 3 retreat houses, 1 novitiate.

Represented in MI: in the Archdiocese of Detroit and in the Dioceses of Gaylord, Grand Rapids, Kalamazoo, Lansing, Marquette and Saginaw. In OH: Cleveland, Columbus, Steubenville, Toledo and Youngstown. Also in India, Nepal, Peru, Nicaragua, Thailand, Tanzania, Uganda and Kenya.

Vocation Director: Fr. Norman Dickson, S.J., Loyola House, 2599 Harvard Rd., Berkley, MI 48072. (810) 399-8132.

JESUITS (S.J.)
(Society of Jesus)

(New York Province), 39 E. 83 St., New York, NY 10028

560 Priests, 36 Brothers, 83 Scholastics

Conduct: 1 university, 3 colleges, 7 high schools, 1 novitiate, 4 retreat houses, 8 parishes, publications, hospital chaplaincies, prison chaplaincy, Society for Blind, Shrine of North American Martyrs.

Apostolic Work: There is no one Jesuit ministry. Ignatius wanted his companions to do whatever the Church needed done and wherever that might be. This is the source of Jesuit devotion to the Church. Jesuits are involved in everything, all "for the greater glory of God."

Represented in the Archdioceses of New York and Newark and in the Dioceses of Albany, Brooklyn, Buffalo, Paterson, Rochester, Rockville Centre and Syracuse. Also in Nigeria, Puerto Rico, Ecuador, Philippines, Japan, Caroline-Marshall Islands, Ghana, Zambia-Malawi and Central America.

Vocation Director: Rev. Joseph Costantino, S.J., 39 E. 83 St., New York, NY 10028. (212) 774-5500.

JESUITS (S.J.)
(Society of Jesus)

(New England Province), 771 Harrison Ave., Boston, MA 02118. (617) 266-7233

443 Priests, 21 Brothers, 30 Seminarians

Conduct: 3 parishes, 2 universities, 1 college, 4 high schools, 2 houses for retreats, 1 seminary, 1 novitiate.

Apostolic Work: Teaching, parish work, hospital, prisons, military chaplaincies, administration, social service, retreats, writing, foreign missions.

Represented in the Archdiocese of Boston and in the Dioceses of Bridgeport (CT), Fall River, Springfield and Worcester (MA), Portland (ME), Norwich (CT) and Manchester (NH) Also, in the international field: Jamaica, W.I., Brazil, Japan, Middle East in Jordan, Lebanon, Egypt, Syria, Bahamas, Iceland, Micronesia, and Malawi.

Vocation Director: Rev. William C. Russell, S.J., P.O. Box 799, Back Bay Annex, Boston, MA 02117-0799. (617) 266-7233.

JESUITS (S.J.)
(Society of Jesus)

(California Province) P.O. Box 519, Los Gatos, CA 95031. (408) 354-6143

422 Priests, 37 Brothers, 60 Scholastics

Conduct: 15 parishes, 3 universities, 5 high schools, 1 novitiate, 1 theologate, 1 retreat house.

Represented in the Archdioceses of Los Angeles and San Francisco and in the Dioceses of Honolulu, Monterey, Oakland, Phoenix, Reno, Sacramento, Salt Lake, San Diego, Stockton and Tucson.

Vocation Director: Rev. John T. Mitchell, S.J., P.O. Box 519, Los Gatos, CA 95031. (408) 354-7408.

JESUITS (S.J.)
(Society of Jesus)

(Oregon Province), 2222 N.W. Hoyt, Portland, OR 97210. (503) 226-6977

277 Priests, 23 Brothers, 33 Scholastics

Conduct: 40 parishes (including 19 Alaskan and 9 Indian missions), 2 universities, 4 high schools, 2 houses of study, 1 novitiate, 2 retreat houses.

Represented in the Archdioceses of Anchorage, Portland, OR and Seattle and in the Dioceses of Baker, Boise, Fairbanks, Great Falls, Helena, Spokane and Yakima. Also in Kenya, Malawi, Peru, Uganda and Zambia.

Vocation Director: Brian Ulrickson, S.J., North 1107 Astor, Spokane, WA 99202. (509) 487-5020.

JESUITS (S.J.)
(Society of Jesus)

(Missouri Province), 4511 W. Pine Blvd., St. Louis, MO 63108-2191.

309 Priests, 25 Scholastics (Men in Formation), 33 Brothers

Conduct: 2 universities, 1 college, 1 junior college, 5 high schools, 1 house of study for Jesuit seminarians, 8 parishes, 2 retreat centers, the Sacred Heart radio program, 1 mission, 1 novitiate.

Apostolic Work: Teaching, parish work, retreats, hospital chaplaincy, campus ministry, publications, social service, arts and communications (writing, radio), domestic and foreign missions.

Represented principally in the states of Missouri, Colorado, Kansas and Oklahoma. Also in the Central American countries of Belize and the Republic of Honduras.

Vocation Director: Rev. William T. Oulvey, S.J., 4511 W. Pine Blvd., St. Louis, MO 63108-2191. (314) 361-7765.

JESUITS (S.J.)
(Society of Jesus)
(New Orleans Province), 500 S. Jefferson Davis Pkwy., New Orleans, LA 70119.

260 Priests, 35 Scholastics, 21 Novices, 32 Brothers

Conduct: 13 parishes, 1 university, 1 college, 4 high schools, 1 novitiate, 5 houses of retreat.

Apostolic Work: Teaching higher and secondary education, parishes, retreats, chaplaincies, spiritual direction, campus ministry, prisons, social ministries, foreign missions in Brazil and Paraguay.

Represented in the Archdioceses of Atlanta, Miami, New Orleans, San Antonio and Santa Fe and in the Dioceses of Alexandria, Austin, Baton Rouge, Charleston, Corpus Christi, Dallas, El Paso, Fort Worth, Galveston-Houston, Lafayette, Las Cruces, Little Rock, Mobile, Natchez-Jackson, Orlando, Palm Beach and St. Petersburg.

Vocation Director: Fr. Marvin Kitten, S.J., 500 S. Jefferson Davis Pkwy., New Orleans, LA 70119-7192. (504) 821-0334.

JESUITS (S.J.)
(Society of Jesus)
(Wisconsin Province) 3400 W. Wisconsin, Milwaukee, WI 53208. (414) 937-6949.

421 Priests, Brothers and Scholastics.

Conduct: 9 parishes, 2 universities, 3 high schools, 2 middle schools, 3 grade schools, 4 retreat centers, Sioux Spiritual Center, 3 Native American missions with 14 parishes and a radio station.

Apostolic Work: Educational, pastoral, social, spiritual and international ministries; arts and communications.

Represented in Wisconsin, Minnesota, North and South Dakota, Nebraska, Iowa and Wyoming, with missions on two Sioux Reservations in S.D. and one mission with Native Americans in Wyoming. Also in South Korea and East Africa.

Vocation Director: Rev. Richard C. Burbach, S.J., 1035 Summit Ave., St. Paul, MN 55105-3034. (612) 224-5593.

JESUITS (S.J.)
(Society of Jesus)
(Province of the Antilles) 13339 S.W. 9th Terrace, Miami, FL 33184. (305) 559-9044.

94 Fathers, 63 Scholastics, 16 Brothers

Conduct: 2 high schools, 1 novitiate, 3 houses of retreat, 2 residences.

Represented in the Archdiocese of Miami. Also in Dominican Republic.

JOSEPHITE FATHERS AND BROTHERS (S.S.J.) (Society of St. Joseph of the Sacred Heart)
138 Fathers, 12 Brothers

Conduct: 70 city and rural parishes, hospital and prison chaplaincies, 1 high school, college house of studies, major seminary, and the Josephite Pastoral Center.

Apostolic Work: Josephites have worked completely among Black Americans for more than 100 years. Josephites are identified with the Black community in a spiritual, educational, and social ministry, and aid one another in achieving goals by the mutual charity of community life.

Represented in the Archdioceses of Los Angeles, Baltimore, Washington, New Orleans, New York, and also in the Dioceses of Arlington, Baton Rouge, Beaumont, Biloxi, Birmingham, Fort Worth, Galveston, Houma-Thibodaux, Houston, Jackson, Lafayette, Lake Charles, Mobile, St. Augustine and Wilmington.

Director of Vocations: Rev. James McLinden, S.S.J., St. Joseph's Seminary, 1200 Varnum St., N.E., Washington, DC 20017. (202) 526-4231.

JOSEPHITE FATHERS (C.J.)
180 Patterson Rd., Santa Maria, CA 93455. (805) 937-5378
Novitiate: 180 Patterson Rd., Santa Maria, CA 93455.

16 Priests, 1 Brother

Conduct: 1 parish, 2 high schools, 1 hospital

Represented in the Archdiocese of Los Angeles; Belgium; England; Africa (Zaire).

Vocation Director: 180 Patterson Rd., Santa Maria, CA 93455.

LA SALETTE MISSIONARIES (M.S.) (Missionaries of Our Lady of La Salette)
(Province of Our Lady of Seven Dolors), 915 Maple Ave., Hartford, CT 06114-2330.

97 Priests, 15 Brothers

Conduct: In the U.S.: 25 parishes, 1 shrine, 1 retreat house, 1 house of study, novitiate.

Apostolic Work: Inner-city and suburban parishes, retreats, shrines, preaching, military & institutional chaplaincies, professional counseling, foreign missions.

Represented in the Archdioceses of Atlanta, Boston, Hartford, New York, St. Paul-Minneapolis and Washington, DC and in the Dioceses of Albany, Manchester, Norwich, Orlando, Raleigh, Springfield and Worcester. Foreign missions in Argentina and Bolivia.

Vocation Directors: Fr. John Dolan, M.S., 915 Maple Ave., Hartford, CT 06114-2330. (203) 956-8870; Fr. Thanh Nguyen, M.S., St. Ann Rectory, 4905 Roswell Rd., NE, Marietta, GA 30062. (404) 552-6400.

LA SALETTE MISSIONARIES (M.S.) (Missionaries of Our Lady of La Salette)
(Province of the Immaculate Heart of Mary) 947 Park St., P.O. Box 2965, Attleboro, MA 02703-0965.

59 Priests, 29 Brothers

Conduct: 1 house of study, 1 novitiate, 1 house of formation.

Apostolic Work: Parish work, retreats, institutional chaplaincies, military chaplaincies, foreign and home missions, pastoral counseling, houses of prayer, shrine work, social work, campus ministry.

Represented in the Dioceses of Fall River, Boston, Manchester, Burlington, San Diego and Tucson; Canada: Dioceses of Montreal, Hull, and London, Ontario.

Vocation Director: Rev. Andre A. Patenaude, M.S., 947 Park St., P.O. Box 2965, Attleboro, MA 02703-0965. (508) 222-9154.

LA SALETTE MISSIONARIES (M.S.) (Missionaries of Our Lady of La Salette)
(Province of Mary Queen) St. Louis, MO 63111.

45 Priests, 6 Brothers

Conduct: 17 houses or parishes in the Province.

Apostolic Work: Parishes, hospital, prison and university chaplaincies, counseling, spirituality center, shrines.

Represented in Texas, Louisiana, Missouri and Michigan as well as foreign missions in Madagascar and Argentina.

Vocation Director: Midwest Province, 4650 S. Broadway, St. Louis, MO 63111. (314) 353-5000.

LA SALETTE MISSIONARIES (M.S.) (Missionaries of Our Lady of La Salette)

(Province of Mary, Queen of Peace) 1607 E. Howard Ave., Milwaukee, WI 53207. (414) 769-7113

18 Priests, 5 Brothers, 1 Student Brother

Apostolic Work: Parish, spiritual direction, shrine and retreat work, hospital and military chaplaincies, foreign missions.

Represented in Illinois, Wisconsin and Madagascar.

Vocation Directors: Bro. Adam Mateja, M.S., La Salette Missionaries, P.O. Box 777, Twin Lakes, WI 53181. (414) 877-3373; Fr. John Gabriel, La Salette Retreat Center, R.R. 1, 5065 Olivet Rd., P.O. Box 403, Georgetown, IL 61846. (217) 662-6671.

LEGIONARIES OF CHRIST (L.C.)

Territorial Directorate: Legionaries of Christ, 393 Derby Ave., Orange, CT 06477. (203) 795-2800

320 Priests, 2,300 Seminarians

Seminaries: High school in New Hamphire for boys interested in the priesthood. Novitiate and Juniorate in Connecticut. Philosophy and Theology in Rome, Italy.

Primary Apostolic Works: Combining a contemplative spiritual life with an urgent apostolate (get people building Christ's Kingdom in society), the priests engage in extensive work with lay apostolate, youth, education, family, missions, the poor, media and catechetics, and run vocation retreats for high school and college-age men.

Represented in the Archdioceses of Hartford, New York, Washington, Detroit and Los Angeles and in the Dioceses of Manchester, Providence, Madison and Dallas. Also in Ireland, Spain, France, Holland, Germany, Italy, Mexico, Venezuela, Colombia, Chile, Brazil and Australia.

Foreign Missions: Diocese of Chetumal, Quintana Roo, Mexico.

Vocation Director: Father Owen Kearns, L.C., Legionaries of Christ, 475 Oak Ave., Cheshire, CT 06410. (203) 271-0805.

LITTLE BROTHERS OF THE GOOD SHEPHERD (B.G.S.)

Generalate: P.O. Box 1003, Hamilton, Ontario L8N 3R1. (905) 528-9109

72 Brothers

Conduct: 5 shelters serving the transient and destitute poor (men, women, children), 2 home facilities for the mentally and physically handicapped, 1 home facility serving the elderly and infirm, 2 centers for AIDS ministry, and 1 center of formation.

Represented in the Archdioceses of Miami, Philadelphia, Santa Fe and Toronto and in the Dioceses of Joliet, Hamilton, Canada, Ossory, Ireland and Birmingham, England.

Vocation Counselor: Bro. David J. Nickerson, B.G.S., Good Shepherd Center, P.O. Box 1003, Hamilton, Ontario L8N 3R1. (905) 528-9109.

LITTLE BROTHERS OF JESUS

1700 Bagley, Detroit, MI 48216. (313) 964-2833.

Apostolic Work: To emulate the life of Jesus at Nazareth.

LITTLE BROTHERS OF SAINT FRANCIS (L.B.S.F.)

General Fraternity: 785-789 Parker St., Mission Hill (Boston), MA 02120. (617) 442-2556

3 Perpetually Professed, 4 Candidates in Formation

Apostolic Work: Combine contemplative life, Eucharistic Adoration and evangelical street ministry, living in radical poverty and prayerful solidarity with the poorest of Christ's poor in the ghettos, favelos or barrios of the world.

Vocations: Bro. James Curran, L.B.S.F., Servant General.

MARIANISTS, SOCIETY OF MARY (S.M.)

(New York Province)

Provincial House: 4301 Roland Ave., Baltimore, MD 21210-2793.

56 Brothers, 26 Priests, 1 Novice, 4 Temporary Professed, 3 Aspirants

Staff: 3 schools, 1 home for disadvantaged youth; 2 retreat centers; 1 adult education center; 2 parishes, 1 university.

Apostolic Work: A community of brothers and priests engaged in: teaching; family renewal; retreat work; skilled trades; mission work; parish work; work with poor and disadvantaged; adult education; special education; campus ministry; universities; formation of lay communities.

Represented in the Archdioceses of Baltimore, Hartford, Miami and Boston and in the Dioceses of Brooklyn, Rockville Center, Trenton and Camden. Also in Dayton, Notre Dame, San Antonio and San Juan, PR. Missions in Puerto Rico and East Africa.

Vocation Director: Bro. Jesse O'Neill, S.M., 4301 Roland Ave., Baltimore, MD 21210-2793. (410) 366-1300, FAX (410) 889-5743.

MARIANISTS, SOCIETY OF MARY (S.M.)

(Province of Cincinnati), 4435 E. Patterson Rd., Dayton, OH 45430.

164 Brothers, 65 Priests

Conduct: 1 university, 5 high schools, 6 parishes, 1 novitiate, 1 renewal center.

Apostolic Work: Secondary schools, university teaching and administration; campus ministry; parish work; adult education; peace and justice centers; counseling; ecumenical centers. Overseas work in Japan, Ireland, Malawi, Kenya, Zambia.

Represented in the Archdiocese of Cincinnati and in the Dioceses of Cleveland, Kalamazoo and Pittsburgh.

Vocation Directors: Bro. Dan Klco, S.M., Marianist Vocation Ministry, Alumni Hall, Room 225, University of Dayton, Dayton, OH 45469-0323. (513) 229-2741; Bro. Michael O'Grady, S.M., 10932 St. Clair Ave., Cleveland, OH 44108. (216) 451-3262.

MARIANISTS, SOCIETY OF MARY (S.M.)

(Province of the Pacific)

Provincial House: P.O. Box 1775, Cupertino, CA 95015-1775. (408) 253-4841

34 Priests, 92 Brothers

Conduct: 5 parishes, 1 university, 5 high schools, 3 middle schools, 1 retreat center, 1 Newman Center, 1 Hispanic evangelization team, 1 community for young laity, 1 inner-city youth group, 1 youth camp, 2 third order laity groups; 1 food kitchen for the needy; 1 religious art studio; individual apostolates in medicine, neighborhood advocacy, religious bookstore, performing arts, journalism, travel advisory for religious, AIDS ministry, summer camp, overnight shelter, Al-Anon leadership, spiritual direction, diocesan chancery work; and professional counseling; mission: Marianist communities and works in Korea.

Represented in the Archdioceses of San Francisco and Los Angeles and in the Dioceses of Honolulu, Monterey and San Jose.

Vocation Ministers: Rev. John McEnhill, S.M., 175 Phelan Ave., San Francisco, CA 94112. (415) 586-8181; Rev. Mario Pariante, S.M., Box 323, 3140 Waialae Ave., Honolulu, HI 96816-1578. (808) 735-4857.

MARIANISTS, SOCIETY OF MARY (S.M.)

(Province of Meribah), Provincial House: 240 Emory Rd., Mineola, NY 11501. (516) 742-5555

6 Priests, 35 Brothers

Conduct: 2 high schools, 2 retreat houses.

MARIANISTS, SOCIETY OF MARY (SM)

(Province of St. Louis), P.O. Box 23130, St. Louis, MO 63156-3130.

183 Brothers, 66 Priests

Apostolic Work: Education, retreats, parish work, foreign missions, campus ministry.

Vocation Director: Rev. Jim Schimelpfening, S.M., Marianist Vocation Ministry, St. Mary's University, One Camino Santa Maria, San Antonio, TX 78228-8556. (210) 431-2193.

MARIANNHILL MISSIONARIES (CMM)

(American-Canadian Province), 23715 Ann Arbor Trail, Dearborn Heights, MI 48127.

22 Priests, 9 Brothers

Conduct: Community house, novitiate, vocation/formation center, parish assistance, youth retreat center.

Apostolic Work: Foreign missions, parish assistance, publications - "Leaves" magazine, youth retreat work and vocation/formation guidance.

Represented in the Archdioceses of Detroit and Chicago and in the Dioceses of Austin, TX and Quebec, Canada. Houses in Germany, Spain, Austria, Holland, Switzerland and Italy. Foreign missions in South Africa, Transkei, Brazil, Zambia, Zimbabwe and Papua New Guinea.

Vocation Director: Bro. Kenn Shatz, CMM, 23715 Ann Arbor Trail, Dearborn Heights, MI 48127. (313) 274-2893. FAX: (313) 561-9486.

MARIANS OF THE IMMACULATE CONCEPTION: PRIESTS AND BROTHERS (M.I.C.)

(St. Stanislaus Kostka Province) Eden Hill, Stockbridge, MA 01262.

23 Priests, 8 Brothers, 3 Professed Members, 4 Novices, 3 Postulants

Conduct: Publishing house, spirituality center, one parish, novitiate, house of studies, 4 religious houses, 1 residence.

Apostolic Work: Parish administration, publishing and printing, pastoral assistance, home missions, foreign missions, Marian pilgrimages, retreats, workshops, spiritual direction, counseling, and specialized apostolates and chaplaincies. Promotes devotion to Our Lady's Immaculate Conception and Our Lord's Divine Mercy.

Represented in the Archdioceses of Detroit (MI), Santa Fe (NM) and Washington (DC) and in the Dioceses of Charlotte (NC), Fairbanks (AK) and Springfield (MA).

Vocation Director: Rev. Larry Dunn, MIC, Marians of the Immaculate Conception, 3885 Harewood Rd. N.E., Washington, DC 20017. (202) 526-8884.

MARIANS OF THE IMMACULATE CONCEPTION (M.I.C.)

(Province of St. Casimir), 6336 S. Kilbourn Ave., Chicago, IL 60629.

34 Priests, 12 Brothers, 4 Novices; 500 Priests & Brothers worldwide

Conduct: 6 parishes, 1 high school, 3 community houses, 2 novitiates.

Apostolic Work: Teaching, publishing, parish work and missions. Spiritual principle: always to serve Christ and His Church, in the spirit of Mary, ministering to all peoples.

Represented in the Archdioceses of Chicago and Milwaukee and in the Dioceses of Joliet, IL, Norwich, CT and Worcester, MA. Also in Italy, England, Wales, Portugal, Poland, Germany, Lithuania, Latvia, Estonia, Byelorussia, Ukraine, Kazakhstan, Australia, Argentine, Brazil and Rwanda.

Vocation Director: Fr. Bill Hayward, M.I.C., Congregation of Marians, Thompson, CT 06277. (203) 923-9565; 2460.

MARIST BROTHERS OF THE SCHOOLS (F.M.S.)

(Province of Poughkeepsie) 26 First Ave., Pelham, NY 10803.

120 Brothers

Apostolic Work: Youth ministry, education (all levels), counseling, catechetical work, retreats, social ministry, foreign missions.

Represented in the Archdioceses of New York, Boston, Chicago and Miami, FL. Also in Japan.

Vocation Director: Bro. Rene Roy, FMS, 4200 W. 115th St., Chicago, IL 60655. (312) 881-0696.

MARIST BROTHERS OF THE SCHOOLS (F.M.S.)

(Province of Esopus) 1241 Kennedy Blvd., Bayonne, NJ 07002.

150 Brothers

Conduct: 10 high schools, 2 grammar schools, 1 summer camp, 1 retreat house, 1 foreign mission.

Apostolic Work: "Christian Education of Youth, particularly the least favored."

Represented in the Archdioceses of New York, Miami, Newark and in the Dioceses of Brooklyn, Brownsville, Rockville Centre and Savannah. Also in Liberia, Africa.

Vocation Directors: Bro. Michael Sheerin, F.M.S., Marist Provincial Office, 1241 Kennedy Blvd., Bayonne, NJ 07002. (201) 823-1115; Bro. John Venturella, F.M.S., Marist Brothers, 218 San Sebastian Ave., Coral Gables, FL 33134. (305) 444-6479.

MARIST FATHERS AND BROTHERS (S.M.) (Society of Mary)

(Boston Province) 27 Isabella St., Boston, MA 02116-5216. (617) 426-5297

85 Fathers & Brothers

Conduct: 15 parishes, 1 high school, foreign missions (in the islands of the Western Pacific), 2 houses of studies for seminarians, 2 shrines in Boston, 4 hospital chaplaincies, 3 college chaplaincies, 2 houses of prayer, 1 retreat house and specialized ministries (preaching parish missions, teaching on college level, military chaplaincy, special education, drug counseling, ministry to the elderly).

Apostolic Work: Parish work, teaching (elementary, college and high school levels), foreign missions, chaplaincies (in hospitals, schools and armed services), retreat work, home missions, charismatic renewal, houses of prayer, specialized ministries.

Represented in the Archdioceses of Boston, Detroit and New York

City; in the Dioceses of Brooklyn, Burlington, Portland (ME), Providence, Rapid City (SD) and Rochester; in the Western Pacific Dioceses of Fiji, New Caledonia, New Guinea, New Hebrides, New Zealand, Samoa, Solomon Islands, and Tonga.

Vocation Director: Fr. Roland Lajoie, S.M., Marist Vocation Office, 518 Pleasant St., Framingham, MA 01701-2898. (508) 875-6075.

MARIST FATHERS AND BROTHERS (S.M.)

(Washington Province) 815 Varnum St., N.E., Washington, DC 20017. (202) 529-4800

97 Priests, 12 Brothers

Conduct: 15 parishes, 1 high school, 2 houses of study and special ministries.

Apostolic Work: Parish work, teaching, chaplaincies, retreats, missions, Hispanic ministry, renewal, communications, foreign missions (Fiji, Solomon Islands, New Caledonia, Samoa, Tonga, Vanuatu, Wallis-Futuna, Brazil, Philippines, Japan, Peru, Venezuela).

Represented in the Archdioceses of Atlanta, New Orleans, St. Paul, Washington, DC and Philadelphia and in the Dioceses of Cleveland, Brownsville, Baton Rouge, Wheeling-Charleston and St. Petersburg.

Vocation Director: Rev. John Ulrich, S.M., Marist School, 3790 Ashford Dunwoody Rd. NE, Atlanta, GA 30319. (404) 458-6875 or 451-1316.

MARIST FATHERS AND BROTHERS (S.M.)

(Western Province), Marist Center, 625 Pine St., San Francisco, CA 94108. (415) 398-3543

32 Priests, 5 Brothers, 5 Theologian Scholastics, 1 Deacon

Conduct: 8 Parishes, campus ministry team, foreign implantation, Brazil.

Represented in the Archdioceses of Portland, OR and San Francisco and in the Dioceses of Boise, Honolulu and Oakland.

Vocation Director: Fr. Michael Galinado, S.M., 2335 Warring St., Berkeley, CA 94704. (510) 486-1232.

MARYKNOLL MISSIONERS (M.M.) (Catholic Foreign Mission Society of America)

Maryknoll, NY 10545.

Conduct: Mission education centers in the U.S. Mission work in Africa, Asia/Pacific, Latin America and Middle East.

Apostolic Work: Specialize in foreign mission work.

Representatives in Buffalo; Chestnut Hill, MA; Chicago; Cincinnati; Cleveland; Denver; Detroit; Gainesville, FL; Houston; Los Angeles; Minneapolis; New York; Philadelphia; St. Louis; San Francisco; Seattle; South Orange, NJ; and Washington, DC.

Vocations Director: Rev. Joseph Thaler, M.M., Maryknoll, NY 10545. Call toll free: (800) 431-2008; NYS Residents Call: (914) 941-7590, ext. 2416.

MERCEDARIANS

See Order of the Blessed Virgin Mary of Mercy.

BROTHERS OF MERCY (F.M.M.)

(American Province) 4520 Ransom Rd., Clarence, NY 14031

14 Brothers, 2 Novices

Apostolic Work: Health care.

Represented in the Diocese of Buffalo.

Vocation Director: Br. Jude Holzfoerster, 4520 Ransom Rd., Clarence, NY 14031. (716) 759-8341.

FATHERS OF MERCY (C.P.M.)

Generalate: 14480 Bowling Green Rd., South Union, KY 42283. (502) 542-6334

13 Priests, 4 Novices, 10 Students

Apostolic Work: The propropagation of the Faith and the salvation of souls, and the preaching of parish missions.

Vocation Director: Very Rev. John O'Brien, C.P.M., Fathers of Mercy, 14480 Bowling Green Rd., South Union, KY 42283. (502) 542-6334.

MILL HILL MISSIONARIES (M.H.M.) (St. Joseph's Missionary Society)

Regional Office: 1377 Nepperhan Ave., Yonkers, NY 10703-1055. (914) 375-0845. FAX (914) 375-0849

17 Fathers, 2 Brothers, 1 Associate

Rev. Terence J. Lee, M.H.M., Society Representative U.S.A.

Conduct: 21 mission territories in Africa, Asia and South America.

Apostolic Work: foreign missions.

Represented in the Archdioceses of New York, Los Angeles and St. Louis.

Vocation Directors: Rev. Emile Frische, M.H.M., 1377 Nepperhan Ave., Yonkers, NY 10703. (914) 375-0845; Rev. Henk Riesthuis, M.H.M., 1841 Camino Palmero, Los Angeles, CA 90046. (213) 876-0505.

MINIM FATHERS (O.M.)

General Motherhouse: Rome, Italy U.S. Delegation: 3431 Portola Ave., Los Angeles, CA 90032. (213) 223-1101

4 Priests

Represented in the Archdiocese of Los Angeles.

Vocation Director: Fr. Gino Vanzillotta, 6043 N. Barranca Ave., Azusa, CA 91702.

MISSIONARIES OF AFRICA

1624 21st St., N.W., Washington, DC 20009.

Apostolic Work: Devoted exclusively to missionary work in Africa.

Represented in the Archdioceses of Washington, Chicago, Los Angeles and in the Diocese of St. Petersburg.

Vocation Director: 1624 21st St., N.W., Washington, DC 20009-1055. (202) 232-5154.

MISSIONARIES OF CHARITY (M.C.)

(founded by Mother Teresa of Calcutta), 1316 South Westlake Ave., Los Angeles, CA 90006. (213) 380-5225

12 Brothers, 3 Novices, 3 Postulants in U.S.

450 Brothers worldwide

Apostolic Work: Work with the homeless, youth, handicapped; minister to people with AIDS and the imprisoned.

Represented in the Archdiocese of Los Angeles.

Vocation Director: Br. Luke Packel, M.C., Missionaries of Charity, 1316 S. Westlake Ave., Los Angeles, CA 90006. (213) 380-5225; (213) 384-6116.

MISSIONARIES OF OUR LADY OF LA SALETTE

See La Salette Fathers.

MISSIONARIES OF THE HOLY FAMILY (MSF)

"Servants of God - Builders of Family"

Provincial House: 210 El Rancho Way, San Antonio, TX 78209.

(210) 826-9815

43 Priests, 5 Brothers, 3 Novices

Apostolic Work: Involved in a large variety of apostolates, always in an attempt to serve the Church's current needs. Work in parishes, schools, hospitals, and homes for the aged, reflecting the order's concern and respect for family life. Staffs 1 house of study, 1 novitiate, 16 parishes, 3 parish missions in Mexico, 3 hospital chaplaincies and 1 nursing home.

Represented in the Archdioceses of St. Louis, MO and San Antonio, TX and in the Dioceses of Duluth, MN, Richmond, VA, Corpus Christi, TX, Brownsville, TX, Saltillo, Mexico and Ottawa, Canada.

Vocation Director: Fr. Philip Sosa, MSF, MSF Vocation Office, 210 El Rancho Way, San Antonio, TX 78209. (210) 826-9815.

MISSIONARIES OF THE HOLY SPIRIT (M.Sp.S.)

American Headquarters: Our Lady of Guadalupe, 500 N. Juanita Ave., Oxnard, CA 93030. (805) 483-0987 / 483-1481

300 Priests, 150 Brothers (Students and Permanent Brothers), 45 Novices, 60 Minor Seminarians

Primary Apostolic Works: All levels of spiritual direction for priests, religious men and women and lay people, retreats, houses of rest and renewal for priests, collaboration in diocesan seminaries, all kinds of parish work.

Conduct: Houses in Mexico, Peru, Italy, Germany, United States (Oxnard, Huntington Park and Fresno, CA), Spain.

Vocation Director: Rev. Fr. Fidencio Silva, M.Sp.S., 6450 Paek Crest St., Long Beach, CA 90808. (310) 421-0808.

MISSIONARIES OF THE SACRED HEART (M.S.C.)

(United States Province), Provincial House: 305 S. Lake St., P.O. Box 270, Aurora, IL 60507. (708) 892-2371

78 Fathers, 26 Brothers

Conduct: 10 parishes, 1 retreat and renewal center.

Apostolic Work: Christian evangelization in the U.S. and in 40 areas of the world pursued through parishes, chaplaincies, and retreat and renewal work.

Represented in the U.S. in the Archdioceses of Chicago and Philadelphia and in the Dioceses

of Rockford, Allentown, Toledo, Providence, Ogdensburg, Youngstown and San Bernardino.

Vocation Director: Br. Christopher J. Kirk, MSC, 305 S. Lake St., P.O. Box 270, Aurora, IL 60507. (708) 892-2371.

MISSIONARIES OF THE SACRED HEARTS OF JESUS AND MARY (M.SS.CC.)

Motherhouse: Naples, Italy

American Headquarters: 2249 Shore Rd., Linwood, NJ 08221. (609) 927-5600

10 Priests, 1 Brother, 2 Brothers in Temporary Vows, 60 Priests worldwide

Conduct: 2 parishes in the Diocese of Camden, NJ; 2 parishes in the Diocese of Harrisburg, 1 novitiate.

Apostolic Work: Inner city and suburban parishes, chaplaincies, retreats, active promotion of devotion to the Sacred Hearts of Jesus and Mary.

Represented in the Dioceses of Camden, NJ and Harrisburg, PA. Foreign missions in Argentina, India and the Republic of Slovakia.

Vocation Contact: Director of Vocations, Missionaries of the Sacred Hearts, 832 S. 4th St., Camden, NJ 08103. (609) 541-7618.

MISSIONARY BENEDICTINE PRIESTS AND BROTHERS

See Benedictine Monks (Schuyler, NE).

MISSIONARY OBLATES OF MARY IMMACULATE (O.M.I.)

(United States Region) A community of brothers and priests held together by a common spirit; their mission takes them where there is urgent need. The Congregation is committed to carrying the Gospel to others, with special preference for the poor and those on the margins of society.

725 Priests and Brothers in U.S.

Apostolic Work: Parishes, retreat centers, college campuses, education, prison and hospital chaplaincies, peace and justice work, ministry with the handicapped, the homeless, in inner cities, with minorities, in foreign missions and many specialized ministries.

Represented worldwide, with 5 U.S. provinces.

Vocation Directors: Vocation hotline national number: (800) 358-4394; (Contact the Vocation Director nearest you): Northern U.S.

Province: Vocation Director, Oblate Provincial Offices, 61 Burns Hill Rd., Hudson, NH 03051. (603) 883-3233; Eastern U.S. Province: Vocation Office, 391 Michigan Ave. NE, Washington, DC 20017. (800) 358-4394; Central U.S. Province: Rev. Louis Studer, O.M.I., Oblate Vocation Office, 5401 S. Cornell Ave., Chicago, IL 60615. (312) 684-7980; Southern U.S. Province: Rev. Arthur Flores, O.M.I., Oblate Vocation Center, 285 Oblate Dr., San Antonio, TX 78216. (210) 341-3496, (800) 350-6647; Western U.S. Province: Bro. Peter Vasquez, O.M.I., Vocation Office, 10390 Remick Ave., Pacoima, CA 91331. (818) 899-0278, (800) 358-4394.

MISSIONARY SERVANTS OF THE MOST HOLY TRINITY

See Trinity Missions.

MISSIONARY SOCIETY OF THE HOLY APOSTLES (M.Ss.A.)

North American Headquarters: 33 Prospect Hill Rd., Cromwell, CT 06416.

Conduct: 1 college seminary and school of theology; 8 parishes, 3 houses of formation, 2 homes for abandoned people, 1 retreat center, 1 high school, 1 house of studies, and assist in 10 parishes.

Apostolic Work: The theological and spiritual preparation of adult men for the priesthood and men and women for positions of leadership in the Church, evangelization and humanization ministry in mission territories and poor parishes in affluent countries.

Represented in the Archdioceses of Hartford and Washington, DC and in the Dioceses of Wheeling-Charleston and Norwich. Also in Africa, Brazil, Canada, Peru and Venezuela.

Vocation Director: Fr. John Patrick Boyhan, M.Ss.A., Holy Apostles, 1335 Quincy St., N.E., Washington, DC 20017.

MISSIONARY SOCIETY OF ST. JAMES THE APOSTLE

24 Clark St., Boston, MA 02109. (617) 742-4715

An association of 73 Diocesan priest volunteers, sent by their Bishops through the Society of St. James to work in mission parishes in South America, from 42 Dioceses of the United States, Canada, England, Scotland, Ireland, Wales, Australia, and New Zealand serving in the Dioceses of Quito and Guayaquil, Ecuador; Lima, Chimbote, Piura and Abancay, Peru; and Santa Cruz and Oruro, Bolivia.

Vocation Directors: Rev. Gabriel Troy, Director, Recruitment and Development; Rev. Patrick Cleary, Assistant to the Director. (617) 742-4715.

MISSIONARY SOCIETY OF ST. PAUL THE APOSTLE

See Paulist Fathers.

MISSIONARY SONS OF THE IMMACULATE HEART OF MARY

See Clarentian Fathers and Brothers.

MONASTERY OF OUR SAVIOR

See Eastern Catholic Religious Communities for Men.

MONKS OF THE MOST HOLY TRINITY MONASTERY

See Eastern Catholic Religious Communities for Men.

MONKS OF MT. TABOR (Holy Transfiguration Monastery)

See Eastern Catholic Religious Communities for Men.

MONTFORT MISSIONARIES (S.M.M.)

101-18 104th St., Ozone Park, NY 11416. (718) 849-5885

45 Members

Conduct: 3 parishes, 5 community houses, 1 house of formation, 2 shrines, 1 publication, 1 spirituality center, 1 center for teenagers in crisis and human services center.

Apostolic Work: Preaching, foreign missions, inner-city apostolate, pastoral work, hospital chaplaincies.

Represented in the Archdioceses of St. Louis and Washington, DC; in the Dioceses of Brooklyn, Fall River and Rockville Centre. The Montfort Missionaries minister in 15 countries and 11 foreign missions.

Vocation Director: Fr. Thomas Poth, St. Teresa of Avila, 3636 N. Market St., St. Louis, MO 63113. (314) 371-1190.

BROTHERS OF OUR LADY, MOTHER OF MERCY (C.F.M.M.)

7140 Ramsgate Ave., Los Angeles, CA 90045. (310) 649-3370

7 Brothers

Conduct: 1 high school, 1 university.

Represented in the Archdiocese of Los Angeles.

NORBERTINE FATHERS (O. Praem.) (Canons Regular of Premontre)

St. Norbert Abbey, 1016 North Broadway, De Pere, WI 54115-2697. (414) 337-4300

86 Priests, 5 Brothers, 3 Novices, 3 Simple Professed

Conduct: 1 dependent priory, 1 seminary, 1 house of studies, 1 novitiate, 1 college, 1 high school, 4 hospital chaplaincies, 14 parishes, 1 campus ministry center, 1 retreat/renewal center, 2 military chaplaincies.

Apostolic Work: Parish work, ecumenical work, chaplaincies, foreign missions, campus ministry work, retreats, teaching and educational administration.

Represented in the Archdioceses of Albuquerque/Santa Fe and Chicago and in the Dioceses of Green Bay, Jackson and Madison.

Vocation Coordinator: St. Norbert Abbey, 1016 N. Broadway, De Pere, WI 54115-2697. (414) 337-4300.

NORBERTINE FATHERS (O. Praem.) (Canons Regular of Premontre)

St. Michael's Abbey, 19292 El Toro Rd., Silverado, CA 92676-9710. (714) 858-0222, ext. 222

35 Priests, 17 Clerics, 6 Novices

Conduct: 2 dependent houses, 1 novitiate, 1 seminary for college resident students, 1 prep high school, 1 summer camp, 1 pious association.

Represented in the Archdiocese of Los Angeles and in the Diocese of Orange.

Vocation Director: Rev. Hugh Barbour, O. Praem.

NORBERTINES (O. Praem.) (Canons Regular of Premontre)

Daylesford Abbey, 220 S. Valley Rd., Paoli, PA 19301. (610) 647-2530

48 Priests, 3 Brothers

Conduct: 2 dependent priories, 1 novitiate, 2 high schools, 4 chaplaincies, and 6 parishes.

Apostolic Work: Teaching, parish work, ecumenical work, chaplaincies, retreats, liturgical apostolate, counseling, sheltering the homeless.

Represented in the Archdioceses of Philadelphia and Baltimore and in the Dioceses of Harrisburg, Wilmington and Washington, DC.

Vocation Director: Fr. Theodore J. Antry, Daylesford Abbey, 220 S. Valley Rd., Paoli, PA 19301-1999.

NORBERTINE FATHERS AND BROTHERS (O. Praem.)

Priory of St. Moses the Black, 653 Claiborne Ave., Jackson, MS 39209-6299. (601) 354-3287

4 Priests, 1 Brother, 3 Novices

Apostolic Work : Ministry primarily among African-Americans; ministry to the poor of any race; parishes, education, retreats.

Represented in the (Arch)diocese of Jackson.

Vocation Director: Xavier G. Colavechio, O. Praem., Vocation Recruiter, Priory of St. Moses the Black, 653 Claiborne Ave., Jackson, MS 39209-6299. (601)354-3287.

OBLATES OF ST. FRANCIS DE SALES (OSFS)

Provincial House: 2200 Kentmere Pkwy., Box 1452, Wilmington, DE 19899. (302) 656-8529

220 Priests, 23 Brothers, 15 Men in Formation

Conduct: 21 parishes, 1 scholasticate, 1 novitiate, 1 college, 1 retreat house, 6 high schools, 4 Newman Centers, 28 community houses.

Apostolic Work: High school teaching, parish work, college teaching, campus ministry, overseas missions, inner-city projects. Armed Forces chaplaincies, adult education, hospital ministry and chaplaincies, conduct retreats and parish missions.

Represented in the Archdioceses of Military Services, Philadelphia and Washington, DC and in the Dioceses of Allentown, Arlington, Camden, Charlotte, Harrisburg, Providence, Raleigh, Richmond, Venice and Wilmington. Also in South Africa, Namibia, Brazil, Uruguay, Mexico and India.

Vocation Director: Rev. Joseph P. Jocco, OSFS, 2200 Kentmere Pkwy., Box 1452, Wilmington, DE 19899. (302) 656-8529.

OBLATES OF ST. FRANCIS DE SALES (O.S.F.S.)

(Toledo-Detroit Province) 2056 Parkwood Ave., Toledo, OH 43620.

94 Priests and Brothers

Minister in 25 parishes including colleges; 11 high schools and 1 grade school; 6 hospitals, elderly and handicapped chaplaincies; 1 military chaplain; missions; prison chaplaincy; 10 community houses, 2 formation houses and 1 summer camp.

Represented in the Dioceses of Buffalo, Toronto, Detroit, Gaylord, Lansing, Toledo, Oklahoma City, Denver, Salt Lake City, San Bernardino, Stockton and mission regions in Brazil, Uruguay, Namibia and S.W. Africa.

Vocation Team: Fr. James Cryan, OSFS, 2056 Parkwood Ave., Toledo, OH 43620. (419) 243-5105.

OBLATES OF ST. JOSEPH (O.S.J.)

(Eastern Province), St. Joseph Oblate Seminary, Rte. 315, Pittston, PA 18640-9618.

13 Fathers, 1 Brother

Conduct: A religious community of brothers and priests working to spread the Gospel in youth ministry, catechesis and parish ministry, under the inspiration of St. Joseph. 4 parishes, 1 community house, 1 house of study.

Represented in the Dioceses of Norwich and Scranton.

Vocation Director: Rev. Gregory Finn, O.S.J., St. Joseph Oblate Seminary, Rte. 315, R.R.4, Pittston, PA 18640-9618. (717) 654-7542.

OBLATES OF ST. JOSEPH (O.S.J.)

(Western Province), 544 West Cliff Dr., Santa Cruz, CA 95060. (408) 427-1614

21 Priests, 3 Brothers

Conduct: A religious family of priests and brothers who serve God in imitation of St. Joseph with total dedication to Jesus, special love for Mary, fidelity to the magisterial teaching of the Church, deep interior prayer life, hard work, and unshakeable trust in Divine Providence; 4 parishes; 2 houses of formation, 1 shrine.

Represented in the Dioceses of Fresno, Monterey and Sacramento. Also in Pennsylvania, Brazil, India, Italy, Mexico, Peru, Bolivia, Philippines and Poland.

Vocation Director: Fr. John Warburton, O.S.J., P.O. Box 547, Loomis, CA 95650. (916) 652-6336.

OBLATES OF THE VIRGIN MARY

1105 Boylston St., Boston, MA 02215.

Apostolic Work: Principally the Spiritual Exercises of St. Ignatius (retreats, parish missions), formation of the clergy, Defense of the Truth, formation of the laity, parishes, foreign missions, social communications and diffusion of good books.

Represented in the Archdiocese of Boston and Los Angeles and in the Dioceses of Springfield, Metuchen, Montreal, Quebec and Trois-Rivieres, Quebec, Canada. Foreign Missions in Argentina, Brazil and Chile.

Vocation Director: Rev. Gregory Staab, OMV, 1105 Boylston St., Boston, MA 02215. (617) 266-5999.

ORATORIANS (C.O.)
(Congregation of the Oratory)

The Oratory of Rock Hill, P.O. Box 11586, Rock Hill, SC 29731. (803) 327-2097

8 Priests, 4 Brothers

Apostolic Work: Parishes, retreats, campus ministry, lay ministry training, spiritual direction.

Represented in the Diocese of Charleston.

Vocation Director: Fr. Ed McDevitt, C.O., P.O. Box 11586, Rock Hill, SC 29731. (803) 327-2097.

ORATORIANS (ORAT.)
(Congregation of the Oratory)

The Oratorian Community of Monterey, P.O. Box 1688, Monterey, CA 93942. (408) 373-0476

4 Priests

Represented in the Diocese of Monterey.

ORATORIANS (C.O.)
(Congregation of the Oratory of St. Philip Neri)

4450 Bayard St., Pittsburgh, PA 15213. (412) 681-3181.

4 Priests, 1 Seminarian

Represented in the Diocese of Pittsburgh.

Vocation Director: Fr. Joseph Linck, C.O., 4450 Bayard St., Pittsburgh, PA 15213. (412) 681-3181.

ORATORIANS (C.O.)
(Congregation of the Oratory)

The Oratory of Pharr, P.O. Box ii, Pharr, TX 78577-1235. (210) 843-8217

2 Priests, 2 Seminarians

Apostolic Work: Services to the poor, Mexican-American cultural services, parish work, health, bicultural Catholic elementary school.

Represented in the Diocese of Brownsville.

Vocation Director: Rev. Leo Francis Daniels, C.O., P.O. Box ii, Pharr, TX 78577-1235. (210) 843-8217.

ORDER OF FRIARS MINOR
See Franciscans.

ORDER OF FRIARS MINOR CAPUCHIN
See Capuchins.

ORDER OF FRIARS MINOR CONVENTUAL
See Franciscan Friars.

ORDER OF THE MOST HOLY SAVIOR
See Brigittine Monks.

ORDER OF PREACHERS
See Dominican Fathers and Brothers.

ORDER OF ST. AUGUSTINE
See Augustinians.

ORDER OF ST. BENEDICT
See Benedictines.

ORDER OF ST. PAUL THE HERMIT
See Pauline Fathers and Brothers.

ORDER OF THE HOLY CROSS
See Crosiers.

ORDER OF THE MOST HOLY TRINITY
See Trinitarian Friars.

ORDER OF THE BVM OF MERCY (Mercedarian Friars) (O. de M.)

Vicariate of the United States of America of the Roman Province

Vicar-Provincial Offices: Mercygrove, 7758 E. Main St., Le Roy, NY 14482-9701. (716) 768-7110

27 Friars, 1 Novice, 4 Postulants

Apostolic Work: In the US, the Friars have five religious houses. With over 950 members in 18 countries, the Mercedarian Friars have continued that same redemptive spirit of their founder, Saint Peter Nolasco, for over seven centuries. Wherever Mercedarians minister: in hospitals, schools, prisons, foreign missions, or parishes, its members seek to redeem those whose faith is in danger because of the situation of their lives and the conditions of society.

Represented in the Archdiocese of Philadelphia and in the Dioceses of Buffalo, Cleveland and St. Petersburg. Also represented within the Diocese of Cochin, India.

Vocation Director: Brother John Michael, O. de M., Mercedarian Friars, 6398 Drexel Rd., Philadelphia, PA 19151-2596. (215) 877-4858.

PALLOTTINES (S.A.C.) (Society of the Catholic Apostolate)
(Immaculate Conception Province) 5552 Rt. 70, Pennsauken, NJ 08109-4798

Priests, brothers, lay associates

Conduct: Staffing parishes, schools, youth and lay ministries across the East and Western seaboard.

Information: Fr. Joseph P. Capella, S.A.C., 5552 Rt. 70, Pennsauken, NJ 08109-4798. (1-800) APOS-TLE (276-7853).

PALLOTTINE FATHERS (S.A.C.) (Society of the Catholic Apostolate)
(Queen of the Apostles, Italian Province) 448 E. 116th St., New York, NY 10029. (212) 534-0681

4 Fathers

Conduct: Parishes, missionary work, diaconate director, schools.

Represented in the Archdiocese of New York and in the Dioceses of Albany and Pensacola-Tallahassee. Other houses, high schools and parishes in Italy and England.

Vocation Director: Fr. Mario Pacini, S.A.C., 448 E. 116th St., New York, NY 10029. (212) 534-0681.

PALLOTTINES (S.A.C.) (Society of the Catholic Apostolate)
(Mother of God Province) 5424 W. Bluemound Rd., Milwaukee, WI 53208.

20 Priests, 1 Brother

Conduct: 3 parishes, 1 Native American mission, 1 retreat house, 7 hospital chaplaincies, 1 high school

Represented in the Archdiocese of Milwaukee and in the Dioceses of Fargo and Wheeling-Charleston.

Vocation Coordinator: Fr. Joe Heinrichs, S.A.C., 5424 W. Bluemound Rd., Milwaukee, WI 53208. (414) 259-0688.

PALLOTTINES (S.A.C.) (Society of the Catholic Apostolate)
(Christ the King Province) 3452 Niagara Falls Blvd., North Tonawanda, NY 14120. (716) 694-4313

10 Priests

Apostolic Work: Retreats, parish work, hospital chaplaincy.

Represented in the Dioceses of Brooklyn and Buffalo. Also in Poland, Austria, Brazil and Africa.

PALLOTTINES (Society of the Catholic Apostolate)
(Irish Province) 3352 Fourth Street, P.O. Box 249, Wyandotte, MI 48192.

23 Priests

Conduct: 13 parishes, 9 missions, 3 hospital chaplaincies, 1 retired.

Represented in the Archdiocese of Detroit and the Dioceses of Fort Worth, Lubbock and Reno-Las Vegas.

Contact: Rev. Stephen Keogh, S.A.C.

PARIS FOREIGN MISSION SOCIETY (M.E.P)
Headquarters: Paris, France. U.S.: 930 Ashbury St., San Francisco, CA 94117. (415) 664-6747

3 Priests

Represented in the Archdiocese of San Francisco.

PASSIONISTS (C.P.) (Congregation of the Passion)
(Province of St. Paul of the Cross) Passionist Province/Pastoral Center, 80 David St., South River, NJ 08882. (908) 257-7177

244 Priests, 33 Brothers, 3 Postulants

Conduct: 8 monasteries, 7 retreat houses, 10 parishes, 7 residences, 1 novitiate, 1 theologate, 1 college residence, 1 Newman Center, 1 volunteer program, missions in the West Indies, Philippine Islands, and Honduras.

Represented in the Archdioceses of Atlanta, Baltimore, Boston, Hartford, Newark, and New York, and in the Dioceses of Brooklyn, Metuchen, Pittsburgh, Raleigh, Rockville Centre, Scranton, Springfield, Palm Beach, Wheeling and Worcester. Also Canada, Jamaica, W.I., the Philippine Islands, and Honduras.

Vocation Director: Very Rev. Richard Burke, C.P., St. Ann's Monastery, 1230 St. Ann's St., Scranton, PA 18504. (717) 347-5691.

PASSIONISTS (C.P.) (Congregation of the Passion)
(Province of the Holy Cross) 5700 N. Harlem Ave., Chicago, IL 60631.

111 Priests, 14 Brothers

Conduct: 4 retreat houses, 5 parishes, renewal preaching, spiritual guidance, hospital and prison ministry.

Represented in the Archdioceses of Chicago, Cincinnati, Detroit, Los Angeles, Louisville and St. Louis and in the Dioceses of Galveston-Houston, Birmingham and Sacramento. Also in Japan, Korea and India.

Vocation Director: Fr. Jim Thoman, C.P., 5700 N. Harlem Ave., Chicago, IL 60631. (312) 631-6336.

PAULINE FATHERS AND BROTHERS
(For Communications Ministry) See St. Paul, Society of.

PAULINE FATHERS AND BROTHERS (O.S.P.P.E.) (Order of St. Paul the First Hermit)
Motherhouse: Czestochowa, Poland

United States Headquarters: National Shrine of Our Lady of Czestochowa, Doylestown, PA 18901.

Members in the United States: 9 Priests, 4 Brothers

Apostolic Work: Contemplative order and apostolic work especially to foster devotion to the Blessed Virgin Mary.

Vocation Director: Pauline Fathers Monastery, Shrine of Our Lady of Czestochowa, P.O. Box 2049, Ferry Rd., Doylestown, PA 18901. (215) 345-0600.

THE PAULIST FATHERS (C.S.P.) (Missionary Society of St. Paul the Apostle)
The Paulists are the first community of priests founded in the U.S. in 1858 by Isaac Hecker. An active missionary community serving North America.

Paulist Office: Scarsdale, NY.

215 Priests, 5 Novices, 15 Candidates in Theology

Apostolic Work: University chaplaincies, adult education, instructions for non-Catholics, parishes, retreat and missionary preaching, the Paulist Press, radio and TV communications, ecumenism and evangelization.

Represented in more than 27 cities throughout the United States and Canada.

Admissions: College preferred; 1 year novitiate followed by theological studies in Washington, DC including a pastoral year.

Vocation Director: Fr. John B. Ardis, C.S.P., 415 W. 59th St., New York, NY 10019. (212) 757-4260 or (800) 235-3456.

PIARIST FATHERS AND BROTHERS (Sch.P.)

(Province of the United States of America) 363 Valley Forge Rd., Devon, PA 19333. (610) 688-7337

24 Priests

Conduct: 1 novitiate, 1 house of studies for candidates to the priesthood and brotherhood, 2 college preparatory schools, 1 diocesan high school

Apostolic Work: The Piarists profess a fourth vow to educate the young. Education for the Piarists means the complete formation of the person. Thus the Piarists fulfill their vow by teaching on the elementary and secondary levels. In addition, they assist local parishes. Their founder, St. Joseph Calasanctius, is the Patron Saint of Christian Schools.

Represented in the Archdioceses of Miami, Philadelphia and Washington, DC and in the Dioceses of Lexington and Buffalo.

Vocation Director: Rev. Leonard J. Gendernalik, Sch.P., 99 Martha's Vineyard, Prestonsburg, KY 41653. (606) 874-9594, (606) 285-3950.

PIARISTS (Sch.P.) (Calasanzian Fathers)

Vice Province: New York & Puerto Rico

25 Priests

Apostolic Work: Christian education, youth pastoral, C.C.D. programs, parish apostolate.

Vocation Director: Fr. Joseph A. Mateo, Sch.P., Annunciation Church, 88 Convent Ave., New York, NY 10027. (212) 234-1919.

PIARIST FATHERS (Sch.P) (The Calasanzians)

(California Vicariate), Casa Calasanz: 3951 Rogers St., Los Angeles, CA 90063. (213) 261-4432

14 Priests, 5 Novices, 10 Pre-Novices, 10 Students

Conduct: 3 parishes, 2 grammar schools, 2 houses of formation.

Apostolic Work: Dedicated to the education of children and youth.

Represented in the Archdiocese of Los Angeles. Also in Tijuana, Mexico.

P.I.M.E. MISSIONARIES (Pontifical Institute for Foreign Missions)

U.S. Regional Headquarters & Promotion Center: 17330 Quincy St., Detroit, MI 48221. (313) 342-4066

20 Priests, 1 Brother

Conduct: in the U.S. and Canada: 1 parish, 1 formation house, 4 mission centers.

Apostolic Work: P.I.M.E. is a foreign mission society engaged in evangelization, church-founding, human development, justice and peace, education, hospitals, orphanages, leprosy relief, dispensaries, homes for the aged, pastoral ministry, interreligious dialogue.

Represented in the Archdioceses of Detroit, Newark and Toronto, Canada and in the Diocese of Columbus, OH. Also in Bangladesh, Brazil, Cambodia, Cameroon, England, Guinea-Bissau, Hong Kong, Italy, India, Ivory Coast, Japan, Mexico, Myanmar, Papua New Guinea, Philippines, Taiwan, Thailand.

Vocation Director: Fr. Claudio Corti, 17330 Quincy St., Detroit, MI 48221. (313) 342-4066.

BROTHERS OF THE POOR OF ST. FRANCIS (C.F.P.)

307 Willow Ave., Hoboken, NJ 07030-3822. (201) 420-1554

30 Brothers

Conduct: 1 novitiate, 3 parochial schools, 1 lodge for troubled boys.

Apostolic Work: Human services, especially the care and education of youth.

Represented in the Archdioceses of Cincinnati, Denver and Newark and in the Dioceses of Covington, Davenport, El Paso and Little Rock.

Vocation Director: Brother Joel Stern, CFP, 324 Donham Ave., Cincinnati, OH 45226. (513) 321-3293.

MISSIONARIES OF THE PRECIOUS BLOOD (C.PP.S.)

(Cincinnati Province)

213 Priests, 40 Brothers

Provincial House: 431 E. Second St., Dayton, OH 45402. (513) 228-9263.

Apostolic Work: Parishes, foreign missions (Chile, Guatemala, Peru), education, hospital and military chaplaincies, retreats, inner-city ministry.

Represented in the Archdioceses of Cincinnati and Detroit and in the Dioceses of Cleveland, Columbus, Fort Wayne-South Bend, Gary, Harrisburg, Lafayette in Indiana, Lansing, Orlando, Pittsburgh, Toledo, Youngstown. Also Lima, Peru; Santiago, Chile; Huancayo, Peru; Guatemala City, Guatemala and Osorno, Chile.

Vocation Director: Rev. Angelo Anthony, C.PP.S., 431 E. Second St., Dayton, OH 45402. (513) 228-6224.

SOCIETY OF THE PRECIOUS BLOOD (C.PP.S.)

(Kansas City Province) Provincial Office, P.O. Box 339, Liberty, MO 64068. (816) 781-4344

76 Priests, 1 Bishop, 5 Brothers

Apostolic Work: Parish work, retreats, teaching, military and hospital chaplaincies, campus ministry, specialized apostolates.

Represented in the (Arch)dioceses of Davenport, Jefferson City, Kansas City-St. Joseph, Salina, San Angelo, Superior and Wichita. Foreign Mission: Tanzania.

Vocation Director: Jack McClure, C.PP.S., P.O. Box 339, Liberty, MO 64068. (816) 781-4344.

MISSIONARIES OF THE PRECIOUS BLOOD (C.PP.S.)

(Atlantic Province) St. Alphonsus Church, 540 St. Clair Ave. West, Toronto, Ontario M6C 1A4, Canada. (416) 653-4486.

9 Fathers

Apostolic Work: parish work, missions both domestic and foreign retreats, parish missions, social work, teaching and specialized apostolates.

Represented in the Archdiocese of Toronto and in the Dioceses of Rochester, Youngstown and London, Ontario.

Vocation Director: Rev. Lui Santi, C.PP.S., St. Mary's Church, 345 Lyle St., London, Ontario N5W 3R3, Canada. (519) 434-9121.

SOCIETY OF THE PRECIOUS BLOOD (C.PP.S.) (Congregation of Missionaries of the Blood of Christ)

(Pacific Province), 2337 West Ave. 134th, San Leandro, CA 94577-4132. (510) 357-4982

24 Priests, 1 Permanent Deacon, 1 Incorporated Seminarian, 1 Brother, 46 Lay Associates (Companions)

Conduct: 7 parishes, 1 chaplaincy, 1 center house, 1 mission house, campus ministry, missions, retreats, spiritual direction.

Represented in the Archdioceses of Los Angeles and San Francisco and in the Dioceses of Oakland, Phoenix, Stockton and Salt Lake City.

Vocation Director: Fr. Jeffrey Finley, St. Edward's Catholic Church, 5788 Thornton Ave., Newark, CA 94560. (510) 797-0395, ext. 18.

PRESENTATION BROTHERS (F.P.M.)

Provincialate: 211 Steeles Avenue East, Willowdale, Ontario, Canada M2M 3Y6.

Apostolic Work: Christian formation, primarily of youth and in particular to the poor and disadvantaged: all forms of education, both elementary and high school, retreat work, social work, pastoral ministry, youth ministry and missionary involvement.

Represented in the Diocese of Orlando. Also in Ireland, England, the West Indies, Canada, Ghana and Peru.

Vocation Director: Bro. Francis Schafer, F.P.M., Presentation Brothers, 1602 N. Pettis Blvd., Kissimmee, FL 34741. (407) 846-2033.

REDEMPTORISTS (EASTERN RITE)

See Eastern Catholic Religious Communities for Men.

REDEMPTORIST FATHERS (C.SS.R.)

(Baltimore Province)

251 Priests, 31 Brothers, 3 Novices

Conduct: 34 parishes, 4 retreat houses, theology residence, pre-theology residence.

Apostolic Work: Conduct both home and foreign missions, Inner City apostolate, parishes, retreat ministry, military and hospital chaplains.

Represented in the Archdioceses of New York, Boston, Philadelphia, Hartford, Baltimore and Washington and in the Dioceses of Brooklyn, Albany, Erie, Pittsburgh, Harrisburg, Toledo, Wilmington, Richmond, Miami, Atlanta, Raleigh, St. Augustine and Charleston. Also in the

Caribbean: Virgin Islands, St. Lucia, Dominica.

Vocation Directors: Fr. James Dowds, C.Ss.R., 3112 7th St. N.E., Washington, DC 20017. (202) 526-7130; Fr. Edmund Falaskie, C.Ss.R., 22-04 Parsons Blvd., Whitestone, NY 11357. (718) 321-1394.

REDEMPTORIST FATHERS AND BROTHERS (C.SS.R.)

(New Orleans Vice-Province) 1527 Third St., New Orleans, LA 70130. (504) 895-0840

63 Priests, 7 Brothers, 2 Theologians, 5 Students

Apostolic Work: Dedicated to the evangelization of the poor and the most abandoned especially through neighborhood and parish mission preaching in the south-central and south-west United States.

Conduct: 7 parishes, 1 retreat center, 2 mission bands, college residence and theology residence.

Represented in the Archdioceses of San Antonio and New Orleans and in the Dioceses of Galveston-Houston, San Angelo, Amarillo, Lafayette, Baton Rouge and Biloxi.

Vocation Director: Rev. Byron J. Miller, C.SS.R., Liguori House, 1523 Iowa St., San Antonio, TX 78203. (210) 533-2406.

REDEMPTORIST FATHERS AND BROTHERS (C.SS.R.)

(Oakland Province), 1300 Juniperro Serra, San Francisco, CA 94132. (415) 452-9634.

86 Priests, 11 Brothers, 7 Students, 2 Novices

Conduct: 14 parishes, 6 mission houses, 3 retreat houses, 8 foreign missionaries.

Represented in the Archdioceses of Anchorage, Los Angeles, Portland, San Francisco and Seattle and in the Dioceses of Boise, Fresno, Great Falls, Monterey, Oakland and Tucson.

Vocation Director: Rev. Stephen Meyer, C.SS.R., P.O. Box 5007, Oakland, CA 94605. (510) 562-9740.

REDEMPTORISTS (C.SS.R.)

(St. Louis Province) 3737 Washington Blvd., St. Louis, MO 63108. (314) 531-2777

220 Priests, 30 Brothers

Conduct: 4 retreat houses, 15 parishes, Liguori Publications, 3 formation communities.

Apostolic Work: Preaching the gospel by missions, retreats and publication ministries; ministry in African-American and Hispanic communities, youth ministry, deaf apostolate, parishes, and foreign missions in Brazil, Thailand and Nigeria.

Represented in the Dioceses of Detroit, Grand Rapids, Chicago, Milwaukee, Minneapolis-St. Paul, Omaha, Davenport, St. Louis, Kansas City, Wichita and Denver.

Contact: Rev. David Polek, C.SS.R., St. John Neumann House, 3737 Washington Blvd., St. Louis, MO 63108. (314) 531-2777.

RESURRECTIONIST (CR) (Congregation of the Resurrection)

(United States of America Province) 2250 N. Latrobe Ave., Chicago, IL 60639.

90 Fathers, 5 Brothers

Conduct: 12 parishes, 2 high schools, 1 retreat center, 3 chaplaincies, 4 missions and stations (1 mission in Mexico).

Represented in the Archdioceses of Chicago, St. Louis and Oaxaca (Mexico) and in the Dioceses of Birmingham, Mobile, Pensacola-Tallahassee, Rockford and San Bernadino.

Vocation Director: Rev. John Nowak, C.R., 2250 N. Latrobe Ave., Chicago, IL 60639. (312) 622-0477.

RESURRECTIONISTS (C.R.) (Congregation of the Resurrection)

(Ontario-Kentucky Province) Provincialate: Resurrection College, Westmound Rd. North, Waterloo, Ontario N2L 3G7, Canada. (519) 885-3030

81 priests (6 in U.S.), 10 Brothers, 2 Permanent Deacons

Apostolic Work: Education of youth (high school and university as teachers and campus ministers), parish and mission work, one college seminary and specialized apostolates.

Represented in the Archdioceses of Toronto, Ontario, Louisville, Kentucky, La Paz, Bolivia, and in the Dioceses of Hamilton, Ontario and Hamilton, Bermuda; London, Ontario and Sault Ste. Marie, Ontario.

Vocation Director: Fr. Timothy Uniac, St. Teresa's Parish, 19 Flamingo Dr., Elmira, Ontario N3B 1V3 Canada. (519) 669-3387.

ROGATIONIST FATHERS AND BROTHERS (R.C.J.) (Rogationists of the Sacred Heart of Jesus)

U.S. Delegation: P.O. Box 37, Sanger, CA 93657. (209) 875-2618

Conduct in the U.S.: 1 parish, 1 center for underprivileged people, 2 formation houses for candidates to the priesthood and brotherhood, 1 vocation center, 1 development office, 1 mission office, 1 publishing office, 1 magazine "Vocations and Prayer", 3 community houses. Also in Italy, Chile, Brazil, Argentina, Africa, Spain, Poland, Philippines and India.

Apostolic Work: Dedicated to heed and spread the command of Jesus: "Pray the Lord of the harvest to send laborers into His harvest." (Mt. 9:38). Both priests and brothers commit their lives to the education of youth, the social assistance of the underprivileged, especially children, orphans and the poor, vocation publications, parishes, missionary activities.

Represented in the Archdiocese of Los Angeles and in the Diocese of Fresno.

Vocation Director: Fr. Enzo Buccheri, R.C.J., 9815 Columbus Ave., North Hills, CA 91343. (818) 895-8924.

ROSMINIAN PRIESTS AND BROTHERS

See Institute of Charity.

BROTHERS OF THE SACRED HEART (S.C.)

(New York Province) Provincialate: P.O. Box 68, Belvidere, NJ 07823. (201) 475-4694

50 Brothers

Conduct: 2 high schools, 2 elementary schools, 1 house of formation, retreat center.

Apostolic Work: Adult education, catechetics, communications, mentally retarded, schools, social service.

Represented in the Dioceses of Brooklyn and Metuchen. Also in Kenya, East Africa.

Vocation Director: Brother Robert Ziobro, S.C., P.O. Box 68, Belvidere, NJ 07823. (1-800) 633-2252, ext. 370.

BROTHERS OF THE SACRED HEART (SC)

(New England Province) Provincial House, 685 Steere Farm Rd., Pascoag, RI 02859-4601. (401) 568-3361.

100 Brothers

Apostolic Work: Christian education and related fields including teaching, counseling, social work, special education, C.C.D. programs, Religious Education coordinators. Also direct and staff schools in three African countries.

Admission: Post high school, college and post college levels. Minimum four years college, 18-month novitiate. Stress on closely knit community participation and lifelong spiritual and academic development.

Represented in the Dioceses of Manchester, Providence, Burlington and Hartford and in England. Also in the southern African countries of Lesotho, Zambia and Zimbabwe.

Vocation Director: Br. Leon Cyr, SC, Vocation Office, St. John's Residence, 159 Earle St., Woonsocket, RI 02895. (401) 766-9677.

BROTHERS OF THE SACRED HEART (S.C.)

(New Orleans Province) Provincial Office, 4540 Elysian Fields Ave., New Orleans, LA 70122. (504) 282-5693

100 Brothers

Conduct: 3 community-owned high schools, 3 diocesan high schools, 11 community houses, 1 house of study, 1 novitiate.

Represented in the Archdioceses of Mobile and New Orleans and in the Dioceses of Baton Rouge, Biloxi, Gallup and Houma-Thibodaux. Mission in Uganda, Africa.

Vocation Director: Brother Ronald Hingle, S.C, 4540 Elysian Fields Ave., New Orleans, LA 70122. (504) 282-2228 or 1-800-633-2252, ext. 390.

SACRED HEARTS COMMUNITY (SS.CC.) (Congregation of the Sacred Hearts of Jesus and Mary)

Eastern Province: Sacred Hearts Provincial House, P.O. Box 111, 77 Adams St., Fairhaven, MA 02719-0111. (508) 993-2442

79 Fathers, 8 Brothers

Conduct: 1 provincial house, 1 novitiate, 1 theologate, 1 house of formation, 1 center of the Enthronement of the Sacred Heart in the home, 14 parishes, 3 home mission parishes, 2 inner-city parishes, chaplains, 1 military, 5 hospitals, 1 prison, 1 home for the aged, 1 retreat house, also seminary and formation, vocation work, advanced studies, Marriage Encounter, Cur-

sillo, youth work, renewal, peace and justice, Catholic Charismatic prayer groups.

Apostolic Work: The Sacred Hearts Community is made up of priests, sisters, and brothers. Through a variety of ministries they attempt to proclaim the love of God in Jesus. By a communal life of prayer and service they strive to make real the Gospel imperative to love one another.

Represented in the Archdioceses of Boston, Washington, DC and Albany and in the Dioceses of Rochester, Brownsville, Columbus, Miami and Fall River. Also foreign missions in Japan, Bahamas, Ecuador and India.

Vocation Director: Fr. Robert Charlton, SS.CC., P.O. Box 111, 77 Adams St., Fairhaven, MA 02719-0111. (508) 993-5010.

SACRED HEARTS COMMUNITY (SS.CC.) (Congregation of the Sacred Hearts of Jesus and Mary)

Western Province: 32481 Sage Rd., Hemet, CA 92343. (909) 767-9436

29 Priests, 2 Brothers

Conduct: 4 parishes, 2 high schools, 5 community houses, 1 novitiate for the five English speaking provinces, 1 house of studies for theology, retreats: marriage encounter, Choice, Kairos and Healing Light; young adult ministry, 3 chaplaincies.

Represented in the Archdiocese of Los Angeles and in the Dioceses of San Bernardino and Oakland.

Vocation Director: Rev. Lester Lee, SS.CC., St. Paul the Apostle, 14860 Cherry Dr., Chino Hills, CA 91709. (909) 597-5608.

SACRED HEARTS COMMUNITY (SS.CC.) (Congregation of the Sacred Hearts of Jesus and Mary and of Perpetual Adoration of the Most Blessed Sacrament of the Altar)

Hawaiian Province: Sacred Hearts Center, P.O. Box 797, Kaneohe, Oahu, HI 96744. (808) 247-5035

36 Priests, 7 Brothers

Conduct: 11 churches, 4 chaplaincies, 1 seminarian, mission—Cook Islands.

PRIESTS OF THE SACRED HEART (S.C.J.)

(United States Province)

150 Priests and Brothers in the U.S.; 2,500 worldwide.

Provincialate: P.O. Box 289, Hales Corners, WI 53130-0289.

Apostolic Work: The SCJs, an international congregation of brothers and priests, minister in some of the poorest areas in the nation and the world. In the United States, home missions include work with Native American, Hispanic and African American peoples. Our foreign missions include South Africa, Zaire, the Philippines, Indonesia and India. We also maintain a strong presence in Europe and South America. We strive to live together simply, to pray together and to be, especially among the poor, "prophets of love and servants of reconciliation" to a world which hungers for justice and peace.

Formation Programs: Located in Chicago, San Antonio and Hales Corners (Milwaukee suburb).

Represented in the Archdioceses of Chicago and Milwaukee and in the Dioceses of Green Bay, WI; Rapid City and Sioux Falls, SD; Jackson, MS; and Galveston-Houston and Brownsville, TX.

Vocation Director: Fr. Jack Kurps, SCJ, P.O. Box 206/RM, Hales Corners, WI 53130-0206. (414) 529-4255; FAX: (414) 529-3377; e-mail: 75512.1315@compuserve.com.

MISSIONARIES OF ST. CHARLES BORROMEO (C.S.)
(Scalabrini Fathers and Brothers)
(Province of St. John the Baptist) 546 N. East Ave., Oak Park, IL 60302. (708) 386-4430.

77 Fathers, 4 Brothers

Conduct: 15 parishes (U.S.), 13 parishes, 1 mission (Canada), 2 homes for the aged, 3 centers, 3 houses of formation (U.S., Canada, Mexico)

Primary Work: Missionaries to immigrants and refugees in 25 countries.

Represented in the Archdioceses of Chicago, Cincinnati, Los Angeles, Edmonton, Vancouver and in the Dioceses of Kansas City, Monterey, San Jose, Calgary, Kamloops, Thunder Bay, and in Mexico in Ciudad Juarez, Guadalajara, Zapopan, Purepero and Tijuana.

Vocation Information: Rev. Raniero Alessandrini, C.S., Scalabrini House of Theology, 8235 South Shore Dr., Chicago, IL 60617. (312) 375-8943 or 6597.

MISSIONARIES OF ST. CHARLES/SCALABRINIANS (C.S.) (The Province of St. Charles Borromeo)
Provincial Residence, 27 Carmine St., New York, NY 10014. (212) 675-3993

100 Priests, 4 Brothers, 15 Novices, 40 College Students

Conduct: 2 college houses, 29 parishes, 3 homes for the aged, 1 center for migration studies, 1 vocation office, 6 apostolic centers, 4 ethnic newspapers and radio shows, 1 Scalabrinians magazine.

Represented in the (Arch)dioceses of New York, Brooklyn, Hartford, Providence, Boston, Newark, Montreal, Toronto, Hamilton, Buffalo, Syracuse, Washington, DC, Venice, FL and West Palm Beach, FL, with missions in Columbia, Venezuela, Dominican Republic and Haiti.

Vocation Director: Rev. Mariano Cisco, C.S., 168-41 84th Ave., Jamaica, NY 11432. (718) 526-3917.

ST. COLUMBAN'S FOREIGN MISSION SOCIETY
See Columban Fathers.

ST. FRANCIS XAVIER FOREIGN MISSION SOCIETY
See Xaverian Missionary Fathers.

ST. JOHN OF GOD BROTHERS
See Hospitaller Brothers.

CONGREGATION OF ST. JOSEPH (C.S.J.)
4076 Case Rd., Avon, OH 44011. (Vice Province of St. Leonard Murialdo)

710 Priests and Brothers

Conduct: Parishes, high schools, counseling centers, foreign missions.

Represented in the (Arch)dioceses of Cleveland and Los Angeles. Also in Italy, Spain, Sierra Leone, Brazil, Colombia, Albania, Argentina, Chile, Equador, Guinea Bissau and Mexico.

Vocation Director: Fr. Lawrence Tosco, C.S.J., 4076 Case Rd., Avon, OH 44011. (216) 934-6270.

ST. JOSEPH'S MISSION SOCIETY
See Mill Hill Missionaries.

ST. PATRICK FATHERS (SPS) (St. Patrick's Missionary Society)
American Headquarters: St. Patrick Fathers, 70 Edgewater Rd., Cliffside Park, NJ 07010.

(201) 943-6575

360 Priests

Primary Apostolic Work: Foreign missions.

Represented in the Archdioceses of Newark and Chicago and in the Diocese of San Jose. Foreign Mission Areas: Nigeria, Kenya, Malawi, Zambia, Sudan, Zimbabwe, South Africa, Cameroon, Brazil, Grenada (West Indies).

Vocation Director: Rev. Donald McDonagh (201) 943-6575.

BROTHERS OF ST. PATRICK (F.S.P.)
(California Province) Provincialate: St. Patrick's Novitiate, 7820 Bolsa Ave., Midway City, CA 92655.

10 Brothers in U.S.; 300 worldwide

Apostolic Work: Teaching, counseling, administration, CCD, youth work.

Represented in Ireland, Australia, India, Kenya and New Guinea, Thursday Island, the Archdiocese of Los Angeles and the Diocese of Orange.

Vocation Director: Brother Philip, F.S.P., 2843 San Fernando Rd., Los Angeles, CA 90065. (213) 257-4108.

SOCIETY OF ST. PAUL (S.S.P.) (Pauline Priests and Brothers Communications Ministry)
Provincial House: 6746 Lake Shore Rd., Box 757, Derby, NY 14047.

25 Brothers, 16 Priests

Conduct: 1 novitiate, 3 houses of formation, 7 book and communication centers, 4 houses of apostolate, book publishing, audio visuals, print projects and television and video.

Apostolate Work: Paulines utilize the media of communications-press, tapes, cassettes, filmstrips, CCD material and other telecommunications to spread the Gospel of Jesus. In the U.S., the major apostolic works are Alba House Publishing, Alba House Communications and Alba House Media.

Represented in the Archdioceses of New York and Detroit and in the Dioceses of Buffalo and Youngstown. There are over 1,100 brothers and priests located in 23 countries involved in communications ministry.

Vocation Director: Brother Peter C. Lyne, S.S.P., (Society of St. Paul) Vocation Office, 2187 Victory Blvd., Staten Island, NY 10314. (718) 698-3698.

CLERICS OF ST. VIATOR (C.S.V.)

See Clerics of St. Viator

SALESIAN MONASTIC COMMUNITY (SMC)

Salesian Monastery, HC #1, Box 455, Frantz Rd., Brodheadsville, PA 18322-9630. (717) 992-3448 (abbot), (717) 992-0230 (monastery).

1 Solemnly Professed Monk, 1 Simply Professed Monk, 1 Simply Professed Nun, 25 Associate Members (men & women).

Apostolic Work: Monastic life, Liturgy of the Hours, use of any gift/ talent compatible with monastic life, i.e., retreats, pastoral psychotherapy, nursing, manual labor, and crafts.

Represented in the Diocese of Scranton.

Abbot: Brother Bernard Seif, SMC.

SALESIANS OF DON BOSCO (SDB)

Province of St. Philip the Apostle (Eastern Province), 148 Main St., New Rochelle, NY 10802. (914) 636-4225

172 Priests, 55 Brothers, 43 Men in Formation

Conduct: 5 academic high schools, 2 technical high schools, 1 resident junior high school, 6 youth centers, 20 parishes, 7 home missions, 1 media center, 1 mission office, 1 retreat center, 12 summer camps, 1 center for youth ministry, 1 job training center.

Apostolic Work: Salesians focus on youth ministry, becoming friends of Christ and friends of the young, in the family spirit of St. John Bosco. Their ministry expresses itself in schools, youth centers, parishes, retreat centers, summer camps, missions and wherever the young are found.

Represented in the Archdioceses of Boston, Miami, Newark, New Orleans and New York and in the Dioceses of Birmingham, Columbus, Nassau, Palm Beach, Paterson and St. Petersburg and in the Eparchy of Passaic. Also active in 102 countries around the world, including mission areas throughout Latin America, Asia, and most recently, Africa.

Vocation Directors: Br. Emil Dube, SDB, Salesian Vocation Ministry, Box 9000, West Haverstraw, NY 10993. (914) 429-1457; Fr. Jonathan Parks, SDB, Salesian Vocation Ministry, P.O. Box 1233, Marrero, LA 70073-1233. (504) 341-9109.

SALESIANS OF DON BOSCO (S.D.B.)

(Western Province) 1100 Franklin St., San Francisco, CA 94109. (415) 441-7144

86 Priests, 29 Brothers

Conduct: 7 parishes, 5 high schools, 1 seminary residence, 1 junior college, 2 retreat centers, 4 youth centers, 4 camps, 1 International House of Studies.

Apostolic Work: Youth ministry (youth centers, retreats, schools, parishes).

Represented in the Archdioceses of Los Angeles, San Francisco and Vancouver and in the Dioceses of Corpus Christi, Monterey, Oakland and San Diego.

Vocation Director: Fr. John Roche, SDB, P.O. Box 8067, Bellflower, CA 90706-8067. (310) 925-0963.

SALVATORIAN FATHERS AND BROTHERS

See Divine Savior, Society of the.

SCALABRINIANS

See St. Charles Borromeo, Missionaries of.

SERVANTS OF CHARITY (S.C.)

(U.S.A. Vice Province) 16195 Old U.S. 12, Chelsea, MI 48118-9646. (313) 475-8430

14 Priests, 6 in Formation

Conduct: Residential facilities for people with mental impairments, homes for the aged, services for youth in need, and parishes/pastoral activity around the world.

Apostolic Work: Care for people with mental impairments; pastoral ministry in parishes and various pastoral situations.

Represented in the Archdiocese of Philadelphia, Chicago and Manila, Philippines and in the Dioceses of Lansing, MI and Providence, RI. Also in Italy, Switzerland, Spain, Chile, Brazil, Paraguay, Argentina, Colombia, Mexico, India, Israel, Nigeria, Philippines, Mozambique and Guatemala.

Vocation Directors: Don Guanella Seminary, 1795 S. Sproul Rd., Springfield, PA 19064. (610) 328-3406; and St. Louis Center, 16195 Old U.S. 12, Chelsea, MI 48118-9646. (313) 475-8430.

SERVANTS OF THE GOSPEL (O.S.D.)

(A community of friars and sisters) St. Mary's Church, P.O. Box 499, Fort Covington, NY 12937. (518) 358-4471

Apostolic Work: There is no specific ministry to which the entire community is dedicated. Members seek to be of service to the local church or diocese in whatever way necessary.

Represented in the Diocese of Ogdensburg.

Vocation Contact: Fr. Martin Farrell, O.S.D. or Sr. Gabrielle Humis, O.S.D.

SERVANTS OF MARY

See Servite Fathers.

SERVANTS OF THE PARACLETE (s.P.)

Foundation House: Jemez Springs, NM 87025. (505) 829-3586

31 Priests and Brothers, 3 Novices

Apostolic Work: Ministry in holistic care to our fellow Priests and Brothers.

Represented in the Archdioceses of St. Louis and Santa Fe and in the Diocese of San Bernadino and in England.

Vocation Coordinator: Fr. Benedict Livingstone, s.P., Lourdes Novitiate, Servants of the Paraclete, P.O. Box 10, Jemez Springs, NM 87025-0010. (505) 829-3729; 3586.

SERVANTS OF THE SICK (O.S. Cam.)

See Camillians.

SERVITE FRIARS-EASTERN PROVINCE (O.S.M.) (Order of Servants of Mary)

Provincial Office: 3121 W. Jackson Blvd., Chicago, IL 60612. (312) 533-0360

57 Priests, 10 Brothers

Conduct: 8 parishes.

Apostolic Work: Teaching, parishes, retreats, hospital chaplaincy, military chaplaincy, Compassion and Healing Ministry. Marian Center and Shrine of Our Lady of Sorrows and National Shrine of St. Peregrine (Chicago). Missions in South Africa. Represented in the Archdioceses of Chicago and St. Louis and in the Dioceses of Metuchen, NJ and Orlando, FL.

Vocation Director: Fr. Donald Siple, O.S.M., Seven Holy Founders Priory, 6747 Rock Hill Rd., Affton, MO 63123. (314) 638-5275.

SERVITE FRIARS (O.S.M.)
(Order of Friar Servants of Mary)
(Western Province)
Provincial Center: 5210 Somerset
St., Buena Park, CA 90621-1498.
(714) 523-5810
40 Priests, 7 Brothers
Conduct: 11 communities, 9
parishes, 1 high school, 1 house of
studies, 1 university chaplaincy,
hospital, national shrine, pastoral
supply, prayer ministries, counselling programs including marriage and family and substance
abuse.
Represented in the Archdioceses
of Denver and Portland and in the
Dioceses of Oakland, Orange and
Tucson.
Vocation Contact: Provincial Center, 5210 Somerset St., Buena
Park, CA 90621-1498. (714) 523-
5810.

SMA FATHERS
See African Missions, Society of.

SOCIETY OF AFRICAN MISSIONS
See African Missions, Society of.

SOCIETY OF CHRIST (S.Ch.)
(North American Province) 3000
18 Mile Rd., Sterling Heights, MI
48314-3808. (313) 939-5022.
50 Priests
Apostolic Work: Pastoral ministry
to Polish Catholics worldwide.
Conduct: 13 parishes, 7 pastoral
missions, 5 apostolates, ethnic
radio programs, retreats.
Represented in the Archdioceses
of Baltimore, Chicago, Detroit,
Hartford, Los Angeles, Miami,
Portland, St. Paul-Minneapolis,
San Francisco, Seattle and Wash-
ington (DC) and in the Dioceses of
Dallas, Houston, Phoenix, San
Diego, San Jose and Toledo. Also
in Canada: Antigonish, Calgary,
Halifax, Hamilton, Regina and
Toronto.
Vocation Director: 3000 18 Mile
Rd., Sterling Hts., MI 48314-3808.
(313) 939-5022.

SOCIETY OF JESUS
See Jesuits.

SOCIETY OF OUR MOTHER OF PEACE (SMP)
Maria Fonte Solitude, PO Box
322, High Ridge, MO 63049-0322.
(314) 677-3235

2 Priests, 3 Brothers, 1 Postulant
Apostolic Work: Contemplative
apostolic balance of life in the context of simplicity and poverty;
emphasis on solitary prayer; limited apostolates of retreat work
and spiritual direction; direct evangelization within the African-American community.
Represented in the Archdiocese of
St. Louis and in the Diocese of
Springfield-Cape Girardeau.
Vocation Director: Rev. John
Hansen, SMP, Maria Fonte Solitude, P.O. Box 322, High Ridge,
MO 63049-0322. (314) 677-3235.

SOCIETY OF ST. EDMUND
See Edmundites.

SOCIETY OF ST. JOSEPH OF THE SACRED HEART
See Josephite Fathers and Broth-
ers.

SOCIETY OF ST. PAUL
See St. Paul, Society of.

SOCIETY OF ST. SULPICE
See Sulpician Fathers, The.

SOCIETY OF THE CATHOLIC APOSTOLATE
See Pallottines.

SOCIETY OF THE PRECIOUS BLOOD
See Precious Blood, Society of.

SOMASCAN FATHERS AND BROTHERS (C.R.S.)
Box 162, Allenstown, NH 03275.
(603) 485-7141; 49 Winthrop St.,
Hartford, CT 06103. (203) 527-
6459; 901 Rose Lane, Houston,
TX 77037. (713) 447-6381.
Apostolic Work: The Somascans
carry on the legacy of their
founder, St. Jerome Emiliani, in
taking care of the poor, especially
the troubled children and youth in
Europe, Americas and Asia. In the
US, the Somascans operate a
treatment center for at-risk youth
in New Hampshire, a Hispanic
parish in Connecticut and a bilingual parish in Texas.

SONS OF MARY MISSIONARY SOCIETY (F.M.S.I.) (Sons of Mary, Health of the Sick)
567 Salem End Rd., Framingham,
MA 01701.
Professed 13
Apostolic Work: Medical, social
and catechetical in U.S. and the
Philippines.
Represented in the Archdiocese of

Boston and in Manila, Philippines.
Vocation Director: Bro. Kevin
Courtney, F.M.S.I. (508) 879-
SONS (7667).

SPIRITANS
See Holy Ghost Fathers.

STIGMATINE FATHERS AND BROTHERS (C.S.S.)
(Province of the Holy Spouses,
Mary and Joseph)
Provincial Office: 554 Lexington
St., Waltham, MA 02154. (617)
899-6525
51 Priests, 4 Brothers
Conduct: 1 retreat house, 9 par-
ishes. Give missions and retreats.
Mission in Brazil, Philippines and
Thailand.
Apostolic Work: Assistance to
bishops.
Represented in the Archdioceses
of Boston and New York and in the
Dioceses of Arlington, Springfield
(MA) and Worcester. Also in Manila,
the Philippines and Thailand.
Vocation Director: Rev. Joseph
Henchey, C.S.S., 554 Lexington
St., Waltham, MA 02154. (617)
899-6525.

SULPICIAN FATHERS, THE (S.S.)
(Society of St. Sulpice)
U.S.A. Province: 5408 Roland
Ave., Baltimore, MD 21210.
93 Priests
Apostolic Work: Educating dioce-
san seminarians and priests,
developing vocations for a multi-
cultural church and collaborating
with seminary programs in mission
countries.
Represented in the Archdioceses
of Baltimore, San Francisco,
Washington and Los Angeles and
Lusaka, Zambia. Canadian Prov-
ince: Canada, Brazil, Colombia
and Japan. French Province:
France, Vietnam, Benin, Upper
Volta, Zaire.
Director of Vocations: Rev. Melvin
C. Blanchette, S.S. (410) 323-5070.

COMMUNITY OF TERESIAN CARMELITES (C.T.C.)
See "C" Section – Community of
Teresian Carmelites.

THEATINE FATHERS (C.R.)
Provincial House: St. Andrew
Seminary, 1050 S. Birch St., Den-
ver, CO 80222. (303) 756-5522

19 Priests, 5 Clerics

Conduct: 9 parishes in four dioceses, primarily in Colorado.

Apostolic Work: Parish work, retreats, working with Spanish speaking, other special ministries.

Represented in the Archdioceses of Denver and New York and in the Dioceses of Colorado Springs and Pueblo.

Vocation Director: St. Andrew Seminary, 1050 S. Birch St., Denver, CO 80222. (303) 756-5522.

TRAPPISTS

See also Cistercians of the Strict Observance.

TRAPPISTS (O.C.S.O.) (Cistercians of the Strict Observance)

Saint Joseph's Abbey, Spencer, MA 01562.

Contemplative community of 75 monks: brothers and priests.

Vocation Director: Fr. David Lavich, OCSO, Saint Joseph's Abbey. (508) 885-3901.

TRAPPISTS (O.C.S.O.) (Cistercians of the Strict Observance)

Our Lady of Gethsemani Abbey, 3642 Monks Rd., New Haven, KY 40051.

16 Priests, 55 Brothers

Vocation Director: Br. Gerlac O'Loughlin. (502) 549-4116.

TRAPPISTS (O.C.S.O.) (Cistercians of the Strict Observance)

Monastery of the Holy Spirit, 2625 Hwy. 212 S.W., Conyers, GA 30208.

58 Monks, 33 Priests, 5 Novices

Represented in the Archdiocese of Atlanta.

Vocation Director: Monastery of the Holy Spirit, 2625 Hwy. 212 S.W. Conyers, GA 30208. (404) 483-8705.

TRAPPISTS (O.C.S.O.) (Cistercians of the Strict Observance)

Mepkin Abbey,1098 Abbey Road, Moncks Corner, SC 29461. (803) 761-8509.

31 Monks (21 Brothers, 10 Priests)

Apostolic Work: Contemplative monastic community called to seek the face of God together in a life of liturgical prayer, simple manual labor and meditation.

Vocation Director: Fr. Aelred Hagan, o.c.s.o.

TRAPPISTS (O.C.S.O.) (Cistercians of the Strict Observance)

Abbey of Our Lady of the Holy Cross, Rte. 2, Box 3870, Berryville, VA 22611-9526.

Contemplative Monastic Community

20 Solemnly Professed, 12 Priests, 2 Temporary Vows, 3 Novices, 2 Postulants

Vocation Director: Fr. Maurice Flood, (703) 955-1425.

TRAPPISTS (O.C.S.O.) (Cistercians of the Strict Observance)

Assumption Abbey, Rt. 5, Box 1056, Ava, MO 65608. (417) 683-5110

6 Priests, 14 Monks

A Trappist-Cistercian community of 14 Monks in the Ozark foothills of S.W. Missouri dedicated to the contemplative monastic life and supported by own manual labor.

Vocation Director: Fr. Cyprian Harrison, O.C.S.O.

TRAPPISTS (O.C.S.O.) (Cistercians of the Strict Observance)

New Melleray Abbey, Peosta, IA 52068. (319) 588-2319.

Contemplative community of monks, brothers and priests.

Vocation Director: Fr. Neil Paquette, New Melleray Abbey, 6500 Melleray Circle, Peosta, IA 52068. (319) 588-2319.

TRAPPISTS (O.C.S.O.) (Cistercians of the Strict Observance)

Our Lady of Guadalupe Abbey, 9200 NE Abbey Rd., Lafayette, OR 97127. (503) 852-7174

17 Priests.

TRAPPISTS (O.C.S.O.) (Cistercians of the Strict Observance)

Our Lady of the Holy Trinity Abbey, 1250 South 9500 East, Huntsville, UT 84317. (801) 745-3784

Contemplative Monastic Community

23 Monks, Priests and Brothers

Vocation Director: Brother Lawrence.

TRAPPISTS (O.C.S.O.) (Cistercians of the Strict Observance)

Abbey of the Genesee, Piffard, NY 14533.

Contemplative order, solemn vows

10 Priests

Represented in the Diocese of Rochester. Community of about 40 monks.

Vocation Director: Br. Anthony Weber, O.C.S.O., (716) 243-0660.

TRAPPISTS (O.C.S.O.) (Cistercians of the Strict Observance)

New Clairvaux Abbey, Vina, CA 96092. (916) 839-2161

24 in Community, 9 Priests

Contact: Vocation Director.

TRAPPISTS (O.C.S.O.) (Cistercians of the Strict Observance)

St. Benedict's Monastery, 1012 Monastery Rd., Snowmass, CO 81654. (970) 927-3311

12 Monks, 1 Novice, 2 Juniors.

THE TRINITARIAN FRIARS (O.SS.T.) (Order of the Most Holy Trinity)

(Province of the Immaculate Heart of Mary)

Provincial Office: P.O. Box 5719, 8400 Park Heights Ave. N., Pikesville, MD 21208. (410) 486-5764.

92 Friars

Conduct: 11 parishes, 1 high school, 1 home for homeless men, 15 community houses, 1 retreat house.

Apostolic Work: Parish ministry, youth ministry, hospital chaplaincy, pastoral counseling, ministry to minorities, secondary, college and graduate level education, retreats, prison ministry, campus ministry, homeless men, promoting social justice, international release of Christian captives, missions.

Represented in the Archdioceses of Baltimore, New Orleans, New York, Philadelphia and Washington, DC and in the Dioceses of Corpus Christi, Trenton and Victoria. Internationally in Spain, Italy, Austria, France, Germany, Poland, Puerto Rico, Mexico, South America, Madagascar, Canada and India.

Vocation Director: Rev. Albert Anuszewski, O.SS.T., P.O. Box 5719, Baltimore, MD 21208. (800) 525-3554 or (410) 484-2250.

TRINITY MISSIONS (S.T.)
(Missionary Servants of the Most Holy Trinity)
1215 N. Scott St., Arlington, VA 22209.

112 Priests, 34 Brothers

Conduct: 40 parishes, 58 missions and stations, 1 major seminary, 1 novitiate, 3 pre-novitiate formation houses in the United States for priests and brother candidates and 3 pre-novitiate houses in Mexico.

Apostolic Work: Lay apostle development, inner-city parish and social service ministry, Appalachian and rural missions, Hispanic and Native American missions, ministry to the institutionalized and incarcerated; alcohol, drug and post-detention rehabilitation ministry.

Represented in the United States, Puerto Rico, Mexico and Costa Rica.

Vocation Minister: Fr. Dennis Berry, S.T., Trinity Missions, 9001 New Hampshire Ave., Silver Spring, MD 20903. (800) 272-8850, (800) 221-5740.

VERONA FATHERS
See Comboni Missionaries.

VIATORIANS
See Clerics of St. Viator.

VINCENTIANS (C.M.)
(Congregation of the Mission)
(New England Province) 234 Keeney St., Manchester, CT 06040-7023

35 Priests, 5 Brothers

Conduct: 6 parishes, 1 mission house.

Apostolic Work: Catholic education, mission preaching, chaplaincies, parochial apostolate.

Represented in the Archdiocese of Hartford and in the Dioceses of Syracuse, Brooklyn, Portland, ME, and Manchester, NH.

Vocation Director: Rev. Anthony F. Kuzia, C.M., 234 Keeney St., Manchester, CT 06040-7023. (203) 643-2828.

VINCENTIANS (CM)
(Congregation of the Mission)
(Eastern Province) 500 E. Chelten Ave., Philadelphia, PA 19144.

240 Fathers, 14 Brothers

Conduct: 19 parishes, 2 universities, 2 seminaries.

Apostolic Work: Catholic education, priestly formation, parishes, missions in Panama, preaching, service to the poor.

Represented in the Archdioceses of Baltimore, Philadelphia and New York and in other dioceses on the Eastern Seaboard.

Vocation Director: Rev. James Claffey, C.M., Vincentian Vocation Office, St. John's University, Jamaica, NY 11439. (718) 990-6744.

VINCENTIANS (C.M.)
(Congregation of the Mission)
(Spanish Vincentian Fathers-Barcelona) St. Peter's - St. Paul's - O.L. of Pilar Church, 234 Congress St., Brooklyn, NY 11201. (718) 624-3425

7 Priests

Conduct: 2 parishes, Centro de Evangelizacion, "San Vicente De Paul", Cursillo Movement, Jornada Movement.

Represented in the Diocese of Brooklyn.

VINCENTIANS (C.M.)
(Congregation of the Mission)
(American Spanish Branch) Holy Agony Church, 1834 3rd Ave., New York, NY 10029. (212) 289-5589

10 Fathers

Conduct: 3 churches, 2 schools.

Represented in the Archdioceses of Los Angeles, New York and San Francisco.

VINCENTIANS (C.M.)
(Congregation of the Mission)
(Midwest Province) 13663 Rider Trail North, Earth City, MO 63045. (314) 344-1184

157 Priests, 19 Brothers

Conduct: 16 parishes (13 U.S.), 4 seminaries (3 U.S.), 1 university.

Apostolic Work: Priestly formation, Catholic education, preaching, parishes, chaplaincies and foreign missions.

Represented in the Archdioceses of Chicago, Denver and St. Louis and in the Dioceses of Pueblo,

Cape Girardeau, Jefferson City, Kansas City–St. Joseph, as well as Dioceses in Kenya.

Vocation Director: Fr. Mark Pranaitis, C.M., 13663 Rider Trail North, Earth City, MO 63045. (314) 344-1184.

VINCENTIANS (C.M.)
(Congregation of the Mission)
(Province of the West) 650 W. 23rd St., Los Angeles, CA 90007. (213) 749-1865

53 Priests, 3 Brothers, 3 Deacons, 5 Students in Formation

Conduct: Evangelization of the poor, priestly formation, home missions, parish ministry, foreign mission, hospital chaplaincies, retreat and evangelization centers.

Apostolic Work: Serving the needs of the Church in the spirit of St. Vincent de Paul.

Represented in the Archdiocese of Los Angeles and in the Dioceses of Phoenix, Stockton, Orange and San Benito, Guatamala.

Vocation Directors: Fr. Henry Van Oudheusden, C.M.; Sr. Frances Sullivan, D.C., 650 W. 23rd St., Los Angeles, CA 90007. (213) 749-1865.

VINCENTIANS (C.M.)
(Congregation of the Mission)
(Puerto Rico Province), P.O. Box 19118, Fernandez Juncos Station, San Juan, PR 00910. (809) 727-3963.

53 Priests

Conduct: 15 parishes, 7 schools.

Represented in the Archdiocese of San Juan and in the Dioceses of Ponce; Arecibo and Mayaguez. Also in Dominican Republic and Haiti.

Vocation Director: Fr. Evaristo Oliveras, C.M., P.O. Box 19118, Fernandez Juncos Station, San Juan, PR 00910. (809) 727-4236.

VINCENTIANS (C.M.)
(Congregation of the Mission)
(Southern Province) 3826 Gilbert, Dallas, TX 75219. (214) 526-0234

37 Priests, 1 Brother

Conduct: Preaching missions in parishes, conducting continuing clergy education, parish work, home mission team, parishes in 8 cities, hospital chaplaincies in 2 cities, seminary work in 1 city.

Apostolic Work: A mobile community dedicated to instructing the poor and helping in the formation of diocesan priests.

Represented in the Archdioceses of New Orleans and San Antonio and in the Dioceses of Gallup (NM), Dallas (TX), San Angelo (TX), Galveston-Houston (TX) and Little Rock (AR).

Vocation Director: Fr. Gilbert Walker, C.M., Vincentian Vocation Office, 3826 Gilbert, Dallas, TX 75219. (214) 526-0234.

VOCATIONIST FATHERS (S.D.V.) (Society of the Divine Vocations)

St. Michael's, 172 Broadway, Newark, NJ 07104. (201) 484-7100.

Apostolic Work: The Vocationist Fathers are a Community of Priests and Brothers who strive to search, recruit and guide vocations to both Religious life and Diocesan Priesthood. They pursue this goal through their work in parishes, missions and special vocation houses called Vocationaries.

Represented in numerous Dioceses of Italy and Brazil. In the U.S. in the Dioceses of Newark and Paterson.

Vocation Director: Fr. Louis Caputo, S.D.V., 172 Broadway, Newark, NJ 07104. (201) 484-7100.

WHITE FATHERS OF AFRICA

See Missionaries of Africa.

XAVERIAN BROTHERS (C.F.X.)

(American Northeastern Province) 704 Brush Hill Rd., Milton, MA 02186.

130 Brothers

Conduct: 6 high schools, 1 formation center, secondary schools in Kenya and Uganda East Africa and the Republic of Zaire.

Apostolic Work: Education in high schools, elementary schools, colleges, CCD, catechetical centers, prison work, hospital chaplaincy, American Indian Reservation School, African mission schools, centers for the homeless.

Represented in the Archdioceses of Baltimore, Boston, Los Angeles, New York and Newark and in the Dioceses of Charleston, Louisville,

Manchester, Monterey, Norwich, Richmond, Syracuse and Worcester.

Vocation Director: Vocation Director, Xaverian Brothers, 704 Brush Hill Rd., Milton, MA 02186. (617) 333-0970.

XAVERIAN BROTHERS (C.F.X.)

(American Central Province) 10318B Baltimore National Pike, Ellicott City, MD 21042. (410) 750-2850

125 Brothers

Conduct: 6 high schools, 1 teacher's college for mission territory teachers, 33 community houses.

Apostolic Work: Teachers (elementary, high school, college), DRE and parish ministers, retreats/encounters, educational specialists in prison ministry, counselors (alcoholic, career, personal), social ministry, and missions in Bolivia and Haiti.

Represented in the Archdioceses of Baltimore, Boston, Los Angeles, Louisville, New York, Newark and Washington and in the Dioceses of Birmingham, Brooklyn, Fairbanks, Houma-Thibodaux, Memphis, Metuchen, Rapid City, Richmond, Rockville Centre, St. Augustine, St. Petersburg and Wheeling-Charleston and in the Dioceses of Aiquile, Cochabamba and Coroico, Bolivia and Hinche, Haiti.

Vocation Director: Brother Richard Murphy, C.F.X., 10318B Baltimore National Pike, Ellicott City, MD 21042. (410) 750-2850.

XAVERIAN MISSIONARIES (S.X.)

U.S. Provincial Office: 12 Helene Court, Wayne, NJ 07470-2813.

Conduct: In the U.S.: 4 vocation and mission education centers, and 1 international theology community.

Apostolic Work: Pastoral and community work, leadership training, justice and peace work in poor, non-Christian, and cross-cultural areas.

Represented in the Archdioceses of Boston, Chicago and Milwaukee and in the Dioceses of Paterson (NJ) and San Jose (CA). Also in Colombia, Mexico, Brazil, Japan, Indonesia, Bangladesh, Philippines, Taiwan, Burundi, Zaire, Sierra Leone, Cameroon, Chad, Italy, Spain and Great Britain.

Vocation Minister: Fr. Dario Maso, sx, 12 Helene Ct., Wayne, NJ 07470-2813. (201) 942-2975.

EASTERN CATHOLIC RELIGIOUS COMMUNITIES FOR MEN

BASILIAN FATHERS, BASILIAN ORDER OF ST. JOSAPHAT (O.S.B.M.) (Order of St. Basil the Great)

(Assumption of B.V.M. Province) 31-12 30th St., Long Island City, NY 11106.

In Canada: 737 Bannerman Ave., Winnipeg R2X-1J9, Canada.

Conduct: 3 monasteries, 7 parishes, 4 parochial schools. The order works in the USA and throughout the world mainly among Ukrainians, Carpatho-Ukrainians/Ruthenians, Rumanians, Hungarians and Croatians.

Represented in the Archdioceses of Chicago, Detroit and New York and in the Dioceses of Passaic and Stamford.

Vocation Directors: Rev. Cyril Iszczuk, O.S.B.M., East Beach Dr., Glen Cove, NY 11542. (516) 671-0545. In Canada: Rev. Isidore Dziadyk, 737 Bannerman Ave., Winnipeg R2X-1J9, Canada. (204) 582-6695.

BASILIAN FATHERS OF MARIA POCH (O.S.B.M.)

360 Monastery Lane, Matawan, NJ 07747. (908) 566-8445.

Apostolic Work: Retreat center, area social center, pilgrimage shrine.

Vocation Directors: Rev. Joseph Erdei, O.S.B.M., Rev. Basil Rakaczy, 360 Monastery Lane, Matawan, NJ 07747. (908) 566-8445.

BASILIAN SALVATORIAN FATHERS (B.S.O.)

American Headquarters: St. Basil Seminary, 30 East St., Methuen, MA 01844. (508) 683-2471.

20 Priests in U.S.

Conduct: 1 seminary, 1 novitiate, 1 center for ecumenical studies and retreats, 1 r & r house, 9 parishes.

Apostolic Work: Specialize in parishes, ecumenical activities, Cursillos, Teen Encounters, retreats, teaching, special ministries.

Represented in the (Arch)dioceses of Atlanta, Boston, Cleveland,

Manchester, Norwich, Miami and in Canada, Mexico and South America.

Vocation Director: Fr. Roderick McRae, BSO, St. Ann's Melkite Catholic Church, 41 Crossroads, Waterford, CT 06385. (203) 442-2211.

BROTHERS OF THE ANNUNCIATION OF MARY

103 Ambassador Dr., Akron, OH 44312-4407. (216) 733-7774

Apostolic Work: Following the Franciscan Rule, work among God's poor, especially the mentally challenged and multiply addicted.

Vocation Director: Bro. M. Raphael Joseph, Director of Formation, 103 Ambassador Dr., Akron, OH 44312-4407. (216) 733-7774.

BYZANTINE FRANCISCAN CUSTODY OF SAINT MARY OF THE ANGELS (O.F.M.) (Franciscan Fathers)

Custodial Office, Byzantine Franciscans, P.O. Box 270, Sybertsville, PA 18251. (717) 788-1212

Ministries: The Byzantine Custody was formed by the Franciscans for men who are called to work as Franciscan brothers and priests within the Byzantine Ukrainian and Ruthenian Rite Catholic Churches. As Franciscans, we are open to doing all types of ministry within the Eastern Rite Churches throughout the world.

Represented in most Byzantine and Ukrainian dioceses in the United States.

Vocation Director: Fr. William Skurla, O.F.M., Vocation Office, Byzantine Franciscans, P.O. Box 270, Sybertsville, PA 18251. (717) 788-1212.

HOLY TRINITY MONASTERY-BENEDICTINE MONKS - Byzantine Rite

P.O. Box 990, Butler, PA 16003-0990. (412) 287-4461

8 Priests, 4 Brothers

Apostolic Works: Hospitality, private retreats, parochial work, and Eastern Christian religious articles.

Represented throughout the Byzantine Metropolitan Province of Pittsburgh.

Vocation Director: Fr. Leo R. Schlosser, O.S.B., Holy Trinity Monastery, P.O. Box 990, Butler, PA 16003-0990. (412) 287-4461.

HOLY TRANSFIGURATION MONASTERY- MONKS OF MT. TABOR

17001 Tomki Rd., P.O. Box 217, Redwood Valley, CA 95470-0217. (707) 485-8959

14 Monks

Apostolic Work: Contemplative; retreats, hospitality, care of the poor, publishing.

Represented in the (Arch)dioceses of St. Nicholas in Chicago and Marquette.

Vocation Contact: Archimandrite Boniface, 17001 Tomki Rd., P.O. Box 217, Redwood Valley, CA 95470-0217.

MARONITE MONKS OF MOST HOLY TRINITY MONASTERY (Eucharistic Adoration/ Strictly Contemplative)

Box 605, 67 Dugway Rd., Petersham, MA 01366-0605. (508) 724-3347

16 Monks in Community (11 Priests)

Represented in the Diocese of St. Maron, U.S.A.

Vocation Director: Rev. William Driscoll, Box 605, 67 Dugway Rd., Petersham, MA 01366-0605. (508) 724-3347.

MARONITE MONKS OF MOST HOLY TRINITY MONASTERY (Eucharistic Adoration/ Strictly Contemplative)

Holy Nativity Monastery, Bethlehem, SD 57708. (605) 787-4606

4 Priests, 11 Monks

Represented in the Diocese of Rapid City.

Vocation Director: Fr. Louis Marie Dauphinais, O. Mar., Superior.

REDEMPTORISTS

St. Joseph's Monastery, 250 Jefferson Ave., Winnipeg R2V 0M6 Canada. (204) 339-4512

Apostolic Work: Parish work, missions, retreats, teaching and formation work. Serve in U.S. and Canada.

Vocation Director: Mr. Mark Gnutel, St. Joseph's Monastery, 250 Jefferson Ave., Winnipeg R2V 0M6 Canada. (204) 338-6823.

As we progress in this way of life...

we shall run on the path

of God's commandments,

our hearts overflowing

with the inexpressible delight

of LOVE.

St. Benedict

Religious Communities for Women

ADORERS OF THE BLOOD OF CHRIST (A.S.C.)

(Columbia Province)

Apostolic Work: Teaching on all levels, ministry to the elderly, health care, domestic service, pastoral ministry, social services, campus ministry, child care, care of children with AIDS, ministry in diverse cultures, religious education.

Represented in the Archdioceses of Chicago and Baltimore and in the Dioceses of Altoona-Johnstown, Harrisburg, Newark, New York, Savannah and Youngstown. Also in Guatemala.

Vocation Director: Sr. Maria Louise Hughes, A.S.C., St. Joseph Convent, 3950 Columbia Ave., Columbia, PA 17512. (717) 285-9596.

ADORERS OF THE BLOOD OF CHRIST (A.S.C.)

(Ruma Province), #2 Pioneer Lane-Ruma, Red Bud, IL 62278. (618) 282-3848

240 Sisters

International Community of 11 provinces

Apostolic Work: Health care, education (university, secondary, elementary), parish ministry, retreat work, social services, sanctuary ministry, refugee resettlement, dietetics/domestic service, geriatrics, youth ministry, prison ministry, religious education, special outreach to women, the poor and the alienated in society and the Church.

Represented in the Archdiocese of St. Louis and in the Dioceses of Belleville, Springfield, Joliet, Springfield-Cape Girardeau, Jefferson City, Covington, Owensboro, Gallup and Phoenix. Foreign Missions in La Paz and Riberalta, Bolivia, Liberia West African cities of Grand Cess, Klay, Gardnersville and Monrovia.

Vocation Director: Sr. Raphael Ann Drone, A.S.C., 2 Pioneer Lane-Ruma, Red Bud, IL 62278. (618) 282-3848.

ADORERS OF THE BLOOD OF CHRIST (A.S.C.)

(Wichita Province), 14000 S. Sheridan, Wichita, KS 67213. (316) 943-1203

243 Sisters

Apostolic Work: Education (elementary-college), religious education, health care, parish ministry, dietetics and domestic services, care of the aging.

Represented in the (Arch)dioceses of Dodge City, Kansas City, Salina and Wichita, KS; Oklahoma City and Tulsa, OK; Tyler, Fort Worth, Beaumont, TX; El Paso and San Antonio, TX; Springfield, IL; Owensboro, KY; Lincoln, NE; Kansas City-St. Joseph, Jefferson City and St. Louis, MO; Gallup, Las Cruces, NM and Washington, DC. Foreign Missions in Masan, Seoul and Pusan, Korea.

Formation Director: Sr. Mary Kevin Rooney, 1165 Southwest Blvd., Wichita, KS 67213.

SISTERS ADORERS OF THE PRECIOUS BLOOD (A.P.B.)

700 Bridge St., Manchester, NH 03104. (603) 623-4264

28 Professed Sisters, 1 Junior Professed, 2 Novices

Apostolic Work: Cloistered, contemplative.

Represented in the Diocese of Manchester.

Contact: Directress of Novices.

SISTERS ADORERS OF THE PRECIOUS BLOOD (A.P.B.)

1106 State St., Lafayette, IN 47905. (317) 742-8227

Apostolic Work: Cloistered, contemplative.

Represented in the Diocese of Lafayette.

Contact: Director of Novices.

SISTERS ADORERS OF THE PRECIOUS BLOOD (A.P.B.)

166 State St., Portland, ME 04101. (207) 774-0861

Apostolic Work: Cloistered, contemplative.

Represented in the Diocese of Portland, ME.

Contact: Sr. Therese.

SISTERS ADORERS OF THE PRECIOUS BLOOD (A.P.B.)

54th St. and Fort Hamilton Pkwy., Brooklyn, NY 11219. (718) 438-6371

19 Nuns

Apostolic Work: Cloistered, contemplative.

Represented in the Diocese of Brooklyn.

Contact: Sr. Mary of the Precious Blood, APB, Director of Novices.

SISTERS ADORERS OF THE PRECIOUS BLOOD (A.P.B.)

Precious Blood Monastery, 400 Pratt St., Watertown, NY 13601. (315) 788-1669

Apostolic Work: Cloistered, contemplative, intercessory prayer.

Represented in the Diocese of Ogdensburg.

Contact: Director of Novices.

ANGELIC SISTERS OF ST. PAUL (A.S.S.P.)

St. Anthony Convent, 770 Washington St., Easton, PA 18042. (610) 258-7792

7 Sisters in U.S., 400 Sisters worldwide

Apostolic Work: Teaching, mission work, parish work, C.C.D. teaching, social work, youth group coordinator.

Represented in the Diocese of Allentown (PA).

Vocation Directress: Sister Donna Pascarella, A.S.S.P.

ANTONINE SISTERS (MARONITE)

See Eastern Catholic Religious Communities for Women.

APOSTLES OF THE SACRED HEART OF JESUS (A.S.C.J.)

Provincial House: Mt. Sacred Heart, 265 Benham St., Hamden, CT 06514.

207 Sisters in U.S.A.

Apostolic Work: Teaching in high schools, elementary schools, schools for children who are mentally handicapped or learning disabled, kindergartens and day nurseries, pastoral ministry, health care, legal services to the poor.

Represented in the (Arch)dioceses of Greensburg, Hartford, Metuchen, New York, Newark, Pensacola/Tallahassee, Pittsburgh, Providence, Sacramento, St. Louis, St. Petersburg, Palm Beach. Also in Africa, Albania, Argentina, Brazil, Chile and Italy.

Vocation Director: Sr. Janet Kofron, A.S.C.J., Mount Sacred Heart Provincialate, 265 Benham St., Hamden, CT 06514. (203) 248-4225.

RELIGIOUS OF THE ASSUMPTION (R.A.)

Provincial House: 227 N. Bowman Ave., Merion, PA 19066. (610) 664-3074.

1,500 Religious worldwide; 22 in the U.S.

Apostolic Work: Teaching, catechetics, campus ministry; nursing, retreats, ecumenical work, Europe, USA, Africa, Central and South America, India, Japan and Philippines.

Represented in the Archdioceses of Philadelphia, PA; Worcester, MA and in 32 foreign countries.

Vocation Director: 227 N. Bowman Ave., Merion, PA 19066. (610) 664-3074.

SISTERS OF THE ASSUMPTION OF THE B.V. (S.A.S.V.)

Provincial House: Worcester, MA 01605.

128 Sisters

Apostolic Work: Teaching, pastoral ministry, religious education, music instruction, campus ministry, spiritual renewal, foreign missionary work.

Represented in the Archdioceses of Boston and Hartford, in four other dioceses and in four foreign countries.

Vocation Team Director: Sr. Sandra Dupre, S.A.S.V., 26 Sylvester St., Brockton, MA 02402. (508) 583-7420.

AUGUSTINIAN CLOISTERED NUNS (O.S.A.)

Mother of Good Counsel, 4328 Westminister St., St. Louis, MO 63108. (314) 533-2054

Cloistered contemplatives

Apostolate: through community charity to grow in the love of God by living the Gospel message; serving the Church through prayer and penance. Work includes: making vestments and habits, needle and art work, household tasks, etc.

Vocations: Sr. Mary Grace, O.S.A., Superior

AUGUSTINIAN SISTERS (O.S.A.) (Servants of Jesus and Mary)

St. John School, Brandenburg, KY 40108. (502) 422-2088

350 Sisters worldwide; 4 Sisters in U.S.

Represented in the Archdiocese of Louisville.

BASILIAN NUNS AND SISTERS

See Eastern Catholic Religious Communities for Women.

BENEDICTINE NUNS (O.S.B.)

Abbey of St. Walburga, 6717 S. Boulder Rd., Boulder, CO 80303-4397. (303) 494-5733.

22 Nuns

Apostolic Work: Cloistered contemplative nuns at the foot of the Rocky Mountains. Work includes retreats, arts and crafts, farm. Full monastic Office.

Represented in the Archdiocese of Denver.

Vocations: Sr. Genevieve Glen, O.S.B.

BENEDICTINE NUNS (O.S.B.)

(Cloistered) St. Scholastica Priory, Box 606, 271 N. Main St., Petersham, MA 01366-0606. (508) 724-3213

12 Nuns in Solemn Vows, 1 in Simple Vows, 2 Novices

Apostolic Work: Prayer.

Vocation Contact: Sr. Scholastica Crilly, O.S.B.

BENEDICTINE NUNS OF THE CONGREGATION OF SOLESMES (O.S.B.)

U.S. Foundation: Monastery of the Immaculate Heart of Mary, H.C.R. #13, Box 11, Westfield, VT 05874. (802) 744-6525.

Cloistered Contemplative Nuns

13 Professed Nuns, 2 Temporary Professed

Apostolic Work: Divine Office, in Latin with Gregorian Chant, according to the Rule of Saint Benedict and the Vatican II Constitution on the Liturgy.

Represented in the Diocese of Burlington. 21 monasteries of monks and 8 monasteries of nuns in 10 countries.

Vocation Director: Rev. Mother Marguerite T. Derome, O.S.B., Prioress.

BENEDICTINE NUNS OF THE PRIMITIVE OBSERVANCE (O.S.B.)

Abbey of Regina Laudis, Bethlehem, CT 06751. (203) 266-7727

Cloistered. 1 Abbey

25 Professed Nuns, 7 in Temporary Vows, 5 Novices, 2 Postulants

Represented in the Archdioceses of Hartford and Seattle.

Vocation Contact: Rt. Rev. Mother Benedict Duss, O.S.B., Abbess.

BENEDICTINE SISTERS (O.S.B.)

St. Benedict Monastery, 2100 5th Ave., Canyon, TX 79015. (806) 655-9317.

3 Professed Sisters

Ministry: The primary ministry is to seek God through monastic life: community, Liturgy of the Hours, contemplation and work.

Vocation Contact: Sr. Marcella Schmalz, O.S.B.

BENEDICTINE SISTERS (O.S.B.)
St. Emma Monastery, 1001 Harvey Ave., Greensburg, PA 15601-1494. (412) 834-3060.
22 Sisters
Apostolic Work: Monastic life, retreat house.
Represented in the Diocese of Greensburg.
Vocations: Mother Mary Anne, O.S.B.

BENEDICTINE SISTERS (O.S.B.)
Mount St. Scholastica, 801 S. 8th St., Atchison, KS 66002.
258 Sisters
Apostolic Work: Education (elementary, secondary, college and special education), religious education, pastoral ministry, hospital chaplaincy, retreats, spiritual direction, counseling, social service, ministry to the sick & the aged, child day care & preschool, health care, ministry of the press, missionary ministry.
Represented in the Archdioceses of Chicago, New Orleans, LA; Kansas City KS; St. Louis and Washington and in the Dioceses of Kansas City-St. Joseph, MO; Shreveport-Monroe, LA; Springfield-Cape Giradeau; Des Moines; Tulsa; Brazil: Mineiros.
Vocation Minister: Sr. Marcia Ziska, O.S.B., Mount St. Scholastica, 801 S. 8th St., Atchison, KS 66002. (913) 367-6110.

BENEDICTINE SISTERS (O.S.B.)
St. Joseph Monastery, 303 Church St., St. Marys, PA 15857.
48 Sisters
Apostolic Work: Education, retreats, office work, family ministries, pastoral ministry, tutoring and domestic services and crafts.
Represented in the Diocese of Erie.
Vocation Director: Sr. Kathleen Warner, St. Joseph Monastery, St. Marys, PA 15857. (814) 834-2267.

BENEDICTINE SISTERS (O.S.B.)
Mt. St. Benedict Priory, 6101 E. Lake Rd., Erie, PA 16511. (814) 899-0614
152 Sisters
Apostolic Work: Administration, care of the handicapped, education, food management, homes for the aged, homemaking, liturgy, music, nursing, pastoral ministry, peace and justice, social work, technicians, hospitality/conference center.

Represented in the Dioceses of Arlington, Cleveland, Erie, Orlando and Richmond.
Vocation Director: Sr. Diane Rabe, O.S.B. (814) 454-4514.

BENEDICTINE SISTERS (O.S.B.)
St. Scholastica Priory, 7430 N. Ridge Blvd., Chicago, IL 60645. (312) 764-2413
100 Sisters
Conduct: 2 community-owned high schools.
Apostolic Work: Education, social service, pastoral ministry, peace and justice, spiritual development programs. Community policy accepts plurality of ministries.
Represented in the Archdioceses of Chicago, St. Louis and in Southern Colorado.
Vocation Director: Sr. Suzanne Zuercher, O.S.B., St. Scholastica Priory, 7430 N. Ridge Blvd., Chicago, IL 60645. (312) 764-2413.

BENEDICTINE SISTERS (O.S.B.)
1910 Maple Ave., Lisle, IL 60532-2184. (708) 969-7040
58 Sisters
Conduct: senior citizen residence, education, hospitality to the needy, pastoral ministry in hospitals and parishes, administrators, counseling and community support services, making of altar breads, secretaries, domestic services.
Represented in the Archdiocese of Chicago and in the Diocese of Joliet.
Vocation Contact: Sr. Charlotte Mack, O.S.B.

BENEDICTINE SISTERS (O.S.B.)
Our Lady of Sorrows Priory, 5900 W. 147th St., Oak Forest, IL 60452. (708) 687-2877
11 Sisters
Apostolic Work: Primarily dedicated to teaching. However, each sister's ability is taken into consideration through obedience and community living.
Represented in the Archdiocese of Chicago.

BENEDICTINE SISTERS (O.S.B.)
Saint Walburga Monastery, 851 N. Broad St., Elizabeth, NJ 07208.
(908) 352-4278.
75 Sisters, 1 Scholastic, 1 Novice, 1 Affiliate
Apostolic Work: Praise of God in the Eucharist and the Liturgy of the Hours; ministries in the fields of education, health care, pastoral

work, domestic arts, counseling, retreat work and administration. Other ministries may also be chosen, provided that these are compatible with the primary monastic commitment to community life and prayer.
Represented in the Archdioceses of New York, Newark and Washington, DC, and in the Dioceses of Paterson, Trenton and Metuchen.
Vocation Ministry: Sr. Marlene Milasus, O.S.B. (908) 352-4278.

BENEDICTINE SISTERS OF PITTSBURGH (OSB)
4530 Perrysville Ave., Pittsburgh, PA 15229.
93 Sisters
Apostolic Work: High school, elementary education, parish ministry, CCD, social justice, adult services, chaplaincy, social services, care of the aged, day care, visual arts, administration, hospital ministry, foster parenting, tutoring, counseling, spiritual direction.
Represented in the Dioceses of Greensburg, Lexington and Pittsburgh.
Vocation Director: Sr. Beth Carrender, OSB. (412) 931-2844.

BENEDICTINE SISTERS (O.S.B.)
Red Plains Monastery, 1132 N.W. 32nd St., Oklahoma City, OK 73118. (405) 528-2715
12 Sisters
Apostolic Work: Pastoral ministry, religious education coordination, spiritual direction and retreats, arts & crafts.
Represented in the Archdiocese of Oklahoma City.
Vocation Director: Sr. Joanne Yankauskis, O.S.B., 1132 N.W. 32nd St., Oklahoma City, OK 73118. (405) 528-2715.

BENEDICTINE SISTERS (O.S.B.)
St. Joseph Monastery, 2200 S. Lewis, Tulsa, OK 74114. (918) 742-4989
37 Sisters
Apostolic Work: Monastic community life and prayer, 1 private school grades pre-school through 8th grade coeducational, other ministries, nursing, teaching, social services, pastoral ministry, catechetics, church and diocesan service, Catholic Charities.
Represented in the Archdiocese of Oklahoma City and in the Diocese of Tulsa.
Vocation Minister: 2200 S. Lewis, Tulsa, OK 74114. (918) 742-4989.

BENEDICTINE SISTERS (O.S.B.)

St. Gertrude Monastery, 14259 Benedictine Lane, Ridgely, MD 21660.

45 Sisters, 1 Novice

Ministry: Prayer and community life. A sister with the prioress discerns a ministry of service. Presently sisters are involved in the Benedictine School for developmentally disabled children, Benedictine Job Training Center for developmentally disabled young adults, elementary and high school teaching, religious education, nursing, social work, pastoral ministry, ministry to the poor and social justice efforts.

Represented in the Archdiocese of Washington, DC and in the Dioceses of Wilmington, DE and Camden, NJ.

Vocation Minister: Sr. Eleanor Murray, O.S.B.,14259 Benedictine Lane, Ridgely, MD 21660. (410) 634-2497.

BENEDICTINE SISTERS (O.S.B.)

St. Walburg Monastery, 2500 Amsterdam Rd., Villa Hills, KY 41017.

125 Sisters

Ministries: Archdiocesan and diocesan offices; hospital and home health care; senior citizen residential and health care; seminary, college, secondary, elementary and preschool education; pastoral and social ministries; prayer and hospitality ministry.

Conduct: 1 academy (1-12); preschool center, senior citizen residences and nursing home; prayer and hospitality center.

Represented in the Dioceses of Covington, Lexington, KY and Pueblo, CO and in the Archdiocese of Cincinnati.

Contact: Vocation Office, St. Walburg Monastery, 2500 Amsterdam Rd., Villa Hills, KY 41017.

BENEDICTINE SISTERS (O.S.B.)

Sacred Heart Monastery, Cullman, AL 35056

70 Sisters

Apostolic Work: Teaching, administration, pastoral ministry, nursing, social work, promoting liturgical works, praying, witnessing to community, responding to present needs of the church.

Represented in the Archdioceses of Atlanta and New Orleans and in the Dioceses of Birmingham, Mobile and Orlando.

Vocation Directress: Sr. Bernadette Sachs, O.S.B., P.O. Box 488, Cullman, AL 35056. (205) 734-2199 or 734-4622.

BENEDICTINE SISTERS OF VIRGINIA (O.S.B.)

9535 Linton Hall Rd., Bristow, VA 22013. (703) 361-0106

50 Sisters

Apostolic Work: Education, health care, parish ministry, retreats, administration.

Represented in the Dioceses of Richmond and Arlington.

Vocation Director: Sr. Mary Ellen Black, O.S.B., St. Benedict Monastery, 9535 Linton Hall Rd., Bristow, VA 22013. (703) 361-0106.

BENEDICTINE SISTERS (O.S.B.)

Monastery: St. Scholastica Monastery, 416 W. Highland St., Boerne, TX 78006. (210) 249-2645

23 Sisters

Apostolic Work: Education, health care, pastoral outreach, community development, public policy, retreat.

Represented in the Dioceses of Gallup and San Antonio.

Vocation Director: Sr. Kathleen Higgins, O.S.B., St. Scholastica Monastery, 416 W. Highland St., Boerne, TX 78006. (210) 249-2645.

BENEDICTINE SISTERS (O.S.B.)

St. Lucy's Priory, 19045 E. Sierra Madre, Glendora, CA 91741. (818) 335-1682

30 Sisters

Ministries: Education, pastoral ministry, ministry to disabled persons.

Represented in the Archdioceses of Los Angeles and San Diego.

BENEDICTINE SISTERS OF FLORIDA (O.S.B)

Holy Name Priory, Box H, St. Leo, FL 33574-4002.

25 Sisters, 3 Scholastics, 2 Affiliates

Apostolic Work: Educational, pastoral and community services.

Represented in the Diocese of St. Petersburg.

Vocation Director: Sr. Lisa-Judene Erazmus, O.S.B., Holy Name Priory, Box H, St. Leo, FL 33574-4002. (904) 588-8320.

BENEDICTINE SISTERS (O.S.B.)

Benet Hill Monastery, 2555 N. Chelton Rd., Colorado Springs, CO 80909. (719) 633-0655

46 Sisters

Apostolic Work: Seeking God in the monastic community, praise of God in liturgy and serving in the area of each sister's giftedness and the needs of the People of God.

Represented in the Archdiocese of Denver and in the Dioceses of Colorado Springs and Pueblo. Also in Jamaica.

Vocation Director: Sr. Mary Jane Vigil, O.S.B.

BENEDICTINE SISTERS (O.S.B.)

Mother of God Monastery, 120 S.E. 28th Ave., Watertown, SD 57201.

90 Sisters

Apostolic Work: Nursing and pastoral care in hospitals, teaching in many areas of education, retreats, parish work and foreign mission work in Guatemala, ministry to Native Americans and social work.

Vocation Director: Sr. Rose Palm, Mother of God Monastery, 120 S.E. 28th Ave., Watertown, SD 57201. (605) 886-6777.

BENEDICTINE SISTERS (O.S.B.)

Sacred Heart Monastery, Yankton, SD 57078.

184 Sisters

Apostolic Work: The building of community is central to the Benedictine way of life and from this all other ministries flow. Individual and communal gifts and resources are used for the building of God's kingdom in a variety of ways. Ministry is characterized by a continual openness and response to the changing needs of the area and the times.

Represented primarily in rural areas in the Archdiocese of Omaha, NE and in the Dioceses of Sioux Falls, SD; Lincoln, Grand Island, NE and Pueblo, CO.

Vocation Minister: Sr. Marietta Kerkvliet, Sacred Heart Monastery, 1005 West 8th, Yankton, SD 57078. (605) 668-1011.

BENEDICTINE SISTERS (O.S.B.)

Sisters of St. Benedict, Mount Saint Benedict Monastery, 620 Summit Ave., Crookston, MN 56716-2799.

167 Sisters, 1 Novice

Ministry: The primary work of the Benedictine is to seek God in community and to praise Him through prayer and ministry. The Sisters work in health care, education, pastoral care, parish ministry, retreat work, social work, domestic services, arts and crafts.
Represented primarily in the Dioceses of Crookston and Brownsville.
Vocation Director: Sr. Kathleen McGeary, O.S.B., Mount Saint Benedict Monastery, 620 Summit Ave., Crookston, MN 56716-2799. (218) 281-3441.

BENEDICTINE SISTERS (O.S.B.)
Sacred Heart Monastery, P.O. Box 364, Richardton, ND 58652. (701) 974-2121
47 Sisters
Ministries:1 nursing home, 2 retirement apartments, 1 parish ministry, 3 chaplains, 2 social services, 1 high school, 1 youth ministry, 1 medical field, 2 Native American ministries, 1 occupational therapy, 2 college instructors, 3 spiritual directors.
Represented in the Diocese of Bismarck.
Vocation Director: Sacred Heart Monastery, P.O. Box 364, Richardton, ND 58652. (701) 974-2121.

BENEDICTINE SISTERS (OSB)
St. Martin's Priory of the Black Hills, 2110-C, St. Martin's Dr., Rapid City, SD 57702. (605) 343-8011
47 Sisters, 2 Novices
Conduct: Learning center, adult education classes, infant day care, elementary school, ministry to the Hispanic poor, youth ministry, hospital and parish ministries, counseling, retreat center and chancery work.
Represented in the Dioceses of Rapid City, Helena, Great Falls-Billings, Orange and Tyler. Dependent priory in Columbia Falls, MT.
Vocation Contacts: Sr. Mary Wegher, OSB, Sr. Florence McManann, OSB, 2110-C, St. Martin's Dr., Rapid City, SD 57702. (605) 343-8011.

BENEDICTINE SISTERS (O.S.B.)
Monastery Immaculate Conception, 802 E. 10th St., Ferdinand, IN 47532-9239.
250 Sisters
Apostolic Work: We are monastic women who live the Benedictine tradition of seeking God through prayer and work. We witness Jesus Christ by our community life, our hospitality, and our service. We are dedicated to leadership in spirituality and in education, and we are committed to stewardship of God's creation. We have 240 members with 23 women in formation (12 in the United States and 11 in our foreign missions located in Guatemala and Peru). We encourage women, ages 20-45, who are earnestly seeking God and want to live a balanced life of prayer and work to inquire about our monastic lifestyle.
Vocation Director: Sr. Rose Mary Rexing, Monastery Immaculate Conception, 802 E. 10th St., Ferdinand, IN 47532-9239. (1-800-738-9999).

BENEDICTINE SISTERS (O.S.B.)
Monastery of St. Gertrude, HC 3, Box 121, Cottonwood, ID 83522-9408. (208) 962-3224
92 Sisters, 3 Temporarily Professed
Conduct: 1 Catholic high school, 3 parochial schools, teach in public schools, parish ministry, ministry to the poor, elderly, Hispanic, disadvantaged, chemically dependent, 1 foreign mission, 2 hospitals.
Represented in the Diocese of Boise.
Vocation Directors: Sr. Cecile Uhlorn, Sr. Corinne Forsman, (208) 962-3224.

BENEDICTINE SISTERS (O.S.B.)
Monastery of Saint Benedict Center, Box 5070, Madison, WI 53705.
7 Members
Monastic Work: an interfaith offering of hospitality, education and prayer.
Represented in the Dioceses of Madison and Sioux City.
Vocation Director: Adel Sautner, O.S.B., (608) 836-1631, ext. 158.

BENEDICTINE SISTERS (O.S.B.)
Queen of Angels Monastery, 840 S. Main St., Mt. Angel, OR 97362. (503) 845-6141
64 Sisters
Apostolic Work: Hospitality, education, health care, social work, pastoral ministry, retreat and prayer ministry, shelter.
Represented in the Archdiocese of Portland, OR.
Vocation Directress: Sr. Marietta Schindler, O.S.B.

BENEDICTINE SISTERS (OSB)
St. Scholastica Monastery, P.O. Box 3489, Fort Smith, AR 72913-3489. (501) 783-4147
140 Sisters
Ministry: Essential ministry is to seek God in community and to praise Him through prayer and work. Some sisters involved in teaching, retreat work, spiritual direction, pastoral care, parish work, youth ministry, social work, and service to one another in community.
Represented in the (Arch)dioceses of Little Rock, Amarillo, Springfield/Cape Girardeaux, Tulsa and Kansas City/St. Joseph, MO.
Vocation Director: Sr. Stephanie Schroeder, O.S.B.

BENEDICTINE SISTERS (O.S.B.)
Our Lady of Peace Monastery, 3710 W. Broadway, Columbia, MO 65203.
Apostolic Work: Wide variety of ministries flowing out of monastic prayer and presence: pastoral ministry, catechetics, care of sick, elderly, disabled, and those in crisis situations, counseling, prison ministry and legal services.
Represented in the (Arch)dioceses of Jefferson City, MO, Kansas City-St. Joseph, MO, Springfield, IL, Springfield-Cape Girardeau, MO, and St. Louis, MO.
Vocation Director: Sr. Mary Jo Polak, O.S.B., 3710 W. Broadway, Columbia, MO 65203.

BENEDICTINE SISTERS (O.S.B.)
Queen of Peace Monastery, Belcourt, ND 58316. (701) 477-6167
6 Professed Sisters
Apostolic Work: Administration, religious education and pastoral ministry, retreat ministry.
Vocation Contact: Sr. Wilma J. Davis, Initial Formation Director, Queen of Peace Monastery, Box 370, Belcourt, ND 58316. (701) 477-6167.

BENEDICTINE SISTERS (O.S.B.)
Holy Spirit Monastery, 22791 Pico St., Grand Terrace, CA 92313. (909) 783-4446
14 Sisters
Apostolic Work: Elementary and high school education, nursing, adult education, parish ministry, pastoral associates, retreats, counseling, sick and elderly and to handicapped.
Represented in the Dioceses of Orange and San Bernardino.

B-61

BENEDICTINE SISTERS (O.S.B.)
Saint Benedict's Convent, Saint Joseph, MN 56374.

450 Sisters

Benedictine Ministry: Seeking God especially in the context of Monastic Community, Liturgy of the Hours and serving in whatever area the giftedness of the Sisters and the needs of the people require.

Represented in the foreign countries of Puerto Rico and Brazil.

Vocation Coordinator: Marlene Meierhofer, O.S.B., St. Benedict's Convent, Saint Joseph, MN 56374. (612) 363-7100.

BENEDICTINE SISTERS (O.S.B.)
St. Scholastica Priory, 1200 Kenwood Ave., Duluth, MN 55811.

198 Professed Sisters

Apostolic Work: Education and health care plus pastoral ministry and retreat work.

Represented in the Archdioceses of Chicago and St. Paul-Minneapolis and in the Dioceses of Duluth and Phoenix.

Vocation Director: Sr. Michelle Dosch, O.S.B., St. Scholastica Priory, 1200 Kenwood Ave., Duluth, MN 55811. (218) 723-6539.

BENEDICTINE SISTERS (O.S.B.)
St. Bede Priory, 1190 Priory Rd., P.O. Box 66, Eau Claire, WI 54702. (715) 834-3176

55 Sisters

Ministries: Seeking God in a monastic community life; serving the needs of the people in a retreat and conference center, and by pastoral ministry, education, retreat work, health care, parish administration, and missionary activities.

Represented in Wisconsin, Minnesota, Missouri, Texas and Jamaica.

Contact: Sr. Clarita Selz, O.S.B.

BENEDICTINE SISTERS (O.S.B.)
Saint Mary Monastery, P.O. Box 128, Nauvoo, IL 62354-0128.

80 Sisters

Ministries: Seeking God in their primary ministry of monastic community and the Liturgy of the Hours the Sisters extend Benedictine Hospitality while serving in the areas of education, administration, social services, pastoral care, spiritual direction, retreats and what-

ever ministries are compatible with monastic life, their own giftedness and the needs of God's people.

Represented primarily in the Diocese of Peoria, IL.

Vocation Director: Sr. Mary Core, O.S.B., St. Mary Monastery, P.O. Box 128, Nauvoo, IL 62354-0128. (217) 453-2227.

BENEDICTINE SISTERS (O.S.B.)
Annunciation Priory, 7520 University Dr., Bismarck, ND 58504.

104 Sisters

Apostolic Work: Seeking God through prayer and community life overflow into ministries of education, health care, campus and parish ministry, social work and whatever best suits the talents of the sister and the needs of the people of the area.

Vocation Coordinator: Sr. Mariah Dietz, O.S.B., Annunciation Priory, 7520 University Dr., Bismarck, ND 58504. (701) 255-2028.

BENEDICTINE SISTERS (OSB)
St. Paul's Priory, 2675 Larpenteur Ave. E., St. Paul, MN 55109.

(612) 777-8181

97 Sisters, 2 in temporary profession

Ministries: Seeking God in monastic life, Liturgy of the Hours and contemplation; parish and liturgical ministry, education, spiritual direction, retreats, psychotherapy, pastoral care of the aged, child care, health care, food management, and other ministries needed by the people.

Represented in the (Arch)diocese of St. Paul/Minneapolis.

Vocation Contact: Sr. Marie Fujan, OSB, St. Paul's Priory, 2675 Larpenteur Ave. E., St. Paul, MN 55109. (612) 777-8181.

BENEDICTINE SISTERS (O.S.B.)
St. Placid Priory, 500 College St., N.E., Lacey, WA 98516. (360) 438-1771

27 Sisters, 3 Temporary Professed, 1 Novice, 2 Postulants

Apostolic Work: Hospitality and ministry flow from commitment to community and prayer.

Represented in the Archdiocese of Seattle.

Vocation Director: Sr. Monika Ellis, O.S.B., 500 College St., N.E., Lacey, WA 98516. (360) 438-1771.

BENEDICTINE SISTERS (O.S.B.)
Regina Pacis, 333 Wallace Rd., Bedford, NH 03102. (603) 472-3239.

Apostolic Work: 1 novitiate and 1 kindergarten (with nursery school), planning a retreat home with a special program for all kinds of people, to strengthen Faith in every person, in every possible way with word and example.

Represented in the Diocese of Manchester.

Vocation Director: Mother Raphaela, O.S.B., Superior.

SISTERS OF ST. BENEDICT (O.S.B.)
Our Lady of Grace Monastery, 1402 Southern Ave., Beech Grove, IN 46107.

98 Sisters

Apostolic Work: Teaching, administration, health care, directors of religious education, parish ministry, youth ministry, music ministry, retreat/education center.

Represented in the Archdioceses of Cincinnati and Indianapolis.

Vocation Directress: Sr. Joan Marie Massura, O.S.B., Our Lady of Grace Monastery, 1402 Southern Ave., Beech Grove, IN 46107. (317) 787-3287.

BENEDICTINE SISTERS (O.S.B.) (Olivetan Benedictines)
Holy Trinity Monastery, P.O. Box 298, St. David, AZ 85630-0298. (520) 720-4642

5 Sisters, 2 Oblate Sisters

Represented in the Diocese of Tucson, AZ.

Vocation Director: Fr. Louis Hasenfuss, O.S.B., Prior.

BENEDICTINE SISTERS (O.S.B.)
Epiphany Monastery, P.O. Box 121, Columbia Falls, MT 59912. (406) 892-4670

3 Sisters

Apostolic Work: As a new community we seek God through communal and personal prayer, stewardship of the earth and service to one another in community. Varied ministries outside the community.

Represented in the Diocese of Helena.

Vocation Director: Sr. Lorane Coffin, OSB, P.O Box 121, Columbia Falls, MT 59912. (406) 892-4670.

BENEDICTINE SISTERS OF BALTIMORE (O.S.B.)

Emmanuel Monastery, 2229 W. Joppa Rd., Lutherville, MD 21093. (410) 821-5792

16 Sisters

Apostolic Work: Education, retreat work, social work, parish ministry, justice and peace, administration.

Represented in the Archdioceses of Baltimore and Newark.

Vocation Director: Sr. Marianne Yannarell, O.S.B., Emmanuel Monastery, 2229 W. Joppa Rd., Lutherville, MD 21093.

BENEDICTINE SISTERS OF PERPETUAL ADORATION (OSB)

Benedictine Monastery (Motherhouse), 8300 Morganford Rd., St. Louis, MO 63123. (314) 638-6427

145 Sisters

Apostolic Work: Contemplative community.

Represented in the (Arch)dioceses of Kansas City-St. Joseph, St. Louis, Tucson, Tulsa and Casper.

Vocation Director: Sr. Lupita Barajas, O.S.B., Benedictine Monastery, 8300 Morganford Rd., St. Louis, MO 63123-6815. (314) 638-6427.

BENEDICTINE SISTERS OF THE BYZANTINE RITE

See Eastern Catholic Religious Communities for Women.

BERNARDINE FRANCISCAN SISTERS (O.S.F.)

(United States Province), Office of Communications, 460 St. Bernardine St., Reading, PA 19607. (610) 777-4174

505 Sisters

Apostolic Work: 1 liberal arts college, secondary and elementary schools, education centers and reading clinics, Montessori, special education, retreat ministry, pastoral/parish ministries, youth ministry, ministry to the poor and ever-widening services to the people of God.

Represented in the Archdioceses of Boston, Detroit, Los Angeles, Philadelphia, San Antonio and Washington and in the Dioceses of Allentown, Bridgeport, Harrisburg, Metuchen, Richmond, Saginaw, San Juan, Scranton and Trenton. Missions in Africa, Brazil, Dominican Republic, Poland and Romania.

Vocation Director: Sr. Rosemary Stets, OSF, Vocation Office, 460 St. Bernardine St., Reading, PA 19607. (610) 796-8971.

SISTERS OF BETHANY (C.V.D.)

850 N. Hobart Blvd., Los Angeles, CA 90029. (213) 665-6937

18 Sisters in U.S.

Conduct: Religious education, social service and 1 women's residence.

Represented in the Archdiocese of Los Angeles.

Vocation Director: Sr. Florelia Salazar, C.V.D., 850 N. Hobart Blvd., Los Angeles, CA 90029. (213) 665-6937.

BETHLEMITA DAUGHTERS OF THE SACRED HEART OF JESUS (BethL.)

St. Joseph Residence, 330 W. Pembroke St., Dallas, TX 75208. (214) 948-3597

6 Sisters in U.S.

Apostolic Work: Teaching, mission work, social work, work with the elderly in Central and South America, Canary Islands, Italy, Africa, India and in the U.S. in the Diocese of Dallas only.

Represented in the Diocese of Dallas.

Contact: Sr. Adelaide Bocanegra.

SERVANTS OF THE BLESSED SACRAMENT (S.S.S.)

American Provincial House: 1818 Coal Pl., S.E., Albuquerque, NM 87106

20 Sisters in U.S.

Apostolic Work: Eucharistic contemplative life – adoration of the Blessed Sacrament and sharing of prayer life with laity.

Represented in the Dioceses of Portland, ME, Pueblo and Sante Fe, NM. Also in nine foreign countries.

Vocation Directresses: 101 Silver St., Waterville, ME 04901. (207) 872-7072; 1818 Coal Pl., S.E. Albuquerque, NM 87106. (505) 242-3692; 1426 N. Grand Ave., Pueblo, CO 81003. (719) 545-7729.

SISTERS SERVANTS OF THE BLESSED SACRAMENT (S.J.S.)

U.S. Vice Provincial: 215 Lomita St., El Segundo, CA 90245. (310) 615-0766

63 Sisters

Apostolic Work: Education.

Represented in the Archdiocese of Los Angeles and in the Dioceses of Fresno, Sacramento and San Diego.

Vocation Director: 215 Lomita St., El Segundo, CA 90245. (310) 615-0766.

SISTERS OF THE BLESSED SACRAMENT (SBS)

Motherhouse: 1663 Bristol Pike, Bensalem, PA 19020-8502.

Members: about 280 (multi-racial, multi-cultural)

Apostolic Work: Share the Gospel message with the poor and oppressed, especially among Black and Indian peoples through a life of prayer, community and service education, religious instruction, counseling, parish ministry, health care, social service, etc. in urban, rural and reservation areas.

Represented in the Archdioceses of Atlanta, New York, Philadelphia, Boston, Chicago, New Orleans, Santa Fe, Seattle and Los Angeles and in the Dioceses of Camden, Savannah, Lafayette, Lake Charles, Gallup, Tucson, San Diego, Palm Beach and Tulsa. Also foreign mission in Haiti.

Vocation Director: Sr. Christa McGill, 1663 Bristol Pike, Bensalem, PA 19020. (215) 638-8482.

CONGREGATION OF BON SECOURS (C.B.S.)

Provincial House and Novitiate: 1525 Marriottsville Rd., Marriottsville, MD 21104.

51 Sisters, 70 Associate Members

Apostolic Work: To help the people of God to wholeness through health care service in its various forms. Special care is given to the poor and to the dying. Membership includes vowed and associate memberships for men and women.

Represented in the Archdioceses of Baltimore, Detroit and Philadelphia and in the Dioceses of Miami, St. Petersburg, Naples, Richmond and Charleston. Also in Riobamba (Ecuador).

Vocation Director: Sr. Victoria Segura, CBS, 1525 Marriottsville Rd., Marriottsville, MD 21104.

BRIGITTINE SISTERS (O.SS.S.)

Convent of St. Birgitta, Vikingsborg, Tokeneke Trail, Runkenhage Rd., Darien, CT 06820. (203) 655-1068

10 Sisters

Apostolic Work: Guest house, private retreats, active contemplative life.

Represented in the Diocese of Bridgeport. Houses in 8 foreign countries, Missions in India (9 houses).

Contact: Convent of St. Birgitta, Vikingsborg, Tokeneke Trail, Runkenhage Rd., Darien, CT 06820.

BYZANTINE NUNS OF ST. CLARE

See Eastern Catholic Religious Communities for Women.

CABRINI SISTERS

See Missionary Sisters of the Sacred Heart of Jesus.

CALIFORNIA INSTITUTE OF THE SISTERS OF THE MOST HOLY AND IMMACULATE HEART OF THE BLESSED VIRGIN MARY (I.H.M.)

3431 Waverly Dr., Los Angeles, CA 90027. (213) 664-1124

25 Sisters

Conduct: high schools, grammar schools, 1 retreat house, engage in parish ministry and retreat work, Braille instruction, hospital ministry.

Represented in the Archdiocese of Los Angeles.

Vocation Director: 3431 Waverly Dr., Los Angeles, CA 90027. (213) 664-1124.

CANOSSIAN DAUGHTERS OF CHARITY (FdCC)

(Canossian Sisters)

Provincial House: 5625 Isleta Blvd., SW, Albuquerque, NM 87105. (505) 873-2854

4,000 Sisters worldwide.

Apostolic Work: Mission of evangelization carried out by religious education and catechesis, youth ministry, family ministries, schools, visiting and assisting the sick and elderly, human promotion.

Represented in the Archdioceses of Santa Fe and San Francisco and in the Diocese of Sacramento and in Canada, Mexico and 5 African countries, 2 South American countries, Australia, 9 Asian countries and 4 European countries.

Vocation Director: Sr. Sharon Brannen, Canossian Sisters, 8228 Pickard Court, NE, Albuquerque, NM 87110. (505) 298-2734.

CARMELITE COMMUNITY OF THE WORD (C.C.W.)

1304 13th Ave., Altoona, PA 16601. (814) 943-0088

23 Sisters

Apostolic Work: Diocesan administration of pastoral centers, religious and academic education (all levels), parish ministry, family life ministry, ministry to the imprisoned, the homeless and the literal poor, 2 family soup kitchens, shelter for homeless

women & children and/or homeless intact families.

Represented in the Diocese of Altoona-Johnstown.

Vocation Director: Sr. Marjorie P. McGuire, C.C.W., Formation Director, 1304 13th Ave., Altoona, PA 16601. (814) 943-0088.

MISSIONARY CARMELITES OF ST. TERESA (C.M.S.T.)

Motherhouse: Fresno 150, 06400 Mexico, D.F.

Provincialate: 9548 Deer Trail Dr., Houston, TX 77038. (713) 445-5520

675 Sisters worldwide, 71 Sisters in U.S.

Apostolic Work: Education, health care, pastoral ministry, spirituality and one community in a seminary.

Represented in the Archdioceses of St. Louis and Oklahoma City and in the Dioceses of Galveston-Houston, Corpus Christi and Tulsa. Also in Mexico, El Salvador, Guatemala, Honduras, Nicaragua, Costa Rica, Bolivia, Brazil and Peru (S.A.).

Vocation Director: 9548 Deer Trail Dr., Houston, TX 77038. (713) 445-5520.

CARMELITE NUNS (O. Carm.)

Carmel of the Sacred Heart, 430 Laurel Ave., Hudson, WI 54016.

6 Nuns

Apostolic Work: In a life of contemplative prayer centered on Jesus Christ and in union with Mary, the Carmelite listens in silence and responds in joyful service, supported by the warmth of a caring community.

Represented in the Diocese of Superior, WI.

Vocation Director: Sr. Lucia La Montagne, O. Carm., 430 Laurel Ave., Hudson, WI 54016. (715) 386-2156.

CARMELITE NUNS-CALCED (O.Carm.)

Carmelite Monastery of St. Therese, Saint Therese's Valley, 3551 Lanark Rd., Coopersburg, PA 18036-9324.

Cloistered.

Apostolic Work: Contemplation, Perpetual Adoration of the Blessed Sacrament.

Represented in the Dioceses of Allentown and Fargo.

Contact: Mother Joseph Marie, O. Carm., Superior.

CARMELITE NUNS OF THE ANCIENT OBSERVANCE (O. Carm.)

Carmel of Mary, Rte. 3, Wahpeton, ND 58075. (701) 642-2360

14 Solemn Professed, 1 Junior Professed, 3 Postulants

Apostolic Work: Contemplative prayer, Papal Enclosure, Liturgy of the Hours in Gregorian Chant.

Represented in the Diocese of Fargo.

CARMELITE NUNS OF THE ANCIENT OBSERVANCE (O.Carm.)

Monastery of Our Lady of Grace, 1 St. Joseph Pl., San Angelo, TX 76905. (915) 651-4959

5 Professed

Apostolic Work: Joyful praise, adoration, intercession; deep communion with God, fostered by love for Jesus in the Blessed Sacrament and for our Blessed Mother, and with special devotion to Saint Joseph, the Prophet Elijah, Saint John of the Cross and Saint Teresa of Avila.

CARMELITE NUNS, DISCALCED (O.C.D.)

Carmelite Monastery, 1318 Dulaney Valley Rd., Baltimore, MD 21286-1399. (410) 823-7415

Contemplative Community with vibrant liturgical life.

17 Nuns

Contact: Sr. Colette Ackerman, Vocation Director.

CARMELITE NUNS, DISCALCED (O.C.D.)

Carmel of St. Joseph, 9150 Clayton Rd., (Ladue) St. Louis County, MO 63124. (314) 993-6899

8 Professed Nuns, 1 Professed Extern

Apostolic Work: Prayer and penance, lived in a cloistered, contemplative community.

Vocation Director: Mother Mary Joseph of Divine Providence, O.C.D., Prioress.

CARMELITE NUNS, DISCALCED (O.C.D.)

Monastery of St. Joseph and St. Teresa, 73530 River Rd., Covington, LA 70435-2206

10 Nuns

Vocation Director: Mother Mary Alice Grace, OCD, Prioress.

CARMELITE NUNS, DISCALCED (O.C.D.)
61 Mt. Pleasant Ave., Boston, MA 02119.
11 Nuns
Apostolic Work: Contemplative prayer.
Vocation Director: Sr. Therese, O.C.D.

CARMELITE NUNS OF THE BYZANTINE RITE, DISCALED
See Eastern Catholic Religious Communites for Women.

CARMELITE NUNS, DISCALCED (O.C.D.)
8 Nuns
Apostolic Work: A life of prayer and sacrifice for the needs of the universal Church, especially for the sanctification of priests. Papal enclosure is maintained.
Vocation Director: Mother Prioress, Carmelite Monastery, 66 Ave. & Old York Rd., Philadelphia, PA 19126. (215) 424-6143.

CARMELITE NUNS, DISCALCED (O.C.D.)
Monastery of Our Lady of Mount Carmel, 745 St. John's Pl., Brooklyn, NY 11216.
Cloistered, 17 Professed Nuns
Mother Marie Ange, D.C., Prioress.

CARMELITE NUNS, DISCALCED (O.C.D.)
Carmelite Monastery of the Infant Jesus, 1000 Lincoln St., Santa Clara, CA 95050. (408) 296-8412
16 Solemnly Professed, 1 Postulant
Vocations: Sr. Roseanne of Jesus, O.C.D., Prioress.

CARMELITE NUNS, DISCALCED (O.C.D.)
St. Joseph's Monastery, 2215 N.E. 147th St., Shoreline, WA 98155. (206) 363-7150
8 Nuns, 1 Postulant
Represented in the Archdiocese of Seattle.
Vocation Director: Sr. Margaret Mary.

CARMELITE NUNS, DISCALCED (O.C.D.)
Carmel of the Queen of Heaven, 17937 250th St., Eldridge, IA 52748. (319) 285-8387
11 Nuns
Apostolic Work: Prayer.
Contact Person: Sr. Mary Joan Loebig, O.C.D.

CARMELITE NUNS, DISCALCED (O.C.D.)
Carmelite Monastery, 1740 Newburg Rd., Louisville, KY 40205.
11 Professed Nuns
Apostolic Work: Prayer and penance.
Vocation Director: Rev. Mother Prioress, Carmelite Monastery, 1740 Newburg Rd., Louisville, KY 40205.

CARMELITE NUNS, DISCALCED (O.C.D.)
Carmel of St. Teresa, 215 E. Alhambra Rd., Alhambra, CA 91801. (818) 282-2387
16 Nuns
Vocation Director: Sr. Maria, O.C.D.

CARMELITE NUNS, DISCALCED
Carmelite Monastery, 4300 Mount Carmel Dr. N.E., Ada (Parnell), MI 49301-9740.
Cloistered Nuns - 20 (3 Novices, 2 Postulants); Externs - 2 Professed, 1 Novice

CARMELITE NUNS, DISCALCED (O.C.D.)
Carmel of St. Joseph, 139 DePuyster Ave., Beacon, NY 12508-3540.
Contemplative. 10 Professed Nuns.
Vocations: Sr. Marjorie Robinson, O.C.D. (914) 831-5572.

CARMELITE NUNS, DISCALCED (O.C.D.)
Monastery of Discalced Carmelites, 75 Carmel Rd., Buffalo, NY 14214. (716) 837-6499
16 Cloistered Nuns, 4 Extern Nuns, 3 Novices
Apostolic Work: Prayer.
Contact: Mother Marie Therese, O.C.D.

CARMELITE NUNS, DISCALCED (O.C.D.)
2500 Cold Springs Rd., Indianapolis, IN 46222. (317) 926-5654
16 Nuns.
Vocation Director: Sr. Jean McGoff, O.C.D., Prioress

CARMELITE NUNS, DISCALCED (O.C.D.)
Carmel of Holy Family, 3176 Fairmount Blvd., Cleveland Heights, OH 44118-4199. (216) 321-6568
17 Nuns.

CARMELITE NUNS, DISCALCED (O.C.D.)
St. Teresa of Jesus Monastery, 428 Duane Ave., Schenectady, NY 12304.
12 Nuns, 1 Novice, 1 Postulant
Apostolate of prayer and penance, lived in strict cloister.
Vocation Director: Mother Elia, O.C.D., Prioress.

CARMELITE NUNS, DISCALCED (O.C.D.)
Monastery of Our Lady and St. Therese, 27601 Hwy. 1, Carmel, CA 93923. (408) 624-3043
Cloistered, contemplatives.
16 Nuns
Vocation Director: Mother Therese, O.C.D., Prioress.

CARMELITE NUNS, DISCALCED (O.C.D.)
Monastery of the Most Blessed Virgin Mary of Mount Carmel, 189 Madison Ave., Morristown, NJ 07960.
10 Nuns
Vocation Director: Mother Teresa of the Trinity, O.C.D., Prioress.

CARMELITE NUNS, DISCALCED (O.C.D.)
Carmelite Monastery of the Trinity, 5158 Hawley Blvd., San Diego, CA 92116. (619) 280-5424
14 Nuns, 2 in Formation
Vocation Director: Sr. Pia Anderson, Prioress.

CARMELITE NUNS, DISCALCED (O.C.D.)
11 Nuns, 2 Postulants
Apostolic Work: A contemplative and apostolic Order, modeled on the life of Mary, Mother of the Church. Continual intercession for the needs of the Church, the sanctification of priests, and the salvation of souls.
Vocation Director: Reverend Mother Prioress, O.C.D., 35750 Moravian Dr., Clinton Township, MI 48035-2138. (810) 790-7255.

CARMELITE NUNS, DISCALCED (O.C.D.)
Carmel of St. Therese of Lisieux, P.O. Box 57, Loretto, PA 15940. (814) 472-8620
10 Professed Nuns, 1 Extern Sister
Contact: Mother Teresa of Jesus, O.C.D., Prioress.

CARMELITE NUNS, DISCALCED (O.C.D.)
Carmelite Monastery of Cristo Rey, 721 Parker Ave., San Francisco, CA 94118-4297.
18 Nuns
Apostolic Work: Cloistered contemplatives.
Vocation Director: Mother Elena de San Juan de la Cruz, O.C.D., Prioress.

CARMELITE NUNS, DISCALCED (O.C.D.)
Carmel of Jesus, Mary and Joseph, 4835 Pearl St., Las Vegas, NV 89121-6009
7 Professed Nuns, 1 Novice, 2 Postulants
Apostolic Work: Cloistered contemplatives.
Vocation Director: Mother Teresa of Jesus, O.C.D., Prioress.

CARMELITE NUNS, DISCALCED (O.C.D.)
Monastery of Discalced Carmelites, 600 Flowers Ave., Dallas, TX 75211.
9 Nuns
Vocation Director: Rev. Mother Prioress.

CARMELITE NUNS, DISCALCED (O.C.D.)
Our Lady/St. Joseph Monastery, 1931 W. Jefferson Rd., Pittsford, NY 14534.
11 in Community
Apostolic Work: Contemplative prayer within enclosure.
Contact: Rev. Mother Prioress, O.C.D., 1931 W. Jefferson Rd., Pittsford, NY 14534. (716) 427-7094.

CARMELITE NUNS, DISCALCED (O.C.D.)
Monastery of Our Lady of Mount Carmel and St.Theresa of the Child Jesus, 25 Watson Ave., Barrington, RI 02806. (401) 245-3421
14 Nuns.
Vocation Contact: Sr. Vilma Seelaus, O.C.D., Prioress.

CARMELITE NUNS, DISCALCED (O.C.D.)
Monastery of the Infant Jesus of Prague and Our Lady of Guadalupe, 6301 Culebra Ave. at St. Joseph's Way, San Antonio, TX 78238-4909. (210) 680-1834
10 Nuns
Vocation Director: Mother Therese Leonard, O.C.D., Prioress.

CARMELITE NUNS, DISCALCED (O.C.D.)
Carmel of the Holy Family and St. Therese, 6981 Teresian Way, P.O. Box 1720, Georgetown, CA 95634. (916) 333-1617
14 Nuns
Vocation Director: Mother Christine, Prioress.

CARMELITE NUNS, DISCALCED (O.C.D.)
Monastery of Mary, Mother of Grace, 1250 Carmel Ave., Lafayette, LA 70501. (318) 232-4651
20 Nuns, 2 Postulants
Vocation Director: Sr. Elia Zepeda, O.C.D.

CARMELITE NUNS, DISCALCED (O.C.D.)
Carmel of St. Joseph, 20000 N. County Line Rd., Piedmont, OK 73078. (405) 348-3947
11 Nuns
Vocation Director: Sr. Therese Ranallo, O.C.D., Prioress.

CARMELITE NUNS, DISCALCED (O.C.D.)
Carmel of Mother of God, Meadowbrook Rd., Pewaukee, WI 53072-4599. (414) 691-0336
8 Nuns
Apostolate Work: Apostolate of Prayer.
Vocation Contact: Sr. Mary Agnes, O.C.D.

CARMELITE NUNS, DISCALCED (O.C.D.)
Carmelite Monastery, 716 Dauphin Island Pkwy., Mobile, AL 36606.
6 Nuns
Vocation Director: Mother Agnes of the Infant Jesus, O.C.D., Prioress.

CARMELITE NUNS, DISCALCED (O.C.D.)
Discalced Carmelite Monastery, 49 Mount Carmel Rd., Santa Fe, NM 87501-4597. (505) 983-7232
12 Nuns
Contemplative Community

CARMELITE NUNS, DISCALCED (O.C.D.)
275 Pleasant St., Concord, NH 03301-2590.
10 Nuns
Contemplative Community

Represented in the Diocese of Manchester.
Contact Person: Sr. Emmanuel (603) 225-5791.

CARMELITE NUNS, DISCALCED (O.C.D.)
St. Joseph's Monastery, 59 Allendale, Terre Haute, IN 47802. (812) 299-1410
12 Professed Nuns
Apostolic Work: A purely contemplative apostolate, excluding all forms of active ministry. Member of a worldwide order composed of almost 800 monasteries, represented in over 60 dioceses in the U.S.

CARMELITE NUNS, DISCALCED (O.C.D.)
Carmel of the Holy Spirit, 6138 S. Gallup St., Littleton, CO 80120. (303) 798-4176
9 Nuns
Vocation Director: Reverend Mother Prioress.

CARMELITE NUNS, DISCALCED (O.C.D.) Carmel of St. Joseph, P.O. Box 379, Solvang, CA 93464.
12 Nuns
Vocation Director: Mother Mary Veronica, O.C.D., Prioress

CARMELITE NUNS, DISCALCED (O.C.D.)
The Carmel of Mary Immaculate and St. Mary Magdalen, P.O. Box 785, Flemington, NJ 08822.
Cloistered Contemplatives.
Vocations: Mother Teresa, Prioress.

CARMELITE NUNS, DISCALCED (O.C.D.)
Monastery of Infant Jesus of Prague, 3501 Silver Lake Rd., Traverse City, MI 49684. (616) 946-4960
12 Nuns
Vocation Director: Mother Teresa Margaret, O.C.D.

CARMELITE NUNS, DISCALCED (O.C.D.)
Carmelite Monastery of Christ, the Exiled King, 68 Rincon Rd., Kensington, CA 94707.
7 Nuns
Vocation Contact: Sr. Mary Magdalen, Prioress.

CARMELITE NUNS, DISCALCED (O.C.D.)
Monastery of the Holy Cross, P.O. Box 397, Iron Mountain, MI 49801. (906) 774-0561
15 Cloistered Nuns, 2 Externs
Apostolic Work: Contemplative prayer for the Church.
Vocation Director: Reverend Mother Prioress, O.C.D., Monastery of the Holy Cross, P.O. Box 397, Iron Mountain, MI 49801.

CARMELITE NUNS, DISCALCED (O.C.D.)
Monastery of the Immaculate Heart of Mary, Beckley Hill, Barre, VT 05641. (802) 476-8362
9 Nuns.

CARMELITE NUNS, DISCALCED (O.C.D.)
Monastery of St. Teresa of Jesus, 7201 W. 32nd St., Little Rock, AR 72204. (501) 565-5121
10 Nuns, 3 First Vows
Vocation Director: Sr. Cecilia Chun, O.C.D.

CARMELITE NUNS, DISCALCED (O.C.D.)
2155 Terry Rd., Jackson, MS 39204. (601) 373-1460
5 Nuns
Vocation Director: Sr. Margaret Mary, Prioress.

CARMELITE NUNS, DISCALCED (O.C.D.)
Carmel of the Immaculate Heart of Mary, 5714 Holladay Blvd., Salt Lake City, UT 84121. (801) 277-6075
10 Nuns
Apostolate Work: Contemplation.
Vocation Director: Mother Mary Ann.

CARMELITE NUNS, DISCALCED (O.C.D.)
St. Joseph's Monastery, 68 Franklin Ave., Saranac Lake, NY 12983. (518) 891-0655
Contemplative Order
11 professed nuns
Vocations: Sr. Marie Gertrude, O.C.D.

CARMELITE NUNS, DISCALCED (O.C.D.)
Carmel of O.L. of Divine Providence, 8251 De Montreville Trail, N., Lake Elmo, MN 55042. (612) 777-3882.

8 Sisters, 1 Novice, 1 Postulant
Vocation Director: Sr. Rose of the Sacred Heart, O.C.D., Prioress

CARMELITE NUNS, DISCALCED (O.C.D.)
Carmelite Monastery, 70 Monastery Rd., Elysburg, PA 17824-9697.
18 Nuns
Apostolate: Contemplative religious life.
Vocation Director: Sr. Christine O'Brien, O.C.D. (717) 672-2935.

CARMELITE NUNS, DISCALCED (O.C.D.)
Monastery of Our Lady of the Mountains, 1950 La Fond Dr., Reno, NV 89509-3099. (702) 323-3236
14 Nuns
Vocation Director: Sr. Carol, O.C.D.

CARMELITE NUNS, DISCALCED (O.C.D.)
Carmel of Maria Regina, 87609 Green Hill Rd., Eugene, OR 97402. (503) 345-8649
12 Nuns
Apostolic Work: Primary work is prayer. Community active in most countries of the world.
Vocation Director: Mother Elizabeth Mary, O.C.D., Prioress

CARMELITE NUNS, DISCALCED (O.C.D.)
Monastery of Holy Family, 510 E. Gore Rd., Erie, PA 16509. (814) 825-0846
Cloistered Contemplatives
Vocations: Mother Emmanuel, Prioress.

CARMELITE NUNS, DISCALCED (O.C.D.)
6 Nuns
Apostolic Work: Contemplative life of prayer.
Vocation Director: Sr. Carmela Marolda, O.C.D., Carmelite Monastery, 11 W. Back St., Savannah, GA 31419. (912) 925-8505.

CARMELITE NUNS, DISCALCED (O.C.D.)
Monastery of the Most Holy Trinity, 5801 Mt. Carmel Dr., Arlington, TX 76017. (817) 468-1781
10 Nuns
Vocation Director: Mother Anne Teresa of Jesus, O.C.D., Prioress.

CARMELITE NUNS, DISCALCED (O.C.D.)
Carmel of the Most Holy Trinity, 1100 Parthenon Pl., New Caney, TX 77357. (713) 399-0270
13 Nuns
Vocation Director: Sr. Angel Teresa, O.C.D., Novice Mistress.

CARMELITE NUNS, DISCALCED (O.C.D.)
River Rd. and Central, Des Plaines, IL 60016. (708) 298-4241
18 Nuns
Vocation Contact: Mother Catherine of the Mother of God, Prioress.

CARMELITE NUNS, DISCALCED (O.C.D.)
(Cloistered)15 Mt. Carmel Rd., Danvers, MA 01923.
15 Professed Nuns, 1 Novice, 1 Postulant
Prioress: Rev. Mother Michael, O.C.D. (508) 774-3008.

CARMELITE NUNS, DISCALCED (O.C.D.)
Monastery of the Sacred Heart and St. Joseph, 2201 W. Main St., Jefferson City, MO 65109. (314) 636-3364.
10 Nuns
Vocation Contact: Mother Mary Teresa, O.C.D., Prioress.

CARMELITE NUNS, DISCALCED (OCD)
Carmel of the Assumption, R.D. #6, Box 28, Center Dr., Latrobe, PA 15650. (412) 539-1056
15 Nuns
A cloistered contemplative community.
Vocation Director: Sr. Barbara Sitter, OCD.

CARMELITE NUNS, DISCALCED (O.C.D.)
Monastery of the Discalced Carmelite Nuns, 2901 S. Cecelia St., Sioux City, IA 51106. (712) 276-1680
15 Nuns
Vocation Director: Mother Agnes of Divine Love, Prioress.

CARMELITE NUNS, DISCALCED (O.C.D.)
Carmelite Monastery, 4047 Chapel Dr., New Franken, WI 54229.
9 Professed, 2 Novices,1 Extern

CARMELITE NUNS, DISCALCED (O.C.D.)

Carmelite Monastery of the Mother of God, 530 Blackstone Dr., San Rafael, CA 94903. (415) 479-6872

4 Nuns, 3 Novices

Apostolic Work: Contemplative prayer for the Church; special emphasis to pray for the people of Russia.

Vocation Director: Mother Anna Marie of Jesus Crucified, O.C.D., Prioress.

CARMELITE NUNS, DISCALCED (O.C.D.)

St. Anne Carmel, 424 E. Republic Rd., Springfield, MO 65807. (417) 881-2115

5 Solemn Professed Nuns, 1 Novice

CARMELITE SISTERS (Corpus Christi) (O. Carm.)

Motherhouse: Tunapuna, Trinidad, WI; Regional House: 412 W. 18th St., Kearney, NE 68847. (308) 237-2287

14 Nuns, 103 Nuns worldwide

Apostolic Work: Catechetics, care of the elderly, and Christian unity.

Represented in the Archdiocese of Portland and in the Dioceses of Grand Island and Providence. Also in England, South America and five Caribbean islands in the West Indies.

CARMELITE SISTERS FOR THE AGED AND INFIRM (O. Carm.)

Motherhouse: St. Teresa's, 600 Woods Rd., Germantown, NY 12526. (518) 537-5000.

300 Sisters, 2 Novices, 1 Postulant

Conduct: 27 homes for the aged.

Represented in 6 Archdioceses and 13 Dioceses. Also in Ireland.

Vocation Director: Sr. Madeline Angeline, St. Teresa's, 600 Woods Rd., Germantown, NY 12526. (518) 537-5000.

CARMELITE SISTERS, INSTITUTE OF THE SISTERS OF OUR LADY OF MT. CARMEL (O. Carm.)

Motherhouse: Rome, Italy; U.S. Headquarters: Carmelite Sisters' Novitiate, 5 Wheatland St., Peabody, MA 01960. (508) 531-4733

16 Nuns (in U.S.)

Apostolic Work: Religious education, nursing, teaching.

Represented in the Archdioceses of Boston and Washington.

Vocation Directress: Sr. M. Benedetta, O.Carm.

CARMELITE SISTERS OF CHARITY (C.C.V.)

Formation House: 701 Beacon Rd., Silver Spring, MD 20903. (301) 431-3773

Apostolic Work: Ministry in clinics, education of youth and adults, parish work and social service with Hispanics and homeless.

Represented in the Archdiocese of Washington and in the Diocese of Brooklyn.

Vocation Representative: Sr. Claudia Paredes, C.C.V., 272 Marcy, Brooklyn, NY 11211. (718) 387-1783.

CARMELITES (TERESIAN)

See "C" section – The Community of Teresian Carmelites.

CARMELITE SISTERS OF ST. THERESE OF THE INFANT JESUS (C.S.T.)

Villa Teresa Convent, 1300 Classen Dr., Oklahoma City, OK 73103-2447. (405) 232-7926

30 Final Professed, 1 Novice, 3 Candidates

Apostolic Work: Education, (including pre-school and day care), parish ministry, archdiocesan offices, allied health.

Represented in the Archdiocese of Oklahoma City.

Vocation Director: Villa Teresa Convent, 1300 Classen Dr., Oklahoma City, OK 73103-2447. (405) 232-7926.

CARMELITE SISTERS OF THE DIVINE HEART OF JESUS (Carmel D.C.J.)

Northern Province: 1230 Kavanaugh Pl., Milwaukee, WI 53213. (414) 453-4040

Central Province: 10341 Manchester Rd., St. Louis, MO 63122. (314) 965-7616

Southwestern Province: 8585 La Mesa Blvd., La Mesa, CA 92041. (619) 466-3116

450 Sisters worldwide; 110 in U.S.

Conduct: 3 homes for children, 11 homes for the aged, 5 day nurseries, mission work in Africa, Brazil, Nicaragua and Venezuela .

Represented in the Archdioceses of Detroit, Milwaukee, St. Louis and San Antonio. Also in the Dioceses of Gary, Grand Rapids, Jefferson City, Owensboro and San Diego.

Vocation Directors: Sr. Mary Zachary, Northern Province, (414) 453-4040; Sr. Mary Rose, Central

Province, (314) 965-7616; Sr. Gertrude, Southwestern Province, (619) 466-3116.

CARMELITE SISTERS OF THE MOST SACRED HEART OF LOS ANGELES (O.C.D.)

Generalate: 920 E. Alhambra Rd., Alhambra, CA 91801. (818) 289-1353; (216) 521-5605; (602) 364-7658; (305) 446-9950; (305)663-1704

130 Professed Sisters, 5 Novices, 1 Postulant

Conduct: 9 grammar schools, teach in one Archdiocesan high school, 1 general hospital, 1 skilled nursing facility for the care of the aged, 2 nursery schools with day care center and kindergarten, 1 retreat house.

Represented in the Archdioceses of Los Angeles and Miami and in the Dioceses of Tucson and Cleveland.

Vocation Director: Sr. Marisa, O.C.D. (818) 289-1353, ext. 259.

CONGREGATION OF OUR LADY OF MT. CARMEL (O. Carm.)

Generalate: P.O. Box 476, Lacombe, LA 70445. (504) 882-7577

98 Professed Sisters in U.S.

Apostolic Work: Education, health care, social work, parish and campus ministry, retreat work.

Represented in the Archdiocese of Chicago, New Orleans and Washington, DC, and in the Dioceses of Alexandria, Lafayette and Houma-Thibodaux. Also in the Philippine Islands and Mexico.

Vocation Directress: Sr. Aloysia Duhon, O. Carm., P.O. Box 476, Lacombe, LA 70445. (504) 882-7577.

SISTERS OF THE CATHOLIC APOSTOLATE

See Pallottine Sisters

RELIGIOUS OF THE CENACLE (r.c.) (Congregation of Our Lady of the Retreat in the Cenacle)

Province of the East, North America: The Cenacle, 312 Cenacle Rd., Ronkonkoma, NY 11779-2202

Province of the Midwest:

The Cenacle, 513 Fullerton Parkway, Chicago, IL 60614.

Apostolic Work: "Awakening and deepening faith – in the form of retreats, spiritual direction, education in the faith, or other spiritual ministries...to honor and be attentive to the Spirit's action in others as well as in ourselves. Ministry flows out of prayer and community life, and it necessarily leads back to prayer and community..."

Represented in several archdioceses and dioceses across the United States and in British Columbia.

Vocation Director: Sr. Pamela J. Falkowski, r.c., 312 Cenacle Rd., Ronkonkoma, NY 11779-2202. (516) 737-8491.

SISTERS OF CHARITY OF LEAVENWORTH (SCL)

Motherhouse: 4200 S. 4th St., Leavenworth, KS 66048-5054. (913) 682-7500

485 Sisters

Apostolic Work: Health care: hospitals and clinics for the uninsured poor. Education: college, high school, elementary. Pastoral ministry: parish associates, administrators, religious education, spiritual direction, campus ministry, and youth ministry. Social services: Catholic Charities, AIDS ministry, social justice. Foreign missions: Peru.

Represented in the Archdioceses of Kansas City (KS), Los Angeles, Denver, Oklahoma City, Omaha and in the Dioceses of Kansas City, (MO), Helena, Great Falls-Billings, Pueblo, Cheyenne, Jefferson City and Spokane. Also in Peru.

Vocation Director: Sr. Noreen Walter, SCL, 4200 S. 4th St., Leavenworth, KS 66048-5054. (913) 758-6522.

SISTERS OF CHARITY OF MONTREAL (Grey Nuns)

Provincial House: 10 Pelham Rd., Lexington, MA 02173. (617) 862-4700

Apostolic Work: As an apostolic community, the Sisters serve those persons in need, especially the most forsaken, with compassionate love, through various ministries, as the care of the sick, the homeless and abandoned children; also, as pastoral ministers; handcrafting for the poor and by trying to alleviate the social injustices of our day.

Represented in Maine, Massachusetts, New Hampshire, Ohio, South America, and throughout Canada.

Vocation Director: Sr. Marie Mansfield, S.G.M., 10 Pelham Rd., Lexington, MA 02173. (617) 862-4700.

SISTERS OF CHARITY OF THE BLESSED VIRGIN MARY (B.V.M.)

Mount Carmel, Dubuque, IA 52003. (319) 588-2351

1,000 Sisters

Apostolic Work: The Sisters choose their ministry in keeping with the BVM mission: of being freed and helping others enjoy freedom in God's steadfast love. This mission finds expression in the traditional commitment to education and in ministries emerging from new needs in Church and society. The Sisters are called to live in any part of the world where there is promise of furthering the mission of Jesus through works of education, justice and peace.

Represented in 29 states, 69 dioceses throughout the U.S. and in two countries in Central and South America, Ghana, Africa, and Rome, Italy.

Vocation Director: Sr. Mary Ann DeNicolo, Mount Carmel, 1150 Carmel Dr., Dubuque, IA 52003.

SISTERS OF CHARITY OF CINCINNATI (S.C.)

Motherhouse: Mount St. Joseph, 5900 Delhi Rd., Mount St. Joseph, OH 45051.

728 Sisters

Apostolic Work: Ministering as teachers and religious educators, nurse-midwives and health-care professionals of all types, social workers and counselors, environmentalists and consciousness-raisers; sponsoring institutions and programs that address education, health-care and social service needs with particular concern for building a more just society and providing direct service to the poor.

Represented in the (Arch)dioceses of Boston, Brownsville, Buffalo, Chicago, Cincinnati, Cleveland, Colorado Springs, Columbus, Covington, Denver, Detroit, El Paso, Galveston/Houston, Gaylord, Helena, Indianapolis, Knoxville, Lafayette, Lansing, Las Cruces, Lexington, Memphis, Nashville, New Orleans, New York, Newark, Oakland, Orlando, Palm Beach, Phoenix, Pueblo, Raleigh, Reno, Saginaw, San Francisco, Santa Fe, Spokane, St. Petersburg, Steubenville, Toledo, Venice, Washington, DC, and Wichita. Also in Ecuador, Guatemala and Peru.

Contact: S. Mary Bookser, S.C., Mount St. Joseph, OH 45051. (513) 347-5471.

SISTERS OF CHARITY OF HALIFAX (S.C.H.)

26 Phipps St., Quincy, MA 02169. (617) 773-6085

910 Sisters

Apostolic Work: All areas of education, health care, social service, and pastoral ministry.

Represented in several places in the U.S.: MA, NH, NY, MN, KY; in several provinces in Canada; in Bermuda; in Peru, South America; and Bani, Dominican Republic.

Vocation Directors: Sr. Kathleen Crowley, S.C., 8 Curtis St., Medford, MA 02155. (617) 396-7970 or Sr. Maryann Seton Lopiccolo, 84-32 63rd Ave., Middle Village, NY 11379. (718) 651-1685.

SISTERS OF CHARITY OF THE INCARNATE WORD (C.C.V.I.)

Motherhouse: Incarnate Word Convent, 4707 Broadway, San Antonio, TX 78209. (210) 829-7561; Provincial Office: (210) 820-0987

Provinces: United States, Mexico and Region in Peru.

571 Sisters, 98 Lay Associates, 12 Volunteer in Mission

Apostolic Work: Serving the Christian community in Catholic schools, hospitals, children's centers, and as parish workers and in various other ministries in the United States, Mexico and Peru.

Vocation Director: Sr. Bertha Franco, C.C.V.I., 7800 Natural Bridge, St. Louis, MO 63121. (314) 385-1733.

SISTERS OF CHARITY OF THE INCARNATE WORD-HOUSTON (CCVI)

Motherhouse: Villa de Matel, 6510 Lawndale Ave., P.O. Box 230969, Houston, TX 77223-0969. (713) 928-6053

300 Sisters

Apostolic Work: Serving the Christian community in clinics, hospitals, schools and parishes in Africa, El Salvador, Guatemala, Ireland and the United States.

Vocation Ministry: Sr. Maureen Costello, CCVI, Kairos Vocation Office, 6510 Lawndale Ave., P.O. Box 230969, Houston, TX 77223-0969. (713) 928-6053.

SISTERS OF CHARITY OF NAZARETH (S.C.N.)

General Motherhouse: Nazareth, KY 40048.

830 Sisters

Apostolic Work: EDUCATION: seminary, university, high school, elementary, Montessori, E.S.L. nonformal education, adult literacy. PASTORAL MINISTRY: parish associates, chaplains, religious education, retreat center, spiritual direction, campus ministry, youth ministry, centering prayer, the arts, clinical pastoral education, peace and justice, media. SOCIAL SERVICES: troubled youth, drug and alcohol, counseling, migrants, low-income senior housing and housing for the handicapped, spouse abuse shelters, legal aid, advocacy. HEALTH CARE: multi-hospital system, nursing home, clinics, home health, massage, healing touch, nurse practitioners, parish nurses, AIDS ministry.

Represented in the Archdioceses of Cincinnati, Louisville, Chicago, Boston, Washington, DC, Philadelphia, St. Louis, Indianapolis and Miami and in the Dioceses of Baton Rouge, Boca Raton, Charleston, Columbus, Covington, Evansville, Green Bay, Jackson, Jacksonville, Knoxville, Lexington, Little Rock, Memphis, Nashville, Owensboro, Palm Beach, St. Petersburg, Richmond, San Jose, Steubenville, Wheeling-Charleston and Worcester. Also in India, Nepal and in Belize, Central America.

Vocation Directress: Sr. Janice Downs, S.C.N., Box 172, Nazareth, KY 40048. (502) 348-1521.

SISTERS OF CHARITY OF OTTAWA (S.C.O.) (Grey Nuns of the Cross)

St. Joseph Province, 975 Varnum Ave., Lowell, MA 01854. (508) 453-4993

56 Sisters in the U.S.; 920 worldwide

Apostolic Work: Teaching, foreign missions: (South Africa, Japan, Central Africa, Brazil, Haiti; Papua New Guinea), nursing, care of the aged, parish work and social work.

Represented in the Archdiocese of Boston.

Vocation Director: Vocation Director, 975 Varnum Ave., Lowell, MA 01854. (508) 453-4993.

SISTERS OF CHARITY OF OUR LADY OF MERCY

General Motherhouse, P.O. Box 12410, Charleston, SC 29422. (803) 795-6083

44 Sisters

Apostolate Work: Education, health care, social service and child care.

Vocation Director: Sr. Donna, Motherhouse, P.O. Box 12410, Charleston, SC 29422. (803) 795-6083.

SISTERS OF CHARITY OF OUR LADY, MOTHER OF MERCY (S.C.M.M.)

Provincial House: 520 Thompson Ave., East Haven, CT 06512. (203) 469-7872

21 Sisters in U.S.; 1,375 total

Apostolic Work: works of charity.

Represented in the Archdioceses of Hartford, St. Paul-Minneapolis and Detroit and in the Dioceses of Bridgeport and San Diego.

Vocation Director: 520 Thompson Ave., East Haven, CT 06512. (203) 469-7872.

SISTERS OF CHARITY OF QUEBEC (SCQ) (Grey Nuns)

Motherhouse: Maison generalice, 2655, rue Le Pelletier, Beauport, Quebec G1C 3X7. (418) 628-8860

902 Sisters

Apostolic Work: Direct service to the poor, home visits, care of the sick and the elderly, assistance to the handicapped, education in its different forms, CCD program, parish work, foreign missions in South America and Japan.

Represented in the Archdiocese of Boston and in the Diocese of Fall River. Also in Canada.

Vocation Directress: Sr. Monique Morin, SCQ, 333 Pawtucket St., Lowell, MA 01854. (508) 441-1696.

SISTERS OF CHARITY OF ST. AUGUSTINE (C.S.A.)

Motherhouse: Mt. Augustine, 5232 Broadview Rd., Richfield, OH 44286.

118 Sisters

Apostolic Work: Education: college, high school, grade school; pastoral ministry: parish associates, spiritual direction, Directors of Religious Education; health care: hospitals, nursing home administration, AIDS ministry, pastoral care, CSA health system; missionary: team in El Salvador.

Represented in the Dioceses of Cleveland, Charleston and Youngstown.

Vocation Director: Sr. Ruth Ann Patrick, C.S.A., Mt. Augustine, 5232 Broadview Rd., Richfield, OH 44286. (216) 659-4161.

SISTERS OF CHARITY OF SAINT ELIZABETH (S.C.)

Convent of Saint Elizabeth, Convent Station, NJ 07961.

758 Sisters

Apostolic Work: 1 college, 5 academies, 13 high schools, 65 elementary schools, 5 hospitals, 1 residence for women, 1 long term care nursing home, 2 homes for the aged, 4 homes for aged and retired sisters, 1 novitiate,1 mission in the Virgin Islands, parish work.

Represented in the (Arch)dioceses of Arlington, Boston, El Paso, Galveston-Houston, Santa Fe, Newark, New York, Omaha, Orlando, Richmond, Scranton, St. Louis, Washington, DC; Bridgeport, Charlotte, Fairbanks, Fall River, Hartford, Jackson, Metuchen, Palm Beach, Paterson, Pensacola-Tallahassee, Providence, St. Petersburg, Syracuse, Trenton, Venice, Wheeling-Charleston, Wilmington, St. Thomas, VI. Also in Canada, El Salvador and Mexico.

Director of Vocation Promotion: Sr. Maryanne Tracey, S.C., Convent of St. Elizabeth, Convent Station, NJ 07961. (201) 292-6399.

SISTERS OF CHARITY OF ST. HYACINTHE (S.C.S.H.) (Grey Nuns)

Sisters' Residence, 98 Campus Ave., Lewiston, ME 04240. (207) 784-2349 (Bilingual - French and English)

24 Sisters in U.S.

Apostolic Work: General hospital, nursing homes, home for the aged, child care center, pastoral care, C.C.D., pastoral ministry and missionary works in foreign country, and education to the Indians.

Represented in the Dioceses of Manchester (NH) and Portland (ME).

Vocation Director: Sr. Diane Beaudoin, 1137 Washington Ave., Portland, ME 04103-3624. (207) 797-8607.

SISTERS OF CHARITY OF ST. JOAN ANTIDA (SCSJA)

Regina Mundi, 8560 N. 76th Pl., Milwaukee, WI 53223. (414) 354-9233

51 Sisters in the American Province; approximately 5,000 sisters in 7 European, 7 African, 5 Asian, and 2 South American countries.

Apostolic Work: Teaching, nursing, care of the elderly, pastoral work, parish work, home visiting, social work, and missionary work.

Represented in the Archdiocese of Milwaukee and in the Diocese of Amarillo in the U.S.
Director of Vocations: Sr. Andrea Peters.

SISTERS OF CHARITY OF ST. LOUIS (S.C.S.L.)
Regional House: 4907 So. Catherine St., Plattsburgh, NY 12901.
Novitiate: 6 Secada Dr., Clifton Park, NY 12065.
International Congregation: 864 members, American Province: 21 Sisters
Apostolic Work: Teaching: elementary, secondary, C.C.D.; Nursing: in nursing homes for the aged and hospitals; retreat, parish and social work.
Represented in the Dioceses of Albany and Ogdensburg.
Vocation Directress: Sr. Louise Marceau, S.C.S.L., 6 Secada Dr., Clifton Park, NY 12065.

SISTERS OF CHARITY OF ST. VINCENT DE PAUL OF NEW YORK (S.C.)
Sisters of Charity Center, 6301 Riverdale Ave., Mt. St. Vincent, Bronx, NY 10471.
611 Sisters
Apostolic Work: Schools on all levels from pre-school through college, adult education, 4 general hospitals, 2 mental health facilities, child care institutions, small group homes and social services for dependent children, intercommunity involvement in Houses of Prayer, Justice and Peace Center, court advocacy, parish ministry, work with aged, handicapped, alcoholics, AIDs patients, abused women & children, drug addicts, soup kitchens, homeless.
Represented in the Archdiocese of New York and in the Dioceses of Brooklyn and Rockville Centre. Also, mission centers in Appalachia, New Jersey, Connecticut, Florida, Indiana, North Carolina, Maryland, Bahama Islands, Latin America, Atlanta, Shreveport, Oakland, Gary, Ponce, P.R. and Italy.
Vocation Director: Sr. Mary Lou McGrath, SC, 6301 Riverdale Ave., Mt. St. Vincent, Bronx, NY 10471. (718) 549-9200.

SISTERS OF CHARITY OF ST. VINCENT DE PAUL (S.V.Z.)
U.S. Foundation; 171 Knox Ave., West Seneca, NY 14224. (716) 825-5859

26 Sisters
Apostolic Work: Nursery schools, C.C.D., parish services, hospital and health services.
Represented in the Archdioceses of Chicago and St. Louis and in the Dioceses of Buffalo; Hamilton and Oakville (Toronto) Canada.
Vocation Director: Sr. Adeline, 171 Knox Ave., West Seneca, NY 14224. (716) 825-5859.

SISTERS OF CHARITY OF SETON HILL (S.C.)
De Paul Center, Mt. Thor Rd., Greensburg, PA 15601.
500 Sisters
Apostolic Work: Administration, campus ministry, computer programming, counselling, education (early childhood, elementary, secondary, college, university, and special education), law, health care, medicine, geriatrics, social work, pastoral ministry, religious education, secretarial, speech and occupational therapy, pharmacy, multi-cultural ministry, spiritual direction, retreat ministry.
Represented in the Archdiocese of Washington and in the Dioceses of Altoona-Johnstown, Greensburg, Pittsburgh, Phoenix, Tucson, Wheeling/Charleston, and various others. Foreign missions in Korea.
Vocation Directors: Mary Clark, S.C., Seton House, 1343 Sheridan Ave., Pittsburgh, PA 15206. (412) 661-8545.

SISTERS OF CHRISTIAN CHARITY (S.C.C.)
(Daughters of the Blessed Virgin Mary of the Immaculate Conception)
North American Eastern Province, Membership: 350; worldwide 1,100
Apostolic Work: teaching, retreat ministry, catechetics, nursing, health services.
Represented in (Eastern Province) Paterson, NJ, Metuchen, NJ, Newark, NJ, Camden, NJ, Scranton, PA, Harrisburg, PA, Philadelphia, PA, Allentown, PA, New York, NY and in (Western Province) Chicago, IL, Peoria, IL, Lansing, MI, New Ulm, MN, St. Paul and Minneapolis, MN, St. Louis, MO, New Orleans, LA. Also provinces in Germany, Chile, Uruguay and Argentina with houses in Italy, Switzerland and the Philippines.
Vocation Directress: Sr. Joanna Pappicco, S.C.C. and Sr. Joelle

Thren, S.C.C., Mallinckrodt Convent, Mendham, NJ 07945. (201) 543-6528 or (908) 766-5638.

SISTERS OF CHRISTIAN CHARITY (S.C.C.)
(Daughters of the Blessed Virgin Mary of the Immaculate Conception)
North American Western Province, Motherhouse: Maria Immaculata Convent, 1041 Ridge Rd., Wilmette, IL 60091-1560. (708) 853-3400
Membership: 170; 1,200 Sisters worldwide
Apostolic Work: Academic education, care of abused and neglected children, religious education, parish ministry, social service and prayer ministry, and ministry to Native Americans and Amerasians.
Represented in the Archdioceses of Chicago, New Orleans, St. Louis and Santa Fe and in the Dioceses of Jefferson City, Lansing and Rapid City. Also in Germany, Switzerland, Italy, Chile, Argentina, Uruguay.
Vocation Director: Sr. Monica Cormier, S.C.C., Rt. 1, Box 11, Cimarron, NM 87714. (505) 376-2553.

RELIGIOUS OF CHRISTIAN EDUCATION (R.C.E.)
Provincial House: 14 Bailey Rd., Arlington, MA 02174
44 Sisters
Apostolic Work: Religious education centers, education, teaching.
Represented in the Archdiocese of Boston and in the Diocese of Charlotte.
Vocation Directress: Sr. Martha Brigham, R.C.E., 14 Bailey Rd., Arlington, MA 02174. (617) 643-3032.

CISTERCIAN NUNS (O. Cist)
Valley of Our Lady Monastery, E. 11096 Yanke Dr., Prairie du Sac, WI 53578-9737. (608) 643-3520
16 Sisters
Apostolic Work: Contemplative monastic life.
Represented in the Diocese of Madison.
Contact Person: Sr. Ann Marie, O.Cist.

CISTERCIAN NUNS OF THE STRICT OBSERVANCE
See Trappistines.

CLARETIAN MISSIONARY SISTERS (R.M.I.) (Religious of Mary Immaculate, Claretian Missionary Sisters)
9600 West Atlantic Ave., Delray, FL 33446. (407) 498-9239; 18450 N.W. 12th Ave., Miami, FL 33169. (305) 652-4593; 7080 SW 99 Ave., Miami, FL 33173. (305) 274-6148.

524 Sisters, 10 in U.S.

Apostolic Work: Missions, education, youth, migrant, social and parish ministry. Theological formation in seminaries and institutes.

Represented in the Archdiocese of Miami and in the Diocese of Palm Beach. Also in Argentina, Cuba, Colombia, Dominican Republic, Panama, Venezuela, Honduras, Mexico, Philippines, Spain, Italy, Poland, Japan and Zaire (Africa).

COLUMBAN SISTERS
See Missionary Sisters of St. Columban.

COMBONI MISSIONARY SISTERS (C.M.S.)
U.S. Headquarters: 1307 Lakeside Ave., Richmond, VA 23228.

1,969 Sisters

Apostolic Work: Foreign missions in Africa, Latin America, and Middle East. Their charism is to share with the poorest of the poor God's love: to initiate and/or to collaborate in the building and strengthening of the local Christian community in union with the universal Church through their lives, words and works in schools, catechetical and pastoral centers, hospitals, dispensaries and leprosy centers; by fostering Christian family life and women's promotion and education; by collaborating in the formation of native clergy, sisters and laity; by working, living and dying for the realization of justice for the poor.

Represented in the Diocese of Richmond and in the Archdioceses of Philadelphia and Chicago. The entire international community is represented in 29 different countries of the world.

Vocation Director: Sr. Bianca Bresciani, C.M.S., Comboni Missionary Sisters, 1125 E. 50th St., Chicago, IL 60615. (312) 624-1122.

COMMUNITY OF THE HOLY SPIRIT (C.H.S.)
6151 Rancho Mission Rd. #205, San Diego, CA 92108. (619) 584-0809

17 Sisters

Apostolic Work: Education, health care, social services.

Represented in the Dioceses of Oakland, Orange, Portland, Reno-Las Vegas, San Diego and San Jose.

General Coordinator: Susann Kernaghan, C.H.S., 6151 Rancho Mission Rd. #205, San Diego, CA 92108. (619) 584-0809.

COMMUNITY OF TERESIAN CARMELITES (C.T.C.)
(A community of Nuns and Friars)
Box 826, Worcester, MA 01613-0826. (508) 752-5734

Religious: 6 Solemn Professed, 1 Simple Professed, 1 Novice; Lay: 7 Final Professed Members, 4 Simple Professed.

Apostolic Work: Contemplatives: spiritual life center, evangelization, music ministry, pilgrimages.

Represented in the Diocese of Worcester.

Vocation Directors: Sister Susan-Elizabeth, C.T.C. or Brother Daniel-Francis, C.T.C., Community of Teresian Carmelites, Box 826, Worcester, MA 01613-0826. (508) 752-5734.

COMMUNITY OF THE MOTHER OF GOD OF TENDERNESS
See Eastern Catholic Religious Communities for Women.

COMPANY OF MARY (O.D.N.)
Motherhouse: 16791 E. Main St., Tustin, CA 92680. (714) 541-3125
67 Sisters in U.S.; 2,236 worldwide

Apostolic Work: Kindergartens, grammar schools, religious instruction centers, residences, parish ministry, retreat center.

Represented in the Archdiocese of Los Angeles and in the Dioceses of Orange and San Bernardino.

Vocation Directress: Sr. Leticia Salazar, O.D.N., 16791 E. Main St., Tustin, CA 92680. (714) 836-1098.

THE COMPANY OF THE SAVIOR (C.S.)
820 Clinton Ave., Bridgeport, CT 06604. (203) 368-1875
60 Sisters, 2 Novices, 1 Postulant

Represented in the Diocese of Bridgeport.

Vocation Director: Sr. Araceli Fernandez, 820 Clinton Ave., Bridgeport, CT 06604. (203) 368-1875.

CONGREGATION OF THE CENACLE
See Cenacle, Congregation of the.

CONGREGATION OF THE INFANT JESUS
See Infant Jesus, Congregation of the.

CONGREGATION OF THE SISTERS OF JESUS CRUCIFIED
See Jesus Crucified, Congregation of the.

CONGREGATION OF THE DIVINE SPIRIT (C.D.S.)
Motherhouse (Domus Caritas), 409 W. Sixth St., Erie, PA 16507.
47 Sisters

Apostolic Work: Parish schools, CCD centers, home for senior citizens.

Represented in the Dioceses of Erie and Youngstown.

Vocation Directress: 409 W. Sixth St., Erie, PA 16507. (814) 455-3590.

CONSOLATA MISSIONARY SISTERS (MC)
6801 Belmont Ave., NE, Belmont, MI 49306-0096 (616) 361-2072

Total members in Congregation: just under 1,000, 21 Sisters in U.S.

Apostolic Work: Primary work is evangelization among the poor which is carried out by ministries of teaching, nursing, social work, and pastoral ministry.

Represented in Michigan and Alabama, in 8 African countries, in 5 South American countries, and in 5 European countries.

Vocation Director: Sr. Zelia M. Cordeiro, M.C., P.O. Box 96, Belmont, MI 49306-0096. (616) 361-9609 or 2072.

CONTEMPLATIVE SISTERS OF THE GOOD SHEPHERD (CGS)
(Sisters of Our Lady of Charity of the Good Shepherd, St. Louis Province), 2711 Mullanphy Rd., Florissant, MO 63031-3798. (314) 837-1719.

21 Sisters in St. Louis Province, 984 total internationally.

Apostolic Work: Prayer for the salvation of souls, especially those served by active Good Shepherd Sisters; altar breads, sewing, art work to support cloistered community.

Vocation Office: 2711 Mullanphy Lane, Florissant, MO 63031-3798. (314) 837-1719.

See also listing for Good Shepherd Sisters.

SISTERS OF THE CROSS OF THE SACRED HEART OF JESUS (R.C.S.C.J.)

U.S. Foundation: 1320 Maze Blvd., Modesto, CA 95351. (209) 526-3525. Motherhouse: Francisco Sosa 109, Delegacion Coyoacan, 04000 Mexico, D.F.

375 Sisters, 35 Novices

Apostolic Work: Contemplative.

Represented in the Diocese of Stockton. Also in Rome, Guatemala, Costa Rica, Mexico and Madrid, Spain.

Vocation Director: Sr. Luz Eugenia Alvarez, R.C.S.C.J.

DAUGHTERS OF CHARITY OF THE MOST PRECIOUS BLOOD (D.C.P.B.)

500 Sisters

Apostolic Work: Education of the youth, care for the sick and the elderly. Apostolates in Italy, Brazil, Nigeria and India.

Conduct: 3 day nurseries, 1 rest home for elderly women.

Represented in the Dioceses of Albany, NY, Bridgeport, CT and Paterson, NJ.

Vocation Directress: Sr. M. Goretti Chaloux, D.C.P.B., 46 Preakness Ave., Paterson, NJ 07522. (201) 956-1921.

DAUGHTERS OF THE CHARITY OF THE SACRED HEART OF JESUS (F.C.S.C.J.)

U.S. Provincialate: Mt. Sacred Heart, P.O. Box 642, Littleton, NH 03561. (603) 444-5346

80 Sisters

Apostolic Work: Education of children in schools, day care programs, health care and hospice work, the care of the elderly in homes for the aged, religious education, adult education, pastoral work, community service, retreat work.

Represented in the Archdiocese of Boston and in the Dioceses of Fall River, MA, Burlington, VT, Manchester, NH, Ogdensburg, NY and Portland, ME. Foreign missions in Western Africa, South Africa, Brazil, Tahiti, Madagascar.

Vocation Director: Sr. Monique Couture, F.C.S.C.J., Grove St.-

Box 642, Littleton, NH 03561. (603) 444-5346.

DAUGHTERS OF CHARITY OF ST. VINCENT DE PAUL (D.C.)

(Emmitsburg Province-Southeast)

Provincial House: Emmitsburg, MD 21727. (301) 447-3121

333 Sisters

Ministries: 3 high schools, 4 elementary schools, 6 hospitals, 4 ministry with the aged, 1 school of nursing, 2 homes for unmarried mothers, 2 day care, 11 parish and social services, 4 Hispanic ministry, 2 soup kitchens, 3 diocesan work, 1 St. Elizabeth Seton Shrine, 1 migrant ministry.

Represented in the Archdioceses of Atlanta, Baltimore, Miami, and Washington and in the Dioceses of Arlington, Charleston, Charlotte, Richmond, St. Augustine, Orlando, Palm Beach, Pensacola-Tallahassee, Raleigh, St. Petersburg, Savannah, Venice and Wheeling-Charleston.

Vocation Directress: Sr. Catherine Norton, D.C., 123 Franklin St., Petersburg, VA 23803-3308. (804) 732-6414.

DAUGHTERS OF CHARITY OF ST. VINCENT DE PAUL (D.C.)

(Northeast Province)

Provincialate: De Paul Provincial House, 96 Menands Rd., Albany, NY 12204-1499.

253 Sisters

Apostolic Work: Campus ministries, catechetical centers, child care centers, day care centers, elementary school, family shelters, general hospitals and clinics, high schools, homes for special needs children, home for unwed mothers, parish visiting, maternity hospital, multi-service center, neighborhood centers, pastoral/parish ministries, psychology clinics, special child study center, schools of nursing, social work with Catholic Charities, visiting home nursing.

Represented in the Archdioceses of Boston, Newark, New York and Philadelphia and in the Dioceses of Albany, Allentown, Bridgeport, Brooklyn, Buffalo, Metuchen, Ogdensburg, Rochester, Syracuse and Wilmington. Also in over 50 foreign countries.

Vocation Director: Sr. Mary Ellen Thomas, De Paul Provincial House, 96 Menands Rd., Albany, NY 12204-1499.

DAUGHTERS OF CHARITY OF ST. VINCENT DE PAUL (D.C.)

(West Central Province), 7800 Natural Bridge Rd., St. Louis, MO 63121. (314) 382-2800

265 Sisters

Work in: parochial schools, high schools, hospitals, leprosarium, psychiatric hospitals, parish ministry, social service centers, day care centers, clinics, prison ministries, homes for aged, homes for children, shelter for women, neighborhood centers, Catholic Charities offices, refugee resettlement, senior citizens programs, higher education, diocesan offices, youth programs.

Represented in the Archdioceses of New Orleans, St. Louis and San Antonio and in the Dioceses of Amarillo, Austin, Baton Rouge, Brownsville, Dallas, Davenport, El Paso, Fort Worth, Kansas City, Little Rock, St. Joseph, San Angelo, Springfield-Cape Girardeau.

Vocation Director: Sr. Germaine Price, D.C., 7800 Natural Bridge Rd., St. Louis, MO 63121. (314) 382-2800.

DAUGHTERS OF CHARITY OF ST. VINCENT DE PAUL (D.C.)

(East Central Province), 9400 New Harmony Rd., Evansville, IN 47720.

237 Sisters

Apostolic Work: Elementary schools, high schools, alternative high school, diocesan education offices, religious education center, directors of religious education, parish ministry, campus ministry, diocesan program for the deaf, skilled nursing facilities, multi-hospital system, clinics, handicapped facility, day care and neighborhood services, homes and programs for unwed mothers, services and residences for the aged, social service bureau and/or Catholic Charities offices, shelters/homeless, children's residences, home for retired sisters, rural ministry and outreach services.

Represented in the Archdioceses of Chicago, Detroit, Indianapolis, Milwaukee and Mobile and in the Dioceses of Belleville, Biloxi, Birmingham, Evansville, Nashville, Jackson, Peoria, Saginaw, South Bend-Fort Wayne and Springfield in IL.

Vocation Director: Sr. Patricia Finerty, D.C., Vocation Director, 9400 New Harmony Rd., Evansville, IN 47720. (812) 963-3341.

DAUGHTERS OF CHARITY OF ST. VINCENT DE PAUL (D.C.)

(Province of the West), 26000 Altamont Rd., Los Altos Hills, CA 94022. (415) 941-4490

163 Sisters

Conduct: 1 high school, 6 parochial elementary schools, 5 hospitals, 3 homes for children, 1 day care center, 1 home for unwed mothers, 1 pastoral ministry center, 1 senior citizens apostolate, 1 free dining room, transitional housing program, cocaine-addicted babies programs and Family Preservation Rehabilitation Center for Adults.

Represented in the Archdioceses of Los Angeles and San Francisco and in the Dioceses of Fresno, Phoenix, Reno, Salt Lake City, San Jose and Oakland.

Vocation Director: Sr. Noreen McPartland, D.C., 26000 Altamont Rd., Los Altos Hills, CA 94022. (415) 941-4490.

DAUGHTERS OF DIVINE CHARITY (F.D.C.)

(St. Joseph's Province) Provincial House: 205 Major Ave., Staten Island, NY 10305. (718) 720-4377

83 Sisters

Apostolic Work: Education (elementary & secondary), religious education, residence for young working women, pastoral ministry, and residence for homeless women and their children.

Represented in the Archdioceses of New York and Newark and in the Dioceses of Trenton, San Diego, San Bernardino, Bridgeport and Metuchen.

Vocation Directors: Sr. Josita De Vita, 850 Hylan Blvd., Staten Island, NY 10305. (718) 727-5700, 273-3222; Sr. Marie Claire Weaver, 162 Bidwell Ave., Jersey City, NJ 07305. (201) 413-1556; Sr. Denise Martin, 10294 Eagle Rock Ave., San Diego, CA 92126. (619) 271-1451.

DAUGHTERS OF DIVINE CHARITY (F.D.C.)

(Holy Trinity Province), 1315 N. Woodward Ave., Bloomfield Hills, MI 48304. (810) 645-5318

34 Sisters

Conduct: 2 grammar schools, 1 residence for women, 2 homes for the aged in Midwest.

Represented in the Archdiocese of Detroit and in the Diocese of Ft. Wayne-So. Bend. Also on the East and West coast of the U.S., Europe and No. and So. Brazil.

Contact: Sr. M. Paschal, F.D.C., 1315 N. Woodward Ave., Bloomfield Hills, MI 48304. (810) 645-5318.

DAUGHTERS OF DIVINE CHARITY (F.D.C.)

(St. Mary's Province) Provincial Motherhouse and Novitiate, 39 N. Portage Path, Akron, OH 44303. (216) 867-4960

24 Sisters

Apostolic Work: Education, home for working women, home for elderly senior men and women.

Represented in the Archdioceses of Milwaukee and Miami and in the Dioceses of Cleveland and Pittsburgh.

Vocations: Sr. Maria Bakich, F.D.C., Provincial Superior.

DAUGHTERS OF THE CROSS (D.C.)

Motherhouse: 1000 Fairview St., Shreveport, LA 71104. (1-318) 869-3482

17 Sisters

Apostolic Work: 1 novitiate, 2 grammar schools, nursing, pastoral ministry; other ministries according to aptitude and professional training.

Represented in the Diocese of Shreveport.

Contact: Sr. M. Joan Koen, 1000 Fairview St., Shreveport, LA 71104.

DAUGHTERS OF THE CROSS OF LIEGE (F.C.)

Principal House: St. Bernard Convent, 165 W. Eaton Ave., Tracy, CA 95376. (209) 835-7391

5 Sisters

Represented in the Diocese of Stockton.

DAUGHTERS OF THE HEART OF MARY (D.H.M.)

Provincial House: 1339 Northampton St., Holyoke, MA 01040. (413) 532-7406

U.S. Province: 140; 2,500 professed members worldwide

Apostolic Work: Ministries are diversified according to gifts of individual women committed to Gospel values in the service of the Church. Presently in U.S. founded corporate works: Nardin Academy, Buffalo, NY; St. Joseph's School for the Deaf, Bronx, NY; 3 retreat centers: Marian Center, Holyoke, MA; Regina Maria, Plattsburgh, NY; Maryhill, St. Paul, MN. Serve on 5 continents in 30 countries.

Represented in the Archdioceses of New York, Baltimore, Boston, Philadelphia, Chicago, Newark, St. Paul, Detroit and St. Louis and in the Dioceses of Buffalo, Camden, Cleveland, Las Cruces, Lincoln, Ogdensburg, Phoenix, Springfield, Trenton and Venice.

Vocation Counselor: Joan Sweeney, 1365 Northampton St., Holyoke, MA 01040. (413) 534-5717.

DAUGHTERS OF THE HOLY SPIRIT (D.H.S.)

East Coast: Holy Spirit Provincial House, 72 Church St., Putnam, CT 06260. (203) 928-0891

225 Sisters

Apostolic Work: Education: preschool through college; hospital and home nursing; pastoral work; migrant ministry; campus ministry; hospital chaplaincy; prison work; advocacy in the name of justice; missions in U.S., South America and Africa. Serving in NY, New England, Appalachia, Alabama and California.

Vocation Directress: Sr. Therese Vanasse, D.H.S., St. Mary Convent, 40 N. Main St., Jewett City, CT 06351. (203) 376-4020.

DAUGHTERS OF THE HOLY SPIRIT (F.Sp.S.)

3318 Randolph St., Lincoln, NE 68510. (402) 477-7646

300 Sisters worldwide; 4 Sisters in U.S.

Apostolic Work: Evangelization and acculturation of the Hispanic community, the promotion of vocations to the priesthood.

Represented in the Diocese of Lincoln. Motherhouse in Mexico. Also in Rome, Italy.

DAUGHTERS OF MARY AND JOSEPH (D.M.J.)

Provincialate: 5300 Crest Rd., Rancho Palos Verdes, CA 90274.

76 Sisters

Conduct: 1 novitiate, 1 retreat center, 10 grammar schools, 2 high schools, 7 parish ministry, 3 health ministry, 1 prison ministry.

Apostolic Work: Education at all levels, parish ministry, health care ministry, counseling and retreat ministry, detention ministry.

Represented in the Archdioceses

of Los Angeles and San Francisco and in the Dioceses of San Bernardino and San Diego.

Vocation Information: Sr. Brigid Johnston, 5300 Crest Rd., Rancho Palos Verdes, CA 90274. (310) 377-4867, ext. 236.

DAUGHTERS OF MARY HELP OF CHRISTIANS (F.M.A.)
(Salesian Sisters of St. John Bosco)

Provincial House: St. Philip Apostle (SUA) Province, 655 Belmont Ave., Haledon, NJ 07508-2398. (201) 790-7964

147 Sisters

Apostolic Work: Education of young people, especially the poorest and most abandoned.

Represented in the Archdioceses of Newark, Miami and New York and in the Dioceses of Paterson, St. Petersburg and Birmingham.

Vocation Directress: Sr. Antoinette Cedrone, F.M.A., 659 Belmont Ave., Haledon, NJ 07508-2397. (201) 790-6204.

DAUGHTERS OF MARY HELP OF CHRISTIANS (F.M.A.)
(Salesian Sisters of St. John Bosco)

(Western Province), 6019 Buena Vista St., San Antonio, TX 78237. (512) 432-0089; or Mary Help of Christians Youth Center, 605 Enos Lane, Corralitos, CA 95076. (408) 728-4700

120 Sisters; 17,000 Sisters worldwide

Conduct: 15 grammar schools, 1 high school, 1 retreat house (spirituality center), 2 youth centers, 6 summer camps, 20 catechetical centers, pre-novitiate program.

Apostolic Work: Youth ministry (youth centers, schools, catechetical centers, summer camps, retreat centers).

Represented in the Archdioceses of Los Angeles, New Orleans, San Antonio and San Francisco and in the Dioceses of Phoenix, Monterey, Corpus Christi and Austin. Also in 72 countries in North, Central and South America, Africa, Asia, Australia and Europe.

Vocation Directress: Sr. Phyllis Neves, F.M.A., Mary Help of Christians Youth Center, 605 Enos Lane, Corralitos, CA 95076. (408) 728-4700 (convent); (408) 728-5518 (school).

CONGREGATION OF THE DAUGHTERS OF MARY IMMACULATE (Marianists) (F.M.I.)

251 W. Ligustrum Dr., San Antonio, TX 78228. (512) 433-5501

21 Sisters in United States Province

Apostolic Works: Teaching and education administration, campus ministry, social work, support services, adult faith development, formation of lay communities, hospital and hospice chaplaincy. Novitiate in Dayton, OH.

Represented in the Archdioceses of San Antonio and Cincinnati and in the Diocese of Toledo.

Contact: Sr. Grace Walle, F.M.I., Vocation Team, 251 W. Ligustrum Dr., San Antonio, TX 78228.

DAUGHTERS OF MARY OF THE IMMACULATE CONCEPTION (D.M.)

Motherhouse of the Immaculate Conception, 314 Osgood Ave., New Britain, CT 06053.

77 Sisters

Apostolic Work: 1 academy, 3 parochial schools, 1 home for the aged, 3 residences for women, 1 reading clinic, 3 catechetical centers, 2 skilled care facilities, 1 day care center.

Represented in the Archdioceses of Boston, Hartford and New York and in the Diocese of Springfield.

Office of Vocations: Sr. M. John, D.M., Vocation Director, 532 Burritt St., New Britain, CT 06053. (203) 223-2123.

DAUGHTERS OF OUR LADY OF THE HOLY ROSARY (F.M.S.R.)

1492 Moss St., New Orleans, LA 70119. (504) 486-0039

38 Sisters in U.S.

Apostolic Work: Education of young people, especially the poorest. Parish ministry, nursing and counseling, and CCD. Ministry to both Vietnamese and American.

Represented in the Archdiocese of New Orleans and in Mississippi and Texas.

Vocation Director: Sr. Mary Frances Dang, F.M.S.R., 1102 Beach Blvd., Long Beach, MS 39560. (610) 864-5291.

DAUGHTERS OF OUR LADY OF MERCY (D.M.)

Provincial House & Novitiate: Villa Rossello, R.R.1, Box 159, Catawba Ave., Newfield, NJ 08344. (609) 697-2983

70 Sisters

Apostolic Work: Teaching primary work, 1 day nursery and 1 convalescent hospital, C.C.D., parish ministry.

Represented in the Dioceses of Camden, Harrisburg, Scranton and Springfield (MA). Also in Italy, South America (Argentina, Brazil, Chile), England, Germany, Africa and India.

Vocation Directress: Sr. Eileen McGowan, D.M., 305 W. Areba Ave., Hershey, PA 17033-1602. (717) 533-2864.

DAUGHTERS OF OUR LADY OF THE SACRED HEART (F.D.N.S.C.)

St. Francis de Sales Convent, 424 E. Browning Rd., Bellmawr, NJ 08031. (609) 931-8973

15 Sisters in U.S., 1,800 Sisters worldwide

Province: South Africa

Apostolic Work: Nursing, teaching, pastoral ministry.

Represented in the (Arch)dioceses of Camden, Greensburg and Philadelphia.

Conduct: 4 schools.

Vocation Director: Sr. Patricia Burnes, FDNSC, St. Francis de Sales Convent, 424 E. Browning Rd., Bellmawr, NJ 08031. (609) 931-8973.

DAUGHTERS OF ST. FRANCIS OF ASSISI (D.S.F.)

Our Lady of Angels Province, St. Joseph Convent, 507 N. Prairie St., Lacon, IL 61540.

34 Sisters

Apostolic Work: Health care ministry, CCD and social work.

Represented in the Dioceses of Peoria and Springfield-Cape Girardeau.

Vocation Director: Sr. Vaclava, 507 N. Prairie St., Lacon, IL 61540. (309) 246-2175.

DAUGHTERS OF ST. MARY OF PROVIDENCE (D.S.M.P.)

Motherhouse: St. Mary of Providence Institute, 4200 N. Austin Ave., Chicago, IL 60634. (312) 545-8300

100 Sisters in U.S.; 1,000 Sisters worldwide

Apostolic Work: 7 schools for retarded, 1 hospital, 2 homes for the aging, child care. Foreign mission in Colombia, Mexico, Canada (Indian Missions).

Represented in the Archdioceses of Chicago, Detroit, Philadelphia, Boston, Providence and in the Dioceses of New Ulm, Sioux Falls; Kam-Loops and Vancouver, B.C. Also in Bogota, Cuouta, Florencia, Colombia and Mexico.

Vocation Director: Sr. Ann Schaffer, D.S.M.P., 4200 N. Austin Ave., Chicago,IL 60634. (312) 545-8300.

DAUGHTERS OF ST. PAUL (F.S.P.)

United States Province: 50 St. Paul's Ave., Boston, MA 02130.

Apostolic Work: International congregation of 2,600 women religious serving the Church in 53 countries in evangelizing with the communications media: press, films, radio, music ministry, television, audio and video cassettes, etc. In the U.S., Pauline Book and Media is the publishing house of the Daughters of St. Paul. Sisters staff the Pauline Book and Media Centers throughout the U.S.

Vocation Drectress: Sr. Mary Martha, F.S.P., 50 St. Paul's Ave., Jamaica Plain, Boston, MA 02130. (617) 522-8911.

DAUGHTERS OF WISDOM (D.W.)

(American Province) Provincial House: 385 Ocean Ave., Islip, NY 11751-4600. (516) 277-2660

157 Sisters

Apostolic Work: The mission of evangelization is primary for the congregation. A Daughter of Wisdom commits herself to the service of justice and the liberation of persons in the name of Jesus Christ.

Represented in the Archdiocese of Washington, DC and in the Dioceses of Brooklyn, Hartford, Portland (ME), Richmond, Rockville Centre, Wheeling, Arlington, Raleigh, Chicago, Bridgeport, Charleston, Denver, Manchester, St. Augustine, Metuchen and Mobile. Also in Africa, Asia, South America, Europe and Haiti.

Vocations: Daughters of Wisdom, 385 Ocean Ave., Islip, NY 11751-4600. (516) 277-2660.

SISTER DISCIPLES OF THE DIVINE MASTER (P.D.D.M.)

3700 North Cornelia Ave., Fresno, CA 93722. (209) 275-1656.

48 Sisters in the U.S.

Apostolic Work: Contemplative-active life style, Perpetual Adora-

tion, collaboration with the priesthood, liturgical apostolate.

Represented in 27 nations throughout the world and in the Archdioceses of Boston, New York, Los Angeles, Fresno, Youngstown and San Jose.

Vocation Directress: Sr. Paula Magana, 60 Sunset Ave., Staten Island, NY 10314. (718) 494-8597.

SISTERS OF THE DIVINE COMPASSION (R.D.C.)

Motherhouse and Novitiate: Good Counsel Convent, 52 N. Broadway, White Plains, NY 10603. (914) 949-2950

131 Sisters

Apostolic Work: Education, hospital ministry, nursing, counseling, social service, parish ministry, Mexican migrant ministry, retreat ministry.

Represented mostly in the Archdiocese of New York.

Vocation Director: Sr. Maureen McMahon, Good Counsel Convent, 52 N. Broadway, White Plains, NY 10603. (914) 949-2950.

COMMUNITY OF DIVINE PROVIDENCE (C.D.P.)

279 County Rd., Demarest, NJ 07627. (201) 768-8131 or 8106

Apostolic Work: House of prayer and hospitality, building Christian community thru associate membership, retreats, spiritual direction, teaching, ministry to the sick.

Represented in the Archdiocese of Newark.

Vocation Directors: Sr. Catherine Reddy or Sr. Gloria Jean Henchy.

CONGREGATION OF DIVINE PROVIDENCE (C.D.P.) SAN ANTONIO, TX

Generalate: P.O. Box 197, Helotes, TX 78023. (210) 695-8721

375 Sisters

Apostolic Work: Colleges and universities, elementary, secondary, and high schools, pastoral services, hospitals and clinics, social services, diocesan offices, retreats, counseling, spiritual direction.

Represented in the Archdioceses of Boston, Mexico City, Milwaukee, New Orleans, Oklahoma City, San Antonio, Santa Fe, St. Paul-Minneapolis, Washington, DC, and in the Dioceses of Alexandria, Allentown, Austin, Baton Rouge, Brownsville, Corpus Christi, Dallas, El Paso, Fort Worth, Ft.

Wayne-So. Bend, Fresno, Gallup, Galveston-Houston, Lafayette, (LA), Lake Charles, Las Cruces, Lexington, Oakland, Ogdensburg, Peoria, Rockville Centre, San Angelo, Shreveport, Springfield-Cape Girardeau, St. Cloud, Tulsa, Victoria, Wheeling-Charleston and Wichita. Also in Germany (U.S. Military), Brazil and Mexico: Queretaro, Saltillo, San Cristoban, Tehuantepec.

Vocation Director: Sr. Ann Umschaid, C.D.P., P.O. Box 197, Helotes, TX 78023. (210) 695-8721.

DAUGHTERS OF DIVINE PROVIDENCE (F.D.P.)

3100 Mumpfrey Rd., Chalmette, LA 70043. (504) 279-4617

300 Sisters worldwide; 8 in the U.S.

Apostolic Work: Education, catechesis, parish ministry, social work, ministry to the sick, elderly, poor and needy.

Represented in the Archdiocese of New Orleans. Also in Italy, India, Chile, Switzerland and Spain.

Vocation Director: 3100 Mumpfrey Rd., Chalmette, LA 70043. (504) 279-4617.

SISTERS OF DIVINE PROVIDENCE (C.D.P.)

(Province of Our Lady of Divine Providence)

Provincial House: 363 Bishops Hwy., Kingston, MA 02364.

Apostolic Work: Education at all school levels – pre-primary through high school, catechetical and spiritual leadership, counseling, pastoral ministry and nursing care.

Represented in the Archdiocese of Boston and in the Dioceses of Fall River and Richmond. Also in Germany, Puerto Rico, Peru and South Korea.

Vocation Directress: Sr. Mary Francis Fletcher, Visitation Convent, 341 Bishops Hwy., Kingston, MA 02364. (617) 585-7724.

SISTERS OF DIVINE PROVIDENCE (C.D.P.)

St. Peter's Province, Pittsburgh, PA 15215.

Provincial: Providence Heights, 9000 Babcock Blvd., Allison Park, PA 15101.

300 Sisters

Apostolic Work: Higher education, high schools, elementary schools, religious education and special education, pastoral ministry, campus ministry, social service, hospital, clerical, domestic service and pastoral care, House of Prayer, day care, ministry with the aging, social concerns and health care.

Represented in nine dioceses and in Puerto Rico.

Vocation Director: Sr. Jan Pritchard, 9000 Babcock Blvd., Allison Park, PA 15101. (412) 635-5408 or 931-5241.

SISTERS OF DIVINE PROVIDENCE (C.D.P.)

St. Louis Province, 8351 N. Florrisant Blvd., St. Louis, MO 63121.

70 Sisters

Apostolic Work: Education, health services, parish ministry, work with refugees and homeless.

Represented in the Archdioceses of St. Louis and Chicago and in the Dioceses of Brownsville, Jefferson City, Kansas City-St. Joseph, Nashville and Springfield (IL).

Vocation Directress: Sr. Margaret Mertens, C.D.P., Mt. Providence, 8351 N. Florissant Blvd., St. Louis, MO 63121. (314) 524-3803.

SISTERS OF DIVINE PROVIDENCE OF KENTUCKY (C.D.P.)

St. Anne Convent, Melbourne, KY 41059

215 Professed Sisters

Apostolic Work: Education (Montessori, elementary, secondary, college), social services, religious education, pastoral ministry, health care, foreign missions, peace and justice ministry.

Represented in the Archdioceses of Baltimore, Cincinnati, New York and Washington and in 13 dioceses. Also in Latacunga, Ecuador and in Ghana, West Africa.

Vocation Director: Sr. Barbara Rohe, C.D.P., St. Anne Convent, Melbourne, KY 41059. (606) 441-0679.

SISTERS OF THE DIVINE REDEEMER (S.D.R.)

Divine Redeemer Motherhouse, 999 Rock Run Rd., Elizabeth, PA 15037. (412) 751-8600

63 Sisters

Apostolic Work: Care of the sick, the poor, and the elderly; education, domestic service, parish ministry, retreat work and pastoral care.

Represented in Pennsylvania, Ohio and New York.

Vocation Director: Sr. Joanne Tricsko, S.D.R. (412) 751-8600.

SISTERS OF THE DIVINE SAVIOR (S.D.S.) (Salvatorians)
(North American Province)

144 Sisters

Apostolic Work: All areas of health care professions; teaching at all levels (grade school through college and special education); justice and peace work; serve minority groups in bilingual schools and clinics; retreat work; counseling; clerical work; pastoral ministry in hospitals, parishes and among the poor and elderly; missionary work; diocesan planning; nutritional counseling and food service.

Represented in the Dioceses of Birmingham, AL; Jackson, MS; Phoenix, Tucson, AZ; Rapid City, Sioux Falls, SD; Chicago, IL; Lexington, KY; Saginaw, MI; Baltimore, MD; Green Bay, La Crosse, Madison, and Milwaukee, WI. Also in Europe, Africa, East Asia, South America and the Middle East.

Vocation Directress: Sr. Jenada Fanetti, S.D.S., 4311 N. 100 St., Milwaukee, WI 53222-1393. (414) 466-0810.

CLOISTERED DOMINICAN NUNS (O.P.)

Monastery of the Infant Jesus, 1501 Lotus Ln., Lufkin, TX 75901. (409) 634-4233

23 Sisters

Vocation Director: Sr. Mary William.

DOMINICAN CONTEMPLATIVE SISTERS, O.P.

Monastery of the Heart of Jesus, 155 Church St., Lockport, LA 70374. (504) 532-2411

4 Professed Sisters, 1 Novice, 1 Candidate

Cloistered Contemplative Life.

Represented in the Diocese of Houma-Thibodaux.

Prioress: Mother Mary Henry, O.P.

DOMINICAN NUNS (O.P.)

Monastery of Our Lady of Grace

47 Sisters, 6 in Formation

Apostolic Work: Contemplative community in the monastic tradition of the Church, responding to the gospel through a life of prayer, solitude, community life and work.

Vocation Director: Sr. Diane, O.P., Monastery of Our Lady of Grace, North Guilford, CT 06437. (203) 457-0599.

DOMINICAN NUNS (O.P.)

Saint Dominic's Monastery, 4901 16th St., N.W., Washington, DC 20011-3839.

10 Sisters

Apostolic Work: Monastic contemplative life.

Vocation Director: Sr. Mary Amata, O.P., 4901 16th St., N.W., Washington, DC 20011-3839. (202) 726-2107.

DOMINICAN NUNS (O.P.)

Corpus Christi Monastery, 215 Oak Grove Ave., Menlo Park, CA 94025. (415) 322-1801

25 Sisters

Apostolic Work: Adoration of the Blessed Sacrament; Solemn Liturgy; study; work; silence; solitude.

Vocation Director: Sr. Mary of the Holy Family, O.P.

DOMINICAN NUNS (O.P.)
(The Cloistered Nuns of the Order of Preachers)

Monastery of St. Dominic, Newark, NJ 07103.

22 Nuns

Apostolic Work: Monastic contemplative life; full choral celebration of Liturgy of the Hours; daily Eucharistic exposition and adoration; a balance of community life and solitude, of prayer, study and work; a hidden apostolate of intercession and penance providing fruitful support for the Dominican Order, the universal Church and the needs of all people.

Vocation Directress: Sr. Mary Magdalen, O.P., Monastery of St. Dominic, 375 13th Ave., Newark, NJ 07103. (201) 622-6622.

DOMINICAN NUNS, CLOISTERED (O.P.)
(Nuns of the Sacred Order of Preachers)

(Corpus Christi Monastery) 1230 Lafayette Ave., Bronx, NY 10474-5399. (718) 328-6996

Perpetual Adoration of the Most Blessed Sacrament, Contemplatives

19 Professed, 1 Novice, 2 Postulants

Prioress: Sr. Lee Pendergast, O.P.

DOMINICAN NUNS (O.P.)

Monastery of Our Lady of the Rosary, 543 Springfield Ave., Summit, NJ 07901.

19 Nuns, 1 Junior Professed, 1 Novice

Apostolic Work: Monastic contemplative community dedicated to the apostolic needs of the Church and the Dominican Order with the special apostolate of perpetual adoration and perpetual rosary.

Represented in the Archdiocese of Newark.

Contact: Vocation Directress, (908) 273-1228.

DOMINICAN NUNS (O.P.)

(Province of St. Joseph) Mother of God Monastery, 1430 Riverdale St., West Springfield, MA 01089.

Apostolate Work: A life of contemplation and intercessory prayer. A cloistered, monastic community of 31 nuns, daily celebrating the entire Liturgy of the Hours and having as the focal point of the day the solemn and joyful celebration of the Eucharistic Liturgy. Devotion to Mary, Mother of God, especially through praying the Rosary, is characteristic of the community.

Vocation Directress: Sr. Mary of the Pure Heart, O.P. (413) 736-3639.

DOMINICAN NUNS (O.P.)

Monastery of Mary the Queen, 1310 W. Church St., Elmira, NY 14905.

15 Nuns

Apostolic Work: We have dedicated ourselves to the following of Jesus Christ within the monastic, contemplative tradition given to us by St. Dominic. We do this principally through: Prayer offered both in a common liturgy, and in solitude which issues from an attentive listening to the Lord speaking in the Scriptures and the study of sacred truth; Community life marked by a freedom of spirit arising from our poverty, chastity, and obedience, a common labor and a sisterly love; An Apostolic Spirit which finds expression in a joyful hospitality and a universal solidarity with all people in their needs.

Vocation Directress: Sr. Miriam, O.P.

DOMINICAN NUNS (O.P.)

Monastery of the Blessed Sacrament, 29575 Middlebelt Rd., Farmington Hills, MI 48334.

42 Sisters

Apostolic Work: Our monastic contemplative vocation balances a life of solitude with life in community. The whole of our life is aimed at the continual remembrance of God, especially through prayer, study and work.

Novice Directress: Sr. Mary Trinity, O.P., Monastery of the Blessed Sacrament, 29575 Middlebelt Rd., Farmington Hills, MI 48334. (810) 626-8253.

DOMINICAN NUNS OF PERPETUAL ADORATION (O.P.)

Monastery of the Angels, 1977 Carmen Ave., Los Angeles, CA 90068. (213) 466-2186

25 Sisters

Apostolic Work: A cloistered community observing norms of a full contemplative life.

Prioress: Sr. Mary Thomas, O.P.

DOMINICAN NUNS OF THE PERPETUAL ROSARY (O.P.)

Dominican Monastery of St. Jude, P.O. Box 170, Marbury, AL 36051. (205) 755-1322

9 Sisters

Cloistered Contemplative.

Vocation Director: Mother Mary Aimee, O.P., Prioress.

DOMINICAN NUNS OF THE PERPETUAL ROSARY (O.P.)

14th and West Sts., Union City, NJ 07087.

Cloistered. 8 Professed Sisters, 1 Novice

Prioress: Mother Mary Clare, O.P.

DOMINICAN NUNS OF THE PERPETUAL ROSARY (O.P.)

Monastery of Our Lady of the Rosary, 335 Doat St., Buffalo, NY 14211-2199. (716) 892-0066

28 Nuns, 3 Temporary Professed

Apostolic Work: Contemplative: Perpetual Adoration and Perpetual Rosary.

Vocation Director: Sr. Mary Gemma, O.P.

DOMINICAN NUNS OF THE PERPETUAL ROSARY (O.P.)

Monastery of the Perpetual Rosary, 1500 Haddon Ave., Camden, NJ 08103.

8 Nuns

Contact: Mother M. Immaculate Heart, O.P., Prioress.

DOMINICAN NUNS OF THE PERPETUAL ROSARY (O.P.)

Monastery of the Immaculate Heart of Mary, 1834 Lititz Pike, Lancaster, PA 17601-6585. (717) 569-2104

13 Nuns, 1 Aspirant

Apostolic Work: Contemplative monastic life.

Contact: Mother Prioress.

DOMINICAN NUNS OF THE PERPETUAL ROSARY (O.P.)

(Contemplative Community)

802 Court St., Syracuse, NY 13208. (315) 471-6762

12 Sisters

Prioress: Sr. M. Augustine, O.P.

DOMINICAN SISTERS, CABRA (O.P.)
(Our Lady of the Rosary)

Regional House: 1930 Robert E. Lee, New Orleans, LA 70122. (504) 288-1593

14 Sisters in U.S.; 530 Sisters worldwide

Apostolic Work: A variety of educational ministries, pastoral work, spiritual direction, retreats, community organizing.

Represented in the Archdiocese of New Orleans, and in the Diocese of Fort Worth.

Vocation Director: 1930 Robert E. Lee, New Orleans, LA 70122. (504) 288-1593.

DOMINICAN SISTERS OF ADRIAN (O.P.)

1257 E. Siena Heights Dr., Adrian, MI 49221.

1,200 Members

Apostolic Work: Education at all levels, pastoral work, health care, social work, direct social action, theology, preaching and the fine arts.

Vocation Director: Sr. Joann Plumpe, O.P., 1257 E. Siena Heights Dr., Adrian, MI 49221.

DOMINICAN SISTERS OF AKRON (O.P.)

Our Lady of the Elms Motherhouse, 1230 W. Market St., Akron, OH 44313-7185. (216) 836-4908

116 Sisters

Apostolic Work: Education on all levels preschool through college including religious education and pastoral ministry in parishes, counseling, youth ministry. Hospital ministry, ministry to elderly and shut-ins. Preaching, retreat work and spiritual direction, campus ministry. Library work, clerical, food service, administration, applied and fine arts, Guatamalan missions.

Represented in the Archdioceses

of Chicago, Denver, St. Louis and Washington, DC and in the Dioceses of Cleveland, Lansing, Phoenix, Seattle, Toledo and Youngstown.

Vocation Contact: Sr. Theresa Damicone, O.P.

DOMINICAN SISTERS OF AMITYVILLE (O.P.)

Queen of the Rosary Convent, Albany Ave., Amityville, NY 11701. (516) 842-6000

865 Sisters

Apostolic Work: Teaching, hospital ministry, parish ministry, congregational service, counseling, religious education, campus ministry, house of prayer, social work, law, medicine, preaching teams and others.

Represented in five Archdioceses and 12 Dioceses. Also in Puerto Rico.

Vocation Director: Sr. Margaret Ciccolella, O.P.

DOMINICAN SISTERS OF BLAUVELT (O.P.)

Motherhouse: St. Dominic Convent, Blauvelt, NY 10913.

Vowed and Associate Membership

Apostolic Work: Education, college, high schools, elementary, child care, ministry with the blind, retarded, migrant children, pastoral, social and health care.

Represented in (Arch)dioceses in New York, New Jersey, Providence, RI, St. Petersburg, FL and Jamaica, W.I.

Vocation Minister: Sr. Theresa Rickard, O.P., Convent of St. Dominic, Blauvelt, NY 10913. (914) 359-0696/5600.

DOMINICAN SISTERS OF CALDWELL, NEW JERSEY (O.P.)

Motherhouse: Mt. St. Dominic, Caldwell, NJ 07006. (201) 403-3331.

250 Sisters

Apostolic Work: Education at all levels, diocesan administration, pastoral ministry, health and human services.

Represented in the Archdiocese of Newark and in six other dioceses in the US and in the Bahamas.

Vocation Director: Sr. Pat Wormann, O.P., Our Lady of the Lake Convent, 22 Lakeside Ave., Verona, NJ 07044. (201) 239-4767.

DOMINICAN SISTERS OF EDMONDS (O.P.)
(Congregation of Holy Cross)

Motherhouse: P.O. Box 280, Edmonds, WA 98020. (206) 542-7511

82 Sisters

Conduct: Serving apostolates in university, high school, elementary school, parish, hospital pastoral ministry, religious education, ministry to the aging, health services, Indian apostolate, prison ministry, lay ministry formation, consultant in leadership, diocesan tribunal and political arena.

Represented in the Archdioceses of Los Angeles, St. Paul-Minneapolis, San Francisco, Santa Fe, NM, Seattle and in the Dioceses of San Diego, Boise, Covington and Fairbanks. Also in Haiti, Mexico and Poland.

Vocation Director: Sr. Maureen Rose, O.P., Dominican Sisters of Edmonds, P.O. Box 280, Edmonds, WA 98020. (206) 542-7753.

DOMINICAN SISTERS OF GRAND RAPIDS (OP)

Motherhouse: Marywood, 2025 E. Fulton St., Grand Rapids, MI 49503-3895.

360 Sisters

Apostolic Work: Education at all levels, parish and campus ministry, health care, social service, liturgy, social justice ministries, retreat work, diocesan personnel.

Represented in 6 Michigan Dioceses, New Mexico and 21 other states. Foreign mission in Chimbote, Peru.

Vocation Director: Sr. Mary Ann Barrett, OP, Marywood, 2025 E. Fulton St., Grand Rapids, MI 49503-3895. (616) 459-2910.

DOMINICAN SISTERS OF GREAT BEND (O.P.)

3600 Broadway, Great Bend, KS 67530. (316) 792-1232

150 Sisters

Apostolic Work: Teaching, nursing, parish ministry, religious education, care of aging, social service, foreign missions in Africa, home health, retreat and spirituality center, ministry to alcoholics and handicapped, pastoral care, holistic health, permaculture farming, ministry to Native Americans.

Represented in the Dioceses of Dodge City, Salina, and Wichita, KS; Oklahoma City, OK; San Angelo, TX; Denver and Pueblo, CO; Phoenix, AZ, Sokoto and Kaduna, Nigeria, Africa.

Vocation Director: Sr. Renee Dreiling, O.P., 3600 Broadway, Great Bend, KS 67530. (316) 792-1232.

DOMINICAN SISTERS OF HAWTHORNE (O.P.)
(Servants of Relief for Incurable Cancer)

Motherhouse and Novitiate: Rosary Hill Home, 600 Linda Ave., Hawthorne, NY 10532. (914) 769-4794

Apostolic Work: Confined entirely to the care of incurable cancer patients.

Represented in the Archdioceses of New York, Philadelphia and St. Paul and in the Dioceses of Cleveland, Fall River and Atlanta.

Formation Directress: Sr. Marie Edward, O.P.

DOMINICAN SISTERS OF HOPE (O.P.)

(formerly three Dominican congregations from Fall River, MA and Newburgh and Ossining, NY)

350 Sisters

Apostolic Work: Proclaiming and witnessing to the life-giving and healing Word of God through education, health care, pastoral services, social services and other types of advocacy and human services.

Represented in 21 states and Puerto Rico and 34 dioceses primarily in the Northeast.

Vocation Director: Sr. Rosanna Quinn, OP, 299 N. Highland Ave., Ossining, NY 10562. (914) 941-4455.

DOMINICAN SISTERS OF HOUSTON (O.P.)

Dominican Sisters, 6501 Almeda Road, Houston, TX 77021. (713) 747-3310

158 Sisters: 156 Sisters Professed, 1 Temporarily Professed, 1 Novice.

Apostolic Work: Education at all levels, pastoral work, health care, social work, direct social action, theology, preaching and the fine arts, foreign mission.

Represented in Dioceses of Galveston-Houston, Austin, Beaumont, San Antonio, TX; Archdioceses of Los Angeles and San Francisco, CA; Dioceses of San Bernardino, CA; and Guatemala City, Guatemala, Central America.

Vocation Director: Sr. Adrian Dover, O.P., 6505 Almeda Rd., Houston, TX 77021-2001. (713) 741-7076.

DOMINICAN SISTERS OF JUSTICE (O.P.)
(Congregation of the Immaculate Conception)
Motherhouse: Poland; Provincial House, 9000 W. 81st St., Justice, IL 60458. (708) 458-3040

10 Sisters

Represented in the Archdioceses of Chicago and Milwaukee. Also in Calgary and Alberta, Canada; Rome and Naples, Italy; Cameroon, Africa.

DOMINICAN SISTERS OF KENOSHA (O.P.)
P.O. Box 1288, Kenosha, WI 53141-1288.

36 Sisters

Apostolic Work: Teaching, health care ministry, care of the aged, social services, parish ministry, foreign mission.

Represented in the Archdioceses of Milwaukee and San Francisco and in the Dioceses of Baker and Fresno.

Vocation Director: P.O. Box 1288, Kenosha, WI 53141-1288. (414) 694-2067.

DOMINICAN SISTERS OF NASHVILLE (O.P.)
General Motherhouse: St. Cecilia Convent, 801 Dominican Dr., Nashville, TN 37228-1909. (615) 242-8505

150 Sisters; 50 in Formation

Conduct: 1 college, 1 private academy, 2 academies, 2 high schools, 14 elementary schools, 2 private elementary schools, 2 private kindergartens.

Represented in the Archdioceses of Baltimore and Cincinnati and in the Dioceses of Arlington, Birmingham, Memphis, Knoxville, Nashville and Richmond.

Vocation Directors: Sr. Catherine Marie, O.P., Sr. Mary John, O.P., St. Cecilia Convent, 801 Dominican Dr., Nashville, TN 37228-1909. (615) 242-8505.

DOMINICAN SISTERS OF OAKFORD (O.P.)
U.S. Regional Center: 1855 Miramonte Ave., Mountain View, CA 94040. (415) 965-1903.

20 Sisters

Conduct: 1 regional center, 1 novitiate, 1 geriatric center. Serve in parishes, Newman Center.

Represented in the Dioceses of San Jose and Oakland, CA and Tucson, AZ. Serve in So. Africa, Germany, Rome, England, California and Arizona (USA), and Argentina (South America).

Vocation Director: Sr. Nicolina Kohler, O.P., 327 Woodland Park Dr., San Leandro, CA 94577.

DOMINICAN SISTERS OF OXFORD
775 W. Drahner, Box 167, Oxford, MI 48371.

49 Sisters

Apostolic Work: Education administration, pastoral ministry, nursing home administration and ministry, peace/justice ministry, teaching, pre-school management, secretarial work, domestic work and retreat work.

Represented in the Dioceses of Detroit, Gaylord, Lansing and Saginaw, MI.

Vocation Director: Sr. Teresita Lipar, O.P., 775 W. Drahner, Box 167, Oxford, MI 48371. (810) 628-2872.

DOMINICAN SISTERS OF THE PERPETUAL ROSARY (O.P.)
(Cloistered, Contemplative)
217 N. 68th St., Milwaukee, WI 53213. (414) 258-0579

13 Professed Sisters

Vocations: Mother Miriam, O.P., Prioress.

DOMINICAN SISTERS OF THE PRESENTATION (O.P.)
3012 Elm St., Dighton, MA 02715.

82 Sisters

Apostolic Work: 1 hospital, caring for the aged, rural health, pastoral care, education, parish ministry, 1 house of studies, ministry to the disabled, home health care, social work, ministry to immigrants, ministry to Hispanics, mission in India.

Represented in the Archdiocese of Washington, DC and in the Dioceses of Fall River, MA, Brownsville, TX and Providence, RI.

Vocation Directress: Sr. Carole V. Marie, O.P., 3012 Elm St., Dighton, MA 02715. (508) 669-5023.

DOMINICAN SISTERS OF RACINE (O.P.)
St. Catherine of Siena Convent, 5635 Erie St., Racine, WI 53402-1900.

285 members

Apostolic Work: All levels of education, health care, social services, pastoral ministry, retreat

work, social justice concerns.

Represented in 16 states, Kenya and Mexico.

Vocation Director: Sr. Diane Poplawski, O.P., 5635 Erie St., Racine, WI 53402-1900. (414) 639-4100.

DOMINICAN SISTERS OF THE ROMAN CONGREGATION (O.P.)
Provincial Residence: 304 Oberlin St., Iowa City, IA 52245-4034

38 Sisters in U.S.; 715 in the World

Apostolic Work: Education at all levels, parish and pastoral ministries, mission work on the Navajo Reservation, health care, social work.

Represented in the Archdioceses of New York and Chicago and in the Dioceses of Davenport, Des Moines, Gallup, Phoenix, Portland, ME and Portland, OR. In countries of: U.S., Canada, Brazil, Belgium, Sweden, France, Italy, Switzerland, Benin, Japan, Spain.

Vocation Directress: Sr. Monique Belanger, O.P., Dominican Sisters, 18 Tampa St., Lewiston, ME 04240.

DOMINICAN SISTERS OF MISSION SAN JOSE (O.P.)
Motherhouse: P.O. Box 3908, Mission San Jose, CA 94539. (510) 657-2468

337 Sisters

Conduct: 1 college, 6 high schools, 19 elementary schools, 1 kindergarten, 1 school of music.

Apostolic Work: Preachers of the Good News of Jesus Christ through the ministry of Christian education in elementary and high schools, parish ministry, campus ministry and pastoral ministry in hospitals.

Represented in the Archdioceses of Los Angeles, Portland (OR) and San Francisco and in the Dioceses of Oakland, Orange and Tucson. Also in Mexico and Germany.

Vocation Director: Sr. Gloria Marie Jones, O.P., P.O. Box 3908, Mission San Jose, CA 94539. (510) 657-2468.

DOMINICAN SISTERS OF ST. CATHERINE DE' RICCI (OP)
750 Ashbourne Rd., Elkins Park, PA 19027-2596.

109 Sisters

Apostolic Work: Retreat ministry, residence for women, religious education, parish ministry, ministry with the poor, social services.

Represented in the Archdioceses of Miami, Detroit, Albany, Philadelphia, Santa Fe and Baltimore and in 15 dioceses.

Candidate Director: Sr. Carol Davis, O.P., 1 Tryon Ave., B1, A6, Scotia, NY 12302-3623.

DOMINICAN SISTERS OF ST. CATHARINE OF SIENA (O.P.)
St. Catharine Motherhouse, 2645 Bardstown Rd., St. Catharine, KY 40061. (606) 336-9303.

338 Sisters

Apostolic Work: Preaching through our ministries as educators, health-care providers, advocates for the homeless, pastoral ministers in parishes and retreat centers, counselors and through other ministries that address contemporary needs.

Represented in the Dioceses of Boston, Brooklyn, Chicago, Grand Island, Louisville, Memphis and Omaha; in about 17 other dioceses in lesser numbers.

Vocation Director: Sr. Joann Mascari, O.P., 4331 Hazelwood Ave., Louisville, KY 40215. (502) 367-6696.

DOMINICAN SISTERS OF ST. MARY OF THE SPRINGS (O.P.)
2320 Airport Dr., Columbus, OH 43219-2098.

345 Sisters

Conduct: 2 colleges, high schools, elementary schools, learning center, parish ministry, senior citizens apartment building, involvement in many aspects of pastoral ministry. Foreign mission-Chimbote, Peru.

Apostolic Work: Diversified ministries which include education at all levels, parish ministries, health care, spirituality ministry, social work, foreign missions, etc.

Represented in (Arch)dioceses in Bolivia, S.A., Arizona, Colorado, Connecticut, Florida, Illinois, Indiana, Louisiana, Maryland, Massachusetts, Michigan, Missouri, New Mexico, New York, Ohio, Pennsylvania, Peru, S.A., Puerto Rico, Rhode Island, Virginia, Washington, DC, West Virginia and Wisconsin.

Vocation Director: Sr. Caroline Castellini, O.P., St. Mary of the Springs, 2320 Airport Dr., Columbus, OH 43219-2098. (614) 252-2950.

DOMINICAN SISTERS OF SAN RAFAEL (O.P.)
Motherhouse: San Rafael, CA 94901. (415) 453-8303

170 Sisters

Conduct: 1 college, 2 high schools, 10 grammar schools, 4 hospitals, 1 retreat and conference center.

Represented in the Archdioceses of Los Angeles and San Francisco and in the Dioceses of Oakland, Reno, Sacramento, San Jose, Santa Rosa, Stockton and Seattle.

Vocation Director: Sr. Maureen McInerney, O.P., 1500 Butterfield Rd., San Anselmo, CA 94960-1099. (415) 459-4178.

DOMINICAN SISTERS OF SINSINAWA (O.P.)
(Sinsinawa Dominican Congregation of the Most Holy Rosary)
Generalate: The Mound, Sinsinawa, WI 53824-9999.

965 Sisters

Apostolic Work: A variety of educational ministries, pastoral ministries and health and welfare ministries.

Represented in 37 states, Europe, South and Central America, Mexico, Trinidad, West Indies and Canada.

Vocation Directors: Mary Therese Johnson, O.P., Mary Ellen O'Grady, O.P., Mary Ann Casey, O.P., Membership Office, Dominican Motherhouse, Sinsinawa, WI 53824-9999. (608) 748-4411.

DOMINICAN SISTERS OF SPARKILL (O.P.)
(Dominican Congregation of Our Lady of the Rosary)
175 Route 340, Sparkill, NY 10976.

487 Sisters

Apostolic Work: Elementary schools, high schools, college, child care, housing, foreign missions, nursing, religious education, pastoral ministry, secretarial, administration, campus ministry, health related, counseling, aging, art, communication, handicapped, Indian missions.

Represented in the Archdioceses of New York and St. Louis and in five dioceses. Also in Pakistan and Peru.

Vocation Contact: Sr. Madeleine Murphy, O.P., Dominican Convent, 175 Rt. 340, Sparkill, NY 10976. (914) 359-6400.

DOMINICAN SISTERS (O.P.)
(Congregation of St. Mary)
Motherhouse: 580 Broadway, New Orleans, LA 70118. (504) 861-8183.

72 Professed Sisters, 3 Temporarily Professed

Ministries: Administration, teaching, including religious education, campus ministry in 6 elementary, 1 high school; on arch/diocesan level, directing music, superintending schools; counseling, spiritual direction, retreats, writing books, pastoral ministry in many parishes, 1 nursing home, hospice; directing/staffing 2 conference/retreat centers, apartment residence for elderly; community organizing in New Orleans and Baton Rouge, pastoral ministry with the deaf, full-time study, full-time prayer.

Represented in the Archdiocese of New Orleans and in the Dioceses of Baton Rouge, Biloxi, Houma-Thibodaux and Lafayette.

Vocation Contact: Sr. Shirley Bodisch, O.P., 7300 St. Charles Ave., New Orleans, LA 70118. (504) 866-0541.

DOMINICAN SISTERS OF SPOKANE (O.P.)
W. 3102 Ft. George Wright Dr., Spokane, WA 99204. (509) 328-8033

38 Sisters

Apostolic Work: Health care ministry, pastoral ministry, education and social service.

Represented in the Diocese of Spokane.

Vocation Directors: Mary Therese Johnson, O.P., Mary Ellen O'Grady, O.P., Mary Ann Casey, O.P., Membership Office, Dominican Motherhouse, Sinsinawa, WI 53824-9999. (608) 748-4411.

DOMINICAN SISTERS OF SPRINGFIELD (O.P.)
Sacred Heart Convent, 1237 W. Monroe St., Springfield, IL 62704.

352 Professed Sisters, 7 in Formation

Apostolic Work: Preaching to the unserved and underserved through: pastoral ministries in daycare and learning centers, elementary and secondary schools, hospitals, religious education centers, retirement centers, retreat and renewal centers, sisters' infirmary. Sisters also minister in administrative positions in diocesan offices and parishes; in parish roles as pastoral associate, DRE, liturgist/musician, and visitor to elderly, shut-ins; as pastoral care persons in hospitals, hospices, nursing homes and prisons; to hearing impaired and to the poor; in spiritual direction, campus ministry, counseling, communication, social service and Peruvian missions.

Represented in the Archdioceses of Chicago, Lima (Peru) and St. Paul/Minneapolis and in the Dioceses of Baton Rouge, Duluth, Jackson, La Crosse, Little Rock, Belleville, Joliet, Peoria, Rockford, Springfield-in-Illinois and Huancayo (Peru).

Vocation Contact: Sr. M. Gael Daley, O.P., Dominican Renewal Center, 7th & Adams, Box 679, Riverton, IL 62561. (217) 629-8471.

DOMINICAN SISTERS OF TACOMA (O.P.)

Motherhouse: 935 Fawcett Ave. S., Tacoma, WA 98402. (206) 272-9688.

92 Sisters

Apostolic Work: Members participate in education, parish ministry, pastoral care, counseling, ministry to refugees, elderly and poor.

Represented in the Archdiocese of Seattle and in the Dioceses of Fresno, San Diego, Yakima and Baker.

Vocation Director: c/o Vocation Director, 935 Fawcett Ave. S., Tacoma, WA 98402.

EUCHARISTIC FRANCISCAN MISSIONARY SISTERS (E.F.M.S.)

Motherhouse: 943 S. Soto St., Los Angeles, CA 90023. (213) 264-6556

Novitiate: Nativity Convent, 1421 Cota Ave., Torrance, CA 90501. (213) 328-6725

Mission Center: Blessed Sacrament Convent, 1205 N. San Joaquin St., Stockton, CA 95202. (209) 462-3906.

20 Sisters

Apostolic Work: Missionary work through Adoration of the Blessed Sacrament, catechetical ministry at all levels, parish ministry (social work), education, secretarial, multi-cultural ministry, retreats, out-reach programs and diocesan work.

Represented in the Archdiocese of Los Angeles and in the Diocese of Stockton, CA.

Vocation Director: Sr. Gloria DeJesus, E.F.M.S., Blessed Sacrament Convent, 1205 N. San Joaquin St., Stockton, CA 95202. (209) 462-3906.

EUCHARISTIC MISSIONARIES OF ST. DOMINIC (O.P.)

Motherhouse: 3801 Canal St., Ste. 400, New Orleans, LA 70119. (504) 486-0098; (504) 486-6146

50 Sisters

Apostolic Work: Religious education ministry, diocesan offices, parish census, social service ministry, centers for the deaf, day care centers, ministry to the sick, home nursing, hospital nursing, pastoral care of sick in homes, hospitals and nursing care institutions.

Represented in the Archdiocese of New Orleans and in the Dioceses of Baton Rouge, Houma-Thibodeaux, Lake Charles and Lafayette (LA), Phoenix and Tucson (AZ), Biloxi (MS), St. Petersburg and West Palm Beach (FL).

Vocation Director: Sr. Luisa Derouen, O.P., 3801 Canal St., Ste. 400, New Orleans, LA 70119. (504) 486-0098.

FAITHFUL COMPANIONS OF JESUS (F.C.J.)
(Society of the Sisters, Faithful Companions of Jesus)

Saint Philomena Convent, Portsmouth, RI 02871. (401) 683-2222

37 Sisters

Apostolic Work: Grammar schools, high schools, colleges; catechetics with youth and adults; retreat work; hospital chaplaincy; parish ministry; prison ministry; child care; ministry to the elderly; missionary work.

Represented in the Dioceses of Providence and Fall River and in 14 foreign countries. New foundations in the Philippines and Indonesia.

Vocation Directess: Sr. Joanna Walsh, F.C.J., Blessed Sacrament Convent, 350 Mt. Pleasant Ave., Providence, RI 02908. (401) 274-6578.

FELICIAN SISTERS (C.S.S.F.)

(Immaculate Conception Province) Provincial House: Immaculate Conception Convent, 260 S. Main St., Lodi, NJ 07644-2196.

260 Sisters in the Province

Apostolic Work: Primary work: education on all levels: 25 elementary schools, 3 high schools, 1 college, 1 school for exceptional children, 3 religious education offices, a reading center, 2 child care centers and a language lab. Also: 6 hospitals, 1 nursing home, 1 infirmary, 2 diocesan offices, 1 urban youth center, 1 AIDS institu-

tion, 1 retreat center, 1 home for children, 1 drug rehabilitation program, and 4 pastoral assistants/associates, 1 foreign mission in Kenya, Africa.

Represented in the Archdioceses of Baltimore, Newark and Philadelphia and in the Dioceses of Camden, Metuchen, Paterson, Trenton and Wilmington.

Vocation Director: Sr. Marilyn Marie Minter, C.S.S.F., 260 S. Main St., Lodi, NJ 07644-2196. (201) 473-5923.

FELICIAN SISTERS (C.S.S.F.)

(Our Lady of the Angels Province) Motherhouse and Novitiate: Our Lady of the Angels Convent, 1315 Enfield St., Enfield, CT 06082.

160 Sisters in Province

Apostolic Work: Ministry in fields of health and education, adult day care, pastoral care.

Represented in the Archdioceses of Boston, Hartford and New York and in the Dioceses of Albany, Manchester, Norwich, Portland (ME), Providence and Springfield.

Vocation Directress: Sr. Frances Marion, C.S.S.F., 1315 Enfield St., Enfield, CT 06082. (203) 745-7791.

FELICIAN SISTERS (C.S.S.F.)

(Immaculate Heart of Mary Province) Motherhouse and Novitiate: Villa Maria, 600 Doat St., Buffalo, NY 14211.

358 Sisters in the Province

Apostolic Work: 1 college, 1 academy, 4 high schools, 1 day care center, 28 elementary parochial schools, 9 religious education centers, 1 school for exceptional children, 1 institute of music, nursing, social work, tutorial work, pastoral ministry, general clerical/administrative work, diocesan work, retreat work, counseling.

Represented in the Dioceses of Buffalo and Syracuse and Erie, PA. Also in Canada.

Vocation Director: Sr. Mary Lucette Kinecki, 600 Doat St., Buffalo, NY 14211. (716) 892-4141.

FELICIAN SISTERS (C.S.S.F.)

(Our Lady of Sacred Heart Province) Motherhouse and Novitiate: Our Lady of the Sacred Heart Convent, 1500 Woodcrest Ave., Coraopolis, PA 15108.

166 Sisters in the Province.

Apostolic Work: Private high

school, parochial schools, religious education centers, hospitals, nursing home, home for exceptional children, home for aged. On faculty of regional high schools, consolidated high school, consolidated elementary schools, college, domestic service, foreign missions in Brazil; retreats and renewals, summer school work and tutorial programs, medical, social and secretarial work in hospitals, parish ministry, youth ministry, campus ministry and occasional special apostolates.

Represented in the Dioceses of Pittsburgh, Venice, Wheeling-Charleston, Altoona-Johnstown, Cleveland, Greensburg and Harrisburg.

Vocation Director: Sr. Mary Andrew Budinski, C.S.S.F., 1500 Woodcrest Ave., Coraopolis, PA 15108. (412) 264-2890.

FELICIAN SISTERS (C.S.S.F.)

(Presentation of the Blessed Virgin Mary Province) Motherhouse and Novitiate: Presentation of the B.V.M. Convent, 36800 Schoolcraft Rd., Livonia, MI 48150.

294 Sisters in the Province

Apostolic Work: 1 university, 4 high schools, 29 elementary schools, 7 catechetical centers, 8 religious education centers, 1 Montessori center, 1 day care center, 2 nursing homes, 1 hospital, 2 medical centers, 1 assisted living center, community out-reach programs, 1 hospice in-patient facility and home care program, 2 retreat centers, 1 child care center, 1 prayer center, 1 youth ministry, 3 parochial pastoral centers, foreign missions in Brazil and Kenya, archdiocesan tribunal, 1 parish soup kitchen, 1 senior clergy residence, secretarial services in seminary.

Represented in the Archdiocese of Detroit and in the Dioceses of Saginaw, Lansing, Kalamazoo, Gaylord, Toledo, Fort Wayne-South Bend; Sao Paulo, Brazil and Rome, Italy.

Vocation Director: Sr. Mary De Sales, C.S.S.F., 36800 Schoolcraft Rd., Livonia, MI 48150. (313) 591-1730.

FELICIAN SISTERS (C.S.S.F.)

(Mother of Good Counsel Province) Provincial and Novitiate: Mother of Good Counsel Convent, 3800 W. Peterson Ave., Chicago, IL 60659.

303 Sisters in the Province

Apostolic Work: 1 junior college, 2 high schools, instruction and administration in 16 elementary schools, 1 day care center, 2 hospitals, 2 homes for the aged, 1 assisted-living facility for the elderly, 1 skilled-care facility, 1 counseling program for high-risk children, teens and parents, social service especially among the poor, youth ministry, pastoral ministry, religious education, evangelization, diocesan work, domestic service, clerical work, foreign missions in Brazil and Kenya.

Represented in the Archdioceses of Chicago and Milwaukee and in the Dioceses of Green Bay, La Crosse, Belleville, Joliet and Rockford. Also in Rome and Brazil.

Vocation Director: Sr. Paula Mary, C.S.S.F., 3800 W. Peterson Ave., Chicago, IL 60659. (312) 463-3020.

FELICIAN SISTERS (C.S.S.F.)

(Assumption of the B.V.M. Province) 4210 Meadowlark Ln., S.E., Rio Rancho, NM 87124. (505) 892-8862

78 Sisters-Franciscans

Conduct: 3 high schools, 11 grammar schools, 40 Christian Doctrine classes, 4 religious education centers, counseling, youth ministry, adult education, pastoral ministry, handicapped, missionary ministry, domestic service, Eucharistic ministry, home visiting and other spiritual and corporal works of mercy.

Represented in the Archdioceses of Santa Fe, Los Angeles and San Antonio and in the Dioceses of Austin, Fort Worth and Saltillo, Coahuila, Mexico.

Vocation Directors: Sr. Denise Amato, C.S.S.F., 1180 West Holt Ave., Pomona, CA 91768. (909) 629-1308. Sr. Mary Dorothy Young, C.S.S.F., 4210 Meadowlark Ln., S.E., Rio Rancho, NM 87124 (505) 892-8862.

FILIPPINI SISTERS (M.P.F.)
(Religious Teachers Filippini)

(St. Lucy Province) Motherhouse, Novitiate and Provincial House: Villa Walsh, Western Ave., Morristown, NJ 07960.

300 Sisters

Apostolic Work: Elementary and secondary education, parish ministry, retreat ministry, child day care centers, and foreign missions.

Represented with foundations in the United States, Italy, Brazil, Ethiopia, India, England and Ireland. Another province in Connecticut.

Vocation Director: Sr. Alma Blume, M.P.F., Villa Walsh, Western Ave., Morristown, NJ 07960. (201) 538-2886.

FILIPPINI SISTERS (M.P.F.)
(Religious Teachers Filippini)

(Queen of Apostles Province)
Provincial House: 474 East Rd., Bristol, CT 06010. (203) 584-2138

49 Sisters

Conduct: 1 middle school, 9 grammar schools, 1 mission, 3 religion education centers, 2 shrines.

Represented in the Archdiocese of Hartford and in the Dioceses of Bridgeport, Norwich, Orlando and Providence.

Vocation Directress: Sr. Dorothy Sayers, M.P.F., Holy Family Convent, 3375 Galaxy Way, Orlando, FL 32819. (407) 876-2211.

FRANCISCAN HANDMAIDS OF THE MOST PURE HEART OF MARY (F.H.M.)

15 W. 124th St., New York, NY 10027. (212) 289-5655

28 Sisters

Conduct: 1 nursery, 1 summer camp, 1 house of prayer.

Apostolic Work: Teaching, pastoral work, social work, religious instruction, retreat work.

Represented in the Archdiocese of New York.

Vocation Director: 444 Woodvale Ave., Pleasant Plains, Staten Island, NY 10309. (718) 984-1625.

FRANCISCAN HOSPITALLER SISTERS OF THE IMMACULATE CONCEPTION (F.H.I.C.)

St. Joseph Novitiate: 300 S. 17th St., San Jose, CA 95112-2245. (408) 998-2896

19 Sisters

Apostolic Work: Schools, hospitals, social work, parish.

Represented in the Dioceses of Fresno, Monterey and San Jose. Also represented in Portugal, Brazil, India, Africa, Spain, Philippines and Italy.

Vocation Director: Sr. Lucinda D. Fonseca, 300 S. 17th St., San Jose, CA 95112-2245.

FRANCISCAN MISSIONARIES OF THE IMMACULATE HEART OF MARY (F.M.I.H.M.)

Holy Saviour Convent, 30 Emerald

Ave., Westmont, NJ 08108
St. Jude Convent, 420 S. Black
Horse Pike, Blackwood, NJ
08012.

7 Sisters in U.S., 900 worldwide

Apostolic Work: Teaching, foreign
missions, parish work, nursing and
social services.

Vocation Director: Sr. Dorothy
Aloisio, F.M.I.H.M., St. Jude Convent, 420 S. Black Horse Pike,
Blackwood, NJ 08012. (609) 227-
8658.

FRANCISCAN MISSIONARIES OF MARY (F.M.M.)

Provincial House: Institute of Franciscan Missionaries of Mary, 3305
Wallace Ave., Bronx, NY 10467.

8,500 Sisters worldwide, 210 in
U.S.

Apostolic Work: Medical, educational, social, and pastoral, as well
as special ministries among the
poor and marginalized in 78 countries throughout Africa, Asia,
Europe, Latin America, North
America and Oceania.

Represented in the Archdioceses
of Boston, New York, St. Louis,
Chicago and San Francisco and in
dioceses in Georgia, New Mexico,
Mississippi, Rhode Island and
Florida.

Vocation Directress: F.M.M. Vocation Office, Franciscan Missionaries of Mary, 621 Second St., Fall
River, MA 02721. (508) 673-2892.

FRANCISCAN MISSIONARIES OF OUR LADY (O.S.F.)

4200 Essen Ln., P.O. Box 80376,
Baton Rouge, LA 70809.

31 Sisters in the U.S.A.

Apostolic Work: Parish ministry,
education and health care ministry.

Represented in three Louisiana
dioceses. Sisters are located in 12
other countries.

Vocation Directress: 4200 Essen
Ln., P.O. Box 80376, Baton Rouge,
LA 70809. (504) 926-1627.

FRANCISCAN MISSIONARIES OF THE SACRED HEART

See Franciscan Sisters of Peekskill.

FRANCISCAN MISSIONARY SISTERS FOR AFRICA (O.S.F.)

American Headquarters: 172 Foster St., Box 35095, Brighton, MA
02135.

7 Sisters

Apostolic Work: Education at primary and secondary levels; AIDS
education; mobile AIDS clinics,
dispensaries; pastoral work
among urban poor; facilitating
basic Christian communities;
refugee services; job training in
rural areas; initial and ongoing formation of African Sisters.

Represented in the Archdiocese of
Boston and in 9 foreign countries.

Vocation Director: (617) 254-4343.

FRANCISCAN MISSIONARY SISTERS OF ASSISI (SFMA)

St. Francis Convent, 1039 Northampton St., Holyoke, MA 01040.
(413) 532-8156

Apostolic Work: Pastoral work,
teaching, nursing, social work and
domestic work.

Represented in the Archdiocese of
New York and in the Diocese of
Springfield, MA. Also in missions
in Italy, Germany, Romania,
Kenya, Croatia, Brazil, Zambia,
Japan and Korea.

Contact Person: Vocation Directress, 1039 Northampton St.,
Holyoke, MA 01040. (413) 532-
8156.

FRANCISCAN MISSIONARY SISTERS OF THE DIVINE CHILD (FMDC)

Motherhouse: 6380 Main St.,
Williamsville, NY 14221. (716)
632-3144

33 Sisters

Apostolic Work: Ministries in city
and rural areas alike through:
catechetics, DRE, education (early
childhood, elementary, high schools,
college, adult religious education),
human services, parish religious
surveys, pastoral ministry.

Represented in the Diocese of
Buffalo.

Vocation Director: Sr. Concetta
DeFelice, 6380 Main St., Williamsville, NY 14221. (716) 631-5147.

FRANCISCAN MISSIONARY SISTERS OF THE IMMACULATE CONCEPTION (O.S.F.)

11320 Laurel Canyon Blvd., San
Fernando, CA 91340. (818) 898-
1546.

96 Sisters

Conduct: Provincial home, 1 novitiate, 1 home for the aged, 2
grammar schools, 1 preschool, 2
hospitals, 1 retreat house, 1 house
in catechetical and pastoral ministries, 1 home for senior citizens.

Represented in the Archdioceses

of Los Angeles and in the Dioceses of Orange and Gallup.

Vocation Contact: Sr. Angelica
Tiscareno, 11320 Laurel Canyon
Blvd., San Fernando, CA 91340.
(818) 898-1546.

FRANCISCAN MISSIONARY SISTERS OF THE INFANT JESUS, F.M.I.J.

Delegation (Regional) and Formation House: 1215 Kresson Rd.,
Cherry Hill, NJ 08003-2813. (609)
428-8834; FAX (609) 428-7930

Motherhouse in Assisi (Italy) -
Generalate in Rome.

Apostolic Work: Education, health
care, pastoral assistance to
elderly, youth; catechesis and
other services to evangelization.

Represented in 5 continents and
10 countries.

Vocation Director: Sr. Clare V.
Sabini, F.M.I.J., 1215 Kresson
Rd., Cherry Hill, NJ 08003-2813.
(609) 428-8834. FAX: (609) 428-
7930.

FRANCISCAN MISSIONARY SISTERS OF OUR LADY OF SORROWS (OSF)

3600 S.W. 170th Ave., Beaverton,
OR 97006-5099. (503) 649-7127

50 Sisters

Conduct: 2 novitiates, 1 grammar
school, 2 retreat houses, 2 foreign
missions, 1 group home for Indian
girls.

Represented in the Archdioceses
of Portland, OR and San Francisco and of Taipei, Taiwan and in
the Dioceses of Hong Kong, Monterey and Gallup.

Contact Person: Sr. Anne Marie,
OSF, 3600 S.W. 170th Ave.,
Beaverton, OR 97006-5099. (503)
649-7127.

FRANCISCAN SISTERS (O.S.F.) (Servants of the Holy Child Jesus)

Regional Motherhouse and Novitiate: Villa Maria, 641 Somerset
St., N. Plainfield, NJ 07061. (201)
757-3050

43 Sisters

Apostolic Work: Home for the
aged, residence for mentally
handicapped women, nursing and
related health fields, social work,
AIDS ministry and teaching.

Represented in the Dioceses of
Metuchen, Trenton and in the
Archdiocese of New York.

Vocation Directress: Sr. M. Ilia

Delio, O.S.F., Villa Maria, 641 Somerset St., P.O. Box 708, N. Plainfield, NJ 07061. (908) 757-3050.

FRANCISCAN SISTERS OF ALLEGANY, NY (O.S.F.)

St. Elizabeth Motherhouse, Allegany, NY 14706. (716) 373-0200.

490 Sisters.

Apostolic Work: Ministries: Evangelization in education, health care, social services, pastoral and campus ministries, spiritual ministries, prison ministries, houses of prayer and social advocacy.

Represented in the Archdioceses of New York, Boston, Hartford, Newark, Philadelphia, Miami and Wilmington and in the Dioceses of Buffalo, Syracuse, Albany, Rockville Centre, Paterson, Winston-Salem, Brooklyn, Metuchen, Trenton, Camden, Orlando, Palm Beach, Venice and St. Petersburg. Also in Jamaica, West Indies, Brazil and Bolivia.

Vocation Coordinator: Sr. Pat Reid, OSF, Portiuncula House of Formation, 720 West 231 St., Bronx, NY 10463. (718) 796-2784.

FRANCISCAN SISTERS OF THE ATONEMENT (S.A.)

Graymoor, R1, Box 163B, Garrison, NY 10524-9717.

255 Sisters

Apostolic Work: Religious education at parish and diocesan levels, social services and community development programs, pastoral ministry and evangelization, adult social day care programs, kindergartens and child care programs, camps for underprivileged youth, justice and peace programs and retreat and hospitality ministry.

Represented in the Archdioceses of Boston, Hartford, Newark, New York, San Francisco and Washington, DC and in 22 other dioceses in the United States. Also in Brazil, Canada, Japan, Ireland and Italy.

Vocation Directress: St. Francis Convent, Graymoor, R1, Box 163B, Garrison, NY 10524-9717. (914) 424-3624.

FRANCISCAN SISTERS OF BALTIMORE (O.S.F.)

General Motherhouse: 3725 Ellerslie Ave., Baltimore, MD 21218. (410) 235-2496

53 Sisters

Apostolate: Conduct special education school, social service center, Franciscan lay mission volunteer community, inner city youth center. Individual ministries include catechetics, evangelization (African-Americans and Hispanics), nursing, parish missions, hospital chaplaincy, pastoral ministry, counseling, retreat work, music, bookkeeping, marriage tribunal advocacy, and work with HIV+ infants and toddlers. Ministry rooted in prayer and community.

Represented in the Archdioceses of Baltimore, New York and Washington and in the Dioceses of Trenton and Brownsville.

Vocation Minister: Sr. Beth Anne Herrmann, O.S.F., 3725 Ellerslie Ave., Baltimore, MD 21218. (410) 235-2496 in MD; (914) 356-1300 in NY.

FRANCISCAN SISTERS OF BUFFALO (O.S.F.)

400 Mill St., P.O. Box 275, Williamsville, NY 14231. (716) 632-2155

153 Sisters

Ministry: Choices are made in response to the needs of the Church and one's talents and skills. Present involvements include: health care, care for the elderly, teaching at all levels; justice and peace work; service to the poor; retreat work; counseling; clerical work; pastoral ministry in hospitals, parishes and among the elderly; missionary work; diocesan planning and other emerging needs.

Represented in the Archdiocese of Chicago and in the Dioceses of Buffalo, Rochester, Syracuse, NY; Harrisburg, PA; Charleston, SC. Also in San Juan, Puerto Rico and Meru in Kenya, Africa.

Vocation Director: Sr. Beth Ann Niederpruem, St. Clare Convent, 2844 Main St., Buffalo, NY 14214. (716) 836-4060.

FRANCISCAN SISTERS OF CHICAGO (O.S.F.)

14700 Main St., Lemont, IL 60439-0956.

165 Professed Sisters

(708) 257-7776

Apostolic Work: Ministry to the sick, elderly and the poor; elementary and secondary education; religious education; pastoral ministry and evangelization; child care, counseling and social services; liturgy and parish ministry.

Represented in the Archdiocese of Chicago and in the Dioceses of Cleveland, Gary and Tulsa.

Vocation Director: Sr. Diane Marie, O.S.F., 14700 Main St., Lemont, IL 60439-0956. (708) 257-7776.

FRANCISCAN SISTERS OF CHRISTIAN CHARITY (O.S.F.) (Silver Lake Sisters)

Holy Family Convent, 2409 S. Alverno Road, Manitowoc, WI 54220.

580 Sisters.

Apostolic Work: Catholic education, Catholic health care, and service to our Sisters in community.

Represented in these dioceses in the U.S.; Columbus, Gaylord, Green Bay, Honolulu, Los Angeles, Marquette, Milwaukee, Omaha, Phoenix, Steubenville, Superior and Tucson. Also in Lima, Peru.

Vocation Directress: Holy Family Convent, 2409 S. Alverno Road, Manitowoc, WI 54220. (414) 682-7728.

SCHOOL SISTERS OF ST. FRANCIS OF CHRIST THE KING (O.S.F.)

Mt. Assisi Convent, 13900 Main St., Lemont, IL 60439. (708) 257-7495

82 Sisters in America

Conduct: 1 academy, 6 grammar schools, 1 home for the aged. Serve as Directors of Religious Education and liturgy directors.

Represented in the Archdioceses of Chicago and Milwaukee and in the Diocese of Joliet.

Vocation Director: Sr. Therese Ann, O.S.F., 13900 Main St., Lemont, IL 60439. (708) 257-7495.

FRANCISCAN SISTERS OF THE EUCHARIST (F.S.E.)

Motherhouse: 405 Allen Ave., Meriden, CT 06450. (203) 237-0841

73 Sisters, 1 Novice, 3 Postulants, 1 Pre-Postulant

Represented in the Archdioceses of Hartford, Portland and Seattle and in the Dioceses of Boise, Duluth and Grand Rapids. Also in Rome and Assisi, Italy and Jerusalem.

Vocation Contact: Sr. Barbara Johnson, F.S.E., (203) 238-2243.

FRANCISCAN SISTERS OF HANKINSON (O.S.F.)

Motherhouse: P.O. Box E, Hankinson, ND 58041-0433. (701) 242-7195

82 Sisters

Apostolic Work: 2 elementary schools, college/adult education, parish ministry, 1 hospital, 2 homes for the elderly, liturgical vestments, social service, domestic service, pro-life worship.

Represented in North Dakota, Minnesota and Iowa.

Vocation Director: Sr. M. Jean Louise Schafer, OSF, St. Francis Convent, P.O. Box E, Hankinson, ND 58041-0433. (701) 242-7195.

FRANCISCAN SISTERS OF HASTINGS-ON-HUDSON, NY (OSF)

Sisters of St. Francis Mission of the Immaculate Virgin at Immaculate Conception Motherhouse: 49 Jackson Ave., Hastings-on-Hudson, NY 10706. (914) 478-3930.

Apostolic Work: Child care, social work, education, health and hospitals, parish ministry, Franciscan Center for Retreats.

Represented in the Archdiocese of New York and in New Mexico.

Vocation Director: Sr. Roberta Smith, OSF. (914) 478-3930, 961-3970.

SISTERS OF ST. FRANCIS OF THE HOLY CROSS

3025 Bay Settlement Rd., Green Bay, WI 54311-7301. (414) 468-1828

100 Sisters

Apostolic Work: Education (elementary, high school, college), religious education, parish ministry, health care and related ministries.

Represented primarily in the Diocese of Green Bay. Also in Milwaukee, Mississippi, New Mexico, Louisiana, Indiana and Nicaragua.

Vocation Director: Sr. Francis Bangert.

FRANCISCAN SISTERS OF THE IMMACULATE CONCEPTION (O.S.F.)

Provincial House: 291 W. North St., Buffalo, NY 14201.

10 Sisters

Apostolic Work: Care of the chronically ill – Nazareth Home, Buffalo, NY.

Represented in the Archdiocese of New York and in the Diocese of Buffalo. Also in Germany, Brazil, Argentina and Paraguay.

Vocation Director: Sr. M. Bernard, O.S.F., 291 W. North St., Buffalo, NY 14201.

FRANCISCAN SISTERS OF THE IMMACULATE CONCEPTION (O.S.F.)

Immaculate Conception Convent, 2408 W. Heading Ave., Peoria, IL 61604.

64 Sisters

Apostolic Work: Teaching, parish work, nursing, care of the elderly, religious education and social work.

Vocation Director: Sr. Janice Keenan, O.S.F., Immaculate Conception Convent, 2408 W. Heading Ave., Peoria, IL 61604. (309) 674-6168.

FRANCISCAN SISTERS OF THE IMMACULATE CONCEPTION AND ST. JOSEPH FOR THE DYING (O.S.F.)

Motherhouse: Ave Maria Convent, 1249 Josselyn Canyon Rd., P.O. Box 1977, Monterey, CA 93942. (408) 373-1216

8 Sisters

Conduct: 1 convalescent hospital, teaching, religious education, home visiting.

Represented in the Diocese of Monterey.

Vocation Director: Sr. Rosanna, O.S.F., Ave Maria Convent, 1249 Josselyn Canyon Rd., P.O. Box 1977, Monterey, CA 93942. (408) 373-1216.

FRANCISCAN SISTERS OF LITTLE FALLS (O.S.F.)

St. Francis Convent, Little Falls, MN 56345.

280 Sisters

Evangelical Ministry: Prayer, retreats, foreign missions, teaching and education, nursing and health, counseling, homes for the aged, hospices, pastoral ministry, dietetics, law, religious education, library, social justice, sanctuary movement, refugee ministry, ministry to family, the deaf, prisoners, poor, those seeking justice and civil rights and wherever the needs of the present time calls us.

Represented in Minnesota, Illinois, New Mexico, Tennessee, Wisconsin, Mississippi, Texas, Arizona, California, Iowa, South Dakota, New York, Washington, Missouri, Washington, DC, Virginia, Florida, Pennsylvania and South Carolina. Also in Ecuador, Nicaragua, Guatemala and Tanzania.

Vocation Minister: Sr. Carol Virnig, OSF, 727 East Margaret, St. Paul, MN 55106. (612) 771-0041.

FRANCISCAN SISTERS OF THE MARTYR ST. GEORGE (O.S.F.)

Province: St. Elizabeth, St. Francis Convent, 2120 Central Ave., P.O. Box 9020, Alton, IL 62002-9020.

134 Professed Sisters, 14 Novices, 10 Postulants

Apostolic Work: Teaching, nursing, social work, day care for children, parish work, missions in Brazil, secretarial and domestic work, adoration of the Blessed Sacrament.

Vocation Director: Sr. Regina Pacis, O.S.F., 2120 Central Ave., Alton, IL 62002. (618) 463-2750.

FRANCISCAN SISTERS OF MARY (F.S.M.)

1100 Bellevue Ave., St. Louis, MO 63117.

250 members and associate members

Apostolic Works: Increasingly varied but emphasizing healing, health promotion, restoration, and health education. Focus on wholeness of relationships and life, including communal and congregational life. The Congregation's members serve in hospitals, clinics, birthing centers, parishes, chaplaincies, hospices, schools, counselling situations, group dynamics, etc.

Represented in the Archdioceses of Chicago, IL and Oklahoma City, OK and in the Dioceses of Madison, WI; Belleville, IL; South Carolina; Brownsville, TX; Albany, NY; St. Petersburg, FL; various dioceses in Missouri. Cross-cultural mission in Brazil.

Membership Director: 1100 Bellevue Ave., St. Louis, MO 63117. (314) 768-1826.

CONGREGATION OF THE THIRD ORDER OF ST. FRANCIS OF MARY IMMACULATE (OSF)

520 Plainfield Rd., Joliet, IL 60435. (815) 727-3686

356 Professed Sisters

Apostolic Work: All levels of education, pre-school through adult, music specialists, parish ministry, social services, health care, religious education, care of elderly, holistic health.

Represented in 13 Archdioceses, 22 Dioceses of U.S., 1 other country. One Novitiate in Joliet, IL, U.S. and one Novitiate in Goiania, Brazil, SA.

Vocation Counselor: Sr. Carlene Howell, O.S.F., 520 Plainfield Rd., Joliet, IL 60435.

FRANCISCAN SISTERS OF MARY IMMACULATE OF THE THIRD ORDER OF ST. FRANCIS OF ASSISI (F.M.I.)

St. Francis Convent and Provincial House, 4301 N.E. 18th St., Amarillo, TX 79107. (806) 383-5769

48 Sisters

Conduct: Education in primary, elementary and junior/senior high schools; nursing and catechetics.

Represented in the Archdiocese of Los Angeles and in the Diocese of Amarillo, Monterey and Santa Fe. Missions in Mexico, Central and South America, Switzerland, Luxembourg and Romania.

Vocation Directress: Sr. Mary Magdalene.

FRANCISCAN SISTERS OF MILLVALE (O.S.F.)

146 Hawthorne Rd., Millvale P.O., Pittsburgh, PA 15209.

270 Sisters

Apostolic Work: Elementary education, secondary education, college education, Montessori, day care, hospitals, healthcare, healthcare education, senior citizen housing, family home care, parish ministry, religious education, evangelization, youth ministry, social service ministries, spirituality ministries, lay collaborative ministry.

Represented in the (Arch)dioceses of Pittsburgh, Altoona-Johnstown, Erie, Greensburg, Los Angeles, New York, Cincinnati, Lubbock, Miami, Chicago, Lansing, Newark, Cleveland, Steubenville, Charleston and San Angelo. Also in Caguas and San Juan, PR, St. Thomas, VI, Military Ordinariate, Benin City, Nigeria, Santo Domingo and Guatemala.

Vocation Director: Sr. Mary Jo Mattes, O.S.F., 146 Hawthorne Rd., Pittsburgh, PA 15209. (412) 821-2200.

FRANCISCAN SISTERS OF OLDENBURG (O.S.F.)

Motherhouse and Novitiate: Immaculate Conception Convent, Oldenburg, IN 47036. (812) 934-2475

425 Sisters, 7 in Formation

Apostolic Work: Elementary, secondary, college, and religious education and administration; campus ministry, pastoral and hospital ministry; daycare; spiritual direction and retreat ministry; counseling; social work; nursing; library science; House of Prayer; clerical and supportive services; African-American, Native American, Hispanic and Appalachian ministries.

Represented in the (Arch)dioceses of Charlestown, Chicago, Cincinnati, Cleveland, Columbus, Covington, Davenport, Detroit, Evansville, Gallup, Gaylord, Great Falls/ Billings, Indianapolis, Jefferson City, Lansing, Las Cruces, Lexington, Los Angeles, New York, Peoria, Providence, St. Augustine, St. Louis, St. Petersburg and Toledo. Foreign missions in Mexico and Papua New Guinea.

Vocation Director: Sr. Marge Wissman, O.S.F., Sisters of St. Francis, Oldenburg, IN 47036. (812) 933-6462.

FRANCISCAN SISTERS OF OUR LADY OF PERPETUAL HELP (O.S.F.)

201 Brotherton Ln., St. Louis, MO 63135.

160 Sisters

Apostolic Work: Education, health care, pastoral ministry, social service, contemporary needs of the Church.

Contact: Sr. Mary John Cleary, O.S.F., 201 Brotherton Ln., St. Louis, MO 63135. (314) 522-6800.

FRANCISCAN SISTERS OF PEACE (F.S.P.)

20 Ridge St., Haverstraw, NY 10927. (914) 942-2527

95 Sisters; co-founded in 1986

Ministries: Education (pre-school through college), pastoral and campus ministry, prison ministry, religious education, spiritual direction, counselling, health care, day care, working with the poor and homeless.

Represented in the Archdioceses of New York, Newark, Philadelphia and San Francisco and in the Dioceses of Rockville Centre, Paterson, Albany, Camden, Trenton and Gallup. Also in Guatemala City.

Vocation Director: Franciscan Sisters of Peace, 20 Ridge St., Haverstraw, NY 10927. (914) 942-2527.

FRANCISCAN SISTERS OF PEEKSKILL (F.M.S.C.)
(Franciscan Missionaries of the Sacred Heart)

250 South St., Peekskill, NY 10566-4419.

89 Sisters

Apostolic Work: Education, religious education, educational administration, parish ministry, nursing, prison ministry and community service.

Represented in the Archdioceses of New York and Newark, NJ and in the Diocese of Paterson, NJ. Also in Europe, Africa, South America and Asia.

Vocation Director: Sr. M. Petra Zanghi, F.M.S.C., Mount St. Francis, 250 South St., Peekskill, NY 10566-4419. (914) 737-3373, ext. 36.

FRANCISCAN SISTERS OF PERPETUAL ADORATION (F.S.P.A.)

Generalate: St. Rose Convent, 912 Market St., La Crosse, WI 54601. (608) 782-5610.

600 Sisters

Apostolic Work: Education on primary, secondary, and college levels, pastoral ministry, home and health care services, social services, and diversified ministries.

Represented in over 50 U.S. dioceses and 25 states, with heavy concentration in the Western and Midwestern states. Also in Guam, Africa, El Salvador and the Marshall Islands.

Office of Membership: Sr. Sharon Berger, 912 Market St., La Crosse, WI 54601. (608) 791-5292.

SISTERS OF ST. FRANCIS OF PERPETUAL ADORATION (O.S.F.)

Mount Saint Francis, 7665 Assisi Heights, Colorado Springs, CO 80919. (719) 598-5486

123 Sisters

Apostolic Work: Ministry to the sick, the elderly, the poor, education of multicultural youth, pastoral ministry, facilitation of individual and family wellness, perpetual adoration of the Blessed Sacrament.

Represented primarily in the Archdioceses of Denver, Omaha and Sante Fe and in the Dioceses of Colorado Springs, Grand Island, Lincoln and Gallup.

Vocation Directress: Sr. Dorothy Schlaeger, O.S.F., Mount Saint Francis, 7665 Assisi Heights, Colorado Springs, CO 80919. (719) 598-5486.

SISTERS OF ST. FRANCIS OF PERPETUAL ADORATION (O.S.F.)

(Immaculate Heart of Mary Province), St. Francis Convent, P.O. Box 766, 1515 Dragoon Trail, Mishawaka, IN 46546-0766. (219) 259-5427

200 Sisters, 3 Novices, 4 Postulants

Apostolic Work: Perpetual adora-

tion of the Blessed Sacrament. Health care, education and other ecclesial ministries in Central U.S.
Vocation Director: Sr. Jacinta Krecek, O.S.F., St. Francis Convent, P.O. Box 766, 1515 Dragoon Trail, Mishawaka, IN 46546-0766.

SISTERS OF ST. FRANCIS OF PHILADELPHIA (O.S.F.) (Glen Riddle Franciscans)

Our Lady of Angels Convent, 609 S. Convent Rd., Aston, PA 19014. (610) 459-4125

1,000 Sisters

Conduct: College, high school, elementary school, health system: serve in education, social, health care, spiritual and pastoral ministries.

Mission: Continuous conversion of heart, commitment to a life of contemplation, poverty and humility. Serve all (but especially the economically poor, the marginal and the oppressed) to bring about justice, peace and reconciliation.

Represented in the Archdioceses of Philadelphia and Portland, OR and throughout the U.S. Also in Africa, Antigua, Ireland, Dominican Republic, Ethiopia, Guatemala, Nicaragua and Puerto Rico.

Vocation Directors: Sr. Joan Morris, O.S.F., Our Lady of Angels Convent, 609 S. Convent Rd., Aston, PA 19014. (610) 459-4125; Our Lady of Angels Convent, 0858 SW Palatine Hill Rd., Portland, OR 97219. (503) 697-8078.

SISTERS OF ST. FRANCIS OF THE PROVIDENCE OF GOD, PITTSBURGH (O.S.F.)

3603 McRoberts Rd., Pittsburgh, PA 15234.

200 Sisters (120 in U.S.)

Apostolic Work: Education, health care, social services, pastoral ministry, prison ministry, catechetical work, campus ministry, retreat work.

Represented in 8 dioceses in U.S. Also in Brazil and Lithuania.

Vocation Director: Sr. Althea Anne Spencer, 3603 McRoberts Rd., Pittsburgh, PA 15234. (412) 882-9911 or (412) 771-7791.

FRANCISCAN SISTERS OF THE POOR (S.F.P.)

133 Remsen St., Brooklyn, NY 11201. (718) 643-1919

230 Sisters

Ministry: Varies according to the needs of society in response to the call to "heal the wounds of Christ in poor, suffering humanity."

Included is service in 9 acute care hospitals, 1 women's hospital, 6 long-term care and retirement centers; 2 social service centers; AIDS ministry; work with the poor and homeless in inner-city communities; pastoral care; ministry to Native Americans.

Represented in the Archdioceses of New York, Newark, Detroit and Cincinnati and in four dioceses in the U.S. Present also in Brazil, Italy and Senegal.

Vocation Coordinators: Vocation Office, 133 Remsen St., Brooklyn, NY 11201. (718) 643-1919; Vocation Office, 2360 Kipling Ave., Cincinnati, OH 45239. (513) 681-6071; Sr. Marcia Dahlinghaus, SFP, 7180 Kavanagh Way, Flagstaff, AZ 86004. (602) 527-4808; Sr. Grace Miriam Pleiman, SFP, 144 W. 19th St., New York, NY 10011. (212) 242-0446.

FRANCISCAN SISTERS OF THE RENEWAL (C.F.R.)

Our Lady of the Angels Convent, 420 E. 156th St., Bronx, NY 10455. (718) 993-3405

Apostolic Work: Care of the destitute and evangelization.

Represented in the Archdiocese of New York.

Contact: Sr. Ann Lynn, C.F.R., Vocation Director.

FRANCISCAN SISTERS OF RINGWOOD (F.S.R.)

Motherhouse and Novitiate: Mt. St. Francis, Ringwood, NJ 07456. (201) 962-7411

38 Sisters

Apostolic Work: Elementary schools, religious education, retreat house, pastoral ministry, social work, counseling.

Represented in the Archdioceses of Newark and New York and in the Diocese of Paterson.

Directress of Vocations: Sr. Theresa Marie Firenze, St. Clare's Convent, 474 Sloatsburg Rd., Ringwood, NJ 07456. (201) 962-7411.

FRANCISCAN SISTERS OF ROCHESTER, MN (O.S.F.)

Box 4900, Assisi Heights, Rochester, MN 55903. (507) 282-7441

450 members

Ministry choices are guided by human need, the call to justice and personal talents. Some of our ministries include health care, education, social service, business, law, and pastoral ministry.

Represented in the (Arch)dioceses

of Baltimore, Boston, Brownsville, Charleston, Charlotte, Chicago, Colorado Springs, Columbus, Covington, Denver, Dubuque, Duluth, El Paso, Fargo, Great Falls, Helena, Indianapolis, Joliet, La Crosse, Lafayette, Lexington, Madison, Memphis, Metuchen, Milwaukee, New Ulm, Oakland, Oklahoma City, Orange, Owensboro, Phoenix, Pueblo, St. Louis, San Bernardino, San Diego, Santa Fe, Savannah, Seattle, Sioux Falls, Spokane, Springfield-Cape Girardeau, St. Cloud, St. Louis, St. Paul/Minneapolis, Springfield, Superior, Tucson, Washington and Winona. Also in Cambodia, Colombia, Peru and South Africa.

Vocation Minister: Sr. Barbara Knipp, Assisi Heights, Box 4900, Rochester, MN 55903. (507) 282-7441.

FRANCISCAN SISTERS OF THE SACRED HEART (O.S.F.)

Motherhouse: St. Francis Woods, 9201 W. St. Francis Rd., Frankfort, IL 60423. (815) 469-4895

170 Sisters

Apostolic Work: "Works of Neighborly Love" in education, health care, domestic services, 1 foreign mission, social services, retreat ministry.

Vocation Directors: Sr. Mary Elizabeth, O.S.F., Sr. Deborah Suddarth, St. Francis Woods, 9201 W. St. Francis Rd., Frankfort, IL 60423. (815) 469-4895, 464-3880.

FRANCISCAN SISTERS OF ST. ELIZABETH (F.S.S.E.)

Motherhouse: Rome; Delegate House and Novitiate, 499 Park Rd., Parsippany, NJ 07054.

60 Sisters in U.S.

Apostolic Work: (in U.S.) 1 novitiate, 1 elementary school, 4 day nursery schools, 1 Montessori school and 5 mission houses.

Represented in the Archdiocese of Newark and in the Diocese of Paterson. Also, throughout Italy, Panama, India and the Philippines.

Vocation Directress: Sr. Elizabeth Pinto, F.S.S.E., 499 Park Rd., Parsippany, NJ 07054. (201) 539-3797.

FRANCISCAN SISTERS OF ST. JOSEPH

U.S. Foundation: St. Paul College, 3015 4th St., N.E., Washington, DC 20017. (202) 832-6262; 269-2515

5 Sisters

Apostolic Work: Ministry in domestic areas.

Represented in the Archdiocese of Washington.

FRANCISCAN SISTERS OF ST. JOSEPH (F.S.S.J.)

Immaculate Conception Convent, 5286 S. Park Ave., Hamburg, NY 14075-1596. (716) 649-1205

225 Sisters

Apostolic Work: Education on elementary, secondary and college levels, health care service, pastoral ministry, social services and diversified ministries, foreign missionary work.

Represented in the Archdioceses of Baltimore, Boston, Detroit and Milwaukee and in nine dioceses, and in South America.

Vocation Contact: Vocation Director, 5286 S. Park Ave., Hamburg, NY 14075-1596. (716) 649-1205.

FRANCISCAN SISTERS OF ST. PAUL, MN

Franciscan Regional Center, 1388 Prior Ave. S., St. Paul, MN 55116. (612) 690-1501

International Congregation

700 worldwide; 15 Sisters in U.S.

Apostolic Work: Health related care, teaching, social work.

Represented in the Archdiocese of Minneapolis/St. Paul. Also in Germany, Holland and Brazil.

Vocation Director: 1388 Prior Ave. S., St. Paul, MN 55116.

SISTERS OF ST. FRANCIS OF SAVANNAH, MO (O.S.F.)

Provincial House, LaVerna Heights, P.O. Box 488, 104 East Park, Savannah, MO 64485. (816) 324-3179

30 Professed Sisters, 1 Novice, 1 Postulant, 17 Co-Disciples

Apostolic Work: Education, nursing, C.C.D. ministry, pastoral care, nursing home care, supportive ministries.

Represented in the Archdiocese of Kansas City, KS and in the Dioceses of Kansas City-St. Joseph and Jefferson City.

Vocation Contact: Sr. Rebecca Brennan, O.S.F., P.O. Box 488, 104 East Park, Savannah, MO 64485. (816) 324-3179.

FRANCISCAN SISTERS OF SYRACUSE (O.S.F.)

2500 Grant Blvd., Syracuse, NY 13208.

381 Sisters

Apostolic Work: In the U.S.: elementary and high schools, hospitals, schools of nursing, a rehabilitation center, a geriatric center, a tutorial center, catechetical centers, a retreat center, the Covenant House Program for teenagers in New York City, preschool and day care center, and geriatric day care center. Also, a leprosarium at Molokai, a guest house in Rome, Italy, a parish center in the Diocese of Haucho, Peru, parish ministry, diocesan ministry, and various individual ministries.

Vocation Directress: Sr. James Peter Ridgeo, O.S.F., (315) 425-7413.

FRANCISCAN SISTERS, DAUGHTERS OF THE SACRED HEARTS OF JESUS AND MARY, (Wheaton Franciscans) (O.S.F.)

Our Lady of the Angels Motherhouse, P.O. Box 667, Wheaton, IL 60189. (708) 462-7422

Apostolic Work: Serving people in a variety of health, educational, social, pastoral, cultural and spiritual ministries.

Represented in the Archdioceses of Chicago, Denver, Dubuque, Milwaukee and St. Louis and in the Dioceses of Gary, Green Bay, Joliet, La Crosse, Rockford and Springfield-Cape Girardeau. Also in Brazil, Rome, France, Germany, Holland, Nigeria and Indonesia.

Vocation Director: Sr. Gabriele Uhlein, O.S.F., P.O. Box 667, Wheaton, IL 60189. (708) 462-7422.

SISTERS OF ST. FRANCIS OF ASSISI (O.S.F.)

Motherhouse: St. Francis Convent, 3221 S. Lake Dr., Milwaukee, WI 53235-3799.

450 Sisters and Associates

Apostolic Ministry: Advocates for women, minorities, disabled, disadvantaged and elderly persons. Administrators, teachers, child care workers, counselors, social workers, food service and health care providers, clerical workers, parish ministries, artists and musicians.

Represented in U.S. dioceses from coast to coast and Taiwan.

Contact: Vocation Director, 3221 S. Lake Dr., Milwaukee, WI 53235-3799. (414) 744-1160.

SCHOOL SISTERS OF THE THIRD ORDER OF ST. FRANCIS (Bethlehem) (O.S.F.)

Provincial House: 395 Bridle Path Rd., Bethlehem, PA 18017. (610) 866-2597

66 Sisters Bethlehem Province, 440 Sisters worldwide

Apostolic Work: Parish schools, retreat ministry, CCD centers, day care, high schools, social ministry.

Represented in the Archdiocese of Newark and in the Dioceses of Allentown, Paterson and Springfield. Also in Chile, South Africa and India.

Vocation Contacts: Sr. Carol Ann, O.S.F., Sr. Maria, O.S.F., Vocation Office, 395 Bridle Path Rd., Bethlehem, PA 18017. (610) 866-2597.

SCHOOL SISTERS OF THE THIRD ORDER OF ST. FRANCIS (Pittsburgh) (O.S.F.)

96 Sisters

Motherhouse: Mount Assisi Convent, 934 Forest Ave., Pittsburgh, PA 15202. (412) 761-6004

Apostolic Work: Pastoral ministry, teaching (early childhood, elementary, secondary, adult education), prayer and retreat ministry, hospital chaplaincies, nursing, youth ministry, religious education, parish social services, home for the aged, translator (Rome), counseling, clerical work, missionary work, ministry to Hispanics and Native Americans in Southwest, other works corresponding to the gifts of the members.

Represented in the Archdiocese of San Antonio and in the Dioceses of Erie, Greensburg, Pittsburgh, Phoenix and San Angelo. Also missions in South America and South Africa.

Vocation Director: Sr. Adelina Garcia, O.S.F., 934 Forest Ave., Pittsburgh, PA 15202. (412) 761-6004.

SCHOOL SISTERS OF THE THIRD ORDER OF ST. FRANCIS (Panhandle) (O.S.F.)

North American Region: PO Box 906, Panhandle, TX 79068. (806) 537-3182

29 Sisters

Conduct: 2 grammar schools, 4 confraternity centers, 1 home for the aged.

Represented in the Archdiocese of San Antonio and in the Diocese of Amarillo. Also in Austria, Europe and in Argentina, South America.

SCHOOL SISTERS OF ST. FRANCIS (OSF)

Generalate: St. Joseph Convent, 1501 S. Layton Blvd., Milwaukee, WI 53215. (414) 384-1515

1,132 Sisters

U.S. Province: 1515 S. Layton Blvd. Milwaukee, WI 53215. (414) 384-1515

Apostolic Work: Education, health care, pastoral ministry, social concerns, the arts, sponsorship of institutions.

Represented in dioceses throughout the United States, Latin America, Europe and India.

U.S. Province Vocation Team: Great Plains: Sr. Roberta Klesener, 315 S. Main St., Melcher, IA 50163; South/East: Sr. Julene Stromberg, Rt. 1, Box 142, Holly Springs, MS 38635; South West-Texas: Sr. Barbara Jean Pottbast, P.O. Box 471, Grand Falls, TX 79742; South West AZ/CA: Sr. Kathleen Kluthe, 1949 N. Swan Rd., Apt. 3, Tucson, AZ 85712; Lower Midwest: Sr. Rosemary Reier, 3545 North Nora Ave., Chicago, IL 60634. (815) 385-1455; Upper Midwest: Sr. Rita Mary Phalen, 1515 S. Layton Blvd., Milwaukee, WI. (414) 384-1515; Hispanic Lower Midwest: Sr. Frances Hicks, 220 E. Hillcrest Dr. #3101, DeKalb, IL 60115. (708) 584-0514; African-American: Sr. Catherine Culp, 5046 Ashland Ave., Chicago, IL 60640. (312) 478-4741; Higher Education: Sr. Virginia Wagner, 3401 S. 39th St., Milwaukee, WI 53219. (414) 382-6117.

SISTERS OF ST. FRANCIS (O.S.F.)

6832 Convent Blvd., Sylvania, OH 43560. (419) 882-2016

317 Professed Sisters

Apostolic Work: Religious and academic education at all levels, health care, parish ministries, retreat work, social services.

Represented in the Archdioceses of Baltimore, Cincinnati, Detroit, Indianapolis, Milwaukee, New Orleans, Portland (OR), St. Paul-Minneapolis, Santa Fe and Washington, DC and in the Dioceses of Austin, Biloxi, Cleveland, Columbus, Dallas, Grand Rapids, Jackson, Joliet, Kalamazoo, Lafayette, Lansing, Little Rock, Phoenix, Raleigh, Richmond, Shreveport, St. Cloud, Steubenville, Toledo, Wheeling-Charleston and Winona. Also in Africa.

Vocation Director: Sr. Joy Barker,

6832 Convent Blvd., Sylvania, OH 43560. (419) 882-2016, ext. 632, (419) 882-7912.

SISTERS OF ST. FRANCIS OF THE HOLY EUCHARIST (O.S.F.)

2100 N. Noland, Independence, MO 64050. (816) 252-1673

30 Sisters

Apostolic Work: Teaching in grade school, high school, college, health care, domestic work, retreat center.

Represented in the Dioceses of Kansas City, MO and Kansas City, KS.

Vocation Director: Sr. Doris Engeman, O.S.F., 2100 N. Noland Rd., Independence, MO 64050. (816) 252-1673.

SISTERS OF ST. FRANCIS OF THE HOLY FAMILY (O.S.F.)

3390 Windsor, Dubuque, IA 52001-1311. (319) 583-9786

500 members

Apostolic Work: Education (elementary, secondary, college), religious education, special education, health care, prayer and retreat ministry, social work, campus ministry, the aged, counseling, justice and peace and other varied works depending on the gifts of the members and the needs of people.

Represented in more than 50 dioceses and in 28 states of the U.S. as well as in El Salvador, Mexico and Poland.

Vocation Minister: Mary Lechtenberg, O.S.F., 3390 Windsor, Dubuque, IA 52001-1311. (319) 583-9786.

SISTERS OF ST. FRANCIS OF PENANCE AND CHRISTIAN CHARITY (O.S.F.)

Stella Niagara, NY 14144. (716) 754-4312

230 Sisters

Apostolic Work: Administration, campus ministry, education, college, secondary, primary, health sciences and technicians, library, missionary, pastoral ministry, peace and justice, physical education, retreat directors, rural ministry, secretarial, social work, spiritual direction, art.

Represented in the Dioceses of Buffalo, Cincinnati, Cleveland, Columbus, Metuchen, Miami, Orlando, St. Petersburg, Sante Fe, Trenton, Venice (OH), Wheeling, Youngstown, (OH).

Director of Admissions: Sr. Betty

Neumeister, O.S.F., 4421 Lower River Rd., Stella Niagara, NY 14144. (716) 754-4312.

SISTERS OF ST. FRANCIS OF PENANCE AND CHRISTIAN CHARITY (O.S.F.)

(Sacred Heart Province), 2851 W. 52nd St., Denver, CO 80221. (303) 458-6270

89 Sisters

Conduct: 4 health care facilities, 1 emergency housing, 1 emergency food bank and clothing distribution, 1 home for abused and neglected children.

Apostolic Work: Are involved in a variety of parish ministries, work among Native Americans, Vietnamese and Hispanics, traditional educational ministry, adult education (Biblical and tutorial), peace and justice work, pastoral ministry, motherhouse is available to groups.

Represented in the Archdioceses of Denver, Omaha and Santa Fe and in the Dioceses of Bismarck, Grand Island, Rapid City and Reno-Las Vegas. Also in Chiapas and Hidalgo, Mexico and Tanzania, Africa. International congregation with provinces located in 7 countries.

Vocation Director: Sr. Patricia, O.S.F., 2851 W. 52nd St., Denver, CO 80221. (303) 458-8640.

SISTERS OF ST. FRANCIS OF PENANCE AND CHRISTIAN CHARITY

P.O. Box 1028, Redwood City, CA 94064. (415) 369-1725

112 Sisters

Apostolic Work: Elementary and secondary education, pastoral ministry in parishes and a medical center, administration, Catholic social services, day care center, Seaman's ministry, residence for retired women and men, marriage tribunal ministry, religious education, retreat center, bilingual education, Hispanic ministry.

Represented in the Archdioceses of Los Angeles, Portland, San Francisco and Seattle and in the Dioceses of Oakland, Reno-Las Vegas and Sacramento.

Vocation Director: P.O. Box 1028, Redwood City, CA 94064. (415) 369-1725.

SISTERS OF ST. FRANCIS, TIFFIN (O.S.F.)

200 St. Francis Ave., Tiffin, OH 44883. (419) 447-0435

160 Sisters

Apostolic Works: Education, health care, pastoral work, parish ministry, child care, care of elderly, social work, retreat and renewal programs.

Represented in the (Arch)dioceses of Brownsville, Charlotte, Cincinnati, Columbus, Covington, Davenport (IA), Detroit, Galveston/Houston, Indianapolis, Jackson, Kansas City, Lansing, Lexington, Los Angeles, Orlando, Owensboro, Rapid City, Santa Fe, Toledo, Venice (FL), Wheeling and in Chiapas, Mexico.

Director of New Membership: Sr. Gemma Fenbert, 200 St. Francis Ave., Tiffin, OH 44883.

SISTERS OF THE THIRD ORDER OF ST. FRANCIS (O.S.F.)

St. Francis Ln., E. Peoria, IL 61611.

Apostolic Work: Care of the sick and the poor in health-care facilities, education in colleges of nursing.

Represented in the Dioceses of Peoria and Rockford, IL; Marquette, MI; and Davenport, IA.

Vocation Director: Sr. Dorothy Lampe, O.S.F., Mt. Alverno Novitiate, St. Francis Ln., E. Peoria, IL 61611. (309) 699-9313.

THE LITTLE PORTION FRANCISCAN SISTERS (O.S.F.)

645 Assisi Way, Republic, MO 65738. (417) 732-6684

4 Sisters

Apostolic Work: Being a presence of God's healing love to the needy through spiritual ministry, shelter, food kitchen, low-income residency for elderly, ABE programs, free walk-in clinic, transitional housing units.

Represented in the Diocese of Springfield-Cape Girardeau.

Vocation Director: Little Portion Franciscan Sisters, 645 Assisi Way, Republic, MO 65738. (417) 732-6684.

GLENMARY SISTERS (G.H.M.S.)

The Glenmary Center: 405 W. Parrish Ave., Owensboro, KY 42302. (502) 686-8401

Apostolic Work: The Glenmary Sisters work in the rural areas of Appalachia and the deep South. They are radically involved with the issue of injustice, spiritual and material poverty and the rights of the downtrodden. The Sisters let the people know that they and their Catholic Christian communities do care.

Represented in the Dioceses of Owensboro, Lexington and Savannah.

Vocation Director: Sr. Mae Koenig, G.H.M.S., P.O. Box 22264, Owensboro, KY 42304. (502) 686-8401.

GOOD SHEPHERD SISTERS (R.G.S.)
(Sisters of Our Lady of Charity of the Good Shepherd)

(Province of New York)

New York Provincialate: 82-31 Doncaster Place, Jamaica, NY 11432. (718) 380-3270

123 Apostolic Sisters, 79 Contemplative Sisters

Apostolic Work: An international community whose special interest is teenagers and their families who have social and emotional problems. Forms of service include residential treatment centers for adolescent girls as well as smaller residences, diagnostic centers, special day school programs, community-based social service centers for families, ministry to prisoners, youth and training programs for those in the helping professions.

Represented in the Dioceses of New York, New Jersey and the New England States.

Vocation Office: 82-31 Doncaster Place, Jamaica, NY 11432.

GOOD SHEPHERD SISTERS (R.G.S.) (Sisters of Our Lady of Charity of the Good Shepherd)

(Washington, DC Province), 504 Hexton Hill Rd., Silver Spring, MD 20904. (301) 384-1169

Over 7,000 Sisters worldwide; 77 R.G.S. Sisters and 31 Contemplative Sisters of the Good Shepherd in the Washington Province; approximately 730 Good Shepherd Sisters in North America.

Apostolic Work: Reaching out to persons in personal/spiritual/family/social distress, this international community has a special concern for teenagers and their families who are experiencing social and emotional problems. Forms of service include residential treatment centers for adolescents, specialized day school programs for adolescents and pre-schoolers, community-based multi-service youth and family counseling/ diagnostic/educational centers, parish social ministry, many forms of social work as well as ministry to prisoners, homeless and battered

women, refugees, the elderly homebound and other outreach programs. Sisters serve in a variety of positions including administrators, bookkeepers, teachers, principals, caseworkers, nurses, group leaders, child care workers, psychologists, recreation leaders, residence directors, secretaries and counselors.

Represented in the Archdioceses of Atlanta, Baltimore, Philadelphia, Washington, DC and in the Dioceses of Scranton, Raleigh and Orlando. The entire international community is represented in over 60 nations of the world.

Vocation Director: Sr. Mary Frances, RGS, Sisters of the Good Shepherd, 537 Venard Rd., Clarks Summit, PA 18411. (717) 586-2647.

GOOD SHEPHERD SISTERS (R.G.S.) (Sisters of Our Lady of Charity of the Good Shepherd)

(Province of Cincinnati), 2849 Fischer Pl., Cincinnati, OH 45211. (513) 661-1833

113 Sisters

Apostolic Work: Primary work is directed toward persons in personal, social, and family difficulties, particularly girls and women. The chief work is conducting residential treatment facilities for teenage girls and day treatment programs for girls and boys.

Vocation Person: Sr. Christine Hock, R.G.S., 2440 Dawnlight Ave., Columbus, OH 43211-1934. (614) 471-2626, ext. 248.

GOOD SHEPHERD SISTERS (RGS)

(St. Louis Province), Provincial Convent of the Good Shepherd, 7654 Natural Bridge Rd., St. Louis, MO 63121-4989. (314) 381-3400

90 Sisters in St. Louis Province; 5,649 total internationally

Apostolic Works: St. Louis & San Francisco: women recovering from addiction. Chicago & Los Angeles: battered women w/children. Memphis: troubled teenage girls. New Orleans: women prisoners.

Vocation Office: Provincial Convent of Good Shepherd, 7654 Natural Bridge Rd., St. Louis, MO 63121-4989. (314) 381-3400.

See also Contemplative Sisters of the Good Shepherd, St. Louis Province.

**GOOD SHEPHERD SISTERS
(Sisters of Our Lady of Charity
of the Good Shepherd)
(Apostolic RGS/Contemplative
CGS)**
St. Paul Province, 5100 Hodgson
Rd., St. Paul, MN 55126. (612)
484-0221

60 Sisters

Apostolic Work: Apostolic Active
Sisters of the Good Shepherd; an
international community whose
special ministries are directed
towards youth in crisis; women in
transition and homeless; parish
ministry; single mothers; families
who need counseling; abused
women and children; Hispanic
ministry.

Apostolic Contemplative Sisters of
the Good Shepherd find joy in
prayer, community, work and play,
longing to bring the world to God's
liberating love.

Represented in the Archdioceses
of Omaha, Honolulu, Denver, Portland, St. Paul and Seattle.

Vocation Team: Sr. Maureen
Kunz, 5100 Hodgson Rd., St.
Paul, MN 55126. (612) 484-1601;
Sr. Elsie Fields, 562 N. Portland
Blvd., Portland, OR 97217. (503)
283-4931; Sr. Marge Cashman,
1573 S. Dexter Way, Denver, CO
80222. (303) 753-0248.

GREY NUNS OF MONTREAL
See Charity, Sisters of.

**GREY NUNS OF THE SACRED
HEART (G.N.S.H.)**
Motherhouse: 1750 Quarry Rd.,
Yardley, PA 19067.

199 Vowed Members, 1 Novice, 1
Temporary Professed

Apostolic Work: Education, health
care, social work, pastoral ministry, retreat ministry, religious
education, service on behalf of the
poor.

Represented in the Archdioceses
of Anchorage, Atlanta, Baltimore,
Detroit, New York, Philadelphia
and Washington, DC and in the
Dioceses of Allentown, Brooklyn,
Buffalo, Camden, Charlotte, Erie,
Gaylord, Metuchen, Newark,
Ogdensburg, Richmond, Rockville
Center, Trenton and Toronto,
Canada.

Vocation Directress: Sr. Mary Elizabeth Looby, GNSH, 1750 Quarry
Rd., Yardley, PA 19067. (215)
968-4236.

**SISTERS OF THE
GUARDIAN ANGEL (S.A.C.)**
Motherhouse: Madrid, Spain. U.S.
Foundation: 1245 S. Van Ness,
Los Angeles, CA 90019. (213)
732-7881

Represented in the Archdiocese of
Los Angeles.

**HANDMAIDS OF MARY
IMMACULATE (A.M.I.)**
Holy House Convent, P.O. Box
976, Washington, NJ 07882. (908)
689-7330

5 Sisters

Apostolic Work: Shrine of the
Immaculate Heart of Mary and
World Apostolate of Fatima.

Represented in the Diocese of
Metuchen.

Vocation Director: Sr. Mary Francis, A.M.I., Holy House Convent,
P.O. Box 976, Washington, NJ
07882. (908) 689-7330.

**HANDMAIDS OF THE
PRECIOUS BLOOD (H.P.B.)**
Motherhouse: Cor Jesu Monastery, Jemez Springs, NM 87025.
(505) 829-3906

33 Professed Sisters,1 Postulant,
2 First Professed Sisters

Apostolic Work: Contemplative life
of Perpetual Eucharistic Adoration
for the sanctification of priests and
needs of the entire world.

Represented in the Archdioceses
of Santa Fe and Chicago. Also in
Rome, Italy.

Vocation Director: Rev. Mother
David Marie, H.P.B.

**HANDMAIDS OF REPARATION
OF THE SACRED HEART OF
JESUS (A.R)**
Sacred Heart Villa, R.D. # 3, Sun-
shine Park, Steubenville, OH
43952.

6 Sisters in U.S.

Apostolic Work: Education all levels, religious education, parish and
diocesan ministry, C.C.D. work,
orphanages, missionary work-
Brazil.

Represented in the Dioceses of
Steubenville and Arlington. Also in
Italy, Brazil and Africa.

Contacts: Sr. Rosalba, A.R., R.D.
3, Sunshine Park, Steubenville,
OH 43952. (614) 282-3801; Sr.
Donatella, 9523 Lyra Ct., Burke,
VA 22153. (703) 455-4180.

**HANDMAIDS OF THE SACRED
HEART OF JESUS (a.c.j.)**
(U.S. Province) 616 Coopertown
Rd., Haverford, PA 19041. (610)
642-5715

1,900 Sisters worldwide; 50 Sisters U.S.

Apostolic Work: Adoration of the
Blessed Sacrament, education,
social and pastoral ministries and
spiritual centers.

Represented in the (Arch)dioceses
of Philadelphia, Atlanta, Miami and
Charlotte as well as Latin America,
Africa, Asia, India, Ireland, Great
Britain, Europe and the Philip-
pines.

Contact Person: Sr. Gloria
Petrone, a.c.j., 616 Coopertown
Rd., Haverford, PA 19041. (610)
642-5715.

**HERMANAS CATEQUISTAS
GUADALUPANAS (H.C.G.)**
Motherhouse: Mexico

American Foundation: 4110 S.
Flores, San Antonio, TX 78214.
(210) 532-9344

16 Sisters in U.S.

Apostolic Work: Evangelization,
catechesis and education. The
work is in parishes and in schools.

Represented in the Archdioceses
of Oklahoma City and San Antonio
and in the Diocese of Fort Worth.

Vocation Director: Sr. M. Clara
Ruiz, H.C.G., 4110 S. Flores, San
Antonio, TX 78214.

HERMANAS JOSEFINAS (H.J.)
Motherhouse: Mexico

U.S. Foundation: Assumption
Seminary, 2600 W. Woodlawn
Ave., P.O. Box 28240, San Anto-
nio, TX 78284. (210) 734-0039

8 Sisters

Represented in the Archdioceses
of Chicago, Denver, Los Angeles
and San Antonio and in the Diocese of El Paso.

**SOCIETY OF THE HOLY CHILD
JESUS (S.H.C.J.)**
(American Province), Provincial
House: 460 Shadeland Ave.,
Drexel Hill, PA 19026. (610) 626-
1400

300 Sisters

Apostolic Work: 1 college, a number of secondary and elementary
schools throughout the United
States. The Society is an international congregation of women living an Ignatian spirituality through
a variety of educational, pastoral,

spiritual and socio-political apostolates in order to help others find Christ hidden within our world.

SHCJ sponsors a lay ministry program entitled, "Response-Ability" which sends volunteers to teach in inner city Los Angeles, Philadelphia and New York.

Represented in California, Colorado, Connecticut, Delaware, District of Columbia, Florida, Illinois, Indiana, Kentucky, Louisiana, Maryland, Massachusetts, New Jersey, New Mexico, New York, North Carolina, Oregon, Pennsylvania and Wisconsin.

Vocation Coordinators: Sr. Jeanne Hatch, S.H.C.J., 460 Shadeland Ave., Drexel Hill, PA 19026. (610) 626-1400.

HOLY CROSS SISTERS

700 E. Riverside, Merrill, WI 54452. (715) 536-5445

54 Members (U.S.); 5,800 worldwide

Apostolic Work: All fields carrying out the motto: "The need of the times is the will of God."

Represented in the Archdioceses of Cincinnati, OH, Milwaukee, WI, New Orleans, LA and St. Louis, MO and in the Dioceses of Superior, WI; Green Bay, WI; LaCrosse, WI; Gaylord, MI; Venice, FL; Bismarck, ND; Belleville, IL; Baton Rouge, LA; and Des Moines, IA. Also in Switzerland.

Contact Person: Sr. John Marie Semien, Holy Cross Sisters, 700 E. Riverside Ave., Merrill, WI 54452. (715) 536-5445.

SISTERS OF THE HOLY CROSS (CSC)

Generalate: Saint Mary's, Notre Dame, IN 46556.

760 Sisters

Represented in the U.S. and abroad in Brazil, Peru, Ghana, Uganda, Israel and Bangladesh.

Apostolic Work: Education, health care, parish, retreats, social service.

Vocation Director: Sr. Rita Slattery, CSC, Bertrand Hall, St. Mary's College, Notre Dame, IN 46556. (219) 284-5550.

SISTERS OF HOLY CROSS (C.S.C.)

Regional Office: 377 Island Pond Rd., Manchester, NH 03109-4811. (603) 622-9504

260 Sisters

Apostolic Work: 1 college, 1 preschool; serve in 6 parish and diocesan regional high schools; 17 parish and regional grammar schools; 15 religious education centers. Also in pastoral ministry, Christian Life Centers, hospitals, staff chaplaincies and social work.

Represented in the (Arch)dioceses of Springfield, Manchester, Burlington, St. Petersburg, FL, Norwich, Worcester, Fall River, Portland and New York. Foreign missions in six foreign countries.

Director of Vocation Ministry: Anne Hosffler, CSC, 106 W. River Dr., Apt. 16, Manchester, NH 03104. (603) 624-8047.

CONGREGATION OF THE SISTERS OF THE HOLY FAITH (C.H.F.)

United States Region: 12322 Paramount Blvd., Downey, CA 90242. (310) 923-4013.

267 Sisters, 4 Novices

Conduct: 40 grammar schools, 16 high schools, religious education coordinators, pastoral associates, campus and youth ministers, center for women alcoholics, social work, R.C.I.A. directors, ministry directors, parish sisters, church musicians.

Represented in the Archdioceses of Los Angeles, New Orleans and San Francisco and in the Dioceses of Orange and Sacramento. Also in Ireland, Trinidad, New Zealand, Australia and Peru.

Formation Director: Sr. Dolores Maguire, C.H.F., 11513 Rives Ave., Downey, CA 90241. (310) 861-6698.

SISTERS OF THE HOLY FAMILY OF NAZARETH (C.S.F.N.)

(Immaculate Heart of Mary Province), Marian Heights, 1428 Monroe Tnpk., Monroe, CT 06468.

160 Sisters

Apostolic Work: 1 high school, 1 child-caring institution, 14 elementary schools, 17 Christian Doctrine centers, 1 foster home care center, 1 clinical dispensary, retreats, and social services

Represented in the (Arch)dioceses of Bridgeport, Brooklyn, Hartford, Norwich, Rockville Centre, Syracuse and Worcester.

Vocation Coordinator: Sr. M. Bernice S. (203) 261-0866.

SISTERS OF THE HOLY FAMILY OF NAZARETH (C.S.F.N.)

(The Immaculate Conception Province), 4001 Grant Ave., Philadelphia, PA 19114-2999. (215) 335-6381.

188 Sisters

Apostolic Work: 1 college, 1 high school academy, 1 grade school academy, 4 high schools, 9 elementary schools, 1 kindergarten, 1 nursery, 1 child-care institution, 1 hospital, 1 nursing home, 2 parish ministries, 4 CCD programs, 2 inner city ministries.

Represented in the Archdioceses of Baltimore, Miami and Philadelphia and in the Dioceses of Allentown, Scranton, San Juan.

Vocation Director: Sr. Mary Ann Allton, CSFN.

SISTERS OF THE HOLY FAMILY OF NAZARETH (C.S.F.N.)

(Sacred Heart Province), 353 N. River Rd., Des Plaines, IL 60016.

Apostolic Work: Ministry to families in education, nursing, retirement homes, parish ministry, religious education and retreat work.

Represented in the Archdiocese of Chicago.

Vocation Director: Sr. Sandra Marie, 353 N. River Rd., Des Plaines, IL 60016. (708) 298-3449.

SISTERS OF THE HOLY FAMILY OF NAZARETH (C.S.F.N.)

(St. Joseph Province) Mt. Nazareth, 285 Bellevue Rd., Pittsburgh, PA 15229-2195. (412) 931-4775

173 Professed Sisters

Apostolic Work: Education, nursing and other hospital services, social services, child care, day care, parish ministry, religious education, elder care, family ministry.

Represented in the Archdioceses of Detroit and Washington and in the Dioceses of Pittsburgh, Erie, Cleveland and Altoona-Johnstown.

Membership Director: Sr. Janice Marie Blados, C.S.F.N., Mt. Nazareth, 285 Bellevue Rd., Pittsburgh, PA 15229-2195. (412) 931-4775.

SISTERS OF THE HOLY FAMILY OF NAZARETH (C.S.F.N.)

(Blessed Frances Siedliska Province), 1814 Egyptian Way, P.O. Box 530959, Grand Prairie, TX 75053. (214) 641-4496

46 Sisters

Apostolic Work: 3 elementary schools, 1 community college, 2 hospitals, parish ministry, religious education.

Represented in the Dioceses of Dallas, Fort Worth and Tyler.

Vocation Director: Sr. M. Margaret Langsett, 1814 Egyptian Way, P.O. Box 530959, Grand Prairie, TX 75053. (214) 641-4496.

CONGREGATION OF THE SISTERS OF THE HOLY FAMILY (S.S.F.)

6901 Chef Menteur Hwy., New Orleans, LA 70126. (504) 242-8315

208 Sisters

Conduct: Education at elementary and secondary levels, 1 nursing home, 2 apartments for the elderly and 2 day care centers.

Represented in the Archdioceses of Los Angeles, New Orleans and Washington, DC and in the Dioceses of Alexandria, Baton Rouge, Galveston-Houston, Lafayette and Tyler and in the Diocese of Belize in Central America and in Nigeria, West Africa.

Vocation Director: Sr. Carmen Marie Bertrand, S.S.F., 6901 Chef Menteur Hwy., New Orleans, LA 70126. (504) 241-5418.

SISTERS OF THE HOLY FAMILY (S.H.F.)

P.O. Box 3248, Fremont, CA 94539. (510) 490-8657

165 Sisters

Apostolic Work: Religious ed classes, teacher training for laity, parish home visiting, parent education, family programs, youth ministry programs, pastoral care (hospital chaplains, bereaved and infirmed, AIDS), parish pastoral administrators, social service/social workers, nurses and home health care, child and family counselors, director of worship, librarian, public school teachers, religious education classes for developmentally handicapped children, diocesan religious education directors and coordinators, day care for pre-school children, associate pastors.

Represented in the Archdioceses of Anchorage, Los Angeles and San Francisco and in the Dioceses of Honolulu, Fresno, Monterey, Oakland, Reno, Sacramento, Salt Lake City, San Antonio, San Diego, San Jose, Stockton and in Kentucky, South Dakota and Seattle, WA and California.

Vocation Director: Sr. Mary Ruth Faisca, S.H.F., (510) 490-8657.

SISTERS OF THE HOLY NAMES OF JESUS AND MARY (S.N.J.M.)

(New York Province), 1061 New Scotland Ave., Albany, NY 12208. (518) 489-5469

137 Sisters

Ministries: Elementary, high school, college teachers, religious education directors, involved in parish ministry to elderly, pastoral work, counseling, health care, migrant ministry, advocacy work, missionary work in Africa, Haiti, South America.

Represented in the Archdioceses of Washington and New York and in the Dioceses of Albany, Baltimore, Jackson, Roanoke, St. Petersburg, Orlando, Palm Beach and Venice.

Vocation Director: Sr. Mary E. Glavin, 3214 Marlin Ave., Tampa, FL 33611.

SISTERS OF THE HOLY NAMES OF JESUS AND MARY (S.N.J.M.)

(Province of Oregon), P.O. Box 25, Marylhurst, OR 97036. (503) 635-3621

250 Sisters

Ministries: Elementary, high school, college teachers, religious education directors, parish ministry to elderly, retreat ministry, pastoral associates, pastoral care in hospitals, family education and counseling, various ministries to the disadvantaged.

Represented in the Archdiocese of Portland, OR, in the Diocese of Baker and in many other places throughout the U.S.

Vocation Director: Sr. Eileen Brown, S.N.J.M., Membership Team, P.O. Box 25, Marylhurst, OR 97036. (503) 635-3621.

SISTERS OF THE HOLY NAMES OF JESUS AND MARY (S.N.J.M.)

(Province of California), PO Box 907, Los Gatos, CA 95031. (408) 395-5150

290 Sisters, 90 Associates

Ministries: Education at the pre-school, elementary, secondary, and college level; campus ministry, religious education, retreats and spiritual direction, pastoral and youth ministry, social justice.

Represented in the Archdioceses of Los Angeles and San Francisco and in the Dioceses of Oakland, Orange, Monterey, San Jose, San Bernadino and San Diego. Also in Central and South America, Canada, South Africa and Haiti.

Vocation Director: Sr. Molly Neville, S.N.J.M., 26900 Patrick Ave., Hayward, CA 94544. (510) 785-9197.

SISTERS OF THE HOLY NAMES OF JESUS AND MARY (S.N.J.M.)

(Province of Washington), 2911 West Fort Wright Dr., Spokane, WA 99204. (509) 328-7470

224 Sisters; 69 Associates

Ministries: Educators in the faith, all levels; pastoral ministry, spiritual direction, retreats.

Represented in the Archdiocese of Seattle and in the Diocese of Spokane and Yakima.

Vocation Director: Sr. Mary Rita Rohde, S.N.J.M., 109 North "E" St., Toppenish, WA 98948. (509) 865-3836.

SISTERS OF THE HOLY REDEEMER (CSR)

Provincialate: 521 Moredon Rd., Huntingdon Valley, PA 19006. (215) 938-0540

50 Sisters in U.S., 890 worldwide

Apostolic Work: Minister to the needs of the poor, the sick, the elderly and homeless mothers and children in the Philadelphia and southern New Jersey areas, in the fields of health care, social services and pastoral care. Minister in our hospital, nursing homes, home health and hospice care agencies, or our transitional housing program and low-income residential facilities for senior citizens.

Special Programs: An affiliate program which enables a woman to share in the lifestyle of a sister before making a commitment to religious life; a Long Distance Contact Program for women who desire a close relationship with a religious congregation, but live too far away to visit on a regular basis; Redeemer Ministry Corps lay volunteer ministry program.

Vocation Director: Sr. Anne Marie Haas, CSR; Asst. Vocation Director: Audrey K. McKenzie (215) 938-0540, ext. 29.

SISTERS OF THE MOST HOLY SACRAMENT (M.H.S.)

Administration Office: P.O. Box 30727, Lafayette, LA 70593-0727. (318) 981-8475

47 Sisters

Apostolic Work: Teaching, CCD, pastoral work, social work, health care, home missions.

Represented in the Archdiocese of New Orleans and in the Dioceses of Baton Rouge, LA; Lafayette, LA; Biloxi, MS.

Vocation Director: Sr. Justina Baker, M.H.S., P.O. Box 30727, Lafayette, LA 70593-0727. (318) 981-8475.

HOLY SPIRIT ADORATION SISTERS
(Sister Servants of the Holy Spirit of Perpetual Adoration)
Convent of Divine Love, 2212 Green St., Philadelphia, PA 19130. (215) 567-0123
70 Sisters in U.S.
Apostolic Work: Perpetual Adoration of the Most Blessed Sacrament exposed in the monstrance day and night. Contemplative life.
Represented in the Archdiocese of St. Louis and in the Dioceses of Corpus Christi and Lincoln. Also, in the Philippine Islands, Argentina, Germany, Holland, India, Brazil and Poland.
Vocation Director: Sr. Mary Caritas.

HOLY SPIRIT MISSIONARY SISTERS (S.Sp.S.)
Provincial House: Convent of the Holy Spirit, P.O. Box 6026, Techny, IL 60082. (708) 272-5930
160 Sisters in the U.S.
An international community of 4,000 women called to witness to the presence and power of the Holy Spirit, and to continue the saving mission of Jesus Christ.
Apostolic Work: In schools from pre-school through university; in technical and professional schools; in hospitals as administrators, physicians, nurses, technicians, dieticians, and chaplains; involved with the elderly and the marginalized; in parishes in religious education and youth ministry; in spiritual direction, retreat work, counseling and social work.
Represented in 35 countries: Angola, Argentina, Australia, Austria, Bolivia, Botswana, Brazil, Chile, China, Czech Republic, England, Germany, Ghana, India, Indonesia, Ireland, Italy, Japan, Korea, Mexico, Netherlands, Papua New Guinea, Paraguay, Philippines, Poland, Portugal, Romania, Russia, Slovakia, Spain, Switzerland, Taiwan, Togo, Ukraine and in the United States.
Vocation Ministers: Sr. Rose Martin, S.Sp.S., Sr. Margaret Anne Norris, S.Sp.S., 2600 Waukegan Rd., Techny, IL 60082. (708) 272-5930.

MISSION SISTERS OF THE HOLY SPIRIT (M.S.Sp.)
Motherhouse: 1030 N. River Road, Saginaw, MI 48609.
12 Professed Sisters
Apostolic Work: Religious education, medical work, social work and pastoral ministry.

Vocation Directress: Sr. Margo Tafoya, M.S.Sp., 1030 N. River Rd., Saginaw, MI 48609. (517) 781-0934.

SISTERS OF THE HOLY SPIRIT (S.H.S.)
5246 Clarwin Ave., Pittsburgh, PA 15229.
93 Sisters
Apostolic Work: Pre-school, teaching (kindergarten, elementary, secondary, college, adult and religious education), retreat ministry, home for the elderly, nursing and nursing education, administration, business, social services, pastoral ministry, formation ministry, youth ministry, ministry to the poor, the arts. Open to emerging needs.
Represented in the Dioceses of Pittsburgh, Greensburg and Youngstown.
Vocation Director: Sr. Patricia Eleanor Myers, SHS, 5246 Clarwin Ave., Pittsburgh, PA 15229; (412) 931-1917; 931-9790.

SISTERS OF THE HOLY SPIRIT (C.S.Sp.)
10102 Granger Rd., Garfield Heights, OH 44125. (216) 581-2941
9 Sisters
Apostolic Work: Elementary and secondary education; nursing, nursing home administration, dietary supervision, medical records, physical therapy, occupational therapy, related health care services, other service areas according to the needs of the Church and the particular talents of the community.
Represented in the Diocese of Cleveland.
Superior General: Sr. Mary Assumpta, C.S.Sp., 10102 Granger Rd., Garfield Heights, OH 44125.

SISTERS OF THE HOLY SPIRIT AND MARY IMMACULATE (S.H.Sp.)
Motherhouse: 301 Yucca St., San Antonio, TX 78203. (210) 533-5149
140 Sisters
Apostolic Work: Minister with the poor and marginated in schools, catechetical centers, social services, parish ministry, health care, home for the aged.
Represented in the (Arch)dioceses of San Antonio, Dallas, Fort Worth, Brownsville, Beaumont, Corpus Christi, Galveston-Houston, New Orleans, Houma-Thibodaux, Lafayette, Alexandria; Biloxi, Jackson,

MS, Nayarit and Oaxaca, Mexico and Zambia, Africa.
Vocation Director: Sr. Mary Fagan, S.H.Sp. (210) 533-5149.

SISTERS OF THE HOLY UNION (SUSC)
(Fall River Province) Provincialate: 550 Rock St., Fall River, MA 02720. (508) 678-3616.
125 Sisters
Apostolic Work: Education on elementary, secondary, college level, day care, adult education, religious education, pastoral ministry (parish and diocesan level), outreach ministries, hospital chaplaincy, nursing, health ministries, youth/young adult ministry, campus ministry, social work, secretarial, music ministry, retreat/spiritual direction, prison ministry, work with refugees/aliens, ministry to the elderly, missions.
Represented in Florida, Kentucky, Maryland, Massachusetts, New York and Rhode Island. Also in Italy and Tanzania.
Vocation Director: Sr. Mary Hildegarde Kogler, SUSC, 21-60 31st St., Astoria, NY 11105. (718) 278-5954.

SISTERS OF THE HOLY UNION (susc)
(Sacred Heart Province), Main St., Box 993, Groton, MA 01450.
96 Sisters
Apostolic Work: Elementary, secondary, special education, parish religious education, parish secretarial work, pastoral ministry, social services, adult education, nursing, foreign missions, refugees, outreach ministry, retreat and spiritual direction, work with refugees, with the elderly, language skills for immigrants.
Represented in the Archdiocese of Boston and in the Dioceses of Fall River, Providence and Worcester. Also in 14 countries in Europe, South America and in Africa.
Vocation Director: Sr. Helen Poirier, susc, 45 Eerie Ave., Brockton, MA 02402. (508) 559-7642.

HOME VISITORS OF MARY (H.V.M.)
356 Arden Park, Detroit, MI 48202.
16 Sisters
Apostolic Work: A small religious community founded in 1949, dedicated to the mission of serving Christ among people in the heart

of the city. Pastoral ministry, evangelization, lay leadership development, retreat work, small Christian community development, human relations seminars, African American spirituality center.

Represented in the Archdiocese of Detroit and in the Dioceses of Lansing and Tucson.

Vocation Director: 356 Arden Park, Detroit, MI 48202. (313) 875-1123.

HOSPITAL SISTERS OF ST. FRANCIS (O.S.F.)

St. Francis Convent, Sangamon Ave. Rd., Springfield, IL 62794-9431. (217) 522-3386

270 Sisters

Apostolic Work: All health-related fields including nursing, social service, home health care, pastoral care and administration. Thirteen hospitals in Illinois and Wisconsin. Mission centers in Taiwan and Haiti. International congregation with community members also in Germany, Poland, the Netherlands, Japan and India.

Vocation Directress: Sr. Joan Miller, O.S.F., St. Francis Convent, Sangamon Ave. Rd., Springfield, IL 62794-9431. (217) 522-3386.

CONGREGATION OF THE HUMILITY OF MARY (C.H.M.)

820 W. Central Park, Davenport, IA 52804.

194 Sisters, 69 Associates

Apostolic Work: Education: teaching and administration; pastoral ministry/religious education; social services: jail ministry, homeless and abused women, substance abuse rehabilitation; other individual ministries: law, communications, artist, health services, ministry to the elderly.

Vocation Director: Sr. Joann Kuebrich, C.H.M., 820 W. Central Park, Davenport, IA 52804.

SISTERS OF THE HUMILITY OF MARY (H.M.)

Motherhouse: Villa Maria Community Center, Villa Maria, PA 16155. (412) 964-8861

300 Sisters

Apostolic Work: Diversified ministries, including education, health care, parish ministry, evangelization, social services, work for justice and peace and prayer.

Represented in Ohio and western Pennsylvania, but represented in smaller numbers in 10 other states and 2 foreign countries.

Membership Office: Sr. Kathleen King, H.M., 19220 Lorain Rd., Fairview Park, OH 44126. (216) 333-5373.

I.C.M. MISSIONARY SISTERS (I.C.M.)
(Missionary Sisters of the Immaculate Heart of Mary)

238 E. 15th St., Apt. 5, New York, NY 10003-3901. (212) 677-2959

33 Sisters in U.S.

Apostolic Work: Sisters involved in various forms of educational, pastoral, social, and health care ministries. Similar ministries in foreign missions.

Represented by 1,026 Sisters in 10 mission posts in the U.S. Archdioceses of Los Angeles, New York and Philadelphia and in the Dioceses of Albany and Brownsville, 140 communities overseas in 19 different countries of Africa, Asia, Europe and Latin America.

Vocation Counselor: Sr. Alene Grothues, 238 E. 15th St., Apt. 5, New York, NY 10003-3901. (212) 677-2959.

SISTERS OF THE IMMACULATE CONCEPTION (C.I.C.)

4920 Kent Ave., Metairie, LA 70006-1099. (504) 887-8371

17 Sisters

Apostolic Work: CCD work, child care, ministry to sick and aged, service to retreatants, domestic and managerial work, Ministries develop as the Spirit moves.

Represented in the Archdiocese of New Orleans and in the Diocese of Houma-Thibodaux.

SISTERS OF THE IMMACULATE CONCEPTION (R.C.M.)

Delegation House: 2230 Franklin St., San Francisco, CA 94109. (415) 474-0159

19 Sisters in U.S. (550 around the world)

Conduct: schools, Hispanic apostolate, CCD, missionary work, social & parish work, catechesis, orphanages, youth ministry.

Represented in the Archdiocese of San Francisco and in the Diocese of Fresno. Also in Spain, Italy, Brazil, Venezuela, Dominican Republic, Japan, Zaire, Equatorial Guinea, S. Korea and Filippines.

Vocation Director: Sr.Gloria Gil.

SISTERS OF THE IMMACULATE CONCEPTION OF THE BLESSED VIRGIN MARY (Lithuanian)

Immaculate Conception Convent and Novitiate, 600 Liberty Hwy., Putnam, CT 06260. (203) 928-7955.

33 Sisters

Apostolic Work: Committed to Christ through a life of dedicated service and prayer: Catechetics and religious instruction; spiritual renewal programs; education of pre-school children and youth through day care and camping; health care ministry of the sick and elderly; social service; ministry through the media.

Represented in the Archdiocese of Chicago and in the Dioceses of Norwich, CT and Burlington, VT. Also in Montreal and Toronto, Canada.

Vocation Director: Immaculate Conception Convent and Novitiate, 600 Liberty Hwy., Putnam, CT 06260.

SISTERS OF THE IMMACULATE HEART OF MARY (I.H.M.)

(U.S. Province), 4100 Sabino Canyon Rd., Tucson, AZ 85715. (602) 886-4273

50 Sisters in U.S.

Conduct: 1 novitiate, grammar schools, high schools, religious education programs in parishes.

Represented in the Archdiocese of Miami and in the Dioceses of Oakland and Tucson. Also in Spain, France, Italy, Cuba, Chile and the U.S.

Contact: Vocation Director, 4100 Sabino Canyon Rd., Tucson, AZ 85715.

SISTERS OF THE IMMACULATE HEART OF MARY OF WICHITA (I.H.M.)

605 North Woodchuck, Wichita, KS 67212. (316) 722-9316

9 Sisters, 1 Postulant

Apostolic Work: Education and retreat work.

Represented in the Diocese of Wichita.

Vocation Director: Sr. Marie Bernadette Mertens, I.H.M., 605 N. Woodchuck, Wichita, KS 67212. (316) 722-9316.

SISTERS OF THE INCARNATE WORD AND BLESSED SACRAMENT (S.I.W.)

Motherhouse & House of Formation: 6618 Pearl Rd., Parma Heights, OH 44130.

43 Vowed Members, 1 Temporary Professed, 48 Associate Members

Apostolic Work: Education, pastoral care, hospital chaplaincy, social work, ministry with the retarded and with runaways, retreats and spiritual direction, diocesan office.

Vocation Minister: Sr. Rosemarie Burke, S.I.W., 9139 Broadview Rd., Broadview Heights, OH 44147. (216) 526-4069.

CONGREGATION OF THE INCARNATE WORD AND BLESSED SACRAMENT (C.V.I.)

Motherhouse and Novitiate: 3400 Bradford Pl., Houston, TX 77025. (713) 668-0423

67 Sisters

Apostolic Works: 7 elementary schools, 1 high school, religious education, department for aging, diocesan office, social services, retreat/renewal, hospital chaplaincy, Hispanic/community services, pastoral ministry, nursing.

Represented in the Dioceses of Austin, Beaumont and Galveston-Houston.

Vocation Contact: in Houston: Incarnate Word Convent, Sr. Madeleine Grace, C.V.I., 609 Crawford St., Houston, TX 77002. (713) 223-4143.

CONGREGATION OF THE INCARNATE WORD AND BLESSED SACRAMENT (I.W.B.S.)

Incarnate Word Convent, 1101 N.E. Water St., Victoria, TX 77901. (512) 575-7296

120 Sisters

Conduct: 1 academy (pre-K through 8); 1 academy multi-level learning center (pre-school through K, alternative high school, adult ed.); high schools (2 parochial, 1 private); 10 parochial grade schools; 1 private elementary; 5 C.C.D. centers; 3 day care centers. Minister in other institutions: 4 hospitals; 1 state school for the disabled; 2 parochial grade schools. Special assignments: administration; parish ministry; RCIA; retreats; spiritual direction; counseling; diocesan director of ministries; clerical and domestic work; religious goods shop; spiritual and corporal works of mercy.

Represented in the Archdiocese of San Antonio and in the Dioceses of Beaumont, Corpus Christi, Dallas, Galveston-Houston, Victoria and Rome. Also in Kenya, Africa.

Vocation Directress: Sr. M. Amata Hollas, I.W.B.S., 1101 N.E. Water St., Victoria, TX 77901. (512) 575-7296; 575-2266.

CONGREGATION OF THE INCARNATE WORD AND BLESSED SACRAMENT (I.W.B.S.)
(Sisters of the Incarnate Word and Blessed Sacrament of Corpus Christi)

Motherhouse and Novitiate: 2930 S. Alameda St., Corpus Christi, TX 78404. (512) 882-5413

74 Sisters

Conduct: 1 private high school, 2 private middle schools, 2 private grade schools, 2 kindergartens, 1 Montessori, 2 parochial grade schools, 1 language school, 3 parish ministry, 4 diocesan offices, 3 health care.

Represented in the Dioceses of Brownsville, Corpus Christi, Houston and Fort Worth. Also in Nakuru, Kenya (East Africa).

Vocations: Sr. Rose Miriam Gansle, I.W.B.S.

CONGREGATION OF THE INFANT JESUS (C.I.J.)
(Nursing Sisters of the Sick Poor)

Motherhouse: 310 Prospect Park W., Brooklyn, NY 11215. (718) 965-7300

82 Sisters

Apostolic Work: Healing ministry, sponsor one hospital and one community health agency. Engaged in nursing, administration, social services, physical therapy, services to the handicapped, pastoral care, parish outreach and other works related to health services.

Represented in the Dioceses of Brooklyn and Rockville Centre.

Vocation Director: 310 Prospect Park W., Brooklyn, NY 11215. (718) 965-7300.

INSTITUTE OF THE BLESSED VIRGIN MARY (I.B.V.M.)
(Sisters of Loretto)

Loretto Convent, Box 508, Wheaton, IL 60189.

332 Sisters in Community, 128 in U.S.

Apostolic Work: Education in its broadest sense, pastoral and social ministry.

Represented in the (Arch)dioceses of Marquette, Chicago, Phoenix, Joliet, Rockford, Nashville, Sacramento, San Bernadino, Isle of St. Vincent and in the Canadian Provinces of Ontario and Saskatchewan.

Vocation Directors: Vocation Director, Loretto Convent, P.O. Box 508, Wheaton, IL 60189. (708) 653-4740; Vocation Director, 101 Mason Blvd., Toronto, Ontario, Canada M5M 3E2. (416) 483-2238.

INSTITUTE OF THE BLESSED VIRGIN MARY (I.B.V.M.)
(also known as Loreto Sisters)

Mary Ward House, 2521 W. Maryland Ave., Phoenix, AZ 85017. (602) 433-0658

16 Sisters

Apostolic Work: Teaching, religious instruction, hospital chaplaincy, parish ministry.

Represented in the Diocese of Phoenix; other Provinces in Peru, Kenya, S. Africa, Mauritius, India, Australia, Spain, England, Ireland.

Directress of Formation: Sr. Anne Fitzsimons, IBVM.

IRISH URSULINE UNION (O.S.U.)

Our Lady of Lourdes Convent, 1973 Torch Hill Rd., Columbus, GA 31903. (706) 689-5184

4 Sisters

Apostolic Work: Parish domestic ministry, education.

Represented in the Diocese of Savannah.

Local Superior: Sr. Kathleen Twomey.

POOR SISTERS OF JESUS CRUCIFIED AND THE SORROWFUL MOTHER (C.J.C.)

Our Lady of Sorrows Convent, 261 Thatcher St., Brockton, MA 02402. (508) 588-5070.

63 Sisters

Apostolic Work: Nursing homes, parochial schools, CCD center, retreats.

Represented in the (Arch)dioceses of Boston, Scranton and Allentown.

Vocation Director: Sr. Baptista, CJC, 261 Thatcher St., Brockton, MA 02402. (508) 588-5070.

CONGREGATION OF THE SISTERS OF JESUS CRUCIFIED (J.C.-O.S.B.)

Regina Mundi Priory, Waterloo and Fairfield Rds., Devon, PA 19333. (215) 688-5130

180 Sisters in Congregation, 30 in U.S.

Motherhouse: Prieure S. Joseph, 77177 Brou-sur-Chantereine, France

Other Locations: In U.S.: Diocese of Providence (Newport, RI), France, Holland, Japan.

Apostolic Work: A contemplative, monastic community living in the tradition of St. Benedict; open to women with certain physical limitations as well as those in good health. Good psychological and emotional balance is essential.

Vocation Directress: St. Paul's Priory, 61 Narragansett Ave., Newport, RI 02840. (401) 847-2423.

SISTERS OF THE LAMB OF GOD (A.D.)

2919 Christie Pl., Owensboro, KY 42301. (502) 926-2739

120 Sisters in Congregation; 11 in the U.S.

Motherhouse in Brest, France; one mission in Cameroon

Apostolic Work: Offers to the healthy as well as to those with physical disabilities the opportunity to fulfill their vocation, witnessing to the love of God and serving in diverse apostolates.

Represented in the Diocese of Owensboro.

Vocation Directress: Sr. Audrey, A.D., 9534 Kentucky 144, Philpot, KY 42366. (502) 281-5450; 281-4881.

SISTERS OF LIFE (Sorores Vitae) (S.V.)

198 Hollywood Ave., Bronx, NY 10465. (718) 863-2264.

8 Professed Sisters, 19 Novices, 3 Postulants

Apostolic Work: Contemplative prayer and pro-life activities in behalf of the sacredness of human life in all stages, particularly emphasizing protection and reverence for the life of the unborn and the terminally ill.

Represented in the Archdiocese of New York.

Superior: Mother Agnes Mary, 198 Hollywood Ave., Bronx, NY 10465. (718) 863-2264.

SISTERS OF THE LITTLE COMPANY OF MARY (L.C.M.)

American Provincial House: 9350 S. California Ave., Evergreen Park, IL 60805. (708) 229-5490

35 Sisters in U.S.; 566 worldwide

Apostolic Work: Health care ministry in three hospitals, two extended care/convalescent facilities, three parishes (pastoral ministry) and outreach programs.

Represented in the Archdioceses of Chicago and Los Angeles and in the Dioceses of Toledo, Orange, Evansville, Joliet and Gary. Also in 12 foreign countries including Tonga, Korea, Haiti and Bosnia.

Vocation Director: Sr. Jean Stickney, L.C.M., 9350 So. California Ave., Evergreen Pk., IL 60805.

LITTLE FRANCISCANS OF MARY (P.F.M.)

Regional House: 2 Dupont St., Worcester, MA 01604.

Total membership 350

Apostolic Work: Nursing, teaching, pastoral work, care of the aged, catechetical work, foreign missions in Madagascar and Haiti.

Represented in the Dioceses of Portland and Worcester. Also in Quebec Province. Foreign Missions.

Coordinator of Vocations: Sr. Rena Mae Gagnon, p.f.m., 2 Dupont St., Worcester, MA 01604.

LITTLE MISSIONARIES OF THE EUCHARIST

See Little Missionaries Pious Society.

**LITTLE MISSIONARIES PIOUS SOCIETY (L.M.)
(formerly known as Little Missionaries of the Eucharist)**

St. Theresa House, 50 Brown Ave., Roslindale, MA 02131. (617) 323-4644

1 Sister, 12 Lay Associates

Apostolic Work: Spiritual casework, catechetical, retreat and nursing programs.

Represented in the Archdiocese of Boston.

Vocation Directress: Sr. Mary Elizabeth, L.M. (617) 323-4644.

**LITTLE MISSIONARY SISTERS OF CHARITY (L.M.S.C.)
(Don Orione)**

North American Headquarters: 120 Orient Ave., East Boston, MA 02128. (617) 569-2102.

Generalate: Monte Acero, 5, Rome, Italy

13 Sisters; 1,000 (worldwide)

Apostolic Work: Rooted in prayer and contemplation; various apostolates: minister to the needs of the poor, the sick, the elderly and handicapped, education of the youth, pastoral ministry, religious education, missionary activity.

Represented in the Archdiocese of Boston (MA). Also in Italy, Argentina, Uruguay, Paraguay, Chile, Brazil, Spain, Portugal, Poland, Madagascar, Kenya and the Cape Verdian Islands.

Vocation Directress: 120 Orient Ave., East Boston, MA 02128. (617) 569-2102.

LITTLE SERVANT SISTERS OF THE IMMACULATE CONCEPTION (L.S.I.C.)

Immaculate Conception Provincialate & Novitiate, 1000 Cropwell Rd., Cherry Hill, NJ 08003. (609) 424-1962

75 Sisters; 1,500 Sisters worldwide

Apostolic Work: 1 novitiate, 1 retreat house, 1 nursery school, 4 elementary schools, 1 home nursing service, 1 senior day center, 3 residences for the aged, 2 nursing homes, 1 Archbishop's residence services, 1 mission: Mexico, religious education, prayer cenacle, pastoral work, social services, youth activities.

Represented in the Archdioceses of Newark and Philadelphia and in the Dioceses of Camden, Metuchen and the Diocese of Tijuana (Mexico). Motherhouse: Poland. Also represented in Italy, Austria, Ukraine, Russia, South Africa and Zambia.

Vocation Directress: Sr. M. Philomena, Little Servant Sisters, 1000 Cropwell Rd., Cherry Hill, NJ 08003. (609) 424-1962.

LITTLE SISTERS OF THE ASSUMPTION (L.S.A.)

U.S. Provincialate: 214 E. 30th St., New York, NY 10016. Motherhouse in Paris, France.

48 Sisters

Apostolic Work: Live and work among the poor. Seeking to build, in the Spirit of Jesus Christ, the wholeness of families faced with extreme health, social, and economic problems.

Represented in the Archdioceses of Boston, New York and Philadelphia and in the Diocese of Worcester, MA. Also in 23 countries.

Vocation Directress: Little Sisters of the Assumption. 214 E. 30th St., New York, NY 10016. (212) 889-4310.

LITTLE SISTERS OF THE GOSPEL OF CHARLES DE FOUCAULD
P.O. Box 305, Mott Haven Station, Bronx, NY 10454
4 Sisters
Apostolic Work: Fostering the growth of Christian community among the poor. Apostolate springs from a deep contemplative spirit, prayer and community life.
Vocation Director: Sr. Rita Claus.

LITTLE SISTERS OF THE HOLY FAMILY (P.S.S.F.)
486 Chandler St., Tewksbury, MA 01876-0419. (508) 851-2462
Apostolic Work: Dedicated to the service of priests by prayer, domestic work in rectories, etc.
Represented in the Archdioceses of Boston and Chicago and in the Diocese of Manchester, NH. Also, in Canada and missions in Honduras and Guatemala, Central America.

LITTLE SISTERS OF JESUS
Regional House, 400 N. Streeper St., Baltimore, MD 21224. (410) 327-7863
1,400 Sisters worldwide; 24 Sisters in U.S.
Apostolic Work: Contemplative life in the midst of the world, sharing the life and work of those who are poor and marginalized; a ministry of presence and friendship.
Represented in the Archdioceses of Anchorage, Baltimore, Chicago and Washington and in the Dioceses of Fairbanks, Altoona and Raleigh and in over 120 dioceses worldwide.
Vocations: Sr. Cathy Wright.

LITTLE SISTERS OF JESUS AND MARY (L.S.J.M.)
Joseph House, P.O. Box 1755, Salisbury, MD 21802. (301) 543-1645
6 Sisters, 1 Novice, 1 Postulant
Apostolic Work: Active contemplatives called to cry the Gospel with their lives, particularly in the midst of the poor. Prime purpose is to help stabilize family life. Through crisis centers in poverty-ridden areas, provide direct service to the poor by addressing their social, spiritual and economic problems. Also conduct a religious art and book store.
Represented in the Archdiocese of Baltimore and the Diocese of Wilmington.
Vocations: Sr. Mary Elizabeth Gintling.

LITTLE SISTERS OF THE POOR (l.s.p.)
(Brooklyn Province) Provincialate: Queen of Peace Residence, 110-30 221st St., Queens Village, NY 11429.

(Baltimore Province) Provincialate: Saint Martin's Home, 601 Maiden Choice Ln., Baltimore, MD 21228.

(Chicago Province) Provincialate: 80 W. Northwest Hwy., Palatine, IL 60067.

542 Sisters
Apostolic Work: Welcoming the needy aged to 32 homes in the United States and Canada. Also present in France, Belgium, Spain, Portugal, Malta, Italy, Algeria, Congo, Nigeria, Kenya, Turkey, England, Ireland, Scotland, Jersey (Channel Islands), Colombia, Chile, Argentina, India, Sri Lanka, South Korea, Hong Kong, Malaysia, Singapore, Taiwan, Western Samoa, New Zealand, Australia and New Caledonia.
Represented in the Archdioceses of New York, Boston, Hartford, Philadelphia, Baltimore, Cincinnati, Louisville, Indianapolis, New Orleans, Washington, Chicago, Los Angeles, Mobile, San Francisco, Denver, Saint Paul and Saint Louis, and in 14 other dioceses in the U.S.
Vocation Directress: Sr. Mary Richard, l.s.p., Saint Ann's Novitiate, 110-39 Springfield Blvd., Queens Village, NY 11429. (718) 464-4920.

THE SISTERS OF THE LITTLE WORKERS OF THE SACRED HEARTS (P.O.S.C.)
General Motherhouse: Rome, Italy; Regional House: Our Lady of Grace Convent, 635 Glenbrook Rd., Stamford, CT 06906. (203) 348-5531
22 Sisters in the U.S.; 800 Sisters worldwide
Apostolic Work: Ministry in the fields of academic and religious education at all levels: seminaries, orphanages, parish ministry, CCD, social work, and care of aged and infirm.
Represented in the Dioceses of Bridgeport and in the Archdioceses of Philadelphia and Washington, DC.; also in Italy, Argentina and India.
Vocational Directress: Sr. Gesuina Gencarelli, P.O.S.C., Our Lady of Grace Convent.

SISTERS OF THE LIVING WORD (SLW)
800 N. Fernandez Av.-B, Arlington Heights, IL 60004. (708) 577-5972
80 Sisters, 1 Affiliate
Apostolic Work: Education, parish ministries, religious education, health and elderly care, chaplaincy, social services, retreat ministry, campus ministry, artists, infants, abused women and children, secretarial services.
Represented in the Archdioceses of Chicago, Detroit, New Orleans, St. Paul/Minneapolis, St. Louis and in the Dioceses of Rockford and Joliet, IL; Sioux City, IA; Lafayette, IN; Biloxi and Jackson, MS; Jefferson City, MO; San Angelo, TX and Lansing, MI.
Vocation Director: Sr. Donna M. Williams, SLW, 800 N. Fernandez Av-B, Arlington Heights, IL 60004. (708) 577-5972.

SISTERS OF LORETTO (S.L.) (Sisters of Loretto at the Foot of the Cross),
Loretto Motherhouse, Nerinx, KY 40049. (502) 865-5811.
462 Vowed Members, 173 Co-Members
Conduct: A community of faith & service existing to praise God and minister to people. The works vary according to national and local needs and personal talents; they include education and advocacy, on behalf of women and other minorities and healthcare. Volunteers welcome to participate in works of the community.
Contact: Trish Dunn, Co-L, Outreach Coordinator, 3001 S. Federal Blvd., Denver, CO 80236-2798. (303) 922-8215.

SISTERS OF LORETTO
See Institute of the Blessed Virgin Mary.

LOVERS OF THE HOLY CROSS SISTERS
Holy Cross Convent, 14700 S. Van Ness Ave., P.O. Box 5478, Gardena, CA 90249-5478. (310) 768-1906; (310) 516-0271.
40 Sisters in U.S.
Apostolic Work: Parish ministry, teaching, nursing and social work.
Represented in the Archdioceses of Los Angeles and New Orleans and in the Diocese of Orange.
Contact: Sr. Monica Phi Tran, Superior General, Holy Cross Convent, 14700 S. Van Ness Ave., P.O. Box 5478, Gardena, CA 90249-5478. (310) 768-1906 or (310) 516-0271.

MARIAN SISTERS (M.S.)

Motherhouse: Marycrest Motherhouse, Box 108, Waverly, NE 68462. (402) 786-2750

34 Sisters

Apostolic Work: Home-school for educable retarded children, high schools, grade schools, home for the aged, catechetics.

Represented in the Diocese of Lincoln.

Vocation Director: Rt. 1, Box 108, Waverly, NE 68462.

MARIANIST SISTERS (F.M.I.)

U.S. Foundation: 251 W. Ligustrum Dr., San Antonio, TX 78228. (210) 433-5501.

22 Sisters in U.S. Province

Apostolic Work: Faith community formation, campus ministry, educational, social and pastoral ministry.

Represented in the Archdioceses of Cincinnati and San Antonio and in the Diocese of Toledo.

Vocation Contact: Formation House, 30 Sawmill Rd., Dayton, OH 45409. (513) 224-5896.

MARIANITES OF HOLY CROSS (MSC)

(North American Continent), 1011 Gallier St., N.O. 70117, New Orleans, LA 70131. (504) 945-1620.

206 Sisters

Apostolic Work: Education-primary through adult, pastoral ministry in parishes and hospitals, campus ministry, health care, social ministries, counseling, foreign missions.

Represented in the Archdioceses of New Orleans, New York, San Francisco and Washington and in the Dioceses of Alexandria, Baton Rouge, Beaumont, Biloxi, Camden, Houma-Thibodaux, Jackson, Juneau, Lafayette, Lake Charles, Manchester, Memphis, Paterson and Trenton. Also in the Dioceses of Mt. Laurier and Sherbrooke in Canada. Foreign Missions in Bangladesh, Haiti and Mexico.

Vocation Coordinator: Sr. Marlene Labbe, M.S.C., 31 Cresci Blvd., Hazlet, NJ 07730. (908) 264-3553.

MARIST MISSIONARY SISTERS (S.M.S.M.) (Missionary Sisters of the Society of Mary)

Provincial House: 349 Grove Street, Waltham, MA 02154. (617) 893-0149.

630 Sisters worldwide

Represented in the (Arch)dioceses of Boston, Brownsville, Chicago, Fairbanks (AK), Memphis, St. Petersburg and Venice (FL). Also in Algeria, Australia, Bangladesh, Burundi, Columbia, France, Germany, Italy, Jamaica, Madagascar, Mauritania, New Zealand, Peru, Philippines, Rwanda, Senegal, South Pacific (various islands) and (U.S.) Virgin Islands.

Apostolic Work: Missionary work: religious, pastoral, social, educational and medical.

Vocation Contact: Sr. Claire Rheaume, Marist Missionary Sisters, 5142 Blackstone, Chicago, IL 60615. (312) 324-3352.

MARIST SISTERS (S.M.)

(U.S.A. Province): 810 Peach St., Abilene, TX 79602. (915) 675-5806.

17 Sisters in U.S., 540 worldwide

Apostolic Work: Marist Sisters are missionaries, teachers, nurses, social workers, counsellors, pastoral ministers, retreat directors in 15 countries: U.S.A., Mexico, Brazil, Colombia, The Gambia, Senegal, New Zealand, Australia, Fiji, Italy, France, Belgium, Scotland, England, Ireland, Canada.

Represented in the Archdioceses of Chicago and Detroit and in Diocese of San Antonio.

Vocation Director: Sr. Linda Sevcik, S.M., 4810 South Leamington, Chicago, IL 60638. (312) 767-5392.

SISTERS OF MARY IMMACULATE (S.M.I.)

U.S. Foundation: RD 5, Box 1231, Leechburg, PA 15656-8811. (412) 845-2828

6 Sisters in the U.S.

MARYKNOLL SISTERS OF ST. DOMINIC (M.M.)

Ossining, NY (P.O. Address: Maryknoll, NY 10545-0311.)

800 Sisters

Maryknoll Sisters are invited to journey with people in countries around the world. In the diversity of these cultures, the Sisters walk with the poor, the oppressed and the abandoned. Their lifestyle is in harmony with the people they serve and their ministries are centered in the empowerment of those whom they serve. The world is the Sisters' home, their life is Gospel-centered community, their challenge is, as women of faith in

Jesus, to struggle with the poor for liberation from poverty and oppression.

Represented in Africa, Asia, Pacific, Latin America and the U.S.

Admissions Team: Maryknoll Sisters, Maryknoll, NY 10545-0311. (914) 941-7575.

SISTERS OF MARY REPARATRIX (S.M.R.)

(Society of Mary Reparatrix, American Province), 225 E. 234th St., Bronx, NY 10470. (718) 324-2252.

40 Sisters

Apostolic Work: Retreats, spiritual direction, religious education, parish ministry, pastoral care for the hospitalized and elderly, programs for the poor and needy, counseling, missions.

Represented in the Archdioceses of Detroit, New York, Miami and in the Dioceses of Albany and Brooklyn. Foreign Missions: Africa, South America, Panama.

Vocation Contact: Sr. Joan Pricoli, S.M.R., 183 Surrey Ln., Clarkston, MI 48346. (810) 625-4551.

MARYVALE SISTERS (CLHC) (Congregation of Our Lady Help of the Clergy)

5 Sisters

Motherhouse: Maryvale Motherhouse, 2522 June Bug Rd., Vale, NC 28168.

Apostolic Work: Faith formation on all levels. Home visitation to the sick, elderly, shut-ins, hospital visitations, pastoral assistance in areas of census, counseling, secretarial, youth ministry, day care, evangelization ministry, spiritual direction and retreat ministry; retreat residence available for private or directed individual/group retreats.

Vocation Director: Sr. Mary Norman, C.L.H.C. (704) 276-2626.

MEDICAL MISSION SISTERS (MMS)

(Sector North America), Headquarters: 8400 Pine Rd., Philadelphia, PA 19111.

700 Sisters

Apostolic Work: At the heart of their common call to mission is the deep belief that they are called to be an active presence of Christ, the Healer. Together with the poor, the oppressed, the broken, the Sisters seek to struggle for wholeness, forgiveness, justice, healing and peace. Their ministry then encom-

encompasses a wide variety of activities in Africa, Asia, South America, North America and Europe.

Membership Advisors: Sr. Marie Schmids, 8400 Pine Rd., Philadelphia, PA 19111. (215) 742-6100; Sr. Teresa Jaramillo, 2222 Coronado Ave., #9, San Diego, CA 92154-2037. (619) 424-5502.

MEDICAL MISSIONARIES OF MARY (M.M.M.)

Regional House: 563 Minneford Ave., City Island, NY 10464

460 Sisters

Apostolic Work: An international congregation of religious women, with a lifelong commitment to prayer, and to a participation in the healing mission of Jesus. Ministry as missionaries centers on healing of the whole person. Thus, work is varied: nurses, doctors, social workers, those who work in community development and pastoral ministry, secretaries, to name a few. Live and work particularly with the very poor in areas where the Gospel has not yet been preached: in 10 African countries, Brazil, and Appalachia, Virginia and San Ysidro, CA.

Represented in the Archdioceses of Boston, Chicago and New York and in the Dioceses of Richmond and San Diego.

Vocation Directors: Sr. Mary Donato, MMM, 563 Minneford Ave., City Island, NY 10464-1118. (718) 885-0945; Sr. Jude Walsh, MMM, 3410 W. 60th Pl., Chicago, IL 60629-3602. (312) 737-3458; Sr. Cheryl Blanchard, MMM, P.O. Box 1436, Chula Vista, CA 91912-1436. (619) 690-9237.

MEDICAL SISTERS OF ST. JOSEPH (MSJ)

Motherhouse: India; U.S. Foundation: 3435 E. Funston, Wichita, KS 67218. (316) 686-4746

580 Sisters (worldwide)

Apostolic Work: Health care.

Represented in the Diocese of Wichita and 10 dioceses in India.

MERCEDARIAN MISSIONARIES OF BERRIZ (M.M.B.)

Motherhouse: Berriz, Spain; Generalate: Rome, Italy; 1400 N.E. 42nd Terrace, Kansas City, MO 64116. (816) 454-1344

600 Sisters on the five continents, 28 in the U.S.

Apostolic Work: International missionary congregation; teachers, social workers, nurses, catechists, co-pastors, youth leaders.

Represented in the Dioceses of Hartford, CT; Kansas City-St. Joseph, MO; Lubbock, TX; Guam, Mariana Islands. Foreign Missions: Micronesia, Mariana and Caroline Islands; Mexico; Guatemala; Nicaragua; Peru; Equador; Japan; Taiwan; Philippines; Zaire, Africa.

Vocation Offices: Sr. Jacinta Fernandez, Sr. Flor Maria Alvarez, M.M.B., 1400 N.E. 42nd Terrace, Kansas City, MO 64116. (816) 454-1344 and Sr. Elizabeth Ann Preston, M.M.B., 1035 West Crosby, Slaton, TX 79364. (806) 828-3566.

MERCEDARIANS

See "O" section - Sisters of Our Lady of Mercy.

SISTERS OF MERCY OF THE AMERICAS (R.S.M.) (Regional Community of Albany)

Mercy Administrative Center, 310 South Manning Blvd., Albany, NY 12208-1793. (518) 437-3000.

190 Sisters

Apostolic Work: Education, health services, pastoral ministry, social services.

Represented in the Archdioceses of Anchorage and Newark and in the Dioceses of Albany and Syracuse.

Vocation Directress: Sr. Rhea Bean, R.S.M., 4500 Matilda Ave., Bronx, NY 10470. (718) 994-2503.

SISTERS OF MERCY OF THE AMERICAS (R.S.M.) (Regional Community of Auburn)

Our Lady of Mercy Convent, 535 Sacramento St., Auburn, CA 95603. (916) 887-2000

97 Sisters, 2 Temporary Professed

Apostolic Ministry: Schools, hospitals, parish ministry, Hispanic ministry, outreach clinics, ministry to homeless and aged, retreat and spirituality ministry, hospice and AIDS ministry.

Represented in the Diocese of Sacramento.

Vocation Director: Sr. Michelle Gorman, R.S.M., 2277 Fair Oaks Blvd., Ste. 105, Sacramento, CA 95825-5533. (916) 646-8794.

SISTERS OF MERCY OF THE AMERICAS (R.S.M) (Regional Community of Baltimore)

258 Sisters

Apostolic Work: The spirit of the community is compassion for those in need; the poor, the sick, the uneducated, and all those in any way wounded by contemporary society. Works include: parish ministry, health services, social work, education, diversified works based on unique gifts/interests of members.

Serving in Maryland, Georgia, Alabama, Florida and Washington, DC

Vocation Director: P.O. Box 11448, Baltimore, MD 21239. (410) 435-4400.

SISTERS OF MERCY OF THE AMERICAS (R.S.M.) (Regional Community of Brooklyn)

273 Willoughby Ave., Brooklyn, NY 11205. (718) 622-5840

275 Sisters

Apostolic Work: Elementary schools, high schools, catechetical centers, child-caring institutions, missions in Panama, social work, nursing, mission work, counseling, soup kitchen, women's shelter, parish ministry.

Represented in the Dioceses of Brooklyn and Rockville Centre. Also in Panama.

Director of Vocations and New Membership: Sister Grace Leggio Agate, R.S.M., 60 Anchor Ave., Oceanside, NY 11572. (718) 331-5284; (516) 536-2014.

SISTERS OF MERCY OF THE AMERICAS (R.S.M.) (Regional Community of Buffalo)

Our Lady of Mercy Convent, 5245 Murphy Rd., Orchard Park, NY 14127. (716) 662-9836

221 Sisters, 78 Associates

Ministry: Junior colleges, academy, high schools, elementary schools, hospitals, health system, parish ministry, social service, domestic service, pastoral ministry, speech therapy, religious coordinating, inner city services.

Represented in the Diocese of Buffalo. Also in the Philippines.

Contact Person: Sr. Virginia Marie Grasso, R.S.M.

SISTERS OF MERCY OF THE AMERICAS (R.S.M.) (Regional Community of Burlingame)

Motherhouse: 2300 Adeline Dr., Burlingame, CA 94010-5599. (415) 340-7400

236 Sisters

Conduct: Spirituality and conference center, missionary work in Latin America, elementary, secondary and higher education, pastoral religious education, peace and justice ministry, health care, social services (e.g. low-income housing, psychological counseling, legal services, child care, etc.).

Represented in the Archdioceses of Los Angeles and San Francisco and in the Dioceses of Fresno, Oakland, Orange, Phoenix, San Diego and San Jose.

Vocation Director: Sr. Mary Ann Hills, R.S.M., 2300 Adeline Dr., Burlingame, CA 94010-5599. (415) 340-7400, ext. 261.

SISTERS OF MERCY OF THE AMERICAS (R.S.M.) (Regional Community of Cedar Rapids)

1125 Prairie Dr., N.E., Cedar Rapids, IA 52402. (319) 364-5196.

117 Sisters

Conduct: 1 college, 1 hospital, 1 home for the aged, 1 center for women (education, homeless).

Represented in the Archdioceses of Chicago, Cincinnati, Denver, Dubuque, Hartford, Kansas City (KS), Los Angeles, Miami, Milwaukee and St. Louis and in the Dioceses of Crookston, Davenport, Des Moines, Helena, Joliet, Kansas City/St. Joseph, Rockford and Springfield-Cape Girardeau. Also in Puno (Peru).

Vocation Director: Linda Bechen, RSM, 1125 Prairie Dr. N.E., Cedar Rapids, IA 52402. (319) 364-5196.

SISTERS OF MERCY OF THE AMERICAS (R.S.M.) (Regional Community of Chicago)

10024 S. Central Pk. Ave., Chicago, IL 60642.

430 Sisters

Apostolic Work: Primarily in education, health care, parish ministry and housing.

Represented in the Archdioceses of Chicago, IL; Milwaukee, WI; and Madison, WI and in the Dioceses of Davenport, IA, Peoria, IL, Rockford, IL, and Joliet, IL. Also in Honduras.

Vocation Director: Sister Carol Mucha, RSM, (312) 779-6011.

SISTERS OF MERCY OF THE AMERICAS (R.S.M.) (Regional Community of Cincinnati)

Administrative Offices, 2335 Grandview Ave., Cincinnati, OH 45206

445 Sisters

Conduct: 6 high schools, 1 commercial college, 5 elementary schools, 2 child care homes, 14 hospitals, 5 nursing homes, 2 apartment complexes for the elderly, 2 special education schools, 3 Montessori schools, 1 retreat and renewal center; also serve in colleges and campus ministry, social service programs, parish ministry, parish schools and prison ministry.

Represented in the Archdioceses of Boston, Chicago, Cincinnati, Detroit, Louisville, Washington and Kingston, Jamaica and in the Dioceses of Charlotte, Cleveland, Covington, Memphis, Nashville, Owensboro, Richmond, Toledo and Montego Bay, Jamaica.

Vocation Director: Sister Wanda Smith, R.S.M., 2335 Grandview Ave., Cincinnati, OH 45206. (513) 221-1800.

SISTERS OF MERCY OF THE AMERICAS (R.S.M.) (Regional Community of Connecticut)

Convent of Mercy, 249 Steele Rd., West Hartford, CT 06117. (203) 232-8602

291 Sisters

Apostolic Work: Education from pre-school through college, adult education, religious education, health services, social services, prison ministry, pastoral ministry, parish ministry, diocesan service, housing ministry, care of the elderly, retreat and spiritual direction ministry, counseling, peace and justice ministry.

Represented in the Archdioceses of Hartford and in the Dioceses of Bridgeport and Norwich. Also in Guatemala, Haiti and Belize.

Vocation Contact: Sister Beth Fischer, (203) 232-8602.

SISTERS OF MERCY OF THE AMERICAS (R.S.M.) (Regional Community of Dallas)

Box 369, Dallas, PA 18612-0369.

430 Sisters

Apostolic Work: Education, health care, social services, parish ministry, retreat work, communications, artistic services.

Represented in the Dioceses of Altoona-Johnstown, Brooklyn, Harrisburg, Rockville Centre, Scranton and Georgetown, Guyana.

Vocation Director: Rhea Bean, RSM, 4500 Matilda Ave., Bronx, NY 10470. (718) 994-2503.

SISTERS OF MERCY OF THE AMERICAS (R.S.M.) (Regional Community of Detroit)

29000 Eleven Mile Rd., Farmington Hills, MI 48336. (313) 476-8000

333 Sisters

Apostolic Work: Health care in hospitals, clinics, schools of nursing and public health organizations as nurses, physicans, administrators and chaplains; education from pre-school through college, religious education, special education and campus ministry; social work: prison ministry, care of the elderly and handicapped; Other ministries: retreat work, communications, pastoral ministry and diocesan administration; housing and a variety of direct ministries to the poor.

Represented primarily in the Archdioceses of Detroit and Dubuque and in the Dioceses of Davenport, Gary, Gaylord, Grand Rapids, Kalamazoo, Lansing, Saginaw, Sioux City. Also in Argentina.

Vocation Director: Sr. Rita Valade, R.S.M., 29000 Eleven Mile Rd., Farmington Hills, MI 48336. (313) 476-8000.

SISTERS OF MERCY OF THE AMERICAS (R.S.M.) (Regional Community of Erie)

444 E. Grandview Blvd., Erie, PA 16504. (814) 824-2516

90 Sisters

Apostolic Work: 1 college, 1 high school, 5 grammar schools, 1 hospital, catechetical work, parish ministry and civic community work, 2 houses of prayer, pastoral ministry, inner city ministry, tutoring, work with elderly, work with pre-school children, prison ministry, advocacy for women, music education, shelter for homeless women and children.

Represented in the (Arch)dioceses of Boston, Buffalo, Detroit, Erie, Little Rock, Pittsburgh, Savannah and Washington, DC.

Vocation Director: Sister Rita Panciera, 444 E. Grandview Blvd., Erie, PA 16504. (814) 824-2516.

SISTERS OF MERCY OF THE AMERICAS (R.S.M.) (Regional Community of Merion)
Motherhouse: 515 Montgomery Ave., Merion, PA 19066. (610) 664-6650

463 Sisters

Apostolic Work: 1 college, 6 academies, 13 high schools, 1 vocational institute, 25 elementary schools, 3 hospitals, 1 home for business women, 1 school for special education, 3 hospices for women, social services.

Represented in the Archdioceses of Anchorage, Atlanta, Baltimore, Chicago, Miami, Mobile, New York, Philadelphia, St. Louis and Washington, DC and in the Dioceses of Allentown, Baton Rouge, Camden, Gallup, Lexington, Orlando, Pensacola-Tallahassee, Raleigh, Richmond, St. Petersburg and Wilmington. Also in Rome, Chulucanas (Peru), and the West Indies.

Vocation Director: Sr. Carol Tropiano, R.S.M., 515 Montgomery Ave., Merion, PA 19066. (610) 664-6650.

SISTERS OF MERCY OF THE AMERICAS (R.S.M.) (Regional Community of New Hampshire)
Motherhouse: 21 Searles Rd., Windham, NH 03087-1297

202 Sisters.

Apostolic Work: Teaching, parish ministry, health services, social service.

Represented primarily in the Diocese of Manchester and the Archdiocese of Boston.

Vocation Director: 21 Searles Rd., Windham, NH 03087-1297. (603) 893-6550.

SISTERS OF MERCY OF THE AMERICAS (R.S.M.) (Regional Community of New Jersey)
Motherhouse: Mount Saint Mary, 1645 Hwy. 22, Watchung, NJ 07060.

347 Sisters

Apostolic Work: Education (all levels), parish ministry, social services, health care, religious education. Service to the People of God where and how it is needed. Involved with the elderly, the distressed, the handicapped, the poor.

Represented throughout New Jersey and in parts of California, Maryland, New York, North Carolina and Pennsylvania.

Vocation Director: Sr. Beth Dempsey, R.S.M. (908) 755-5661.

SISTERS OF MERCY OF THE AMERICAS (R.S.M.) (Regional Community of New York)
Administrative Offices: 150 Ridge Rd., Hartsdale, NY 10530.

230 Sisters

Apostolic Work: All levels of education; health care; social services, pastoral ministry; hospital chaplaincy; religious education.

Represented in the Archdiocese of New York and in the Dioceses of Ogdensburg and Worcester.

Vocational Director: Sr. Rhea Bean, St. Anthony Convent, 4500 Matilda Ave., Bronx, NY 10470. (718) 994-2503.

SISTERS OF MERCY OF THE AMERICAS (R.S.M.) (Regional Community of North Carolina)
Sacred Heart Convent, Belmont, NC 28012. (704) 829-5103

140 Sisters, 30 Associates

Apostolic Work: Teaching and nursing with various ministries in social work, pastoral care, campus ministry, religious education, youth ministry.

Represented in the Dioceses of Charlotte, NC, Raleigh, NC, Charleston, SC, Gallup, NM, Lexington, KY, Rockville, MN and Agana, Guam.

Vocation Director: Sr. Marian Arroyo, R.S.M., Sisters of Mercy, Carmel House, 3035 Carmel Rd., Charlotte, NC 28226. (704) 552-2899.

SISTERS OF MERCY OF THE AMERICAS (R.S.M.) (Regional Community of Omaha)
Sisters of Mercy Regional Office, 1801 S. 72nd St., Omaha, NE 68124. (402) 393-8225

301 Sisters

Apostolic Work: Education, health services, parish ministry, social work, housing ministry, peace and justice ministry, retreat ministry and spiritual direction.

Represented in AZ, CA, CO, FL, IL, ID, IA, KS, MO, NE, NM, ND, OR, WA and WY.

Vocation Director: Mary Ann Hills, RSM, 1701 S. 72nd St., Omaha, NE 68124. (402) 397-8266.

SISTERS OF MERCY OF THE AMERICAS (R.S.M.) (Regional Community of Pittsburgh)
3333 Fifth Ave., Pittsburgh, PA 15213. (412) 578-6190

258 Sisters

Conduct: 1 college, grammar schools, 1 school of nursing, 2 hospitals.

Apostolic Work: A variety of health programs, home and foreign missions, parish services and a variety of individual apostolates serving the people of God throughout the United States and the world.

Represented predominantly in the Dioceses of Pittsburgh, Greensburg, Miami, Fort Lauderdale, San Juan in Puerto Rico, Chimbote in Peru, Guatemala and in other areas throughout the United States and the world.

Coordinator for New Membership: Geri Rosinski, RSM.

SISTERS OF MERCY OF THE AMERICAS (R.S.M.) (Regional Community of Portland)
Motherhouse: St. Joseph's Convent, 605 Stevens Ave., Portland, ME 04103.

146 Sisters

Apostolic Work: Teaching: elementary – college; health care, parish work (religious education and social work), transitional housing for the homeless, ministry to Native Americans, spiritual direction.

Represented in the Diocese of Portland, Maine, and have two missions on Andros Island, Bahama.

Formation Director: Sister Mary Morey, R.S.M., St. Joseph's Convent, 605 Stevens Ave., Portland, ME 04103. (207) 797-6957.

DIOCESAN SISTERS OF MERCY OF PORTLAND (R.S.M.)
Our Lady of Mercy Convent, 265 Cottage Rd., South Portland, ME 04106. (207) 767-5804.

11 Sisters

Apostolic Work: Education, social work, pastoral ministry.

Represented in the Diocese of Portland (ME).

Vocation Director: Sr. Eunice Boyd, R.S.M.

SISTERS OF MERCY OF THE AMERICAS (R.S.M.) (Regional Community of Providence)
Administration Office: Highland View Rd., Cumberland, RI 02864. (401) 333-6333

428 Sisters

Apostolic Work: Education at all levels (preschool through college) uniquely developed literacy pro-

grams, social services, pastoral care in hospitals, prisons and parishes, ministry with homeless, religious education.
Represented in the Dioceses of Fall River and Providence and in the countries of Belize and Honduras, Central America.
Vocation Director: Sr. Aliceann Walsh, RSM.

SISTERS OF MERCY OF THE AMERICAS (R.S.M.) (Regional Community of Rochester)
Motherhouse: 1437 Blossom Rd., Rochester, NY 14610.
228 Sisters
Apostolic Work: Continually expanding to serve the poor, the sick, and the uneducated in today's world. Presently involved in all levels of education, administration, nursing, pastoral ministry, and social ministry including a foster home for children and missions in Chile.
Represented in the Dioceses of Rochester, NY; Jackson, MS; Atlanta, GA. Also in Santiago, Chile.
Vocation Director: Sr. Jane Schur, R.S.M., 1437 Blossom Rd., Rochester, NY 14610. (716) 288-2710.

SISTERS OF MERCY OF THE AMERICAS (R.S.M.) (Regional Community of St. Louis)
2039 N. Geyer Rd., St. Louis, MO 63131.
390 Sisters
Apostolic Work: Education, health care, pastoral and social work, religious education.
Represented primarily in the states of Arkansas, Kansas, Louisiana, Mississippi, Missouri, Oklahoma and Texas.
Vocation Director: Our Lady of Mercy Convent, 2039 N. Geyer Rd., St. Louis, MO 63131. (314) 966-4313.

SISTERS OF MERCY OF THE AMERICAS (R.S.M.) (Regional Community of Vermont)
Motherhouse: Mt. St. Mary, 100 Mansfield Ave., Burlington, VT 05401.
96 Sisters
Apostolic Work: 1 college, 1 private elementary school, 1 diocesan high school, 3 diocesan elementary schools, 3 religious education centers. Involvement in social work, spirituality, health care and prison ministry.

Represented in the Diocese of Burlington.
Vocation Director: Sr. Helen O'Brien, R.S.M., 100 Mansfield Ave., Burlington, VT 05401. (802) 863-6835.

MERCY SISTERS (R.S.M.)
Ascension School, PO Box 360937, Melbourne, FL 32935. (407) 254-0725
2 Sisters
Represented in the Diocese of Orlando.
Vocations: Sr. M. Immaculata Knox.

MERCY SISTERS (R.S.M.)
500 S.W. 4th Ave., Boca Raton, FL 33432. (407) 368-6655
5 Sisters
Represented in the Diocese of Palm Beach.

MERCY SISTERS
Holy Infant Convent, 239 Nancy Pl., Ballwin, MO 63021. (314) 391-1528
23 Sisters
Apostolic Work: Education, pastoral ministries.
Represented in the Archdiocese of St. Louis and in the Dioceses of Camden, Orlando and St. Augustine.
Vocation Director: Sr. Laurentia Cusack, Holy Infant Convent, 239 Nancy Pl., Ballwin, MO 63021.

SISTERS OF MERCY (R.S.M.)
Immaculate Conception, 126 W. 45th St., Hialeah, FL 33012. (305) 822-6161
3 Sisters
Conduct: 3 schools.

MERCY SISTERS OF IRELAND (R.S.M.)
6 Sisters in U.S.A.
Apostolic Work: Teaching, social service and pastoral work.
Represented in the Dioceses of Orlando and Mobile. Also in Kenya (Africa) and Paraiba (Brazil).
Vocation Director: St. Mary Convent, 1136 Seminole Dr., Rockledge, FL 32955. (407) 636-1341.

SISTERS OF MERCY (S.M.)
Motherhouse: Carrick-on-Suir, Ireland; U.S. Foundation: St. John's Convent of Mercy, 11154 San Pablo Ave., El Cerrito, CA 94530. (510) 233-6769

10 Sisters
Represented in the Dioceses of San Jose and Oakland.

SISTERS OF MERCY-Elphin Community (S.M.)
Sisters of Mercy, 2960 Mendoza Dr., Costa Mesa, CA 92626. (714) 545-2116
2 Sisters
Represented in the Dioceses of Orange, San Bernardino and San Diego.

SISTERS OF MERCY (Cork and Ross) (S.M.)
Sacred Heart School, 6240 105th St., Jacksonville, FL 32244. (904) 771-3858
7 Sisters
Represented in the Diocese of St. Augustine.

MERCY SISTERS (Galway) (S.M.)
Divine Mercy Convent, 1930 N. Courtenay, Merritt Island, FL 32953. (407) 452-1279, 5955
4 Sisters
Primary Apostolic Work: Education (works of mercy).
Represented in the Diocese of Orlando.

MERCY SISTERS (Cashmel) (C.M.S.)
Motherhouse in Ireland; U.S. Foundation: St. Mel's Convent, P.O. Box 1180, Fair Oaks, CA 95628. (916) 967-9504.
4 Sisters in Community
Apostolic Work: Teaching and pastoral.
Represented in the Archdiocese of San Francisco and in the Diocese of Sacramento.

MERCY SISTERS (R.S.M.)
St. Joseph Convent, 1402 Miller St., Palm Bay, FL 32905. (407) 723-5375; St. Joseph Church, (407) 727-1565
3 Sisters
Represented in the Diocese of Orlando.

MERCY SISTERS (S.M.D.C.) (Daughters of Christian Charity of St. Vincent De Paul)
St. Joseph's Provincial House, Rte. 1, Box 353A, 240 Longhouse Dr., Hewitt, NJ 07421.
3 Sisters.
Apostolic Work: Teaching from kindergarten up to college, nursing

in hospitals and home for aged, care of children, orphanage, novitiate, convent and home for aged. Foreign missions: China Mainland and Taiwan/Formosa.

Represented in the Diocese of Paterson.

Vocation Director: Sisters of Mercy, Rte. 1, Box 353A, 240 Longhouse Dr., Hewitt, NJ 07421. (201) 853-7212.

SISTERS OF MERCY OF THE BLESSED SACRAMENT (H.M.S.S.)

222 W. Cevallos St., San Antonio, TX 78204. (210) 223-5013; 222-1354

32 Sisters in U.S., 1 Aspirant, 1 Postulant, 1 Novice; over 700 worldwide

Apostolic Work: Schools, parish work.

Represented in the Diocese of San Bernardino and in Texas. Also in Mexico, Italy, Spain, Colombia, Chile, Venezuela and El Salvador.

Vocation Directors: Sister Dolores Munoz, H.M.S.S., 222 W. Cevallos St., San Antonio, TX 78204. (210) 223-5013.

SISTERS OF MERCY (R.S.M.) (Sligo)

Generalate: Roscommon, Ireland American Region: 4825 H St., San Bernardino, CA 92407. (909) 886-6172

25 Sisters

Apostolic Work: Religious and academic education, parish ministry, diocesan offices.

Represented in the Dioceses of San Diego, San Bernardino and Orange.

Vocation Director: Sister Rosaline O'Connor, R.S.M., 4825 H St., San Bernardino, CA 92407. (909) 886-6172.

SISTERS OF MERCY (S.M.) (Kerry)

Motherhouse: County Kerry, Ireland; U.S. Foundation: St. John the Evangelist Convent, 5701 Locust Ave., Carmichael, CA 95608. (916) 482-0163

3 Sisters in U.S.

Represented in the Dioceses of Sacramento, San Bernardino and Santa Rosa.

MILL HILL SISTERS (F.M.S.J.) (Franciscan Missionaries of St. Joseph)

Franciscan House, 1006 Madison Ave., Albany, NY 12208. (518) 482-1991

15 Sisters in U.S.; 300 in total

Apostolic Work: Parish ministry, foreign missions, social work, teaching, nursing.

Represented in the Dioceses of Albany and Norwich, CT.

Vocation Director: Sister Joan Kerley, Franciscan House, 1006 Madison Ave., Albany, NY 12208. (518) 482-1991.

MINIM DAUGHTERS OF MARY IMMACULATE (C.F.M.M.)

General Motherhouse: Mexico; U.S.: Our Lady of Lourdes High School, P.O. Box 1865, Nogales, AZ 85628. (602) 287-5659

23 Sisters in the U.S.; 395 Total

Apostolic Work: Academic & religious education, health care, missions.

Represented in the Diocese of Tucson.

SISTERS MINOR OF MARY IMMACULATE (S.M.M.I.)

Holy Name of Jesus Convent, 305 Washington Blvd., Stamford, CT 06902.

55 Sisters

Apostolic Work: All kinds but done as Our Lady would do it and with her.

Represented in the Arch(dioceses) of Bridgeport, Springfield and Fargo.

Vocation Director: Sr. Therese Marie, S.M.M.I., 305 Washington Blvd., Stamford, CT 06902.

MISERICORDIA SISTERS (S.M.)

Generalate: 12435 Ave. de la Misericorde, Montreal, Canada H4J 2G3. (514) 332-0550.

4 Sisters in the U.S.

Apostolic Work: 1 maternity home for unwed mothers.

Represented in 3 Canadian Provinces. Also in the Archdioceses of New York and Milwaukee.

Vocation Director: Sr. Ellen Hunt, S.M., 225 Carol Ave., Pelham, NY 10803. (914) 738-1723.

MISSION HELPERS OF THE SACRED HEART (M.H.S.H.)

1001 W. Joppa Rd., Baltimore, MD 21204-3787. (410) 823-8585, ext. 246 (Sr. Judy Waldt).

125 Sisters

Apostolic Work: Catechists; retreat directors; writers; home visitors; parish administrators; hospital chaplains; counselors; evangelists; campus ministers; justice and peace advocates; liturgists; parish

ministers; directors of religious education on the parish, diocesan and national levels; youth ministers; Hispanic ministers; cable and video programmers; ministers for the deaf, physically and mentally impaired, elderly and family life; advocates for Hispanics and African-Americans.

Represented in 17 states, Puerto Rico and Venezuela, South America, (States: Arizona, California, Colorado, Connecticut, Delaware, District of Columbia, Florida, Georgia, Indiana, Maryland, Massachusetts, Michigan, New Mexico, New York, Ohio, Pennsylvania, Texas, Vermont).

Membership: Sr. Judy Waldt, M.H.S.H., 1001 W. Joppa Rd., Baltimore, MD 21204-3787. (410) 823-8585, ext. 246.

MISSIONARIES OF CHARITY (M.C.)

(North America Province)

4,000 Sisters in the whole congregation

Apostolic Work: Giving wholehearted and free service to the poorest of the poor.

Represented in the (Arch)dioceses of Baton Rouge, Newark, Washington, DC, Little Rock, New York, Denver, Detroit, St. Louis, Miami, Chicago, San Francisco, Covington, Gallup, Philadelphia, Boston, Phoenix, Dallas and Lafayette. Foreign Missions in Albania, Argentina, Australia, Austria, Bangladesh, Belgium, Benin, Bolivia, Brazil, Burundi, Cameroon, Canada, Chile, Columbia, Costa Rica, Cuba, Czechoslovakia, Dominican Republic, El Salvador, Ethiopia, Egypt, Equador, France, East Germany, West Germany, Ghana, Greece, Grenada, Guatemala, Guinea, Guyana, Haiti, Holland, Honduras, Hong Kong, Hungary, India, Ireland, Italy, Ivory Coast, Japan, Jordan, Kenya, Lebanon, Liberia, Macau, Madagascar, Malta, Mauritius, Mexico, Nepal, Nicaragua, Nigeria, Pakistan, Panama, Papua New Guinea, Peru, Philippines, Poland, Portugal, Puerto Rico, Romania, Russia, Rwanda, Seychelles, Sierra Leone, Singapore, South Korea, Spain, Sri Lanka, Sudan, Syria, Tanzania, Trinidad, United Kingdom, Uruguay, Venezuela, Yemen, Yugoslavia, Zaire.

Vocation Director: Sister Sylvia, M.C., 335 E. 145th St., Bronx, NY 10451. (718) 292-0019.

MISSIONARIES OF CHARITY OF THE IMMACULATE MARY (M.C.M.I.)

U.S. Foundation: 2611 W. 39th Ave., Denver, CO 80211. (303) 455-2874.

Motherhouse: Mexico.

215 Sisters

Apostolic Work: Education, foreign missions, nursing, pastoral work.

Represented in the Archdiocese of Denver. Primarily in Mexico. Also in Kenya, Africa and Guatemala.

Vocation Contact: Sr. Luz Flores, M.C.M.I.

MISSIONARIES OF THE SACRED HEART OF JESUS (M.S.C.)

(Cabrini Sisters, Lay Missioners, Collaborators and Volunteers) (Provincial Office), 222 E. 19th St., Apt. 5B, New York, NY 10003. (212) 995-6876; (Sponsorship Office), 434 W. Deming Pl., 3rd Fl., Chicago, IL 60614. (312) 883-7316.

600 Members

Apostolic Work: Colleges, high schools, elementary schools, special education, hospitals, dispensaries, child care institutions, day nurseries, parish work, social services, pastoral care, rest homes, retreat and foreign mission work.

Represented in 8 U.S. dioceses and in Central America, South America, Europe, Africa, Asia and Australia.

Vocation Director: Sr. Regina Peterson, M.S.C., Cabrini College, 610 King of Prussia Rd., Radnor, PA 19087-3698. (610) 902-8232.

MISSIONARY BENEDICTINE SISTERS (O.S.B.)

(Congregation of Missionary Benedictine Sisters)

58 Sisters, 12 in Formation

Represented in Dioceses in the U.S., New Ulm (MN) and Omaha (NE) and in the foreign countries of Angola, Australia, Brazil, Bulgaria, China, Germany, Italy, Kenya, Korea (South), Philippine Islands, Portugal, South Africa, Southwest Africa and Tanzania.

Apostolic Work: Education, health care, catechetics, domestic and pastoral ministry, special apostolates among Native Americans and Korean immigrants.

Vocation Director: Sr. Carmel Simpauco, O.S.B., Immaculata Convent, 300 N. 18th St., Box R, Norfolk, NE 68701-3687. (402) 371-3438.

MISSIONARY CATECHISTS OF DIVINE PROVIDENCE (M.C.D.P.)

2318 Castroville Rd., San Antonio, TX 78237-3520. (210) 435-4626.

54 Sisters

Apostolic Work: Working with children, youth, young adults, adults in religious education within the parish. Also counselors, teachers, social work, consultants at the diocesan, state and local level.

Represented in California, Las Vegas, New Mexico, Texas.

Vocation Director: Sr. Janette Hernandez, M.C.D.P., 2318 Castroville Rd., San Antonio, TX 78237-3520. (210) 435-4626.

MISSIONARY CATECHISTS OF THE SACRED HEARTS OF JESUS AND MARY (M.C.S.H.J.M.)

Regional Office, 805 S. Liberty St., Victoria, TX 77901. (512) 578-9302. (Central Headquarters: Mexico City)

200 Sisters; 46 Sisters, 3 Novices in U.S.

Apostolic Work: Pastoral assistants, family orientation and formation, religious education ministry (C.C.D.), evangelization and catechesis in ministries, home visiting ministry, pastoral and liturgical activities at parish and diocesan levels.

Represented in the Archdiocese of San Antonio and in the Dioceses of Victoria, Galveston-Houston, Ft. Worth, Lubbock, Metuchen and Trenton. Also in Mexico, Africa and Spain.

Vocation Contacts: Sr. Eva Sanchez, MCSHJM, Regional Superior, Sister Alma Lilia Garcia, MCSHJM, Vocation Ministry, 805 S. Liberty St., Victoria, TX 77901. (512) 578-9302.

MISSIONARY DAUGHTERS OF THE MOST PURE VIRGIN MARY

919 N. 9th St., Kingsville, TX 78363. (512) 595-1087

500 Members

Apostolic Work: Education, social work, missions (in Mexico), pastoral work, novitiate in Mexico and U.S.

Represented in the Dioceses of Brownsville, Corpus Christi, Yakima and Trenton.

Vocation Director: Sr. Consuelo Ramirez, 919 N. 9th St., Kingsville, TX 78363. (512) 595-1087.

MISSIONARY FRANCISCAN SISTERS OF THE IMMACULATE CONCEPTION (O.S.F.)

Provincial House: 790 Centre St., Newton, MA 02158.

275 Sisters

Apostolic Work: High schools, grammar schools, catechetical centers, nursing, social apostolate, parish ministry, migrant parish work.

Represented in the Archdioceses of Boston, Newark, New York and Philadelphia and in 7 dioceses and in 10 foreign countries.

Vocation Director: 790 Centre St., Newton, MA 02158. (617) 527-1004.

MISSIONARY SERVANTS OF THE MOST BLESSED TRINITY (M.S.B.T.)

3501 Solly Ave., Philadelphia, PA 19136. (215) 335-7550

290 Sisters

Apostolic Work: Social services, pastoral ministry, religious education, health services, campus ministry, education and retreat ministry.

Represented in dioceses throughout the U.S., Puerto Rico and Mexico.

Vocation Minister: Sr. Theresa Ahearn, M.S.B.T., 3501 Solly Ave., Philadelphia, PA 19136. (215) 335-7533; 7500.

MISSIONARY SERVANTS OF ST. ANTHONY (M.S.S.A.)

100 Peter Baque Rd., San Antonio, TX 78209. (210) 824-4553

6 Sisters

Apostolic Work: Ministering to children in learning centers, caring for retired priests.

Represented in the Archdiocese of San Antonio.

MISSIONARY SISTERS OF THE HOLY ROSARY (M.S.H.R.)

741 Polo Rd., Bryn Mawr, PA 19010. (610) 520-1974

400 Sisters

Apostolic Work: Teaching, medical work, pastoral work, social work, counseling, community building, and organizing.

Represented in the Archdiocese of Philadelphia. Also in Nigeria, Sierra Leone, Cameroon, Ghana, Kenya, Zambia, Ethiopia, South Africa, Brazil, Mexico, Ireland, England and Scotland.

Vocation Director: Sr. Paula Molloy, 741 Polo Rd., Bryn Mawr, PA 19010. (610) 520-1974.

MISSIONARY SISTERS OF THE IMMACULATE CONCEPTION OF THE MOTHER OF GOD (S.M.I.C.)

Franciscan Sisters, 779 Broadway, Paterson, NJ 07514. (201) 279-3790.

Generalate: (201) 279-1484.

67 Sisters in U.S.A.; 475 worldwide

Apostolic Work: Health care, education, social services, parish, retreats and art (any talent is utilized).

Represented in the Archdioceses of Newark and San Antonio and in the Dioceses of Paterson, Trenton, Portland, Austin, Galveston-Houston, Brownsville, Victoria, Gallup and San Bernadino. Also in Brazil, Germany, Taiwan and Africa.

Vocation Director: Sr. Eleanor Goekler, S.M.I.C., Vocation Ministry Office, P.O. Box 3026, Paterson, NJ 07509. (201) 279-3790.

MISSIONARY SISTERS OF THE IMMACULATE HEART OF MARY

See ICM Missionary Sisters.

MISSIONARY SISTERS OF JESUS, MARY AND JOSEPH (J.M.J.)

12940 Up River Rd., Corpus Christi, TX 78410. (512) 241-1955

23 Sisters

Apostolic Work: Among Hispanic poor, social work, day care with children of working mothers, pastoral ministry, delinquency prevention program.

Represented in the Dioceses of Corpus Christi, El Paso and San Antonio. Also in Spain, Chile, Africa and Reynosa (Mexico).

Vocation Director: Sr. Rachel Vallarta, J.M.J., 12940 Up River Rd., Corpus Christi, TX 78410. (512) 241-1955.

MISSIONARY SISTERS OF THE MOST BLESSED SACRAMENT (M.SS.S.)

Mary Immaculate Convent, 1109-1111 Wordin Ave., Bridgeport, CT 06605.

Represented in the Archdioceses of Boston and Newark and in the Diocese of Bridgeport.

MISSIONARY SISTERS OF THE MOST SACRED HEART OF JESUS (M.S.C.) U.S.A.

U.S.A. Province Center: St. Michael Convent, 51 Seminary Ave., Reading, PA 19605.

150 Sisters in the U.S.A. and 1,140 Missionary Sisters worldwide

Ministries: Works of love in home and overseas missions: education, health care, pastoral care, homemaking, parish ministry, counseling, social work, spiritual ministries and community leadership.

Represented in 10 dioceses in the U.S.A. and in 15 other countries, internationally.

Vocation Director: Sr. Barbara Daniels, M.S.C., (610) 929-0695.

MISSIONARY SISTERS OF MOTHER OF GOD

See Eastern Catholic Religious Communities for Women.

MISSIONARY SISTERS OF OUR LADY OF AFRICA (M.S.O.L.A.)

3715 Williams Ln., Chevy Chase, MD 20815. (301) 654-2047

10 Sisters in U.S., 1,444 worldwide

Apostolic Work: Working in 17 African countries for the development of a local African Church: Primary evangelization, parish leadership training, social development of women, youth retreats, media, primary health care and other forms of medical work, teaching, counseling, development projects together with the local people, formation of small Christian communities and local Sisterhoods.

Represented in the Archdiocese of Washington, DC. (U.S. Headquarters)

Vocation Director: Sr. Demetria, M.S.O.L.A., 3715 Williams Ln., Chevy Chase, MD 20815. (301) 654-2047.

MISSIONARY SISTERS OF OUR LADY OF MERCY (M.O.M.)

388 Franklin St., Buffalo, NY 14202. (716) 854-5198

3 Professed Sisters

Represented in the Diocese of Buffalo.

MISSIONARY SISTERS OF THE PRECIOUS BLOOD (C.P.S.)

Provincial House and Novitiate: Precious Blood Convent, P.O. Box 97, Reading, PA 19607-0097 (610) 777-1624

24 Sisters in U.S., 1,000 worldwide

Apostolic Work: Ministry to the aged, Hispanic apostolate, teaching, parish sisters, nurses, doctors, ministry to the handicapped,

retreat/direction ministry, pastoral care, AIDS ministry.

Represented in the Dioceses of Allentown and Gallup. Missions in Africa, New Guinea, Europe and South Korea.

Vocation Director: Sr. Francis Bisland, P.O. Box 97, Reading, PA 19607-0097. (610) 777-1624.

MISSIONARY SISTERS OF ST. CHARLES BORROMEO-SCALABRINIANS (MSCS)

Provincial House: 1414 N. 37th Ave., Melrose Park, IL 60160. (708) 343-2162

827 Sisters in 20 countries.

Apostolic Work: Evangelical and missionary service to the undocumented refugees and immigrants. Realized through teaching, nursing, pastoral work and social services.

Represented in the Archdioceses of Chicago, New York, Washington, DC and Toronto and in the Diocese of San Jose, CA; Manila, Philippines; Tijuana, Guadalajara, and Mexico City, Mexico. Also in Albania, Argentina, Brazil, Columbia, Dominican Republic, Ecuador, France, Germany, Honduras, Italy, Mozambique, Paraguay, Poland, Portugal, South Africa and Switzerland.

Vocation Directress: Sr. Antoinette Scaletta, MSCS, 1414 N. 37th Ave., Melrose Park, IL 60160. (708) 343-2162.

MISSIONARY SISTERS OF ST. COLUMBAN (S.S.C.)

International Novitiate: Birmingham, England

250 Sisters

Apostolic Work: Missions.

Represented in the Archdioceses of Boston, Chicago and Los Angeles and in the Diocese of Buffalo. Also in Hong Kong, Korea, the Philippines, South America and Pakistan.

Vocation Directress: Sr. Margaret Devine, 4031 Dozier St., Los Angeles, CA 90063. (213) 261-2874.

MISSIONARY SISTERS OF ST. PETER CLAVER (S.S.P.C.)

667 Woods Mill Rd. S., P.O. Box 1058, Chesterfield, MO 63006-1058. (314) 434-8084

Contemplative in action and active in contemplation at the service of the Universal Church.

20 Sisters, 3 Novices, 1 Postulant

Represented in the Archdioceses of St. Louis, St. Paul and Chicago.

Vocation Director: Sr. M. Aidan, S.S.P.C., 667 Woods Mill Rd. S., P.O. Box 1058, Chesterfield, MO 63006-1058. (314) 434-8084.

MONASTIC FAMILY OF BETHLEHEM AND OF THE ASSUMPTION OF THE VIRGIN

Our Lady of Lourdes Camp, Livingston Manor, NY 12758. (914) 439-4300

12 Nuns in U.S.; 420 total

Apostolic Work: A life of contemplative prayer.

Represented in the Archdiocese of New York and in France, Austria, Belgium, Spain, Israel, Italy, Germany, Argentina and Canada.

Vocation Director: Sr. Amena, Prioress.

SISTERS OF THE MOST HOLY TRINITY (O.SS.T.)

21281 Chardon Rd., Euclid, OH 44117. (216) 481-8232

29 Sisters

Apostolic Work: Teaching, volunteer hospital ministry, National Shrine of Our Lady of Lourdes.

Represented in the Archdiocese of Philadelphia and in the Diocese of Cleveland, OH. Foreign mission in Madagascar. Generalate house in Rome.

Vocation Directress: Sr. M. Ursula, O.SS.T., Vocation Directress, Sisters of the Most Holy Trinity, 21281 Chardon Rd., Euclid, OH 44117-1591. (216) 481-8232.

SISTERS OF THE MOST PRECIOUS BLOOD (C.PP.S.)

318 Sisters

Apostolic Work: Education, parish ministry, geriatrics, special education, foreign missions, prison ministry, ecclesiastical art (the making of banners, vestments and accessories), domestic service, nursing, hospital ministry, health care services and social work. Represented in 12 states in the U.S. Foreign missions in Bolivia, Finland, Italy and Peru.

Vocation Directress: Sr. Marie Orf, C.PP.S., 204 N. Main St., O'Fallon, MO 63366-2299. (314) 240-3420.

MOTHERS OF THE HELPLESS (M.D.)

432 W. 20th St., New York, NY 10011. (212) 929-5790

7 Sisters

Apostolic Work: in New York: 1 day nursery and 1 residence for young women. Worldwide: Houses in Spain (Motherhouse); Puerto Rico; Mexico; Chile; Argentina and Rome, Italy; Novitiates in Spain and Colombia. Foreign missions in Guatemala and Colombia. Home for the aged and orphaned children; schools, retreat house, residence and day care centers.

Represented in the Archdiocese of New York and 8 foreign countries.

Vocation Directress: Sr. Mary Amparo, M.D., 432 W. 20th St., New York, NY 10011. (212) 929-0839.

SISTERS OF THE NEW COVENANT (S.N.C.)

Motherhouse: Covenant House, 10620 Livingston Dr., Northglenn, CO 80234. (303) 451-8677

Mission: Following Jesus in the style of St. Francis. Evangelization, spreading the Good News of Jesus Christ.

Represented in the Archdiocese of Denver.

Contact: Sr. Brigid Meierotto, S.N.C.

CONGREGATION OF NOTRE DAME OF MONTREAL (C.N.D.)

Blessed Sacrament Province

Provincial House: 223 W. Mountain Rd., Ridgefield, CT 06877. (203) 438-5282

205 Sisters

Apostolic Work: To bring the good news of Jesus to those in need, especially by greater connections for, and with, the poor and oppressed through all kinds of educational projects, and by living and praying together.

Represented in the Archdioceses of Chicago, New York, Hartford and Louisville and in the Dioceses of Albany, Bridgeport, Brownsville, Joliet, Pensacola, Providence, Rapid City, Richmond, Gallop and Oklahoma City. International missionary experience in Africa, Japan, Guatemala, Honduras and El Salvador. Houses in Troyes, France.

Vocation Contact: Mary Ann Rossi, CND, 106 Almy St., Providence, RI 02909-1813. (401) 621-5347.

NOTRE DAME de SION CONGREGATION (N.D.S.)

Novitiate: 349 Westminster Rd., Brooklyn, NY 11218

1,200 Sisters worldwide; 13 Sisters in U.S.

Apostolic Work: Characterized by a commitment to the Church, to the Jewish people and to a world of justice, peace and love.

Represented in 22 countries and in the Archdiocese of Chicago and in the Dioceses of Brooklyn and Kansas City-St. Joseph.

Vocation Contact: Sr. Audrey Gerwing, N.D.S., 160 Marion St., Toronto, Ontario M6R 1E8 Canada. (416) 533-7734.

NOTRE DAME SISTERS (N.D.)

Provincial Motherhouse: 3501 State St., Omaha, NE 68112. (402) 455-2994

80 Sisters

Apostolic Work: Teaching, pastoral ministry, religious education, counseling, nursing, nursing home care, social work, day care work, hospital chaplaincy, campus ministry, mission work on Sioux Reservation, SD.

Represented in the Archdioceses of Omaha, Dubuque and Kansas City and in the Dioceses of Lincoln and Rapid City.

Vocation Director: Sr. Margaret Proskovec, N.D., 3501 State St., Omaha, NE 68112. (402) 455-2994.

SISTERS OF NOTRE DAME (S.N.D.)

(Cleveland Province), 13000 Auburn Rd., Chardon, OH 44024. (216) 286-7101

487 Sisters; 5 in initial formation

Apostolic Work: The Sisters of Notre Dame are called to proclaim the goodness of God and be in solidarity with the poor. They serve in education, parish ministry, spiritual development, pastoral care, community service and other educationally related ministries.

Minister in the dioceses of Cleveland and Youngstown, OH and several other archdioceses and dioceses across the United States, in the Dominican Republic and Rome.

Vocation Director: Sr. Jennifer Kramer, S.N.D., 13000 Auburn Rd., Chardon, OH 44024. (216) 286-7101, ext. 174.

SISTERS OF NOTRE DAME (S.N.D.)

(Covington Province) St. Joseph Heights, 1601 Dixie Hwy., Covington, KY 41011. (606) 291-2040

215 Sisters

Conduct: 1 college, 1 academy, 1 high school, 20 elementary

schools, 3 special education schools, 2 child-care homes, 1 nursing home, 1 hospital, 1 mission among Afro-American people, 1 in Appalachia and 1 African mission.

Represented in the Archdiocese of Cincinnati and in the Dioceses of Birmingham, Covington and Lexington. Also in Uganda.

Vocation Directress: Sr. M. Shauna Bankemper, S.N.D., 1601 Dixie Hwy., Covington, KY 41011. (606) 291-2040.

SISTERS OF NOTRE DAME (S.N.D.)

(Toledo Province) 3837 Secor Rd., Toledo, OH 43623.

317 Sisters

Primary works are education, health care and pastoral ministries.

Conduct: 1 academy, 25 elementary schools, 1 school of music, 1 school for exceptional children, 1 child care center, 8 parish D.R.E.'s, 5 pastoral ministers, 4 diocesan office staff members (schools, vocation), spiritual life ministries, foreign mission, 4 pastoral associates.

Represented in the Archdiocese of Detroit (MI) and in the Dioceses of Fort Wayne (IN), Joliet (IL), St. Augustine (FL), and Toledo (OH). Also in Papua New Guinea.

Vocation Coordinator: Sr. Rita Marie, 3837 Secor Rd., Toledo, OH 43623. (419) 474-5485.

SISTERS OF NOTRE DAME (S.N.D.)

(Los Angeles Province) 1776 Hendrix Ave., Thousand Oaks, CA 91360. (805) 496-3243

106 Sisters

Conduct: 1 college study program for its novitiate, 1 academy, 4 high schools, 17 elementary schools.

Apostolic Work: Teaching in elementary, high school, college; catechetical work; DRE's; Eucharistic ministry to sick; community services; and nursing in Sisters' infirmary.

Represented in the Archdiocese of Los Angeles and in the Diocese of Oakland.

Vocation Directress: Sr. Mary Kathleen Burns, S.N.D., Notre Dame Center, 1776 Hendrix Ave., Thousand Oaks, CA 91360. (805) 496-3243.

SISTERS OF NOTRE DAME DE NAMUR (SNDdeN)

(Connecticut Province) Provincial House: 468 Poquonock Ave., Windsor, CT 06095. (203) 688-1832

170 Sisters

Apostolic Work: Elementary, high school and college teaching, religious education coordination, parish ministry, prison counseling, social action, urban centers, community organization, nursing, paralegal work, hospital pastoral care, adult education.

Represented in the Archdioceses of Hartford, Jacksonville, Newark, Boston and Washington, DC. Also in the Dioceses of Bridgeport, Burlington, Norwich, Springfield, MA, Worcester and Providence. Also in Brazil, Nicaragua, Peru and Italy.

Vocation Contact: Administrative Team, 468 Poquonock Ave., Windsor, CT 06095. (203) 688-1832.

SISTERS OF NOTRE DAME DE NAMUR (SNDdeN)

(Maryland Province) 1531 Greenspring Valley Rd., Stevenson, MD 21153

175 Sisters

Apostolic Work: Higher education, elementary, secondary, religious and special education, pastoral and social ministry in a wide variety of settings; community organizing; peace and justice work.

Represented in the Archdioceses of Baltimore, Washington, New York and Philadelphia and in the Dioceses of Brooklyn, Wilmington, Atlanta, Charleston and Rockville Centre. Overseas Missions in Kenya, Zaire, S. Africa, Nigeria, Zimbabwe, Peru, Nicaragua, Brazil and Japan.

Vocation Director: Sr. Geraldine Meyer, 1531 Greenspring Valley Rd., Stevenson, MD 21153.

SISTERS OF NOTRE DAME DE NAMUR (S.N.D.)

(Ipswich Province) Provincial Residence: 30 Jeffreys Neck Rd., Ipswich, MA 01938. (508) 356-4381

302 Sisters

Apostolic Work: Elementary schools, secondary schools, college, parish ministry, campus ministry, counseling, religious education directors, ministry to the poor, youth ministry, hospital ministry, spiritual development, communication and other developing

Church ministries.

Represented in the (Arch)dioceses of Birmingham, Boston, Fall River, Portland (ME), Springfield and Worcester (MA). Also in Africa, Japan, Rome and South America.

Vocation Director: Sr. Mary Boretti, S.N.D., 30 Jeffreys Neck Road, Ipswich, MA 01938. (508) 356-4381.

SISTERS OF NOTRE DAME DE NAMUR (S.N.D.)

(Boston Province) 351 Broadway, Everett, MA 02149. (617) 387-2500

272 Sisters

Conduct: 1 college, 2 high schools, 6 elementary schools, 2 Montessori schools.

Represented in the Archdiocese of Boston and in 8 provinces in the U.S., Asia, Africa, Europe and South America.

Vocation Director: Formation Office, 351 Broadway, Everett, MA 02149.

SISTERS OF NOTRE DAME DE NAMUR (S.N.D.)

(California Province) Provincial House: 14800 Bohlman Rd., Saratoga, CA 95070. (408) 741-0325

193 Sisters

Ministries: Education, counseling, social work, parish ministry, hospital ministry, religious education, communication, spiritual development and other developing ministries in today's Church especially with the poor.

Represented in the Archdioceses of Los Angeles, San Francisco and Seattle and in the Dioceses of Burlington, Fairbanks, Honolulu, Monterey, Oakland, Sacramento, San Jose, Stockton and Wheeling-Charleston. Also in Brazil, Japan, Kenya, Nicaragua, Nigeria, Peru, Zaire and Zimbabwe.

Vocation Team: Sr. Marie Annette Burkart, S.N.D., Sr. Carol Kenning, S.N.D., 14800 Bohlman Rd., Saratoga, CA 95070. (408) 741-0325.

SISTERS OF NOTRE DAME DE NAMUR (S.N.D. de N.)

(Ohio Unit) Mount Notre Dame, 701 E. Columbia Ave., Cincinnati, OH 45215.

285 Sisters

Apostolic Work: Education on all levels, elementary through college and adult; religious education, parish ministry, retreat work, guidance, social services, social action and health care.

Represented in the Archdioceses of Chicago, Cincinnati, St. Louis, Boston and Miami and in the Dioceses of Austin, Columbus, Covington, Gallup, Lexington, Joliet, Palm Beach, Phoenix, Saginaw, Salt Lake City and Tucson. Also in Brazil, Peru, Nicaragua, Kenya, Zaire, Nigeria, South Africa, Zimbabwe, Japan, Britain, Belgium and Italy.

Vocation Director: Sr. Mary Ellen Dow, 5440 S. Talman Ave., Chicago, IL 60632. (312) 737-2081.

SCHOOL SISTERS OF NOTRE DAME (S.S.N.D.)

(Northeastern Province)

475 Sisters

Motherhouse: 345 Belden Hill Rd., Wilton, CT 06897.

Apostolic Work: Education - preschool through university levels, special education, pastoral ministry, adult education, religious education, campus ministry, prison ministry, medical, nursing professions and legal profession.

Represented in the Archdioceses of Boston, Hartford, Newark and New York and in the Dioceses of Bridgeport, Brooklyn, Manchester, Albany, Paterson, Providence, Rochester and Rockville Centre. Also in Puerto Rico, Brazil, Chile, Kenya, Peru and Ghana.

Affiliate Director: Sr. Brenda Lynch, SSND, 345 Belden Hill Rd., Wilton, CT 06897. (203) 762-3318.

SCHOOL SISTERS OF NOTRE DAME (S.S.N.D.)

(Eastern Province) 6401 N. Charles St., Baltimore, MD 21212.

438 Sisters, 5 Novices, 4 Postulants

Apostolic Work: Head start, day care, child care, kindergarten, elementary education, secondary education, college education, special education, campus ministry, Spanish apostolate, parish ministry, religious education, retreats, spiritual direction, social services, health care, hospital chaplaincy, adult education, counseling, gay ministry, prison ministry.

Represented in the Archdioceses of Baltimore, Boston, Hartford, Los Angeles, Miami, Milwaukee, Newark, Philadelphia, St. Louis and Washington, DC. Also in the Dioceses of Arlington, Birmingham, Brooklyn, Camden, Charleston, Jackson, Lexington, Palm Beach, Pittsburgh, Richmond, St. Petersburg, Venice and Wilmington. Also in Bolivia, El Salvador,

Ghana, Italy and Nigeria.

Vocation Director: Sr. Marguerite Weiler, S.S.N.D., 6401 N. Charles St., Baltimore, MD 21212. (410) 377-5179.

SCHOOL SISTERS OF NOTRE DAME (S.S.N.D.)

(Milwaukee Province) 1233 N. Marshall St., Milwaukee, WI 53202.

688 Sisters, 35 Associate Members and 2 Lay Volunteers; 5,500 worldwide

Apostolic Work: Teaching (elementary, secondary, college), special education, religious education, pastoral ministry, campus ministry, youth ministry, social services, medical and nursing professions, communications, group homes, social justice positions, missionary, community service.

Represented in the (Arch)dioceses of Milwaukee, Green Bay, La Crosse, Superior, Madison, WI, Fort Wayne-South Bend, Gary, Lafayette, IN; Detroit, Gaylord, Grand Rapids, Marquette, Saginaw, MI; Phoenix, AZ; Chicago, Rockford, IL; Lexington, KY; Duluth, St. Cloud, St. Paul-Minneapolis, Winona, MN; Cincinnati, OH; Venice, FL; Baker, OR; Gallup, NM; Tulsa, OK; Seattle, Spokane, WA and Wheeling-Charleston, WV. Also in Guam, Marshall and Caroline Islands, and in the countries of Ghana, Kenya, Nigeria, Honduras, Guatemala, Italy and Germany.

Vocation Director: Sr. Jane Mary Lorbiecki, 1233 N. Marshall St., Milwaukee, WI 53202. (414) 278-7300.

SCHOOL SISTERS OF NOTRE DAME (S.S.N.D.)

(St. Louis Province) 320 E. Ripa Ave., St. Louis, MO 63125. (314) 544-0455

832 Sisters

Represented in the Archdioceses of Los Angeles and St. Louis and in the Dioceses of Belleville, Davenport, Fresno, Jefferson City, San Bernardino, San Diego, Springfield-Cape Girardeau and Springfield in Illinois plus a region in Japan and houses in Africa, Honduras and Nepal.

Vocation Director: Sr. Nancy Becker, S.S.N.D., 320 E. Ripa Ave., St. Louis, MO 63125. (314) 544-0455.

SCHOOL SISTERS OF NOTRE DAME (S.S.N.D.)

(Mankato Province) 170 Good Counsel Dr., Mankato, MN 56001-3198. (507) 389-4200.

500 Sisters in Province; 5,900 throughout the world

Apostolic Work: Education which enables persons to reach the fullness of their potential: teachers, principals in pre-schools, elementary schools, high schools, colleges, adult ed; parish visitors, parish ministers, parish administrators, youth ministers, spiritual directors; artists, musicians, secretaries, administrators, homemakers; missionaries, social workers, nurses, journalists, photographers, catechists.

Represented in the (Arch)dioceses of Fresno, Oakland, Washington, DC, Boise, Chicago, Joliet, Rockford, Fort Wayne-South Bend, Indianapolis, Dubuque, Davenport, Sioux City, New Orleans, Detroit, Duluth, New Ulm, St. Cloud, St. Paul-Minneapolis, Winona, Jackson, St. Louis, Great Falls, Bismarck, Fargo, Cincinnati, Tulsa, Sioux Falls, Fort Worth, Richmond, Spokane, Milwaukee, Superior. Also in the foreign countries of Austria, Canada, Guatemala, Italy and Kenya.

Vocation Director: Sr. Dianne Perry, S.S.N.D., 222 Wentworth Ave. W., Apt. 304, West St. Paul, MN 55118. (612) 457-0983; (612) 690-9285.

SCHOOL SISTERS OF NOTRE DAME (S.S.N.D.)

(Chicago Province) 1431 Euclid Ave., Berwyn, IL 60402. (708) 749-1380

170 Sisters in Province; 5,750 worldwide

Apostolic Work: Elementary education, secondary education, college education, special education, ESL, parish ministry, religious education, spiritual direction, social services, health care, community service.

Represented in the Archdioceses of Baltimore, Chicago, Los Angeles, Miami, Milwaukee and Washington, DC and in the Dioceses of Gary, Joliet, Peoria and Rockford. Also in foreign missions of Africa, Japan and Paraguay.

Vocation Directors: Sr. Maureen Clancy, S.S.N.D., Sr. Carolyn Jost, S.S.N.D., 1431 Euclid Ave., Berwyn, IL 60402. (708) 749-1380.

SCHOOL SISTERS OF NOTRE DAME (S.S.N.D.)

(Dallas Province) P.O. Box 227275, Dallas, TX 75222-7275. (214) 330-9152

210 Sisters

Represented in the Archdioceses of New Orleans and San Antonio and in the Dioceses of Alexandria, Baton Rouge, Biloxi, Brownsville, Dallas, Fort Worth, Gallup, Galveston-Houston, Houma-Thibodaux, Lafayette, Lake Charles, Little Rock, Jackson, Phoenix, San Angelo, Tucson, Tulsa and Tyler and in mission areas of Mexico, Guatemala and Sunyan (Ghana, West Africa).

Formation Director: Sr. Judy Scheffler, S.S.N.D., 132 City, San Antonio, TX 78204. (512) 271-7433.

NUNS OF THE PERPETUAL ADORATION OF THE BLESSED SACRAMENT (A.P.)

(San Francisco Province) 771 Ashbury St., San Francisco, CA 94117. (415) 566-2743

25 Sisters

Represented in the Archdiocese of San Francisco. Also in Mexico, Spain, Chile and Africa.

NUNS OF THE PERPETUAL ADORATION OF THE BLESSED SACRAMENT (A.P.) (Autonomous Monasteries)

Monastery of Perpetual Adoration, 145 N. Cotton Ave., El Paso, TX 79901. (915) 533-5323

21 Sisters

Spanish speaking community

Represented in the Archdioceses of Anchorage and San Francisco and in the Diocese of El Paso.

NUNS OF SAINT BASIL THE GREAT

See Eastern Catholic Religious Communities for Women.

SISTERS OBLATES TO THE BLESSED TRINITY (O.B.T.)

St. Clare's Convent, 1925 Hone Ave., Bronx, NY 10461. (718) 792-9267; St. Aloysius Gonzaga Novitiate, Beekman Rd., P.O. Box 98, Hopewell Junction, NY 12533. (914) 226-5671

Apostolic Work: Teaching in parish schools, catechetics and retreats.

Represented in the Archdiocese of New York and in the Dioceses of Madison, WI, San Juan and Ponce, Puerto Rico.

Superior General: Mother Gloria Castro, Beekman Rd., P.O. Box 98, Hopewell Junction, NY 12533. (914) 226-5671.

OBLATE SISTERS OF JESUS THE PRIEST (O.J.S.)

General Motherhouse: Arenal 244, Tialpan, Mexico D.F.C.P. 14420.

St. Paul the Apostle Church, 415 W. 59th St., New York, NY 10019. (212) 265-3209

22 Sisters in U.S., 137 Sisters in Mexico

Represented in the Archdioceses of Chicago and New York.

OBLATE SISTERS OF THE BLESSED SACRAMENT (O.S.B.S.)

Motherhouse: St. Sylvester's Convent, Marty, SD 57361. (605) 384-3305; Formation House: Kateri Convent, Rapid City, SD 57701. (605) 343-6261.

American Indian Apostolate

7 Sisters

Represented in the Dioceses of Rapid City and Sioux Falls.

OBLATES OF THE MOST HOLY REDEEMER (O.S.S.R.)

Mother of Good Counsel House, 290 Babylon Turnpike, Roosevelt, NY 11575. (516) 223-1013

25 Sisters in U.S., 800 Sisters worldwide

Apostolic Work: Primary apostolic work of the order is to every woman in need: drug addicts, prostitutes, unwed mothers, abandoned women and immigrants adjusting to a new culture.

Represented in the (Arch)dioceses of Boston, New York and Rockville Centre, NY. Also in Spain, Italy, Puerto Rico, Argentina, Uruguay, Venezuela, Colombia, Mexico, Brazil, Philippines and Portugal.

Vocation Director: Mother of Good Counsel House, 290 Babylon Turnpike, Roosevelt, Long Island, NY 11575. (516) 223-1013.

OBLATE SISTERS OF PROVIDENCE (O.S.P.)

Motherhouse: 701 Gun Rd., Baltimore, MD 21227-3899. (410) 242-8500. Novitiate: Lange House, 1227 E-St. N.E., Washington, DC 20002.

140 Sisters (multi-racial, multi-cultural), 5 Candidates

Apostolic Work: Secondary and elementary school, 1 reading center, Spanish apostolate, Offices of Black Catholic Ministries, day care centers, outreach ministries, parish ministries.

Represented in the Archdioceses of Baltimore, Chicago, Detroit, Philadelphia and Washington, DC and in Dioceses of Alabama, Buffalo, South Carolina and Trenton and three vicariates of Costa Rica and the Dominican Republic.

Vocation Directress: Sr. Magdala Marie Gilbert, OSP, 701 Gun Rd., Baltimore, MD 21227-3899.

OBLATE SISTERS OF THE SACRED HEART OF JESUS (O.S.H.J.)

Villa Maria Teresa, 50 Warner Rd., Hubbard, OH 44425.

21 Sisters

Apostolic Work: Minister with, and to, diocesan priests as Directors of Religious Education, care for elderly priests, pastoral ministry, primary and elementary education, mission work.

For information write: Sr. Joyce Candidi, Villa Maria Teresa, 50 Warner Rd., Hubbard, OH 44425. (216) 759-8468.

OBLATE SISTERS OF ST. FRANCIS de SALES (O.S.F.S.)

399 Childs Rd., Childs, MD 21916. (410) 398-3699

14 Sisters

Apostolic Work: Teaching and social work.

Represented in the Archdiocese of Philadelphia and in the Diocese of Wilmington.

Vocation Director: Sr. John Marie, 399 Childs Rd., Childs, MD 21916.

OLIVETAN BENEDICTINE SISTERS (O.S.B.)

Holy Angels Convent, Off Hwy. 141 N., P.O. Drawer 130, Jonesboro, AR 72403.

62 Sisters, 1 Novice

Apostolic Work: Teaching, hospital work, pastoral care, parish religious education, teaching music, day care center.

Represented in the Dioceses of Little Rock and Fort Worth.

Vocations: Holy Angels Convent, P.O. Drawer 130, Jonesboro, AR 72403. (501) 935-5810.

ORDER OF THE MOST HOLY REDEEMER

See Redemptoristine Nuns.

SISTERS OF OUR LADY OF CHARITY (O.L.C.)

(North American Union of the Sisters of Our Lady of Charity) General Administration Center: Sr. Deana Kohlman, Superior General, P.O. Box 327, Wisconsin Dells, WI 53965. (608) 254-2070 or (304) 242-8000

202 Sisters

Primary Work: For "girls and women in need" both within and outside of institutions; also, day care, nursing homes, religious education, parish ministries (English and Spanish speaking), counseling and guidance.

Represented in the (Arch)dioceses of Buffalo/Rochester, NY; Erie/Pittsburgh, PA; El Paso/San Antonio, TX; Madison/ Green Bay, WI; Wheeling, WV; San Diego, CA and Venice, FL. Also in Canada and Mexico.

Vocation Director: Administration Center, P.O. Box 327, Wisconsin Dells, WI 53965.

SISTERS OF OUR LADY OF CHRISTIAN DOCTRINE (R.C.D.)

23 Haskell Ave., Suffern, NY 10901. (914) 357-0046

41 Sisters

Apostolic Work: Religious education, parish visiting, nursing, counseling, recreational work, spiritual direction and retreat work, pastoral ministry.

Located in New Hampshire, Florida, Illinois, New Jersey and New York. Also in the Dominican Republic.

Vocation Directress: Sr. Patricia Brady, R.C.D., 29 Clinton Pl., Mt. Vernon, NY 10550. (914) 668-4031.

SISTERS OF OUR LADY OF THE GARDEN (O.L.G.)

67 Round Hill Rd., Middletown, CT 06457. (203) 346-5765

1,050 Sisters

Apostolic Work: Teaching, nursing, social work, foreign missions, parish work.

Represented in the Archdiocese of Hartford and the Diocese of Norwich. Also in Italy, South America, Spain, Palestine, India and Africa.

Vocation Directress: Sr. Donna Beauregard, O.L.G.

SISTERS OF OUR LADY OF MERCY (S.O.L.M.) (Mercedarian Sisters)

General Motherhouse Offices: Via Ostriana 24, 00199 Rome, Italy. Telephone: (6) 83.80.428.

Reverend Mother Mary Igina Caddori, S.O.L.M., Superior General.

12 Sisters in U.S.; 500 Sisters worldwide

Apostolic Work: In the U.S. the sisters have two convents and staff two parish grammer schools. With over 500 sisters in eight countries, the Mercedarian Sisters have continued that same Marian spirit of their foundress, Venerable Mother Theresa of Jesus Bacq, S.O.L.M., over 130 years ago. Wherever Mercedarians minister: in hospitals, schools, retreat centers, or evangelizing foreign missions, the Sisters seek to be the presence and gift of His Merciful Love in the Church. Mercedarians are committed to communicate to all the world the freedom of the Merciful Love of Christ, who delivers all from everyday earthly captivity.

Represented in the Diocese of Brooklyn and Camden.

Vocation Director: Sr. Mary Celinda, S.O.L.M., Mercedarian Sisters, 400 Erial Rd., Pine Hill, NJ 08021.

SISTERS OF OUR LADY OF THE HOLY ROSARY (R.S.R.)

Motherhouse: Rimouski, P.Q., Canada G5L 3E3.

Regional House: 25 Portland Ave., Old Orchard Beach, ME 04064. (207) 934-0592

625 Sisters, 10 working in U.S.

Apostolic Work: Christian education.

Represented in the Diocese of Portland, ME.; In the Provinces of Quebec and New Brunswick in Canada and also in Honduras, Peru, Chile.

Vocation: Sr. Juliette Michaud, R.S.R., 20 Thomas St., Portland, ME 04102. (207) 774-3756.

SISTERS OF OUR LADY OF SORROWS (O.L.S.)

American Headquarters: 9894 Norris Ferry Rd., Shreveport, LA 71106. (318) 797-0213

35 Sisters

Conduct: 2 grammar schools, 2 residential facilities and 3 community homes for individuals with mental retardation, 1 day care center and apostolic work in the parishes.

Represented in the Dioceses of Alexandria and Shreveport, LA.

Vocation Directress: Sr. Sandra Norsworthy, O.L.S., Holy Rosary Convent, 1720 Cox St., Shreveport, LA 71108. (1-800) 531-9223; (318) 636-4568.

OUR LADY OF VICTORY MISSIONARY SISTERS (OLVM)

Box 109, Victory Noll, Huntington, IN 46750. (219) 356-0628

215 Sisters in over 20 states and Bolivia

Apostolic Work: Pastoral ministry, religious education, social services and health care in favor of the poor and the dispossessed.

Vocation Director: Sr. Beatrice Haines, OLVM, Box 109, Victory Noll, Huntington, IN 46750. (219) 356-0628.

PALLOTTINE SISTERS (C.S.A.C.) (Sisters of the Catholic Apostolate)

(Immaculate Conception Province)

Provincialate: St. Patrick's Villa, Harriman Heights, P.O. Box 118, Harriman, NY 10926. (914) 783-9007

82 Sisters; 650 worldwide

Apostolic Work: High school, parochial schools, private schools, day nursery, parish/pastoral work.

Represented in the Archdioceses of Newark and New York and in the Diocese of Brooklyn. Also in Europe and South America.

Vocation Directress: Sr. Carmel Therese Favazzo, St. Patrick Villa, Harriman, NY 10926. (914) 774-7585.

PALLOTTINE SISTERS (S.A.C.) (Society of the Catholic Apostolate)

15270 Old Halls Ferry Rd., Florissant, MO 63034-1661.

67 Sisters

Ministries: To increase faith and love using any and all means.

Represented in Archdioceses of St. Louis, MO and Washington, DC and in the Diocese of Wheeling-Charleston, WV.

Vocation Director: Sr. Gail Borgmeyer, S.A.C., 15270 Old Halls Ferry Rd., Florissant, MO 63034-1661. (314) 837-1355.

PARISH VISITORS OF MARY IMMACULATE (P.V.M.I.)

Marycrest Convent, Box 658, Monroe, NY 10950-0658. (914) 783-2251

78 Sisters (including Postulants)

Apostolic Work: Contemplative-missionary community serving the Church in visitation/evangelization, through person-to-person contact by visiting families, individuals or groups; religious education for the total parish; spiritual counseling; social service; in all of this seeking out the spiritually, morally or materially impoverished, the rejected and neglected.

Represented in the Archdioceses of New York and Hartford and in the Dioceses of Brooklyn, Ogdensburg, Syracuse and Scranton. Also in the Diocese of Okigwe, Nigeria.

Vocation Director: Marycrest Convent, Box 658, Monroe, NY 10950-0658. (914) 783-2251.

PASSIONIST NUNS (C.P.)
(The Nuns of The Most Holy Cross and Passion of Our Lord Jesus Christ)

Apostolic Work: Contemplation.

Represented in five independent monasteries in the U.S.: Our Lady of Sorrows Monastery of the Passionist Nuns, 2715 Churchview Ave., Pittsburgh, PA 15227. (412) 881-1155

12 Sisters

St. Gabriel's Monastery, 631 Griffin Pond Rd., Clarks Summit, PA 18411. (717) 586-2791

21 Sisters

St. Joseph's Monastery, 1420 Benita Ave., Owensboro, KY 42301. (502) 683-5483

19 Sisters, 1 Novice

Monastery of the Sacred Passion, 1151 Donaldson Hwy., Erlanger, KY 41018. (606) 371-8568

10 Sisters

Immaculate Conception Monastery, 1032 Clayton Rd., Ellisville, MO 63011. (314) 227-5275

15 Sisters, 1 Novice

PASSIONIST SISTERS (C.P.)
(Sisters of the Cross and Passion)

Holy Family Convent, 1 Wright Ln., North Kingstown, RI 02852.

52 Sisters

Apostolic Work: Education, retreats, pastoral care, social work, catechetics, foreign missions.

Represented in the Archdiocese of Hartford and in the Dioceses of Brooklyn, Fall River, Providence and Rockville Centre. Also in Jamaica, West Indies and five foreign countries.

Vocation Person: Sr. Ann Rodgers, CP, Our Lady of Calvary Retreat House, 31 Colton St., Farmington, CT 06032. (203) 677-8510, 8519.

SISTERS OF PERPETUAL ADORATION (A.P.G.)

U.S. Foundation: 2403 West Travis, San Antonio, TX 78207. (210) 227-5546

13 Sisters.

SISTERS OF THE PIOUS SCHOOLS (Sch.P.)

U.S. Headquarters: 17601 Nordhoff St., Northridge, CA 91325. Motherhouse in Rome.

26 Sisters, 2 Novices, 5 Postulants

Conduct: Schools, religious education.

Represented in the Archdiocese of Los Angeles. Also has missions in Mexico, Latin America, Japan, Africa, Philippines, Spain, Poland and Italy.

Vocation Director: Sr. Maria Jesus, Sch.P., 17601 Nordhoff St., Northridge, CA 91325. (818) 882-5265.

SISTERS OF THE POOR CHILD JESUS (P.C.J.)

American Provincialate: Our Lady of Bethlehem Convent, 4567 Olentangy River Rd., Columbus, OH 43214.

7 Sisters in U.S., 1,000 worldwide

Conduct: 1 elementary school, 1 private kindergarten and day care.

Represented in the Dioceses of Columbus and Wheeling-Charleston. Work in Germany, the Netherlands, Belgium, Luxembourg, Spain, Austria and Rome, Italy; Bogota, Columbia, Indonesia and Latvia.

Vocation Director: Sr. Frances Teresa, P.C.J., 4567 Olentangy River Rd., Columbus, OH 43214. (614) 451-6631 or 3900.

POOR CLARE NUNS (O.S.C.) or (P.C.C.)

The Poor Clare Nuns are a contemplative Order of over 1,000 independent monasteries worldwide. The nuns do not engage in any direct apostolate outside of their monasteries.

POOR CLARE NUNS (O.S.C.)

Monastery of St. Clare, 142 Hollywood Ave., Bronx, NY 10465. (718) 822-7271

14 Sisters

Abbess: Sr. Elizabeth Enoch, OSC.

POOR CLARE NUNS (O.S.C.)

Monastery of St. Clare , 6825 Nurrenbern Rd., Evansville, IN 47712.

18 Sisters

Contact Person: Sr. Anna Scheessele, OSC. (812) 425-4396.

POOR CLARE NUNS (O.S.C.)

St. Clare Monastery, 1310 Dellwood Ave., Memphis, TN 38127. (901) 357-6662

12 Sisters.

POOR CLARE NUNS (O.S.C.)

St. Clare Monastery, 920 Centre St., Jamaica Plain, MA 02130. (617) 524-1760

24 Final Professed, 1 in Formation.

POOR CLARE NUNS
(Cloistered)

St. Clare Monastery, 201 Crosswicks St., Bordentown, NJ 08505. (609) 298-0016

15 Sisters

Contemplative Community.

POOR CLARE NUNS (O.S.C.)
(Contemplative Life Style)

Monastery of Saint Clare, 1271 Langhorne-Newtown Rd., Langhorne, PA 19047-1297.

15 Sisters

Vocation Director: Sr. Evelyn, O.S.C. (215) 968-5775.

POOR CLARE NUNS (O.S.C.)

St. Clare's Monastery, 421 S. 4th St., Sauk Rapids, MN 56379. (612) 251-3556

18 Sisters

Contemplatives with Papal Enclosure.

POOR CLARE NUNS (O.S.C.)

St. Clare Monastery, 8650 Russell Ave. S., Minneapolis, MN 55431-1998. (612) 881-4766

13 Sisters

Franciscan Contemplative Community.

Contact: Vocation Director.

POOR CLARE NUNS
(Strictly Cloistered)

Monastery of the Blessed Sacrament, 3501 Rocky River Dr., Cleveland, OH 44111-2998. (216)

941-2820
24 Cloistered Nuns, 5 Extern Sisters
Apostolic Work: Dedicated to contemplative prayer and the Divine Office, living in joyous penance, poverty and simplicity. Perpetual Adoration of the Blessed Sacrament.
Contact Person: Reverend Mother Abbess.

POOR CLARE NUNS (P.C.C.)
Corpus Christi Monastery, 2111 S. Main St., Rockford, IL 61102. (815) 963-7343
28 Sisters, 1 Novice, 3 Postulants.

POOR CLARE NUNS (O.S.C.)
Monastery of St. Clare, 460 River Rd., Andover, MA 01810-4260. (508) 851-6743
20 Sisters
Contact: Vocation Directress.

POOR CLARE NUNS (O.S.C.)
Monastery of St. Clare, 1916 N. Pleasantburg Dr., Greenville, SC 29609-4080. (803) 244-4514.
17 Sisters
Contemplative.
Contact: Sr. Carolyn, O.S.C.

POOR CLARE NUNS
28 Harpersville Rd., Newport News, VA 23601.
13 Nuns
Vocation Director: Mother Colette, 28 Harpersville Rd., Newport News, VA 23601. (804) 596-5942.

POOR CLARE NUNS (P.C.C.)
Maria Regina Mater Monastery, 1175 N. 300 West, Kokomo, IN 46901.
9 Sisters.
Apostolic Work: Prayer and penance.

POOR CLARE NUNS (O.S.C.)
Christ the King Monastery, 3900 Sherwood Blvd., Delray Beach, FL 33445-5699. (407) 498-3294
11 Sisters
Franciscan Contemplative Nuns.
Contact: Sr. Frances Vass, O.S.C.

POOR CLARE NUNS (O.S.C.)
Monastery of St. Clare, 200 Marycrest Dr., St. Louis, MO 63129-4813. (314) 846-2618
9 Nuns in Solemn Vows
Cloistered contemplatives.

POOR CLARE NUNS (O.S.C.)
St. Clare Monastery, 3626 N. 65th Ave., Omaha, NE 68104-3299. (402) 558-4916
10 Sisters
Contact: Sr. Mary Clare Brown, O.S.C.

POOR CLARE NUNS (O.S.C.)
Order of St. Clare, St. Clare Monastery, 720 Henry Clay Ave., New Orleans, LA 70118. (504) 895-2019
13 Solemnly Professed, 2 Simply Professed
Apostolic Work: Franciscan contemplative community situated in the Archdiocese of New Orleans.
Vocation Director: Sr. Rita Marie Hickey, O.S.C.

POOR CLARE NUNS (O.S.C.)
Monastery of St. Clare, 4419 N. Hawthorne St., Spokane, WA 99205-1399. (509) 327-4479
10 Solemnly Professed Sisters
Apostolic Work: Contemplative prayer.
Vocation Directress: Sr. Mary Rita Dolan, O.S.C.

POOR CLARE NUNS
St. Joseph Monastery, 1671 Pleasant Valley Rd., P.O. Box 160, Aptos, CA 95003-0160. (408) 761-9659
14 Sisters, 1 Novice, 1 Postulant

POOR CLARE NUNS (P.C.C.)
Monastery of Poor Clares, 215 E. Los Olivos St., Santa Barbara, CA 93105. (805) 682-7670
17 Professed, 2 in Formation.

POOR CLARE NUNS (P.C.C.)
Monastery of Our Lady of Guadalupe, 809 E. 19th St., Roswell, NM 88201. (505) 622-0868
39 Sisters
Cloistered contemplative community.

POOR CLARE NUNS
Immaculate Heart Monastery, 28210 Natoma Rd., Los Altos Hills, CA 94022. (415) 948-2947
19 Sisters.

POOR CLARE NUNS (O.S.C.)
Monastery of St. Clare, 868 Finney Trail, Cincinnati, OH 45224-1319. (513) 522-4795.

4 Sisters
Apostolic Work: Contemplative.
Represented in the Archdiocese of Cincinnati.
Vocation Director: Sr. Doris Gerke, O.S.C.

POOR CLARES OF PERPETUAL ADORATION (P.C.P.A.)
St. Joseph Adoration Monastery, 2311 Stockham Lane, Portsmouth, OH 45662.
7 Cloistered Nuns, 1 Postulant, 1 Extern Sister
Apostolic Work: Contemplative prayer, Perpetual Adoration of the Blessed Sacrament.
Contact Person: Mother Mary Agnes, P.C.P.A. (614) 353-4713.

POOR CLARES NUNS OF PERPETUAL ADORATION (P.C.P.A.)
Sancta Clara Monastery, 4200 N. Market Ave., Canton, OH 44714.
12 Sisters
Apostolic Work: Eucharistic Adoration and contemplative prayer, music ministry.
Represented in the Diocese of Youngstown.
Vocation Directress: Sr. Kay Marie.

POOR CLARES OF PERPETUAL ADORATION (P.C.P.A.)
4108 Euclid Ave., Cleveland, OH 44103.
24 Sisters
Autonomous, Contemplative Community
Apostolate Work: Perpetual Eucharistic Adoration
Represented in the (Arch)dioceses of Cleveland, Washington, DC, Youngstown, OH; Columbus, OH and Birmingham, AL. Also in India, Poland, France, Germany and Austria.
Contact Person: Vocation Directress. (216) 361-0783.

POOR CLARES OF PERPETUAL ADORATION (P.C.P.A.)
3900 13th St., N.E., Washington, DC 20017. (202) 526-6808
12 Sisters
Primary Apostolic Work: Perpetual Adoration of the Most Blessed Sacrament (enclosed order).
Vocation Directress: Sr. Mary Rita.

POOR CLARES OF PERPETUAL ADORATION (P.C.P.A.)

O.L. of Angels Monastery, 5817 Old Leeds Rd., Birmingham, AL 35210. (205) 956-5987

28 Nuns

Vocation Directress: Sr. Mary Raphael.

POOR CLARE MISSIONARY SISTERS (M.C.)

Regional House and Novitiate: 1019 N. Newhope, Santa Ana, CA 92703. (714) 554-8850

38 Sisters

Conduct: 2 nursery schools, 1 parochial school, 1 retreat house.

Represented in the Archdiocese of Los Angeles and in the Diocese of Orange.

Vocation Contact: Sr. Angelica Trujillo, M.C.

POOR HANDMAIDS OF JESUS CHRIST (P.H.J.C.)

Convent Ancilla Domini, P.O. Box 1, Donaldson, IN 46513. (219) 936-9936

300 Sisters in American province

Apostolic Work: Health care, education, community and social services and parish ministry.

Represented in the Dioceses of Fort Wayne-South Bend, Chicago, Belleville, Lafayette, Gary, Milwaukee, Springfield, Minneapolis-St. Paul and Cincinnati.

Vocation Director: Sr. Deborah Davis, 4231 Fir St., E. Chicago, IN 46312. (219) 397-6091.

POOR SERVANTS OF THE MOTHER OF GOD (S.M.G.)

Regional Headquarters: Maryfield Convent, 1315 Greensboro Rd., High Point, NC 27260. (910) 454-3014; 886-2444.

25 Sisters

Motherhouse: Maryfield Convent, Roehampton, London SW15 4JA, England

Apostolic Work: Health care, education, retreats, social concerns.

Represented in the (Arch)dioceses of Philadelphia, Richmond, Tulsa, Charlotte and Metuchen. Also in England, Ireland, Italy, France, Scotland, Africa and South America.

Vocation Director: Sr. Clare Frances, S.M.G., Regional Superior, Maryfield Convent, 1315 Greensboro Rd., High Point, NC 27260. (910) 454-3014; 886-2444.

POOR SISTERS OF NAZARETH (P.S.N.)

Regional House and Novitiate: Nazareth House, 3333 Manning Ave., Los Angeles, CA 90064. (310) 839-2361

Apostolic Work: In over 50 Nazareth Houses worldwide we, Nazareth Sisters, aim to give children-in-need a real home and educate them in our own schools. Valuing every opportunity to care for retired, sick priests/brothers, we strive to give our elderly, frail residents loving care in a peace-filled, secure and happy atmosphere.

Represented: Six U.S. Nazareth Houses are in the Archdioceses of Los Angeles and San Francisco and in the Dioceses of San Diego, Fresno, Madison and Pago Pago (American Samoa). Sisters also present in Australia, New Zealand, South Africa, Zimbabwe, Ireland, England, Scotland and Wales.

Vocation Director: Mother Margaret Clare, P.S.N., Nazareth House, 3333 Manning Ave., Los Angeles, CA 90064. (310) 839-2361.

POOR SISTERS OF ST. JOSEPH

U.S. Foundations in Alexandria, VA., Bethlehem, PA, and Reading, PA.

15 Sisters in U.S.

Apostolic Work: Parish ministry, schools, social work, hospitals, day care.

Vocations: Sr. Eloina Alvarez, St. Gabriel Convent, 4319 Sano St., Alexandria, VA 22312. (703) 354-0395.

SISTERS OF THE PRECIOUS BLOOD (C.PP.S.)

Generalate: 4000 Denlinger Rd., Dayton, OH 45426. (513) 837-3302

341 Sisters

Apostolic Work: Teaching (elementary, secondary, university), religious education, pastoral ministry, retreat work, health care, food service, social service and Chilean foreign missions.

Represented in the Archdioceses of Cincinnati, Denver and Detroit and in the Dioceses of Cleveland, Columbus, Dallas, Ft. Wayne, Lafayette, Lansing, Toledo, Phoenix, Saginaw, San Diego, Tucson and Youngstown.

Contact: Sr. Nadine Kaschalk, C.PP.S., 2712 Letchworth Pkwy., Toledo, OH 43606-3632. (419) 472-2467.

UNION OF THE SISTERS OF THE PRESENTATION OF THE BLESSED VIRGIN MARY (P.B.V.M.)

Provincialate: 729 W. Wilshire Dr., Phoenix, AZ 85007. (602) 271-9687

120 Sisters

Apostolic Work: Teaching, religious education, adult education, nursing, social work, parish ministries.

Represented in the Archdioceses of Los Angeles, Mobile, New Orleans, San Antonio and San Francisco and in the Dioceses of Biloxi, Birmingham, Oakland, Orange, Phoenix, Sacramento, San Bernardino, Savannah and Tucson. Sisters in Africa, England, India, Ireland, New Zealand, Pakistan, Philippines and South America.

Vocation Coordinator: Sr. Jane Bonar, P.B.V.M., Presentation Provincialate, 729 W. Wilshire Dr., Phoenix, AZ 85007.

PRESENTATION SISTERS OF ABERDEEN (P.B.V.M.)

Motherhouse: Presentation Heights, Aberdeen, SD 57401.

180 Sisters

Apostolic Work: Education, hospital, nursing homes, parish and youth ministries and social services, ministry with Native American, Hispanic and rural people, Mexican mission, retreat work, campus ministry.

Represented primarily in the Diocese of Sioux Falls, SD. Also in Montana, Minnesota, New Mexico, Illinois, Iowa, Arizona, Louisiana, Nebraska, Michigan, New York, Oregon and Mexico.

Vocation Director: Sr. Phyllis Gill, P.B.V.M., Presentation Heights, Aberdeen, SD 57401. (605) 225-0420, Ext. 401.

PRESENTATION SISTERS OF DUBUQUE (P.B.V.M.)

Motherhouse and Novitiate: 2360 Carter Rd., Dubuque, IA 52001-2997

183 Sisters

Apostolic Work: College, high schools, elementary schools, religious education, pastoral ministry, campus ministry, youth ministry, home and foreign missions.

Represented in the Archdioceses of Dubuque, Chicago, Denver, Indianapolis, Kansas City-St. Joseph, St. Louis, St. Paul and

Washington and in the Dioceses of Beaumont, Brownsville, Covington, Davenport, Jackson, Nashville, Orlando, Pensacola-Tallahassee, Rapid City and Sioux City. Also in Entre Rios, Tarija, Bolivia; Santa Cruz del Quiche, Guatemala.

Vocation Director: Sr. Jennifer Rausch, P.B.V.M., 2360 Carter Rd., Dubuque, IA 52001-2997. (319) 588-2008.

PRESENTATION SISTERS OF FARGO (P.B.V.M.)

Motherhouse and Novitiate: 1101 32 Ave., South Fargo, ND 58103. (701) 237-4857

70 Professed

Apostolic Work: Education, pastoral ministry, health care, domestic services, social work, spirituality centers, Dorothy Day House, home and foreign missions.

Represented in the (Arch)dioceses of Fargo, Bismarck, Crookston, Rapid City, Lexington, Knoxville, Columbus, Springfield-Cape Girardeau, Billings-Great Falls, St. Cloud, St. Louis, St. Paul, La Crosse, Portland, Sioux Falls and Winona. Also in Peru and Zambia, Africa.

Contact: Vocation Director, Sacred Heart Convent, 1101 32 Ave., South Fargo, ND 58103. (701) 237-4857.

PRESENTATION SISTERS OF FITCHBURG (P.B.V.M.)

Motherhouse and Novitiate: Presentation Convent, 99 Church St., Leominster, MA 01453. (508) 537-7108.

95 Sisters

Apostolic Work: High schools, elementary schools, social/pastoral ministry, health care and religious education.

Represented in the Dioceses of Norwich, Providence, Worcester and Manchester.

Vocation Director: Sr. Joan McDermott, P.B.V.M., 70 Island St., Keene, NH 03431. (603) 352-7662.

PRESENTATION SISTERS OF NEWBURGH (P.B.V.M.)

Sisters of the Presentation, Mount Saint Joseph, 880 Jackson Ave., New Windsor, NY 12553.

128 Sisters

Apostolic Work: 8 elementary schools, 2 high schools, college teaching, nursing care, diocesan services, social ministry, retreat center, drug rehab, hospice, correctional, medical.

Represented in the Archdiocese of New York and in the Dioceses of Brooklyn, Metuchen, Paterson and Newark. Also foreign missions in Ghana and Bolivia.

Contact Person: Sr. Anne Massell, P.B.V.M., 466 Westchester Ave., Crestwood, NY 10707.

PRESENTATION SISTERS OF SAN FRANCISCO (P.B.V.M.)

Motherhouse: 2340 Turk Blvd., San Francisco, CA 94118. (415) 751-0406

152 Sisters

Conduct: 1 high school, 7 elementary schools

Apostolic Work: Teaching on elementary, secondary and college levels, social work, retreat work, health care work, parish work, missionary work.

Represented in the Archdioceses of Los Angeles and San Francisco and in the Dioceses of Oakland, San Jose, Santa Rosa, Stockton, Orange, San Bernadino and Marquette, MI.

Vocation Director: Sr. Kathleen Sickly, 2340 Turk Blvd., San Francisco, CA 94118.

PRESENTATION SISTERS OF STATEN ISLAND (P.B.V.M.)

Motherhouse: Our Lady of the Presentation, 419 Woodrow Rd., Annadale, S.I., NY 10312. (718) 356-2121

42 Sisters (members of an international organization of women)

Apostolic Work: Grammar schools, high school, catechetics, retreat work, social justice apostolate, nursing, campus ministry and parish ministry.

Represented in the Archdioceses of New York and Philadelphia.

Vocation Director: Our Lady of the Presentation, 419 Woodrow Rd., Annadale, S.I., NY 10312. (718) 356-2121.

PRESENTATION SISTERS OF WATERVLIET (P.B.V.M.),

St. Colman's Presentation Convent, Watervliet, NY 12189. (518) 273-4911

60 Sisters

Apostolic Work: 2 grammar schools, 1 child caring institution, 2 day nursery centers, 4 classes for pre-school handicapped, residential school for emotionally disturbed & autistic children, social work, pastoral ministry, 1 school of religion.

Represented in the Diocese of Albany.

Vocation Directress: Sr. Mary Michael, P.B.V.M.

SISTERS OF THE PRESENTATION OF MARY (P.M.)

(Manchester Province), 495 Mammoth Rd., Manchester, NH 03104. (603) 669-1080

3,550 Sisters

300 Sisters-Manchester Province

Provincial House: 495 Mammoth Rd., Manchester, NH 03104.

Apostolic Work: 8 elementary schools, 1 college, 2 kindergartens, 3 religious instruction centers, nursing, visiting in hospitals and nursing homes, youth ministries.

Represented in 17 countries; U.S. dioceses of Manchester, NH, Providence, RI and Houston, TX.

Vocation Director: Sr. Paulette Lefebvre, pm, 180 Lowell Rd., Hudson, NH 03051.

SISTERS OF THE PRESENTATION OF MARY (P.M.)

(Methuen Province)

182 Sisters

Provincial House: 209 Lawrence St., Methuen, MA 01844. (508) 687-1369

Apostolic Work: 1 high school, 6 elementary schools, 2 kindergartens, 3 Montessori day nurseries, 2 religious instruction centers, pastoral care, retreat center, discernment house.

Represented in the Archdiocese of Boston and in the Dioceses of Portland, Springfield and Worcester. Foreign mission areas in 17 different countries.

Vocation Director: Sr. Margaret Camire, P.M., 67 Webster St., Lewiston, ME 04240.

SISTERS OF PROVIDENCE (S.P.)

(Sacred Heart Province), 520 Pike St., P.O. Box C11038, Seattle, WA 98111. (206) 464-3355

200 Sisters, 1 Novice, 1 Candidate

Sisters' Ministries: Health care, education, parish/diocesan, shelters, prisons, low-income housing for elderly, pastoral care and administration.

Conduct: 1 high school, 13 hospitals, 3 nursing home/retirement centers, 1 acute care children's nursing center and Montessori school, 2 hospitality shelters for women with children and 1 for single women.

Represented in the Archdioceses of Anchorage, Los Angeles, Portland (OR) and Seattle and in the Dioceses of Oakland and Yakima. Community is in Canada, U.S., Chile, Philippines, Argentina, missions in Haiti, Camaroon, Egypt and El Salvador.

Vocation Director: Sr. Joan Gallagher, S.P., 4800-37th Ave., S.W., Seattle, WA 98126. (206) 932-6272.

SISTERS OF PROVIDENCE (S.P.)

(Province of St. Ignatius), 9 E. 9th Ave., Spokane, WA 99202. (509) 455-4884

124 Sisters,1 Candidate

Ministries: Varied according to the gifts and creativity of each individual. Overall focus, God's Providence, loving and caring in today's world exemplified by Mary's compassion at the foot of the cross. Many sisters working in multi-cultural ministries, health care, parish, and with the elderly.

Represented in the Dioceses of Boise, Great Falls, Helena and Spokane.

Part of an international congregation. Opportunities for foreign mission work.

Vocation Director: Sr. Maria Lourdes Cleto, SP, Provincial Administration, East 9 Ninth Ave., Spokane, WA 99202. (509) 455-4884.

SISTERS OF PROVIDENCE (S.P.)

Providence Motherhouse: Holyoke, MA 01040-4083. (413) 536-7511

142 Members

Apostolic Work: Focus is in health care, social and pastoral works. Sisters work alone and on teams as well as in community-sponsored facilities. Other ministries include work in spiritual life centers, shelters, and other new and creative ventures. Being rooted in the past and open to the future gives meaning and direction to their life styles and ministries.

Represented in the (Arch)dioceses of Springfield, Worcester, Boston and Raleigh.

Vocation Director: Sr. Ann Horgan, SP, Genesis, 53 Mill St., Westfield, MA 01095. (413) 562-3621.

SISTERS OF PROVIDENCE (S.P.)

Motherhouse: Saint Mary-of-the-Woods, IN 47876-1089. (812) 535-4193

743 Sisters

Apostolic Work: Colleges, universities, high schools, grade schools, religious education, youth ministry; adult education; retirement and health care facilities, nursing; spiritual direction, counseling, retreat work, chaplains, parish and pastoral ministry; social/justice work; (arch)diocesan and parish offices; foreign missions.

Represented in the Archdioceses of Atlanta, Baltimore, Boston, Chicago, Cincinnati, Dubuque, Indianapolis, Louisville, Los Angeles, Milwaukee, Mobile, Omaha, San Antonio, San Francisco, St. Paul-Minneapolis, Washington, DC and in the Dioceses of Belleville, Birmingham, Cheyenne, Corpus Christi, Covington, Evansville, Fort Wayne/South Bend, Fresno, Galveston, Gary, Helena, Jackson, Joliet, Kansas City, Lafayette (IN), Lafayette (LA), Lexington, Manchester, Monterey, Norwich, Ogdensburg, Oklahoma, Orange, Palm Beach, Peoria, Rockford, San Bernardino, San Jose, Springfield, St. Petersburg, Trenton, Tulsa, Venice, Winona. Also in Taichung, Taipei, Taiwan; and Manila, Philippines.

Vocation Ministry Office: Sr. Bernice Kuper, S.P., Owens Hall, Saint Mary-of-the-Woods, IN 47876-1089. (812) 535-4193.

REDEMPTORISTINE NUNS (O.SS.R.) (Order of the Most Holy Redeemer)

10 Sisters in this monastery, 550 members in total Order. App. 44 monasteries worldwide

Mother of Perpetual Help Monastery, P.O. Box 220, Esopus, NY 12429

Apostolic Work: Contemplation.

Represented in the Archdioceses of New York and St. Louis.

Vocation Director: Vocation Director, Redemptoristine Nuns, P.O. Box 220, Esopus, NY 12429. (914) 384-6533.

RELIGIOUS DAUGHTERS OF ST. JOSEPH (F.S.J.)

U.S. Foundation: 319 N. Humphreys Ave., Los Angeles, CA 90022

8 Sisters; 880 worldwide

Apostolic Work: Specific mission is to evangelize through the spirit of Nazareth; prayer-work, contemplation in action. Realized through health care, catechesis, Christian education and missionary presence.

Represented in the Archdiocese of

Los Angeles, CA, and in Mexico, Guatemala, Colombia, Argentina, Uruguay, Paraguay, Brazil, Angola (Africa), Spain, Germany and Italy.

Vocation Directress: Sr. Lorna Vanegas, F.S.J., 319 N. Humphreys Ave., Los Angeles, CA 90022. (213) 260-8626 or (213) 266-6500.

RELIGIOUS OF CHRISTIAN EDUCATION

See Christian Education, Religious of.

RELIGIOUS OF THE ASSUMPTION

See Assumption, Religious of the.

RELIGIOUS HOSPITALLERS OF ST. JOSEPH (R.H.S.J.)

(St. Joseph Province), 5621 Canterbury Ave., Montreal, Canada H3T 1S8

765 Sisters

Apostolic Work: Health care, nursing.

Represented in France, Canada, U.S.A (New London, Wisconsin, Chicago, Vermont, Maine), Africa, Antigo, Peru, Dominican Republic.

Vocation Director: (in U.S.A.), St. Bernard Hospital, 326 W. 64th St., Chicago, IL 60621. (312) 962-4100, 4094.

RELIGIOUS OF THE INCARNATE WORD (C.V.I.)

Motherhouse: Mexico City; U.S. Vice Provincial: 153 Rainier Ct., Chula Vista, CA 91911. (619) 420-0231

11 Sisters in U.S.; 490 Sisters worldwide

Apostolic Work: Teaching, boarding school, campus ministry, catechetics, pastoral ministry, Third Order, diocesan office, home for aged and missions.

Represented also in the Diocese of San Diego. Also in Mexico, Spain, France, Guatemala, Argentina and Africa.

Vocation Director: Sr. Camille Crabbe, C.V.I.

RELIGIOUS OF JESUS AND MARY (R.J.M.)

(U.S. Province) Provincial House: 3706 Rhode Island Ave., Mt. Rainier, MD 20712. (301) 277-3594

163 Sisters

Apostolic Work: Teaching at all levels, pastoral team work, catechetical instruction, health care, counseling, community social action, retreat work, nursing. Summer and long-term QUEST experiences with the poor and minority groups. Missions in seven foreign countries.

Represented in the Archdioceses of Boston, New York, Los Angeles and Wa : iington, DC and in the Dioceses of Paterson, Providence, El Paso, Manchester, Fall River and San Diego.

Vocation Director: Sr. Mary Scanlon, R.J.M., St. John's Christian Community, 3029 Godwin Terrace, Bronx, NY 10463. (718) 549-7604.

RELIGIOUS OF MARY IMMACULATE (R.M.I.)

Villa Maria, 719 Augusta St., San Antonio, TX 78215.

15 Sisters

Centro Maria, 539 W. 54th St., New York, NY 10019

1,700 Sisters in 16 countries

Apostolic Work: Residences for young girls of good moral conduct, away from home for work, study or both. Age 17-25 normally, of any age, creed or nationality.

Represented in the Archdioceses of New York and San Antonio.

Vocation Director: Sr. M. Christina Lopez, Centro Maria, 539 W. 54th St., New York, NY 10019. (212) 757-6989.

RELIGIOUS SISTERS OF THE APOSTOLATE OF THE BLESSED SACRAMENT (R.M.S.S.) (Sisters of Mercy of the Blessed Sacrament) (H.M.S.S.)

Motherhouse: Mexico City; Regional Headquarters: 222 W. Cevallos St., San Antonio, TX 78204. (210) 222-1354.

32 Sisters in the US; over 700 worldwide

Apostolic Work: Academic and religious education in schools, C.C.D., parish and diocesan ministries to Hispanics, sick and aged, and imprisoned.

Represented in the Archdiocese of San Antonio, TX; in the Dioceses of Corpus Christi, TX; San Diego and San Bernardino, CA. Also in Mexico, Italy, Spain, Colombia, El Salvador, Chile, Venezuela and Guatemala.

Regional Vocation Director: Sr. Teresa Paz, HMSS, 222 W. Cevallos St., San Antonio, TX 78204. (210) 223-5013.

RELIGIOUS MISSIONARIES OF ST. DOMINIC (O.P.)

Foundation House: 2237 Waldron St., Corpus Christi, TX 78418.

(512) 939-8102.

34 Sisters

Represented in the Diocese of Corpus Christi.

RELIGIOUS OF THE SACRED HEART OF MARY (R.S.H.M.)

(Eastern American Province), Provincial Center, 50 Wilson Park Dr., Tarrytown, NY 10591

350 Sisters

Apostolic Work: Education at all levels, retreat work, parish ministry, health care, social work, law in urban, rural areas.

Represented in the Archdioceses of New York, St. Louis and Washington, DC and in the Dioceses of Arlington, Baltimore, Brooklyn, Metuchen, Norwich, Oakland, Palm Beach, Richmond, Rockville Centre, Trenton, Venice (FL) and Winona. Foreign Missions in Zimbabwe, Africa. Overseas schools in London, Paris and Rome.

Vocation Directress: Sr. Monica Walsh, 50 Wilson Park Dr., Tarrytown, NY 10591. (914) 631-8872.

RELIGIOUS OF THE SACRED HEART OF MARY (R.S.H.M.)

(Western American Province), 441 N. Garfield Ave., Montebello, CA 90640- 2901. (213) 887-8821.

100 Sisters, 1,250 Sisters worldwide

Apostolic Work: Education at all levels, parish ministry, campus ministry, hospital pastoral care, social service ministry, detention ministry.

Represented in the (Arch)dioceses of Los Angeles, San Francisco, San Jose and San Diego. Also in Cuernavaca and Mexico City in Mexico.

Vocation Directors: Sr. Gretchen Hailer, RSHM, 441 N. Garfield Ave., Montebello, CA 90640-2901. (213) 890-9065; Hna. Lourdes Galeazzi, RSCM, Sassoferrato, #136, Colonia Alfonso XIII, Delegacion Alvaro Obregon, 01460 Mexico, D.F. 011-525-563-4745.

RELIGIOUS SISTERS OF CHARITY (R.S.C.)

10664 St. James Dr., Culver City, CA 90230. (310) 838-0654

40 Sisters in California

Apostolic Work: Education, health care, parish ministry, juvenile hall, counseling, religious education, retreat and spirituality work, campus ministry, special outreach to marginalized in all settings.

Represented in the Archdiocese of Los Angeles and in the Diocese of Orange. Also in La Guaira, Venezuela, Ireland, England, Zambia, Ethiopia, Nigeria.

Vocation Director: Sr. Kathleen Bryant, 10664 St. James Dr., Culver City, CA 90230. (310) 838-0654.

RELIGIOUS TEACHERS FILIPPINI

See Filippini Sisters.

RELIGIOUS VENERINI SISTERS (M.P.V.)

23 Edward St., Worcester, MA 01605. (508) 754-1020

39 Sisters in the U.S.; approx. 450 worldwide

Apostolic Work: Teaching, C.C.D., parish work, social work, nursing, pastoral associate.

Represented in the foreign countries of Brazil, Cameroon, India, Italy and Romania.

Vocation Director: Sr. Inez Ferrari, M.P.V., 23 Edward St., Worcester, MA 01605. (508) 754-1020.

SISTERS OF REPARATION OF THE CONGREGATION OF MARY (S.R.C.M.)

Motherhouse: St. Zita Villa, Monsey, NY 10952. (914) 356-2011

16 Sisters

Apostolic Work: 1 home for adult women, 1 novitiate, 1 home for business women and 1 home for retired elderly ladies.

Represented in the Archdiocese of New York.

Vocations: Sr. Grace Philomena, Superior, St. Zita Villa, Monsey, NY 10952. (914) 356-2011.

SISTERS OF THE RESURRECTION (C.R.)

(New York Eastern Province).

Provincial House: Mt. St. Joseph, Castleton-on-Hudson, NY 12033.

Apostolic Work: 1 postulancy, 1 novitiate, elementary schools, 1 high school (archdiocesan) for girls, 2 rest homes, Christian Doctrine programs, nursing, geriatric care, campus ministry, other works as the need arises.

Represented in the Archdiocese of New York and in the Dioceses of Albany, Bridgeport, Fall River and Trenton.

Vocation Directress: Sr. Rosemary Ann, C.R., Mt. St. Joseph, Castleton-on-Hudson, NY 12033. (518) 732-2226.

SISTERS OF THE RESURRECTION (C.R.)

(Chicago Western Province), 7432 W. Talcott Ave., Chicago, IL 60631.

89 Sisters

Apostolic Work: Teaching and administration, nursing and health care, day care centers, retirement center, hospital pastoral care, parish pastoral ministry.

Represented in the Archdioceses of Chicago and Mobile and in the Diocese of Pensacola-Tallahassee.

For Information: Sisters of the Resurrection, 7432 W. Talcott Ave., Chicago, IL 60631-3743. (312) 792-6363.

SACRAMENTINE NUNS (O.S.S.)

Blessed Sacrament Monastery, 23 Park Ave., Yonkers, NY 10703.

Cloistered contemplatives.

Perpetual Adoration.

19 Sisters

Represented in the Archdiocese of New York and in the Diocese of Gaylord, MI.

Vocations: Sr. Mary Devereux, O.S.S., (914) 963-0913.

SACRAMENTINE NUNS (O.S.S.)

Sacramentine Monastery of Perpetual Adoration, U.S. 31, P.O. Box 86, Conway, MI 49722. (616) 347-0447

4 Sisters

Represented in the Diocese of Gaylord.

SISTERS OF THE SACRED HEART OF JESUS (S.S.C.J.)

(Sacred Heart Province) 5922 Blanco Rd., San Antonio, TX 78216. (210) 344-4805

70 Sisters

Conduct: 5 grammar schools, 1 domestic work house, 4 schools of religion, 3 Mexican missions.

Represented in the Archdioceses of Oklahoma City, San Antonio and Santa Fe and in the Dioceses of Brownsville, Galveston-Houston and Fort Worth. Also in Mexico City.

Vocation Directress: Sr. Estafane, S.S.C.J.

SISTERS OF THE SACRED HEART OF JESUS (S.S.H.J.)

Motherhouse: Sacred Heart Villa, 5269 Lewiston Rd., Lewiston, NY 14092. (716) 284-8273

426 Sisters

Apostolic Work: All areas of educa-tion, rest homes and hospitals, social service, catechetical and parish ministry and missions.

Represented in New York and Connecticut. Also in Italy, Canada, Madagascar, Poland and Philippines.

Vocation Contacts: Sr. Irene Russo, 5269 Lewiston Rd., Lewiston, NY 14092; Sr. Ambrogia Alderuccio, 94 Chapel Hill Road, North Haven, CT 06473.

SOCIETY OF THE SACRED HEART (R.S.C.J.) (Religious of the Sacred Heart)

Provincial House: 4389 West Pine Blvd., St. Louis, MO 63108. (314) 652-1500

4,000 Sisters worldwide; 550 Sisters in U.S.

Apostolic Work: Education in schools (elementary through university), work among the economically poor and marginalized, spiritual direction and counseling, diocesan and parish ministry.

Represented in the Archdioceses of Baltimore, Boston, Chicago, Detroit, Miami, New Orleans, New York, Omaha, St. Louis, San Francisco, Seattle and Washington, DC and in the Dioceses of Albany, Lafayette, Galveston-Houston, San Jose, San Diego and Trenton.

Vocation Director: Sr. Georgie Blaeser, R.S.C.J., Mission Outreach, 4389 West Pine Blvd., St. Louis, MO 63108. (314) 652-1500.

SACRED HEARTS COMMUNITY – SISTERS OF SACRED HEARTS AND PERPETUAL ADORATION (SS.CC.)

491 Hood St., Fall River, MA 02720; 1120 5th Ave., Honolulu, HI 96816; 3115-302 Queens Chapel Rd., Mt. Rainier, MD 20712.

95 Sisters

Apostolic Work: A variety of parish ministries, religious education, schools, hospital chaplaincy, visiting and bringing Eucharist to the elderly and the homebound, visiting prisoners, working in shelters for the homeless, education for justice and peace, intercessory prayer, home and foreign missions.

Represented in the Archdioceses of Washington, DC and Los Angeles and in the Dioceses of Fall River and Honolulu. Also in 15 foreign countries.

Vocation Director: Sr. Claire Bouchard, SS.CC.

SISTERS OF SACRED HEARTS OF JESUS AND MARY (S.H.J.M.)

California Region: 8644 Don Carol Dr., El Cerrito, CA 94530. (510) 528-6542

18 Sisters U.S., 270 Sisters worldwide

Conduct: Elementary education, missionary work, Zambia, Africa and Central America, caring ministries to the underprivileged and marginalized, nursing and pastoral care.

Represented in the Dioceses of Fresno, Oakland, Sacramento and Stockton. Also in England, Scotland, Ireland, Wales, Zambia, Africa and Central America.

Vocations: Sr. Catherine Collins, S.H.J.M.

CONGREGATION OF ST. AGNES (C.S.A.)

St. Agnes Convent, 475 Gillett, Fond du Lac, WI 54935. (414) 923-2121

475 Sisters

Apostolic Work: 30 parochial schools, 4 high schools, 1 college, 4 hospitals, 2 homes for the aged. Work in the fields of education, health care, pastoral ministry and social services.

Represented in the Archdioceses of Chicago, New York, Milwaukee and St. Paul as well as 24 dioceses. Also in Nicaragua.

Vocation Director: Sr. Marie Scott, CSA, 475 Gillett, Fond du Lac, WI 54935. (414) 923-2121.

SISTERS OF ST. ANNE (S.S.A.)

(St. Marie Province), 720 Boston Post Rd., Marlboro, MA 01752. (508) 485-3791

169 Sisters

Apostolic Work: 1 college, 2 high schools, 5 elementary schools, 1 Montessori school, adult education, campus ministry, nursing, social work, retreat work, ecumenism, music, pastoral work, missionary work, hospital chaplaincy, prison ministry, home nursing, library work, home hospice care.

Represented in the Archdiocese of Boston and in nine dioceses. Also in Africa, Alaska, Canada, Chile and Haiti.

Vocation Director: Sr. Elaine Potvin, S.S.A., Sisters of St. Anne, 720 Boston Post Rd., Marlborough, MA 01752. (508) 481-4934.

SISTERS OF ST. ANNE (S.S.A.)

1550 Begbie St., Victoria, B.C., Canada V8R 1K8. (604) 592-3133

1,340 Sisters

Apostolic Works: Education, health care and pastoral ministry. Active in Africa, Canada, Chile, Haiti and U.S.A.

Represented in the Archdiocese of Anchorage and in the Diocese of Fairbanks.

Vocation Director: Sr. Donna MacIntyre, S.S.A., c/o 1550 Begbie St., Victoria, B.C., Canada V8R 1K8. (604) 592-3133.

SISTERS OF SAINT ANN (S.S.A.)

Mount Saint Ann, P.O. Box 328, Ebensburg, PA 15931. (814) 472-9354

8 Sisters, total members in Congregation 1,400 Sisters.

Apostolic Work: Teaching in parochial schools, C.C.D. program, foreign missions, social work.

Represented in the Dioceses of Aitoona-Johnstown, Allentown and Corpus Christi. Foreign missions in Italy, India, Switzerland, Brazil, Mexico, Philippines, Peru, Cameroon (Africa) and Cachari (Argentina).

Vocation Director: Sr. Lucia D'Cunha, Mount Saint Ann, P.O. Box 328, Ebensburg, PA 15931. (814) 472-9354.

SISTERS OF SAINT ANN (S.S.A.)

3036 Saratoga Blvd., Corpus Christi, TX 78415.

(512) 853-5772.

4 Sisters

Apostolic Work: Teaching in high school, kindergarten and parish religion education.

Represented in the (Arch)dioceses of Corpus Christi, TX.

Vocation Director: Sr. Anna Maria, 3036 Saratoga Blvd., Corpus Christi, TX 78415. (512) 853-5772.

SISTERS OF ST. BASIL THE GREAT (Byzantine Rite)

See Eastern Catholic Religious Communities for Women.

SISTERS OF THE ORDER OF ST. BASIL THE GREAT

(Ukrainian Byzantine Rite)

See Eastern Catholic Religious Communities for Women.

CONGREGATION OF ST. BRIGID (C.S.B.)

Motherhouse: Ireland; U.S. Foundation: St. Brigid's Convent, 5118 Loma Linda Dr., San Antonio, TX 78201. (210) 733-0701.

20 Sisters

Apostolic Work: Education, parish work, counseling, music ministry, hospital care.

Represented in the Archdioceses of Boston and San Antonio.

Vocation Director: Regional Coordinator, 5118 Loma Linda Dr., San Antonio, TX 78201. (210) 733-0701.

SISTERS OF ST. CASIMIR (S.S.C.)

Motherhouse: 2601 W. Marquette Rd., Chicago, IL 60629.

211 Sisters

Apostolic Work: Education in 2 high schools, 11 parishes, health care in 1 hospital and 2 homes for the aged, 3 missions in Argentina. The ministries reflect Jesus' concern for the whole person as we teach and evangelize; care for the sick, the aging, and others who are hurting; provide a sense of belonging to people of various cultures; share Christ's special love for the poor.

Represented in the Archdioceses of Chicago, Baltimore, Miami, New York, Philadelphia, Santa Fe and Washington, DC and in the Dioceses of Allentown and Joliet.

Contact: IL: Sr. Elizabeth Ann Yocius, 2601 West Marquette Rd., Chicago, IL 60629. (312) 776-1324. PA: Sr. Mary Louise Andrulonis, (215) 335-2132.

SISTERS OF STE. CHRETIENNE (S.S.Ch.)

Provincial House: 297 Arnold St., Wrentham, MA 02093. (508) 384-8066.

80 Sisters in U.S.

Apostolic Work: Teaching, nursing, pastoral ministry, foreign missions.

Represented in the Archdiocese of Boston and in the Dioceses of Portland, Fall River, Worcester, MA, Providence and St. Petersburg. Also, in Canada, France, Austria and Africa.

Vocation Director: Sr. Debra Bow, S.S.Ch., 207 Pleasant St., Marlboro, MA 01752. (508) 481-3850.

SISTERS OF ST. CLARE (O.S.C.)

Generalate: Ireland; U.S. Regional Residence: St. Clare's Convent, 449 S. Pine Ave., Brea, CA 92621.

Conduct: Education, pastoral work, youth ministries, CCD, retreat ministry.

Represented in the Dioceses of Orange, San Diego, St. Petersburg and San Bernardino. Also in Australia, El Salvador, England, Ireland and Wales.

SISTERS OF ST. CLARE (OSC) (Franciscan Spirituality)

10544 Brian Ln., New Port Richey, FL 34654. (813) 862-1487

Apostolic Work: Prayer-retreat ministry; education in all its forms; care of deprived children and the elderly; social and pastoral work in the local church, and evangelization in the Third World.

Represented in Great Britain, North and Central America.

Vocation Contacts: Sr. Phyllis, OSC, (813) 862-1487; Sr. Brona Meehan, OSC, St. John's Convent, 204 Via Tavira, Encinitas, CA 92024. (619) 753-5800; Sr. Phyllis, OSC, St. Clare's, 10544 Brian Lane, New Port Richey, FL, 34654.

ST. COLUMBAN SISTERS

(See Missionary Sisters of St. Columban).

SISTERS OF SAINTS CYRIL AND METHODIUS (SS.C.M.)

Villa Sacred Heart, Danville, PA 17821-1698.

220 Sisters, 85 Lay Associates

Apostolic Work: Educational apostolate in Catholic schools from preschool/kindergarten level through university, religious education, parish and campus ministry, music conservatory, pastoral care, hearing impaired, spiritual direction, retreat ministry, Continuing Care Retirement Community and home for the aged.

Represented in the (Arch)dioceses of Allentown, Bridgeport, Charleston, Chicago, Harrisburg, Johnstown, Scranton, Syracuse.

Director of Vocations: Sr. Joanne Marie Schutz, SS.C.M., Villa Sacred Heart, Danville, PA 17821-1698. (717) 275-3702.

INSTITUTE OF THE SISTERS OF ST. DOROTHY (S.S.D.)

(North American Province) Provincial House and Novitiate: Mt. St. Joseph, 13 Monkeywrench Ln., Bristol, RI 02809. (401) 253-7835

59 Sisters

Apostolic Work: 1 high school, 1 academy, 4 elementary schools, 1 novitiate, missions, catechetical work, social work, retreat work.

Represented in the Archdiocese of New York and in the Dioceses of Brownsville, Fall River and Providence. Also in 11 foreign lands.

Vocation Director: Mt. St. Joseph, 13 Monkeywrench Ln., Bristol, RI 02809. (401) 253-7835.

SISTERS OF SAINT FRANCIS (O.S.F.)

Motherhouse: 400 N. Bluff Blvd., Clinton, IA 52732. (319) 242-5631

127 Sisters

Conduct: 1 college, 1 retirement home.

Represented in the Archdioceses of Chicago, Indianapolis, Louisville and St. Louis and in the Dioceses of Belleville, Charleston, Davenport, Des Moines, Fresno, Jackson, Joliet, Kansas City-St. Joseph, Lansing, Lexington, Oakland, Peoria, Portland, Rockford, San Bernardino, San Diego, Springfield-Cape Girardeau, Wichita, Nassau (Grand Bahamas), and Chulucanas, Peru, South America.

Vocation Director: Sr. Donna Burke, 400 N. Bluff Blvd., Clinton, IA 52732. (319) 242-5631.

ST. JOAN OF ARC SISTERS (S.J.A.)

Motherhouse: 1505 rue de l'Assomption, Sillery, Quebec, G1S 4T3.

187 Sisters in 30 convents

Apostolic Work: Twofold: uniting contemplation with action – through prayer and by performing ordinary household tasks in rectories, bishops' residences, homes for retired priests, etc. Also in areas of parish ministries.

Represented in the Archdioceses of Boston and in the Dioceses of Fall River, Manchester and Providence. Also in Canada.

Vocation Director: Sr. Therese Poirier, S.J.A., 1505 rue de l'Assomption, Sillery, Quebec, GIS 4T3. (418) 527-7859.

SISTERS OF ST. JOHN THE BAPTIST (C.S.JB)

General House: Rome, Italy. (U.S. Province), Provincial Residence: 3308 Campbell Dr., Bronx, NY 10465. (718) 518-7820.

130 Sisters

Apostolic Work: Education, health care for aged men & women, religious education, social work and any ministry connected with the poor and abandoned especially youth.

Represented in the Archdioceses of New York and Newark and in the Dioceses of Paterson and Metuchen. Also, missions in Zambia, India, Chile, Brazil, Argentina, the Philippines, Poland, Korea and Italy.

Vocation Directress: Sr. Candida Marie Esposito, C.S.JB, (718) 931-3000/2709.

SERVANTS OF ST. JOSEPH (S.S.J.)

950 Sisters; 16 in U.S.

Apostolic Work: Evangelization of the poor working world through: teaching, social work, missions, group homes for young working women.

Represented in the Dioceses of Arlington, and Newark, NJ. Also in Spain (Motherhouse), Rome (General House), Philippines, Colombia, Argentina, Peru, Chile, Zaire (Congo), Cuba, Papua and Bolivia.

Vocation Director: 203 N. Spring St., Falls Church, VA 22046. (703) 534-9549.

SISTERS OF ST. JOSEPH OF BOSTON (C.S.J.)

Motherhouse: 637 Cambridge St., Brighton, MA 02135.

843 Sisters

Apostolic Work: Various ministries: education, health care, social services, pastoral ministry, counselling and retreat work.

Represented in the Archdioceses of Boston and New Mexico.

Vocation Awareness Director: Sr. Mary Ann Crowley, CSJ, 637 Cambridge St., Brighton, MA 02135. (617) 782-1547.

SISTERS OF ST. JOSEPH OF BRENTWOOD (C.S.J.)

Motherhouse and Novitiate: St. Joseph Convent, Brentwood, L.I., NY 11717. (516) 273-4531

1,030 Sisters

Apostolic Work: Education, health and hospital service, parish work.

Represented in the Archdiocese of New York and in the Dioceses of Brooklyn and Rockville Centre. Also in Puerto Rico.

Vocation Directress: Sr. Mary Ann Rogers, C.S.J., St. Joseph Convent, Brentwood, L.I., NY 11717. (516) 273-7575.

SISTERS OF ST. JOSEPH OF BUFFALO (S.S.J.)

Administrative Center, 23 Agassiz Cr., Buffalo, NY 14214. (716) 838-4400

167 Sisters

Apostolic Work: 1 college, 8 grammar schools, 1 private elementary school, 1 hospital, 1 infant home, 1 school for deaf, 1 center for justice, parish ministry, campus ministry, prison ministry, foreign mission.

Represented in the (Arch)dioceses of Buffalo, Detroit, Cincinnati and Phoenix. Also in Monteria and Ica (Peru, South America).

Vocation Director: 23 Agassiz Circle, Buffalo, NY 14214. (716) 838-4400.

SISTERS OF ST. JOSEPH OF CARONDELET (C.S.J.)

(Congregational Center) 2307 S. Lindbergh Blvd., St. Louis, MO 63131. (314) 966-4048.

St. Louis Province: St. Joseph Provincial House, 6400 Minnesota Ave., St. Louis, MO 63111.

730 Sisters

St. Paul Province: St. Joseph Administration Center, 1884 Randolph Ave., St. Paul, MN 55105.

531 Sisters

Albany Province: St. Joseph Provincial House, 385 Watervliet-Shaker Rd., Latham, NY 12110.

665 Sisters

Los Angeles Province: St. Mary's Provincialate, 11999 Chalon Rd., Los Angeles, CA 90049.

549 Sisters, 3 Novices

Vice Province of Hawaii: Carondelet Convent, 5311 Apo Dr., Honolulu, Oahu, HI 96821-1829.

51 Sisters

Vocation Contacts:

St. Louis Province: Director of Applicants, 6400 Minnesota Ave., St. Louis, MO 63111. (314) 481-8800

St. Paul Province: Director of Applicants, 1884 Randolph Ave., St. Paul, MN 55105. (612) 690-7000

Albany Province: Director of Applicants, St. Joseph's Provincial House, Latham, NY 12110. (518) 783-3500

Los Angeles Province: Director of Applicants, Carondelet Center, 11999 Chalon Rd., Los Angeles, CA 90049. (213) 272-8016

Vice Province of Hawaii: Director of Applicants, Carondelet Convent, 5311 Apo Dr., Honolulu, Oahu, HI 96821-1829. (808) 373-2096

Apostolic Work: Teaching, nursing, pastoral care, parish work, foreign missions, campus ministry, educating the deaf, social services.

Represented in 182 dioceses in the U.S. Also in Peru, Japan and Chile.

SISTERS OF ST. JOSEPH OF CHAMBERY (C.S.J.)

Provincial House: Convent of Mary Immaculate, 27 Park Rd., W. Hartford, CT 06119. (203) 233-5126.

205 Membership

Apostolic Work: Higher education, secondary and elementary, religious education, special education, health care, day shelter, social services, pastoral ministry, soup kitchen, day care center, prison ministry, retreat ministry, counseling, overseas missions, legal services, AIDS ministry, ministry to the elderly.

Represented in the Archdioceses of New York, Hartford, Mobile and Washington and in the Dioceses of Bridgeport, El Paso, Memphis, Norwich, Rutland, Springfield, Lexington, Trenton and Fairbanks, AK. Also in 10 European countries and in Asia, Africa and South America and Canada.

Vocation Counselor: Sr. Susan Cunningham, C.S.J., 27 Park Rd., West Hartford, CT 06119. (203) 233-5126.

CONGREGATION OF ST. JOSEPH OF CLEVELAND (CSJ)

Motherhouse: St. Joseph Convent, 3430 Rocky River Dr., Cleveland, OH 44111.

230 Members and Co-Members

Ministry: Education, social work, pastoral ministry, peace and justice work, campus ministry, religious education, communications, deaf apostolate, retreat work, jail ministry, counseling, hospital chaplaincy, Catholic bookstore, transitional housing for women & families, mentally handicapped.

Represented in the Diocese of Cleveland with Sisters serving elsewhere, including California, Colorado, Florida, Texas, Washington, DC and Washington State.

Contact: Sr. Pam Owens, CSJ, 3430 Rocky River Dr., Cleveland, OH 44111. (216) 252-0440.

SISTERS OF ST. JOSEPH OF CLUNY (S.J.C.)

(American Novitiate), Mary Immaculate Queen Novitiate, 20955 Halldale Ave., Torrance, CA 90501. (310) 328-1807.

Provincial House: Cluny Convent, 90 Brenton Rd., Newport, RI 02840. (401) 846-4757

45 Sisters in U.S., 3,500 worldwide

Ministry: Engaged in every corporal work of mercy on five continents, but especially concentrated in the Third World.

Represented (in the U.S.) in the Archdiocese of Los Angeles and in the Dioceses of Orange, Providence and Wheeling-Charleston (WV). Also in Canada.

Vocation Director: Sr. Genevieve Marie Vigil, 20955 Halldale Ave., Torrance, CA 90501. (310) 328-1807.

SISTERS OF ST. JOSEPH OF CONCORDIA (C.S.J.)

215 Court St., Box 279, Concordia, KS 66901. (913) 243-2149

271 Sisters, 1 Novice

Represented in the Diocese of Salina and in many dioceses throughout the US.

Vocation Director: Sr. Anna Marie Broxterman, C.S.J., 1801 N. Alabama, Silver City, NM 88061. (505) 538-3350.

SISTERS OF ST. JOSEPH OF ERIE (S.S.J.)

Motherhouse: 5031 W. Ridge Rd., Erie, PA 16506. (814) 838-4100

220 Members

Conduct: Sisters involved in various ministries: All levels of education – preschool through college; health care, social ministries, care of the elderly, poor, shelter for women, campus ministry, pastoral ministry, liturgical ministry, spiritual directors, directors of religious education, fine arts – art, writing plus others.

Represented primarily in northwestern PA, with some in Kentucky, Wisconsin, Tennessee, Florida and Washington, DC.

Vocation Directors: Sr. Mary Drexler, S.S.J., 27 Orchard St.,

Erie, PA 16508; Sr. Nancy Prenatt, S.S.J., 1021 W. 26th St., Erie, PA 16508.

SISTERS OF ST. JOSEPH OF LA GRANGE (C.S.J.)

1515 W. Ogden Ave., La Grange Park, IL 60525. (708) 354-9200.

140 members

Apostolic Work: Any work which enables the mission of uniting people with one another and God. We are a Diocesan Congregation called to the Church of Chicago. Some of our sisters serve in other dioceses.

Contact Person: Sr. Sue Torgersen, CSJ, 1515 W. Ogden Ave., La Grange Park, IL 60525.

SISTERS OF ST. JOSEPH OF NAZARETH (S.S.J.)

Nazareth, MI 49074.

460 Sisters

Apostolic Work: Ministries vary according to the gifts of each Sister and the needs of the times and locale "wherever people lack what is needed for the fully human life that is their right".

Represented in Michigan and other parts of the U.S. Also three missions in Peru.

Vocation Director: Vocation Coordinator, Srs. of St. Joseph, Spiritual and Pastoral Development Office, Nazareth, MI 49074. (616) 381-6290.

SISTERS OF ST. JOSEPH OF ORANGE (C.S.J.)

480 S. Batavia St., Orange, CA 92668. (714) 633-8121

250 Sisters

Conduct: 1 college, 2 high schools, 12 grammar schools, education network, 9 hospitals and health systems, Center for Spiritual Development, foreign missions, pastoral ministries, social justice ministries and ministry with the poor.

Represented in the Archdioceses of Los Angeles and San Francisco and in the Dioceses of Lubbock, Orange, Santa Rosa and San Diego. Foreign missions in: Hungary; Guaymas, Sonora, Mexico; El Salvador, Australia and Israel.

Director of Vocations: Sr. Sarah Jordan, CSJ.

SISTERS OF ST. JOSEPH (LYON, FRANCE) (C.S.J.)

93 Halifax St., Winslow, ME 04901. (207) 873-1444.

64 Sisters

Apostolic Work: Catechetical centers, nursing homes, day care centers, renewal center, pastoral ministry.

Represented in the Diocese of Portland (ME). Foreign missions in seven countries.

Vocation Directress: Sr. Janet Gagnon, C.S.J., 93 Halifax St., Winslow, ME 04901. (207) 873-1444.

SISTERS OF ST. JOSEPH OF MEDAILLE (Medaille) (C.S.J.)

1821 Summit Rd., #210, Cincinnati, OH 45237. (513) 761-2888

240 Sisters

Apostolic Work: Primary, secondary and higher education, health care, campus ministry, parish ministry, religious education, pastoral care, chemical dependency, liturgical ministry, spiritual direction, life care ministry, deaf ministry, prison ministry, foreign missions.

Represented in the Archdioceses of Cincinnati, New Orleans and St. Paul-Minneapolis and in the Dioceses of Baton Rouge, Crookston, Fargo, Green Bay and Superior. Also in Nicaragua, Central America.

Vocation Director: Sr. Ileana Fernandez, C.S.J., 5510 Moorstone Dr., Baton Rouge, LA 70820. (504) 767-6878.

SISTERS OF ST. JOSEPH OF PEACE (C.S.J.P.)

(St. Joseph Province), Shalom Center, 399 Hudson Terr., Englewood Cliffs, NJ 07632. (201) 568-6348

177 Sisters

Conduct: Education all levels: school for multiple handicapped blind, nursing homes-blind and sighted, residence for business women, residence for elderly guests, alternative high school for women, transitional housing for women and children, child development center; other efforts on behalf of poor and powerless, retreat house, formation office, hospital and school of nursing, senior sisters residence, magazine office; sisters are involved in various areas of health, education, social service and in pastoral and religious education.

Represented in the Archdioceses of Newark, Los Angeles and Washington, DC and in the Dioceses of Camden, Paterson,

Trenton, Jacksonville and St. Petersburg. Also in England, Scotland, Wales and Ireland.

Contact: Sr. Mary Kuiken, C.S.J.P.

SISTERS OF ST. JOSEPH OF PEACE (C.S.J.P.)

(Our Lady Province), 1663 Killarney Way, P.O. Box 248, Bellevue, WA 98009. (206) 451-1770

111 Sisters, 19 Associate Members

Apostolic Work: Education, health and hospital services, social services, religious education, parish ministry, retreat ministry, social justice and peace ministry.

Represented in the Archdioceses of Anchorage, Los Angeles, Portland, San Francisco and Seattle and in the Dioceses of Fairbanks, Juneau, San Diego and Spokane. Also in Canada and Dublin, Ireland.

Vocation Director: Sr. Beth Taylor, C.S.J.P., 1663 Killarney Way, P.O. Box 248, Bellevue, WA 98009. (206) 451-1770.

SISTERS OF ST. JOSEPH OF PHILADELPHIA (S.S.J.)

Mount St. Joseph Convent, 9701 Germantown Ave., Philadelphia, PA 19118-2693. (215) 248-7200

14,500 Sisters

Apostolic Work: 1 college, 5 academies, diocesan high schools and grammar schools, Montessori and nursery schools, 1 retreat house, 1 school for the deaf, 3 special education schools, pastoral ministry, nursing and medical services, campus ministry, work with senior citizens, social work, counseling, spiritual direction, research, prison ministry, legal counsel, administration of diocesan and government programs, participation in policy planning and other professional groups at all levels.

Represented in the Archdioceses of Philadelphia, Newark, Baltimore, Wilmington and Washington and in the Dioceses of Allentown, Altoona-Johnstown, Belleville, Fort Wayne-South Bend, San Antonio, Harrisburg, Paterson, Metuchen, Camden, Trenton, Raleigh, Charlotte, Arlington, St. Petersburg, Lexington and overseas in Panama and Peru.

Vocation Director: Sr. Kathy Pales, S.S.J., Mt. St. Joseph Convent, 9701 Germantown Ave., Philadelphia, PA 19118-2693. (215) 248-7236.

SISTERS OF ST. JOSEPH OF PITTSBURGH (C.S.J.)

St. Joseph's Convent, Baden, PA 15005. (412) 869-2151

Apostolic Work: 1 academy, 25 grade schools, preschool-early childhood education staffing in various high schools and universities; health care; parish social service; pastoral ministry in parishes and hospitals; prisons-chaplains; religious education; social service; retreat work; communications ministry; missionary work.

Represented in the (Arch)dioceses of Altoona-Johnstown, Baltimore, Boston, Cheyenne, Chicago, Covington, Fort Wayne, Fresno, Greensburg, Harrisburg, Hartford, Memphis, Miami, New York, Pittsburgh, Tucson, Washington, (DC), Wheeling/Charleston; Prelacy of Borba, Brazil and Porus, Jamaica, West Indies.

Vocation Directors: Sr. Lyn Szymkiewicz, C.S.J., St. Bernard Convent, 470 Clairvaux Dr., Indiana, PA 15701. (412) 349-1778; Sr. Carolyn Wiethorn, C.S.J., 7448 McClure Ave., Pittsburgh, PA 15218. (412) 731-4246.

SISTERS OF ST. JOSEPH OF ROCHESTER (S.S.J.)

4095 East Ave., Rochester, NY 14618-3798.

459 Sisters, 1 Jr. Professed, 2 Novices, 97 Associate Members

Apostolic Work: Educational ministry including elementary schools, high schools, college and graduate school, religious education, school for special children and adults, pastoral ministry, numerous health care works, homes for emotionally disturbed and learning disabled children, evangelization, college campus ministry, social service, justice and peace office, drug dependency programs, prison ministry, spirituality ministry program.

Represented in the Archdioceses of Boston and Mobile and in the Dioceses of Albany, Buffalo, Rochester and Syracuse. Missions in Brazil.

Vocation Directors: Sr. Barbara Lum, S.S.J.; Sr. Deanna Gears, S.S.J., 4095 East Ave., Rochester, NY 14618-3798. (716) 586-1000, ext. 122.

SISTERS OF ST. JOSEPH OF RUTLAND (S.S.J.)

129 Convent Ave., Rutland, VT 05701. (802) 775-0665

53 Sisters

Apostolic Work: Elementary, secondary and college education;

diversity of works according to need of the people and the skill of the Sisters.

Represented in the Diocese of Burlington.

Vocation Director: Sr. Jean Elizabeth, SSJ, 13 Clement Rd., Rutland, VT 05701. (802) 775-4231.

SISTERS OF ST. JOSEPH OF ST. AUGUSTINE, FLORIDA (S.S.J.)

St. Joseph's Convent, Box 3506, St. Augustine, FL 32085. (904) 829-3735

130 Sisters

Apostolic Work: Ministries of "unity and reconciliation" in parishes, schools, hospitals, prison, with the poor, AIDS patients, the elderly, unwed mothers and babies, persons with disabilities, retreatants and those requesting spiritual direction. Any needed ministry for which we are prepared.

Represented throughout the Dioceses of Florida.

Vocation Director: Sr. Kathleen Power, S.S.J., Bishop Kenny Convent, 930 Kingman Ave., Jacksonville, FL 32207. (904) 391-0099.

SISTERS OF ST. JOSEPH OF ST. MARK (S.J.S.M.)

(Cleveland Generalate), 21800 Chardon Rd., Euclid, OH 44117.

25 Sisters

Apostolic Work: Nursing, care of the aged, technicians, social service, administrative, clerical and dietetic work.

Vocation Directress: Sr. M. Cecilia, 21800 Chardon Rd., Euclid, OH 44117. (216) 531-7426.

SISTERS OF ST. JOSEPH OF SPRINGFIELD (S.S.J.)

Mont Marie, Holyoke, MA 01040.

425 Sisters, 42 Associates

Apostolic Work: Members of the congregation are encouraged to discern individual gifts and ministries within the framework of the community goal, to live simply and to work toward alleviating unjust structures. Ministries include educational ministry in elementary schools, high schools, college; religious education, special education, pastoral ministry, health care, social services, spiritual direction, counseling, prison ministry, campus ministry, hospital chaplaincy.

Represented in the Archdioceses of Hartford and Washington, DC and in the Dioceses of Lake Charles, LA, Fall River, MA,

Springfield, MA, Worcester, MA and Providence, RI. Also in Tanzania and Guatemala.

Vocation Education Coordinator: Mildred Marengo, S.S.J., Mont Marie, Holyoke, MA 01040. (413) 536-0853, ext. 249.

SISTERS OF ST. JOSEPH OF TIPTON (C.S.J.)

1440 W. Division Rd., Tipton, IN 46072-9574. (317) 675-4146

55 Sisters

Primary Apostolic Works: Pastoral ministry, education, health care, social service, foreign mission.

Represented in the Dioceses of Lafayette, IN, Indianapolis, IN and Baker, OR. Also in Port au Prince, Haiti.

Vocation Directress: Sr. Wanda Wetli, C.S.J., St. Joseph's Center, 1440 W. Division Rd., Tipton, IN 46072-9574. (317) 675-4146.

SISTERS OF ST. JOSEPH OF WATERTOWN (S.S.J.)

Motherhouse: 1425 Washington St., Watertown, NY 13601. (315) 782-3460

83 Members

Apostolic Work: 1 college, 2 high schools, 10 grade schools, 1 conservatory of music, social service, special education, catechetical classes, tutorial work, domestic and clerical work, pastoral ministry, hospital ministry.

Represented in the Diocese of Ogdensburg.

Vocation Director: Sr. Constance Marie, S.S.J., St. James Convent, Carthage, NY 13601. (315) 493-1672.

SISTERS OF ST. JOSEPH OF WHEELING (S.S.J.)

Mt. St. Joseph, Pogue Run Rd., Wheeling, WV 26003.

114 Sisters

Apostolic Work: Diverse ministries in education, health care and pastoral care.

Represented in Diocese of Wheeling-Charleston.

Vocation Director: Mt. St. Joseph, Pogue Run Rd., Wheeling, WV 26003. (304) 232-8160.

SISTERS OF ST. JOSEPH OF WICHITA (C.S.J.)

3700 E. Lincoln, Wichita, KS 67218. (316) 686-7171

230 Sisters

Apostolic Work: Teaching at all

levels from pre-school through college, adult GED programs and school administration, numerous facets of health care (nursing, pastoral care, alcohol treatment, pharmacy, lab and X-ray technicians, administration), parish ministry, campus ministry, retreat direction, ministry to the disabled, social work, day care, youth and adult education for Asian and Hispanic immigrants and native Americans, foreign missions in Japan.

Represented in the Dioceses of Wichita, Dodge City, Pueblo and Oakland.

Vocation Director: Sr. Joan Burger, 3700 E. Lincoln, Wichita, KS 67218. (316) 686-7171.

SISTERS OF ST. JOSEPH OF THE THIRD ORDER OF ST. FRANCIS (SSJ-TOSF)

Central Offices, 105 Jefferson Centre, Room 312, P.O. Box 688, South Bend, IN 46624. (219) 233-1166

550 Sisters, 44 Lay Associates

Apostolic Work: Members of the Congregation serve in a variety of ministries with the ultimate desire to promote the spiritual and material advancement of the human family including all aspects of education, parish ministry, social work, health care, diocesan services/administration, and community services.

Represented in numerous states including California, Colorado, Connecticut, Illinois, Indiana, Massachusetts, Michigan, Minnesota, Mississippi, Missouri, Montana, Nebraska, New Jersey, Ohio, Pennsylvania, Texas, Washington and Wisconsin. Also in Canada, Puerto Rico, South America and South Africa.

Vocation Information: Sr. Linda Szocik, SSJ-TOSF, 105 Jefferson Centre, Room 312, P.O. Box 688, South Bend, IN 46624. (219) 233-1166.

SISTERS OF ST. JOSEPH THE WORKER (S.J.W.)

General Motherhouse: Saint William Convent, 1 Saint Joseph Lane, Walton, KY 41094. (606) 485-4914, 4256

21 Sisters

Represented in the Dioceses of Covington and Lexington.

Vocation Director: Sr. Celeste Marie, S.J.W.

CONGREGATION OF THE SISTERS OF ST. LOUIS (S.S.L.)
Regional House in U.S.: Louisville Convent, 22300 Mulholland Dr., Woodland Hills, CA 91364. (818) 347-2115
81 Sisters in the U.S.
Conduct: 10 grammar schools, 1 high school, college, parish ministry, hospital ministry, prison ministry and social services.
Represented in the Archdiocese of Los Angeles and in the Dioceses of Orange and San Bernardino. Also in Ireland, England, France, Belgium, Nigeria, Ghana and Brazil.
Vocation Contact: Sr. Donna Hanson, S.S.L., 22300 Mulholland Dr., Woodland Hills, CA 91364. (818) 883-1678.

SISTERS OF ST. MARY OF NAMUR (S.S.M.N.)
(Eastern Province) 250 Bryant St., Buffalo, NY 14222. (716) 884-8221
110 Sisters
Apostolic Work: Diversified; Primary emphasis to stand with the poor and marginalized of the earth. Commitment to missions; to refugees; to women and youth.
Represented in the (Arch)dioceses of Boston (MA), Buffalo (NY), Charleston (SC), Syracuse (NY) and Savannah (GA). Provinces in Texas, Canada, Belgium, Great Britain, Africa and Brazil.
Contact: Sr. Patricia Brady, 200 St. Amelia Dr., Tonawanda, NY 14150. (716) 833-6858.

SISTERS OF ST. MARY OF NAMUR (S.S.M.N.)
(Western Province), Our Lady of Victory, 909 West Shaw St., Fort Worth, TX 76110. (817) 923-8393
74 Sisters, 2 Associates
Apostolic Work: 1 college, 7 elementary schools, 1 high school, 4 social services, 7 missionaries, 1 nursing, 9 pastoral ministries, 1 diocesan office (departments).
Represented in the Dioceses of Dallas, Fort Worth, Galveston-Houston and Victoria. Also in Zaire, Brazil and Rwanda.
Vocation Contact: Sr. Donna Ferguson (817) 560-3300 or 923-5539.

SISTERS OF ST. MARY OF OREGON (S.S.M.O.)
Motherhouse: St. Mary of the Valley, 4440 S.W. 148th Ave., Beaverton, OR 97007. (503) 644-9181
106 Sisters
Apostolic Work: Education: day care, kindergarten, 2 high schools, 15 grammar schools; health care: 1 nursing home. Also parish ministry, religious education, Hispanic ministry.

Represented in the Dioceses of Portland, OR, Sacramento, Seattle and Baker.
Vocation Director: Sr. Catherine Hertel, SSMO, 4440 S.W. 148th Ave., Beaverton, OR 97007.

SISTERS OF ST. MARY OF THE PRESENTATION (S.M.P.)
Maryvale Novitiate: 11550 River Rd., Valley City, ND 58072. (701) 845-2864
70 Sisters
Conduct: 2 elementary schools, 4 hospitals, parish ministry, college, Neuman Center, home health agency, Native American ministry, spirituality center.
Represented in the Archdiocese of St. Paul-Minneapolis and in the Dioceses of Fargo, Peoria and Rockford.

SISTERS OF ST. PAUL OF CHARTRES (S.P.C.)
U.S. Province: 1300 County Rd. 492, Marquette, MI 49855. (906) 226-3932
General House: 193 Via della Vignaccia, Rome, 1-00163 Italy
22 Sisters in U.S.; 4,000 worldwide
Apostolic Work: Academic and religious education, pastoral associates, ministry to the aged.
Represented in the Archdiocese of Washington, DC and in the Diocese of Marquette.
Vocation Director: Sr. Rosalie Hughes, S.P.C., 1300 Country Rd. 492, Marquette, MI 49855. (906) 226-3932.

SISTERS OF ST. PHILIP NERI MISSIONARY TEACHERS (R.F.)
Motherhouse: Apostol Santiago 74, 28017 Madrid, Spain
U.S.: 135 Pascus Pl., Sparks, NV 89431. (702) 331-0708; 2525 S.W. 9th Ave., Fort Lauderdale, FL 33315. (305) 525-3533.
Apostolic Work: Teaching, social work, retreat houses.
Represented in the Archdiocese of Miami and in the Diocese of Reno.

SISTERS OF ST. RITA (O.S.A.)
Motherhouse: Wurzburg, West Germany
U.S.: St. Rita's Convent, 3920 N. Green Bay Rd., Racine, WI 53404. (414) 639-1766 or 5050
200 Sisters worldwide
Apostolic work: Social and family welfare work, health care, care of the aged and poor, conduct kindergartens, C.C.D., pastoral ministry, domestic work at seminaries.
Represented in the Archdiocese of Milwaukee. Also in West Germany and Switzerland.

Vocation Directress: Sr. Angelica Summer, O.S.A., St. Rita's Convent, 3920 N. Green Bay Rd., Racine, WI 53404.

SOCIETY OF ST. TERESA OF JESUS (S.T.J.)
Provincial House: 18080 St. Joseph's Way, Covington, LA 70435-5624. (504) 893-1470
2,000 Members Worldwide; 55 in U.S.
Apostolic Work: Elementary and secondary education, catechetical work, youth groups, youth retreats, prayer groups, Hispanic ministry and foreign missions.
Represented in San Antonio (TX), New Orleans (LA) and Miami (FL). Also in Mexico, Nicaragua, Colombia, Venezuela, Brazil, Uruguay, Costa Rica, Paraguay, Argentina, Chile, Cuba, Portugal, Spain, France, Italy, Angola, Bolivia and Ivory Coast.
Vocation Director: Sr. Marina Aranzabal, S.T.J., Teresian Sisters, Formation House, 18158 St. Joseph's Way, Covington, LA 70435-5624. (504) 893-1557.

CONGREGATION OF SISTERS OF ST. THOMAS OF VILLANOVA (S.S.T.V.)
West Rocks Rd., Norwalk, CT 06851. (203) 847-2885
5 Sisters in U.S.; 400 worldwide
Conduct: 1 convalescent home.
Represented in the Diocese of Bridgeport.
Contact: Mother Edmond, Superior.

SISTERS OF ST. URSULA (S.U.)
Motherhouse: American Novitiate, Linwood Spiritual Center, Rhinebeck, NY 12572. (914) 876-4178
39 Sisters
Apostolic Work: Teaching, religious education, retreats, African missions, ministry to aged, social work, parish ministry, campus ministry, nursing, financial and secretarial service.
Represented in the Archdioceses of New York and Washington, DC and in the Dioceses of Providence and Raleigh. Also in France, Italy and Zaire.
Director of Formation: Sr. Mary Isaac Koenig, S.U., Linwood Spiritual Center, 139 South Mill Rd., Rhinebeck, NY 12572. (914) 876-4178.

SALESIAN MONASTIC COMMUNITY (SMC)
Salesian Monastery, HC #1, Box 455, Frantz Rd., Brodheadsville, PA 18322-9630. (717) 992-3448 (abbot), (717) 992-0230 (monastery).
1 Solemnly Professed Monk, 1 Sim-

ply Professed Monk, 1 Simply Professed Nun, 25 Associate Members (men and women).
Apostolic Work: Monastic life, Liturgy of the Hours, use of any gift/talent compatible with monastic life, i.e., retreats, pastoral psychotherapy, nursing, manual labor and crafts.
Represented in the Diocese of Scranton.
Abbot: Brother Bernard Seif, SMC.

SALESIAN SISTERS OF ST. JOHN BOSCO
See Daughters of Mary Help of Christians.

SALVATORIANS
See Divine Savior, Sisters of the.

SCALABRINIANS
See Missionary Sisters of St. Charles Borromeo.

SERVANTS OF THE GOSPEL (O.S.D.)
(A community of friars and sisters)
St. Mary's Church, P.O. Box 499, Fort Covington, NY 12937. (518) 358-4471
Apostolic Work: There is no specific ministry to which the entire community is dedicated. Members seek to be of service to the local Church or Diocese in whatever way necessary.
Represented in the Diocese of Ogdensburg.
Vocation Contact: Fr. Martin Farrell, O.S.D. or Sr. Gabriel, O.S.D.

SERVANTS OF THE HOLY HEART OF MARY (S.S.C.M.)
145 S. Fourth Ave., Kankakee, IL 60901.
69 Sisters in U.S., 800 Sisters in Congregation
Apostolic Work: Health care, education, pastoral ministry in hospitals, parishes and campuses as well as C.C.D. ministries, counseling and opportunities to use business expertise in a human service system.
Represented in the Dioceses of Joliet, Rockford and Peoria and in the Archdioceses of Chicago and Washington.
Vocation Directresses: Sr. Myra Lambert or Sr. Linda Hatton, S.S.C.M., 717 N. Batavia Ave., Batavia, IL 60510. (708) 879-1296.

SERVANTS OF THE IMMACULATE HEART OF MARY (S.C.I.M.) (also known as Good Shepherd Sisters)
Provincial Residence: 313 Seaside Ave., Saco, ME 04072.
125 Sisters in U.S.

Apostolic Work: Social work – group homes for troubled girls and unwed mothers, adoption agency; education – parish and public schools, religious education centers; health services, a health care facility; and other nursing ministries. Pastoral work and other special ministries; foreign missions in South Africa, Brazil, Haiti.
Represented in the Archdiocese of Boston and in the Diocese of Portland, ME.
Vocation Center: SCIM Vocation Office, 187 Bay View Rd., Saco, ME 04072. (207) 283-3636.

SERVANTS OF JESUS (S.J.)
9075 Big Lake Rd., P.O. Box 128, Clarkston, MI 48347. (810) 625-8483
24 Sisters
Represented in the Archdiocese of Detroit and in the Dioceses of Gaylord, Grand Rapids and Saginaw.
Vocation Director: Sr. Mary Ann Kasper, S.J., Servants of Jesus, 21537 Parke Lane, Grosse Ile, MI 48138. (313) 671-3056.

SERVANTS OF MARY (O.S.M.) (Servite Sisters)
1000 College Ave. West, Ladysmith, WI 54848. (715) 532-3364
105 Sisters
Apostolic Work: Worship, education, healing, social service and justice, i.e. all stages of education, health care, pastoral work, community organizing, law, counseling, and ministry to youth, elderly, unwed mothers, mentally and physically handicapped, minorities and Native Americans.
Represented in Arizona, California, Florida, Illinois, Indiana, Kentucky, Massachusetts, Michigan, Minnesota, West Virginia, Wisconsin.
Vocation Contact: Vocation Director, Servants of Mary, 1000 College Ave. West, Ladysmith, WI 54848. (715) 532-3364.

SERVANTS OF MARY (O.S.M.) (Servites)
U.S. Province: Our Lady of Sorrows, 7400 Military Ave., Omaha, NE 68134.
130 Sisters
Apostolic Work: Teaching, nursing, pastoral ministry, campus ministry, hospital chaplaincy, counseling, marriage tribunal, social work, religious ed, liturgy, spiritual renewal.
Missions: Jamaica, West Indies and Kentucky.
Represented in the (Arch)dioceses of Omaha, Lincoln and Grand Island, NE; Des Moines, Iowa; Tucson, AR; Denver and Pueblo, CO, Covington, KY; Detroit, MI; Ogdensburg, NY; Paterson, NJ; and Port-

land, OR. Also in France, England, Belgium, Austria and Canada.
Vocation Director: Sr. Joan Houtekier, O.S.M. 7400 Military Ave., Omaha, NE 68134. (402) 571-2547.

SERVANTS OF OUR LADY, QUEEN OF THE CLERGY (S.R.C.)
General Motherhouse: 57 Jules-A. Brillant, Rimouski, Quebec G5L 1X1 Canada. (418) 722-4402.
4 Sisters. Also 60 Sisters in Canadian Domestic Departments
Conduct: Domestic work.
Represented in the Dioceses of Fall River, Manchester and Providence.
Contact: Servants of Our Lady, Queen of the Clergy, 175, rue Lavoie Rimouski, Quebec G5L 5Y8. (418) 722-8935.

SERVANTS OF THE MOST SACRED HEART OF JESUS (S.S.C.J.)
United States Province: 866 Cambria St., Cresson, PA 16630-1713. (814) 886-4223.
700 Sisters (32 in U.S.)
Apostolic Work: Teaching, nursing, parish work, mission, social service.
Represented in the Archdiocese of Philadelphia and in the Dioceses of Altoona-Johnstown and Metuchen.
Vocation Director: Sr. Amabilis, S.S.C.J., 866 Cambria St., Cresson, PA 16630-1713. (814) 886-4223.

SERVANTS OF THE SACRED HEART OF JESUS AND OF THE POOR (S.S.H.J.P.)
U.S. Delegation House: 237 Tobin Pl., El Paso, TX 79905. (915) 533-3338
600 Sisters
Apostolic Work: Education, health and missions.
Conduct: Elementary schools, high schools, colleges, boarding schools, children's homes, hospitals, nursing homes, dispensaries, mobile clinics.
Represented in the Dioceses of Corpus Christi and El Paso in the U.S.; in 49 places in Mexico; in 4 places in Guatemala; 1 in Nicaragua; 3 in Colombia; 2 in Italy and 2 in Kenya (E. Africa).
Contact: Sr. Elizabeth Mata, 237 Tobin Pl., El Paso, TX 79905.

SISTERS ADORERS OF THE PRECIOUS BLOOD (A.P.B.)
See "A" Section.

CONGREGATION, SERVANTS OF CHRIST THE KING (S.S.C.K.)
Villa Loretto, Mt. Calvary, WI 53057. (414) 753-3211
11 Sisters, 3 Candidates
Conduct: Nursing homes, residential home.

Represented in the Archdiocese of Milwaukee and in the Diocese of Fargo.

Vocation Director: Sr. Michael, S.S.C.K., Villa Loretto, Mt. Calvary, WI 53057. (414) 753-3211.

SISTERS, SERVANTS OF THE IMMACULATE HEART OF MARY (I.H.M.)

P.O. Box 200, Immaculata, PA 19345-0200.

1,400 Sisters

Apostolic Work: 1 college, 3 academies, 128 parish schools, Also co-staff 35 high schools, 1 Montessori school, 1 visually impaired.

Represented in the Archdioceses of Philadelphia, Hartford, San Francisco, Atlanta and Miami and in nine dioceses. Also in two countries in South America.

Vocation Directress: Sr. Marjorie McCall, I.H.M., Villa Maria House of Studies, P.O. Box 200, Immaculata, PA 19345-0200. (610) 647-2160.

SISTERS, SERVANTS OF THE IMMACULATE HEART OF MARY (IHM)

IHM Center, 2300 Adams Ave., Scranton, PA 18509.

730 Sisters, 3 Novices, 1 Candidate

Apostolic Work: Education, health care, social service and various spiritual and pastoral ministries including: 7 colleges, 2 campus ministry settings, 19 secondary schools, 47 elementary schools, 1 Montessori school, 1 intermediate care center for mentally and physically handicapped children/young adults, 2 educational enrichment centers, 25 catechetical centers, 1 retreat/conference center, 3 spiritual renewal centers, 1 hospital, 1 foreign mission, 1 peace site, multiple sites for direct service to the poor, marginalized and persons with AIDS.

Represented in 27 (Arch)dioceses including: Altoona, Baltimore, Bridgeport, Jackson, MS, Newark, New York, Philadelphia, Pittsburgh, Raleigh, Scranton, Syracuse, Trenton, Washington, Wheeling-Charleston, Wilmington and Yakima. Also in Peru, Canada and Israel.

Director of Vocations: Sr. Kathryn Kurdziel, IHM, IHM Center, 2300 Adams Ave., Scranton, PA 18509. (717) 346-5413.

SISTERS, SERVANTS OF THE IMMACULATE HEART OF MARY (I.H.M.)

General Motherhouse: 610 W. Elm, Monroe, MI 48161. (313) 241-3660

789 Sisters

Apostolic Work: Furthering God's reign in our world through education (all levels/forms); pastoral ministry; religious education; retreat/ spiritual direction ministry; health care; pastoral care of the sick and elderly; social work; counseling; prison ministry; societal ministry; action for justice/peace.

Represented in 60 Dioceses in the U.S. and in 11 Dioceses outside of the U.S. including Puerto Rico, Honduras, Ghana, Brazil, Ontario, South Africa, Zimbabwe, Mexico and Kenya.

Vocation Director: Sr. Frances Ryan, IHM, 8531 W. McNichols, Detroit, MI 48221. (313) 341-1254.

SISTERS SERVANTS OF MARY (S.M.) (Ministers of the Sick)

(United States Province), Provincial House: 800 N. 18th St., Kansas City, KS 66102.

2,300 Sisters (263 in U.S.)

Apostolic Work: Nursing-private and visiting nursing in patients' homes and hospitals.

Represented in the Archdioceses of Kansas City, Los Angeles, New Orleans and New York and in France, Spain, England, Italy, Portugal, U.R. of Cameroon, Mexico, Columbia, Ecuador, Brazil, Argentina, Bolivia, Cuba, Dominican Republic, Puerto Rico, Belgium, Panama, Peru, Uruguay.

Vocation Director: Sr. Ma. Rita Miguel, S.M., 3305 Country Club Rd., Bronx, NY 10465-1296. (718) 829-0428.

SISTERS, SERVANTS OF MARY (O.S.M.)

Provincialate: Mother of Sorrows Convent, 13811 S. Western Ave., Blue Island, IL 60406. (708) 385-2103

24 Sisters

Apostolic Work: Teaching: elementary, kindergarten, C.C.D., foreign mission in South Africa.

Vocation Director: Sr. Eleanor, O.S.M., Mother of Sorrows Convent, 13811 S. Western Ave., Blue Island, IL 60406. (708) 385-2103.

SISTERS SERVANTS OF MARY IMMACULATE (S.S.M.I.)

See Eastern Catholic Religious Communities for Women.

SISTERS, SERVANTS OF MARY IMMACULATE (S.S.M.I.)

(Provincialate and Novitiate), 1220 Tugwell Drive, Catonsville, MD 21228.

36 Sisters in American Province; 1,200 worldwide

Apostolic Work: Primarily pre-school

care of children, health care and social and charitable ministry to the aged.

Represented in the Dioceses of Baltimore, Cleveland and Washington, DC. General Motherhouse in Poland. Also in Rome, Africa and Lithuania.

Vocation Director: Sr. Ce Ann Sambor, S.S.M.I., 1220 Tugwell Dr., Catonsville, MD 21228. (410) 747-1353.

SERVITES

See Servants of Mary.

SISTERS OF OUR LADY OF MERCY (MERCEDARIAN SISTERS)

See "O" - Sisters of Our Lady of Mercy.

SISTERS OF SOCIAL SERVICE (S.S.S.)

U.S. Residence: 440 Linwood Ave., Buffalo, NY 14209.

No institutions by Constitution (Members are free to work for Church-related and secular agencies.)

23 Sisters in U.S.

Apostolic Work: (all forms of) social work with individuals, groups and communities; health ministry, inner-city work; parish ministry; retreat work; religious education; youth ministry, political ministry and education for social justice; Spanish apostolate.

Represented in the (Arch)dioceses of Buffalo, Miami and Ponce P.R. Also in Cuba, Hungary, Rumania and Slovakia.

Vocation Director: 210 Winston Rd., Buffalo, NY 14216. (716) 833-7412.

SISTERS OF SOCIAL SERVICE (S.S.S.)

1120 Westchester Pl., Los Angeles, CA 90019. (213) 731-2117

115 Sisters

Apostolic Work: Social service work in parishes and in diocesan agencies, leadership training of youth and adults, residences for emotionally disturbed adolescents and for employed women, retreats, summer camps for children, and families, programs for the elderly, religious education, settlement houses, health programs, low cost legal services, family counseling services.

Represented in the Archdioceses of Los Angeles, CA, San Francisco, CA, Portland, OR, Great Falls, El Paso, Seattle. Also in Tacambaro, Michoacan; Morelia, Michoacan, Taipei, Taiwan and Imus, Cavite; and in the Dioceses of Oakland, Sacramento and San Diego.

SISTERS OF THE SOCIETY DEVOTED TO THE SACRED HEART (S.D.S.H.)

Motherhouse: 9814 Sylvia Ave., Northridge, CA 91324. (818) 772-9961

48 Sisters, 5 Novices

Ministries: In the light of the all-embracing love of God as expressed in the Sacred Heart of Jesus, Sisters joyfully serve in: religious education, retreat apostolate, family retreats, girls' summer camps, catechist formation, education videos, media and music apostolate, sacramental preparation.

Represented in the Archdiocese of Los Angeles and in the Dioceses of Reno-Las Vegas, San Bernardino and Orange. Foreign mission areas: Taipei, Taiwan, R.O.C., Budapest, Hungary.

Vocation Director: Vocation Director, 10480 Winnetka Ave., Chatsworth, CA 91311. (818) 831-9710.

SOCIETY OF HELPERS (S.H.)

Provincialate: 2956 S. Lowe, Chicago, IL 60616. (312) 842-1039

900 Sisters

The Helpers, an international missionary society, are engaged in the pastoral work of the Church, especially with those who are suffering in any way.

Represented in the Archdioceses of New York, Chicago, Fort Wayne/South Bend, Kansas City, St. Louis and San Francisco. Also in Europe, Asia, Africa and Latin America.

Contact: Sr. Jean Kielty, S.H., Vocation Director, 2039 N. Humboldt Blvd., Chicago, IL 60647. (312) 278-6629.

SOCIETY OF OUR MOTHER OF PEACE (SMP)

Maria Fonte Solitude, P.O. Box 322, High Ridge, MO 63049. (314) 677-3235

21 Sisters

Apostolic Work: Contemplative-apostolic balance of life in the context of simplicity and poverty; emphasis on solitary prayer; limited apostolates of retreat work and spiritual direction; direct evangelization within the black community.

Represented in the Archdiocese of St. Louis and in the Diocese of Springfield-Cape Girardeau.

Vocation Director: Sr. Mary Faith, SMP, Maria Fonte Solitude, P.O. Box 322, High Ridge, MO 63049. (314) 677-3235.

SISTERS OF THE SORROWFUL MOTHER (Franciscan) (SSM)

525 Sisters Internationally

Our Lady of Sorrows Convent, 17600 East 51st St. South, Broken Arrow, OK 74012. (918) 355-5581

Ministries: Teaching and healing the unserved through: literacy and advocacy programs, retreats, religious education, art, music, Native American ministries, nursing, administration, hospice, accounting, social work, counseling, outreach clinics, clerical work, archives, teaching and patient advocacy.

Represented in the Archdioceses of Castries-St. Lucia, Milwaukee and Santa Fe and in the Dioceses of Gallup, Green Bay, La Crosse, Las Cruces, Little Rock, Paterson, St. Augustine, St. Georges (Grenada), Sioux City, Superior, Tucson, Tulsa, Wichita and Winona. Also serve in Austria, Brazil, Germany and Italy.

Vocation Counselors: Sr. Bernadette Marie Palma, SSM, Sr. Michele Malolepsy, SSM, 5409 West Villard Ave., Milwaukee, WI 53218. (414) 438-4780; Sr. Cecile St. Remy, SSM, St. Rose Convent, Gouyave, St. John's, Grenada, West Indies. (809) 444-8111.

COMMUNITY OF TERESIAN CARMELITES (C.T.C.)

See "C" section - Community of Teresian Carmelites.

TRAPPISTINES (O.C.S.O.) (Cistercian Nuns of the Strict Observance)

Mount Saint Mary's Abbey, 300 Arnold St., Wrentham, MA 02093. (508) 528-1282

Contemplative Monastic Order

54 Sisters

Represented in the Archdiocese of Boston.

Vocational Contact: Sr. Miriam Pollard, O.C.S.O.

TRAPPISTINES (O.C.S.O.) (Cistercian Nuns of the Strict Observance)

Monastery of Our Lady of the Angels, 3365 Monastery Dr., Crozet, VA 22932. (804) 823-1452

7 Professed, 2 Novices

Apostolic Work: Contemplative monastic.

Represented in the Diocese of Richmond.

Vocations: Sr. Claire Boudreau, O.C.S.O., Vocation Director.

TRAPPISTINES (O.C.S.O.) (Cistercian Nuns of the Strict Observance)

Our Lady of the Mississippi Abbey, 8400 Abbey Hill, Dubuque, IA 52003. (319) 582-2595

27 Sisters

Represented in the Archdiocese of Dubuque.

Contact Person: Sr. Gail Fitzpatrick, O.C.S.O.

TRAPPISTINES (O.C.S.O.) (Cistercian Nuns of the Strict Observance)

Santa Rita Abbey, HC1 Box 929, Sonoita, AZ 85637-9705. (520) 455-5595

16 Sisters

Represented in the Diocese of Tuscon.

Vocation Director: Sr. Victoria Murray, O.C.S.O.

URSULINE NUNS (O.S.U.)

(Roman Union)(Eastern Province of the U.S.), 323 E. 198th St., Bronx, NY 10458. (718) 365-7410

234 Sisters

Apostolic Work: Education: primary, secondary, college, graduate levels; catechetics, pastoral ministry, social services, health-related services and retreat ministry.

Represented in the Archdioceses of New York and Washington and in the Dioceses of Ogdensburg, Orlando and Wilmington. Three other U.S. provinces have central offices in Archdioceses of Boston, St. Louis and San Francisco. Missions in Europe, Asia, Africa and Latin America.

Vocation Director: Sr. Beth Dowd, O.S.U., 323 E. 198th St., Bronx, NY 10458. (718) 365-7410.

URSULINE NUNS (O.S.U.)

(Roman Union) (Northeastern Province), 45 Lowder St., Dedham, MA 02026-4200. (617) 326-6219

68 Sisters

Apostolic Work: 1 high school, 2 elementary schools.

Represented in the Archdiocese of Boston and in the Diocese of Portland (ME).

Vocation Director: Sr. Dorothy Doyle.

URSULINE SISTERS (O.S.U.)

(Roman Union, Central Province), Ursuline Provincialate, 210 Glennon Heights Rd., Crystal City, MO 63019.

240 Sisters

Apostolic Work: Education for evangelization in schools, parishes, diocesan offices, ministry to the poor, foreign mission, retreat work, counseling, pastoral care in hospitals, social work.

Represented in the (Arch)dioceses of Minneapolis-St. Paul, St. Louis, Springfield, IL, Springfield-Cape Girardeau, Dallas, San Antonio, Corpus Christi, Galveston-Houston, Jackson and New Orleans. Also in Europe, Asia, Africa, Latin America, the Caribbean and Australia.

Vocation Director: Sr. Marianne Mullen, OSU, Ursuline Center, 210 Glennon Heights Rd., Crystal City,

MO 63019. (314) 296-6139 or (314) 937-6206.

URSULINE NUNS (O.S.U.)
(Roman Union), (Western Province), 639 Angela Dr., Santa Rosa, CA 95403-1793. (707) 545-6811
54 Sisters
Apostolic Work: Pre-school, elementary and high school education, spiritual growth centers, work with Native Americans and Hispanics, parish ministry, spiritual direction, counseling and retreats.
Represented in the Archdioceses of Anchorage, Los Angeles and San Francisco and in the Dioceses of Boise, Fairbanks, Santa Rosa, Great Falls/Billings, San Jose and Oakland.
Vocation Contact: Sr. Lois Castillon, O.S.U.

URSULINE SISTERS (O.S.U.)
(Congregation of Paris)
Ursulines of Brown County, Ursuline Center, St. Martin, OH 45118. (513) 875-2020
46 Sisters, 1 Junior Professed
Conduct: 1 academy, 1 three-year college, teaching administration, hospital, social ministry, pastoral, archdiocesan work, college teaching and campus ministry, adult education and senior services.
Represented in the (Arch)dioceses of Atlanta, Cincinnati, Daytona Beach and Toledo.
Vocation Director: Sr. Lucia Castellini, O.S.U., 5661 Happy Hollow, Millford, OH 45150. (513) 831-0258.

URSULINES OF CINCINNATI (O.S.U.)
(Congregation of Paris)
St. Ursula Convent, 1339 E. McMillan St., Cincinnati, OH 45206. (513) 961-3410
32 Sisters
Apostolic Work: Teaching, adult education, parish ministry, Catholic social services, hospice.
Represented in the Archdiocese of Cincinnati.
Vocation Director: Sr. Mary Cabrini Durkin, St. Ursula Convent, 1339 E. McMillan St., Cincinnati, OH 45206. (513) 961-3410.

URSULINE SISTERS (O.S.U.)
(Congregation of Paris)
Convent of O.L. of Lourdes, 901 E. Miami St., Paola, KS 66071. (913) 294-2349
46 Sisters
Apostolic Work: Elementary and secondary education, college teaching and campus ministry, parish ministry, retreat work.
Represented in the Archdioceses of

Kansas City (KS) and New Orleans and in the Dioceses of Kansas City-St. Joseph (MO), Sacramento and Tulsa
Contact: Sr. Pat Lynch, OSU, 901 E. Miami St., Paola, KS 66071. (913) 294-2349.

URSULINE SISTERS (O.S.U.)
(Congregation of Paris)
3105 Lexington Rd., Louisville, KY 40206.
250 Sisters
Apostolic Work: Teachers and administrators in Montessori pre-school, elementary schools, secondary schools, colleges and adult and religious education, music and musical drama education, special education (deaf, speech impaired, mental), administrators of health and social services. Also in pastoral ministry, retreat ministry and spiritual direction, ministry to the sick and elderly. Foreign mission in Peru.
Represented in the Archdioceses of Louisville, Indianapolis, Baltimore, Chicago, Omaha and Philadelphia and in the Dioceses of Charlestown, Lafayette, St. Petersburg, Brooklyn, Greensburg, Peoria, Pittsburgh, Grand Island, Jackson, Lexington, Wheeling-Charleston, Callao and Cajamarca, Peru.
Vocation Director: Sr. Jane Stuckenborg, O.S.U., 3105 Lexington Rd., Louisville, KY 40206. (502) 897-1811.

URSULINE NUNS (O.S.U.)
(Congregation of Paris)
Motherhouse & Novitiate: 2600 Lander Rd., Cleveland, OH 44124.
295 Sisters
Conduct: 1 college, 3 high schools, 22 elementary schools. Also active in pastoral ministry, social service, and foreign missions.
Represented in the Diocese of Cleveland. Also in Florida and El Salvador.
Vocation Director: Sr. Anita Whitely, OSU, 2600 Lander Rd., Cleveland, OH 44124. (216) 449-1200.

URSULINE SISTERS (O.S.U.)
(Congregation of Paris)
Mount St. Joseph, Maple Mount, KY 42356. (502) 229-4103
244 Sisters
Apostolic Work: Christian formation ministry and a clear witness of Christian community.
Represented in the Archdioceses of Louisville, Santa Fe and St. Louis and in the Dioceses of Gallup, Lincoln, Memphis, Owensboro, Richmond, Springfield-Cape Girardeau and Kansas City. Also in Chile.
Vocation Ministry Team: Sr. Elaine

Byrne, O.S.U., 8001 Cummings Rd., Maple Mount, KY 42356. (502) 229-4103, ext. 434.

URSULINE NUNS (O.S.U.)
(Congregation of Paris)
Ursuline Convent of the Sacred Heart, 4045 Indian Rd., Toledo, OH 43606
108 Sisters
Apostolic Ministries: Teaching, administration, hospital chaplain, D.R.E.; pastoral asssociate, spiritual direction, home health care.
Represented in the (Arch)dioceses of Toledo, Fresno and Washington, DC. Foreign mission in Peru.
Vocation Director: Sr. Joy Gray, O.S.U., 4045 Indian Rd., Toledo, OH 43606. (419) 536-9587.

URSULINE SISTERS OF YOUNGSTOWN (O.S.U.)
(Congregation of Paris)
4250 Shields Rd., Canfield, OH 44406. (216) 792-7636.
88 Sisters; also Companions in Mission (lay volunteer ministry), Company of Angela (lay prayer associates)
Conduct: 2 high schools, 9 parochial schools, 1 kindergarten, parish ministry and religious education, diocesan offices, social services, hospital services, higher education school of music, preschool, transitional housing for single homeless women with children, AIDS/HIV ministry, speech and hearing center.
Represented in the Diocese of Youngstown.
Vocations Contact: Sr. Jacquelyn Herpy, OSU, 4250 Shields Rd., Canfield, OH 44406. (216) 792-7636.

URSULINE SISTERS (O.S.U.).
1026 N. Douglas Ave., Belleville, IL 62220. (618) 233-5010 or (618) 234-3326.
18 Professed Sisters
Ministries: Elementary schools, parish retreat work, Director of Religious Education, ministry to home-bound, community service, spiritual direction.
Represented in the Diocese of Belleville.
Vocation Director: Sr. Frances McDonagh, O.S.U., 1026 N. Douglas Ave., Belleville, IL 62220. (618) 233-5010 or (618) 566-2821.

URSULINE SISTERS OF TILDONK (O.S.U.)
Provincialate: 81-15 Utopia Pkwy., Jamaica, NY 11432. (718) 380-3459.
75 Sisters in the U.S.

Apostolic Work: Grammar schools, high schools, retreat house at St. Ursula Center, Blue Point, NY, pastoral ministry, religious education, hospital chaplaincy, social work, spirituality.

Represented in the Archdioceses of New York and Hartford and in the Dioceses of Bridgeport, Brooklyn, Rockville Centre, Burlington, Richmond and Shreveport. Provinces in Belgium, Canada and India. District in Zaire, Africa.

Provincial: Sr. Judith O'Connor, O.S.U., 81-15 Utopia Pkwy., Jamaica, NY 11432. (718) 591-0681.

VERONA MISSIONARY SISTERS
See Comboni Missionary Sisters.

VINCENTIAN SISTERS OF CHARITY (V.S.C.)
8200 McKnight Rd., Pittsburgh, PA 15237.

210 Sisters

Apostolic Work: Education: Montessori, day care, kindergarten, elementary, high schools, college; health care: hospital, nursing homes, crippled children, clinic; religious education: elementary, high school, adult; social services; retreats, hospital chaplaincy, parish pastoral, youth ministry and foreign and domestic missionary work.

Vocation Director: Sr. Elena Almendarez, VSC, 8200 McKnight Rd., Pittsburgh, PA 15237. (412) 364-3000.

VINCENTIAN SISTERS OF CHARITY (V.S.C.)
1160 Broadway, Bedford, OH 44146. (216) 232-4755.

84 Sisters, 1 Candidate

Apostolic Work: Education, health care, pastoral ministry, ministry with the poor, hospice, missionaries in El Salvador, ministry with the elderly.

Represented in the Diocese of Cleveland, OH and Lexington, KY.

Contact: Sr. Ruthann Rody, (216) 232-8237 or 4755.

VISITATION NUNS (V.H.M.)
(Cloistered)

(First Federation of North America), Monastery of the Visitation, 2055 Ridgedale Dr., Snellville, GA 30278. (404) 972-1060.

123 Sisters, 6 Monasteries

President: Mother Mary Jozefa Kowalewski, V.H.M., 2055 Ridgedale Dr., Snellville, GA 30278.

Apostolic Work: Prayer is primary, limited retreats.

Monasteries: 2300 Springhill Ave., Mobile, AL 36607; 5820 City Ave., Philadelphia, PA 19131; Rt. 1, Box 2055, Rockville, VA 23146; 1745 Parkside Blvd., Toledo, OH 43607; 370 North St., Pittsfield, MA 01201; 2055 Ridgedale Dr., Snellville, GA 30278.

Vocation Directress: Sr. Mary Immaculata, V.H.M., Monastery of the Visitation, Federation Headquarters, 2055 Ridgedale Dr., Snellville, GA 30278. (404) 972-1060.

VISITATION NUNS (V.H.M.)
Visitation Monastery, 8902 Ridge Blvd., Brooklyn, NY 11209-5716. (718) 745-5151.

26 Sisters

Represented in the Diocese of Brooklyn.

Apostolic Work: 1 elementary academy.

Vocation Directress: Sr. Marie Anatrella.

VISITATION NUNS (V.H.M.)
Visitation Monastery, 200 E. Second St., Frederick, MD 21701. (301) 662-3322

5 Sisters

Apostolic Work: Contemplative order with apostolate of teaching.

Vocation Director: Sr. Marguerite Therese Leary, V.H.M., Visitation Monastery, 200 E. Second St., Frederick, MD 21701. (301) 662-3322.

VISITATION NUNS (V.H.M.)
Monastery of the Visitation, 1500 35th St., N.W., Washington, DC 20007.

29 Sisters

Apostolic Work: Prayer and education.

Vocation Director: Sr. Jacqueline Burke, Monastery of the Visitation, 1500 35th St., N.W., Washington, DC 20007. (202) 337-0305.

VISITATION NUNS (V.H.M.)
Visitation Monastery, 3020 N. Ballas Rd., St. Louis, MO 63131. (314) 432-5353.

27 Sisters

Apostolic Work: "To give to God women of prayer" was Saint Francis de Sales' intention when, with the cooperation of Saint Jane Frances de Chantal, he founded the Visitation Order in 1610. By calling some persons to a life dedicated to seeking union with God in contemplation, God is indicating the goal of human life, to experience that "in Him we live and move and exist" (Acts 17:27). Community life creates family bonds among the members and also with those entrusted to the Sisters' apostolates of prayer, spiritual direction, and teaching (preschool through 12th grade).

Vocation Director: Sr. Catherine Brady, V.H.M., 3020 N. Ballas Rd., St. Louis, MO 63131. (314) 432-5353.

VISITATION NUNS (V.H.M.)
Monastery of the Visitation, Mt. de Chantal, 410 Washington Ave., Wheeling, WV 26003. (304) 233-3771.

29 Sisters

Apostolic Work: Education.

Directress of Vocations: Monastery of the Visitation, 410 Washington Ave., Wheeling, WV 26003. (304) 233-3771.

VISITATION NUNS (V.H.M.)
Monastery of the Visitation, 2455 Visitation Dr., Mendota Heights, St. Paul, MN 55120. (612) 454-6474

23 Sisters

Service in the Church: Prayer and educational ministry.

Vocation Director: Sr. Katherine Mullin, VHM, 2455 Visitation Dr., St. Paul, MN 55120. (612) 454-6474.

SISTERS OF VISITATION OF THE CONGREGATION OF THE IMMACULATE HEART OF MARY (S.V.M.)
Visitation Convent, 2950 Kaufmann Ave., Dubuque, IA 52001-1655. (319) 556-2440.

9 Sisters

Apostolic Work: Elementary, secondary education. Also engaged in adult education, parish ministry, college counseling.

Represented in the Archdiocese of Dubuque.

VOCATIONIST SISTERS (S.D.V.)
(Sisters of the Divine Vocations)

U.S.A. Foundation: Perpetual Help Day Nursery, 172 Broad St., Newark, NJ 07104, (201) 484-3535; Sr. Joanna Formation House, 88 Brooklake Rd., Florham Park, NJ 07932. (201) 966-9762.

14 Sisters

Apostolic Work: To guide and foster vocation to priesthood and religious life; teaching, parish ministry and missionary work; special emphasis is given to work with the poor and underprivileged.

Represented in the Diocese of Newark and Paterson. Also in Italy, France, Brazil, Argentina, Philippines and India.

Vocation Director: Sr. Romilda A. Borges. (201) 966-9762.

XAVIER SISTERS (X.S.)
(Catholic Mission Sisters of St. Francis Xavier)
37179 Moravian Dr., Clinton Township, MI 48036. (313) 465-5082.
3 Sisters
Represented in the Archdiocese of Detroit.
Vocation Contact: Sr. Miriam Kennedy, 37179 Moravian Dr., Clinton Township, MI 48036.

XAVERIAN MISSIONARY SOCIETY OF MARY (X.M.M.)
242 Salisbury St., Worcester, MA 01609.
10 Sisters in U.S.
Apostolic Work: Evangelization among non-Christian peoples, catechetics, medicine, education, social work.
Represented in Italy (Motherhouse), Zaire, Brazil, Mexico, Japan, Chad-Cameroon, Sierra Leone. Also in U.S.: Archdiocese of New York and Diocese of Worcester, MA.
Vocation Director: Sr. Rita Davoli, X.M.M, 242 Salisbury St., Worcester, MA 01609. (508) 757-0514.

EASTERN CATHOLIC RELIGIOUS COMMUNITIES FOR WOMEN

ANTONINE SISTERS (MARONITE)
2691 North Lipkey Rd., North Jackson, OH 44451.
7 Sisters in U.S.; 200 worldwide.
Apostolic Work: Education, health care, pastoral ministry and social service.
Represented in Ohio. Also in Cyprus, Australia, France, Canada, Syria and Israel.
Vocation Contact: Sr. Marie Madeleine Iskandar, Superior, Antonine Sisters, 2691 North Lipkey Rd., North Jackson, OH 44451. (216) 538-2567.

BASILIANS – NUNS OF SAINT BASIL THE GREAT, O.S.B.M.
(Sacred Heart Monastery), 33 Keasel Rd., Middletown, New York 10940-9624. (914) 343-1308.

Apostolic Work: Contemplative community.
Vocation Contact: Very Rev. Mother M. Georgianna, O.S.B.M., 33 Keasel Rd., Middletown, New York 10940-9624. (914) 343-1308.

BASILIANS – SISTERS OF ST. BASIL THE GREAT (Byzantine Rite) OSBM
500 W. Main St., P.O. Box 878, Uniontown, PA 15401.
99 Sisters
Conduct: 7 grammar schools, 1 home for the aged, 1 nursing home, 1 retreat center, staff religious education offices, pastoral and parochial ministry.
Represented in the Archdiocese of Pittsburgh and in the Dioceses of Parma, Passaic and Van Nuys.
Vocation Director: Basilians - Sisters of St. Basil The Great (Byzantine Rite). (412) 438-8644.

BASILIANS – SISTERS OF THE ORDER OF ST. BASIL THE GREAT (O.S.B.M.) (Ukrainian Byzantine Rite)
74 Sisters
Apostolic Work: Education at all levels, pastoral ministry.
Vocation Directress: Sr. Lydia Anna Sawka, O.S.B.M., 710 Fox Chase Rd., Fox Chase Manor, PA 19046. (215) 342-4222.

BENEDICTINE SISTERS OF THE BYZANTINE RITE (O.S.B.)
Queen of Heaven Monastery, 8640 Squires Ln., N.E., Warren, OH 44484.
12 members
Apostolic Work: Teaching, religious education, pastoral care, parish ministry, office work, child care, retreat work, spiritual direction, domestic services.
Vocation Directress: Sister Cathy Ropchock, O.S.B., 407 Shaw Ave., McKeesport, PA 15132. (412) 672-7104.

BYZANTINE NUNS OF ST. CLARE (B.N.S.C.)
Poor Clares in the Byzantine Rite in the Ruthenian Eparchy of Parma, OH
Monastery of Holy Protection, 6688 Cady Rd., N. Royalton, OH 44133.
6 Professed
Apostolic Work: Contemplatives, Second Order of St. Francis, in Eastern Monasticism.

Vocation Directress: Sr. Mary Barbara Wal, B.N.S.C., 6688 Cady Rd., N. Royalton, OH 44133. (216) 237-6800.

COMMUNITY OF THE MOTHER OF GOD OF TENDERNESS (C.M.G.T.)
79 Golden Hill Rd., Danbury, CT 06811.
3 Sisters
Apostolic Work: Active/Contemplative community.
Vocation Contact: Sr. Mary Ann Socha, C.M.G.T., 79 Golden Hill Rd., Danbury, CT 06811. (203) 794-1486.

DISCALCED CARMELITE NUNS OF THE BYZANTINE RITE (O.C.D.)
Holy Annunciation Monastery, R.R. No. 1, Box 1336, Sugarloaf, PA 18249. (717) 788-1205
8 Professed Nuns, 4 Novices
Contact: Mother Marija of the Holy Spirit, Prioress.

MISSIONARY SISTERS OF MOTHER OF GOD (M.S.M.G.)
111 W. North St., Stamford, CT 06902. (203) 323-1237
11 Sisters
Apostolic Work: Catechetical grammar schools, elementary school, nursery schools, kindergarten.
Represented in the Ukrainian Archdiocese of Philadelphia and in the Ukrainian Diocese of Stamford.
Vocation Director: Sr. Yosaphata, MSMG, Motherhouse: 711 North Franklin St., Philadelphia, PA 19123. (215) 627-7808.

SISTERS SERVANTS OF MARY IMMACULATE (S.S.M.I.)
(Immaculate Conception Province)
Provincialate: Sisters Servants Lane, P.O. Box 6, Sloatsburg, NY 10974. (914) 753-2840
Apostolic Work: Serves the Eastern Catholic Church (Ukrainian & Byzantine). Teaching, nursing, senior citizens, youth ministry, pilgrimages, catechizing, sewing vestments, retreats, pastoral ministries, arts, domestics, administration.
Foreign Countries: Canada, Brazil, Argentina, Italy, Poland, Slovakia (former Yugoslavia), France, England, Germany, Ukraine.
Vocation Contact: Sr. Helena, S.S.M.I., St. Mary's Villa, P.O. Box 6, Sloatsburg, NY 10974. (914) 753-5100.

Lay Ministries

ADORERS OF THE BLOOD OF CHRIST VOLUNTEER PROGRAM
2 Pioneer Ln., Red Bud, IL 62278. (618) 282-3848
Contact: Sr. Sharon Van Horn, ASC, Director
Mission Areas: New Mexico,Texas, Arizona, Illinois, Missouri; foreign: Boliva and Guatemala
Type of Service: cathechetics, community work, education, health care, office work
Term of Service: a few weeks to 2 years or more
Basic Requirements: M/F; single/ married; Christian; 21 and up for foreign service.

AMATE HOUSE
2601 N. Sayre, Chicago, IL 60635. (312) 745-0002
Contact: Director
Mission Area: Chicago
Type of Service: teaching, community work, health care, legal, social services
Term of Service: 1 year
Basic Requirements: M/F; single; between 21 and 29; Catholic.

ANNUNCIATION HOUSE
1003 East San Antonio St., El Paso, TX 79901. (915) 545-4509
Contact: Coordinator for Volunteers
Mission Area: U.S./Mexican border at El Paso, TX and Juarez, Mexico
Type of Service: hospitality to homeless poor, and refugees and internal immigrants from Mexico
Term of Service: 12 or more months; 10-week summer internship program; specific arrival dates throughout the year
Basic Requirements: M/F; single; 20 and up; completely voluntary; Spanish extremely helpful.

ANTHONY FAMILY SHELTER
256 Ohio, Wichita, KS 67214. (316) 264-7233
Contact: Kevin S. Danler
Mission Area: Wichita, KS
Type of Service: homeless shelter
Term of Service: 6 months to 1 year
Basic Requirements: M/F; no dependents, 21 and up.

APOSTOLIC VOLUNTEERS
c/o Membership Office, Sinsinawa, WI 53824. (608) 748-4411; Rosary College, 7900 W. Division St., River Forest, IL 60305. (708) 524-5985.

Contact: Claire Noonan
Mission Areas: Throughout the U.S.
Type of Service: community work, education, health care, office work, social service, recreational coordinator
Term of Service: 1 to 3 years
Basic Requirements: M/F; single/ married; 20 or older.

ASSOCIATE MISSIONARIES OF THE ASSUMPTION
227 N. Bowman Ave., Merion, PA 19066. (610) 664-1736
Contact: Sr. Francis Joseph, R.A.
Mission Areas: U.S., Japan, Mexico, Belgium, Italy, Argentina, France, Spain
Type of Service: catechetics, community work, education, health care, office work
Term of Service: 1 to 2 years (renewable)
Basic Requirements: M/F; single; between 22 and 40; Catholic.

AT-ONE-MENT ASSOCIATES
145 Taylor St., NE, Washington, DC 20017. (202) 529-1117
Contacts: Paul McLaughlin, Linda Ferneyhough
Mission Areas: New York State, Canada, overseas
Type of Service: counseling, health care, office work, pastoral ministry, community work
Term of Service: 1 year (Aug. to Aug.)
Basic Requirements: M/F; single/ divorced/widowed; 21 and up.

BAJA OUTREACH
482 W. San Ysidro Blvd. #2043, San Ysidro, CA 92173. (619) 428-4011
Contact: Betsy McEnerney
Mission Area: Tijuana, Mexico
Type of Service: education, office work, communications, domestic work, fund raising, maintenance, recreation
Term of Service: summer to 2 years
Basic Requirements: M/F; 21 and older; Spanish fluency for some positions.

BENEDICTINE APPALACHIAN VOLUNTEERS
Mt. Tabor Benedictines, 150 Mt. Tabor Rd., Martin, KY 41649. (606) 886-9624
Contact: Sr. Kathleen Weigand, O.S.B.
Mission Area: Appalachian region of Eastern Kentucky
Type of Service: catechetics, community work, education, health care, office work

Term of Service: 1 to 3 months
Basic Requirements: M/F w/o dependents; 21 years and up.

BENEDICTINE LAY ASSOCIATES
St. Scholastica Priory, 1200 Kenwood Ave., Duluth, MN 55811-4103. (218) 728-6539
Contact: Sr. Michelle Dosch, OSB
Mission Area: Duluth
Type of Service: education, health care, geriatric services, parish/pastoral/campus ministries, domestic, maintenance, youth ministry
Term of Service: 1 month - 1 year (renewable)
Basic Requirements: F; single/married, no dependents; age 18-65.

BENEDICTINE LAY VOLUNTEERS
Mother of God Monastery, 120 S.E. 28th Ave., Watertown, SD 57201. (605) 886-6777
Contact: Director
Mission Area: South Dakota
Type of Service: community work, (adult) education, health care, office work, rural ministry, varied ministries within the monastery and in South Dakota
Term of Service: 1 year (renewable); summer program
Basic Requirements: M/F; 21 and up (year long); M/F; 20 and up (summer program).

BENEDICTINE SISTERS - ST. MARTIN'S MINISTRIES
14259 Benedictine Lane, Ridgely, MD 21660. (410) 634-2497
Contact: Sr. Patricia Gamgort, O.S.B.
Mission Area: Eastern shore of Maryland (rural poor and homeless)
Type of Service: child care, counselor, community work, health care, office work, other areas related to service with the poor
Term of Service: 6 months to 1 year (renewable); also college break and summer
Basic Requirements: Long-term program: F; lay/religious; 21 and up; personal interview; short term: M/F; 18 and up.

BENEDICTINE SISTERS VOLUNTEER PROGRAM
840 S. Main St., Mt. Angel, OR 97362-9527. (503) 845-6141

Contact: Sister Marietta Schindler, OSB

Mission Areas: rural Mt. Angel, OR

Type of Service: community work, nurse, gardening, receptionist, computer, library, shelter

Term of Service: varies - 1 week to 1 year

Basic Requirements: M/F; single/married w/o dependents; 18-65.

BETHESDA MISSIONER CORPS
700 S. 15th St., Philadelphia, PA 19146. (215) 985-1004

Contact: Lilin Gaab

Mission Area: inner-city Philadelphia

Type of Service: community work, social work, health care, office work

Term of Service: 1 to 2 years (renewable)

Basic Requirements: M/F; 21 and up.

BETHLEHEM HOUSE INC
1401 Lawrence St. NE, Washington, DC 20017. (202) 526-3222

Contact: Dolores Wilson

Mission Area: Washington, DC

Type of Service: provide Christian community with persons who are developmentally disabled (mental retardation)

Term of Service: 1-2 years (renewable)

Basic Requirements: M/F; 20 and up.

BONA (BENEDICTINE OUTREACH TO THE NATIVE AMERICANS)
Queen of Peace Monastery, Box 370, Belcourt, ND 58316. (701) 477-6167

Contact: Sr. Judith Emge, OSB

Mission Area: Turtle Mt. Indian Reservation, ND

Type of Service: cathechetics, community work, religious teachers, counseling

Term of Service: summer; 3 months to 1 year

Basic Requirements: F; single/divorced/widowed; 21-55.

BOYS HOPE/GIRLS HOPE
12120 Bridgeton Sq. Dr., Bridgeton, MO 63044. (314) 298-1250

Contact: Bruce B. Bradley

Mission Areas: St. Louis, New York, Chicago, New Orleans, Cincinnati, Detroit, Cleveland/Akron, Phoenix, Pittsburgh, Orange County, Denver, Baton Rouge, Jacksonville

Type of Service: Provide surrogate parenting services to hurt and at-risk, yet academically capable, youth in family-like settings

Term of Service: 1 year or more; summer program

Basic Requirements: M/F; single; 21 and up, college degree.

BREAD FOR THE WORLD
1100 Wayne Ave., Ste. 1000, Silver Spring, MD 20910. (301) 608-2400

Contact: Katherine Simmons

Mission Area: Silver Spring

Type of Service: seeks justice for the world's hungry people by lobbying nation's decision makers

Term of Service: varies, great flexibility, summer available

Basic Requirements: M/F; single/married/divorced/separated/religious/disabled; Judeo-Christian.

BROTHER BENNO'S FOUNDATION
P.O. Box 308, Oceanside, CA 92054. (619) 439-1244

Contact: Deacon Hal Kutler

Mission Area: Oceanside, CA

Type of Service: day center, soup kitchen, emergency shelter staff, community work

Term of Service: 1 year

Basic Requirements: M/F; single; 22 yrs. and up.

CABRINI MISSION CORPS
610 King of Prussia Rd., Radnor, PA 19087-3698. (610) 971-0821.

Contact: Sr. Lucille Souza

Mission Area: NY, PA, IL, CO, WA, Europe, Africa, Central America, South America

Type of Service: a faith-based lay mission organization serving in the areas of education, health care, pastoral ministry, child care and other social services

Term of Service: 1 year (US); 18 months to 3 years (overseas)

Basic Requirements: M/F; 21 and up; Christian; college or work experience.

CAPUCHIN FRANCISCAN VOLUNTEER CORPS
EAST: St. Ambrose Friary, 4502 Park Heights Ave., Baltimore, MD 21215-6330. (410) 367-0069.

MIDWEST: 2338 E. 99 St., Chicago, IL 60617. (312) 375-3059.

Contacts: Bill Talentino, O.F.M. Cap. (East); Brian Braun, O.F.M. Cap. (Midwest).

Mission Areas: Baltimore, MD, Washington, DC, Charleston, WV

Type of Service: advocacy, education, community organizing, health care, social service

Term of Service: 1 to 2 years (renewable)

Basic Requirements: M/F; single/married w/o dependents; Catholic; 21 and up.

CAPUCHIN YOUTH AND FAMILY MINISTRIES
P.O. Box 192, Garrison, NY 10524. (914) 424-3609

Contact: Fr. Anthony Vetrano, OFM Cap.

Mission Areas: New York, Connecticut

Type of Service: community work, communications, youth and campus ministry

Term of Service: one year (beginning in Aug.) (renewable)

Basic Requirements: M; Catholic, 21 and older; college graduate.

CARITAS MISSION (Y.P.W.C.)
P.O. Box 129, Frenchville, PA 16836. (814) 263-4177, 4855

Contact: Donna Able

Mission Area: Clearfield County in western PA-rural Appalachia

Type of Service: social service work in the community

Term of Service: 6 months to 1 year and longer; summer program

Basic Requirements: M/F; single; 20 and over.

CASA JUAN DIEGO
4818 Rose, P.O. Box 70113, Houston, TX 77270. (713) 869-7376, (713) 864-4994

Contacts: Mark or Louise Zwick

Mission Area: Houston, TX

Type of Service: refugee work for men and women, battered and/or homeless women and children

Term of Service: No minimum

Basic Requirements: M/F; single/married/widowed; 21 and up; functional Spanish; faith commitment.

CATHOLIC CHARITIES VOLUNTEER CORPS
633 University Ave. W., St. Paul, MN 55104. (612) 222-1250.

Contact: John Le Blanc

Mission Area: 12 counties of the Archdiocese of St. Paul/Minneapolis

Type of Service: community work, counseling, office work

Term of Service: 1 year minimum.

Basic Requirements: M/F; single/married w/o dependents/divorced/widowed; 21 and up.

CATHOLIC MEDICAL MISSION BOARD
10 W. 17th St., New York, NY 10011-5765. (212) 242-7757

Contact: Rev. Joseph A. Latella, S.J.

Mission Areas: Africa, India, Papua New Guinea, Central America, Mexico and the Caribbean

Type of Service: health care

Term of Service: 1-3 years.

Basic Requirements: Licensed and registered to practice nursing, medicine or health care in the United States and Canada.

CATHOLIC NETWORK OF VOLUNTEER SERVICE
4121 Harewood Road, N.E., Washington, DC 20017. (1-800) 543-5046; (202) 529-1100

(Clearinghouse - Referral agency for 165 lay mission programs placing 5,500 lay men and women in missions throughout the U.S.A. and the world).

Contact: Maggie Fogarty, Executive Director

CATHOLIC VOLUNTEERS IN FLORIDA
P.O. Box 702, Goldenrod, FL 32733-0702. (407) 331-6444
Contact: Gina Cawley
Mission Area: Florida (inner city, rural)
Type of Service: community work, education, health care, social work, legal, counseling, shelter and group homes.
Term of Service: 1 year (renewable)
Basic Requirements: M/F; single/married/no dependents; 20 and up; Christian; degree or work experienced; previous part-time volunteer experience: interest in social justice.

CCVI VOLUNTEERS IN MISSION – CONGREGATION OF THE SISTERS OF CHARITY OF THE INCARNATE WORD
4503 Broadway, San Antonio, TX 78209. (210) 828-2224
Contact: Karen Gosetti
Mission Areas: United States, Mexico
Type of Service: catechetics, community work, education, health care
Term of Service: 1 year (U.S.); 2 years (out of U.S.)
Basic Requirements: M/F; single/married/divorced/separated/without dependents; 21 & over; Catholic.

CHANNEL
4524 20th Ave. NE, Seattle, WA 98105-3302. (206) 527-2020
Contact: Greg McNabb
Mission Areas: Seattle and western Washington
Type of Service: parish ministry, education (teachers must be certified), social service
Term of Service: 1 year (renewable)
Basic Requirements: M/F; single/married; between 22 and 30.

CHI RHO CATHOLIC SERVICE CORPS
338 Asylum St., Hartford CT 06103-2091. (203) 246-7010
Contact: John D. Campos
Mission Areas: inner-city neighborhoods of Connecticut (Hartford, New Haven, Waterbury)
Type of Service: teaching, tutoring, youth development, AIDS ministry, work with single mothers and their children, assisting the homeless
Term of Service: 1 year (Aug. - July)
Basic Requirements: M/F; single; Catholic; recent college graduates, ages 21-25.

CHILDREN'S CRISIS CENTER, CASA DE ESPERANZA DE LOS NINOS, INC.
P.O. Box 66581, Houston, TX 77266-6581 (713) 529-0639
Contact: Susan Molitor
Mission Area: Houston, TX
Type of Service: child care work; group home staff for homes for young children who are at high risk for abuse/neglect or children at risk for HIV/AIDS.
Term of Service: 6 months to two years (1 year+ preferred).
Basic Requirements: F; prefer experience with children; 18 + (Spanish is not required).

CHRIST HOUSE
1717 Columbia Rd., N.W., Washington, DC 20009. (202) 328-1100
Contact: Coordinator of Residential Volunteers
Mission Area: Washington, DC
Type of Service: health care and social services for the homeless. Doctors, nurses, social workers, nursing and social work assistants, activities coordinator, administrative assistants, cooking and maintenance assistants, van driver and general services needed.
Term of Service: to 1 year or more; 1 month minimum
Basic Requirements: M/F; single/married; 18 or older: short term, 21 or older: long term.

CHRISTIAN APPALACHIAN PROJECT - VOLUNTEER PROGRAM
235 Lexington St., Lancaster, KY 40444. (800) 755-5322; (606) 792-2219
Contacts: Kathy Kluesener, Carla Durand
Mission Area: Appalachian region of Eastern Kentucky
Type of Service: professional and general workers needed year-round for child development centers, GED and adult education programs, elderly outreach, residential programs, home repair, emergency assistance, maintenance, health education, summer camps, teen centers, and much more.
Term of Service: 1 year (renewable); Long Term (9 months-1 year); Short Term (3 weeks-9 months).
Basic Requirements: M/F; single/married w/o dependents; 21 and up for 1-year and long-term; 18 and up for short-term.

CHRISTIAN BROTHERS VOLUNTEER PROGRAM
33 Pryor Terrace, New Rochelle, NY 10804. (914) 636-6194
Contact: Br. Grondin
Mission Areas: New York City, migrants in SW Florida
Type of Service: education, campus ministers, coaches
Term of Service: 1 year (renewable for 1 more year)
Basic Requirements: M/F; single; Christian; college degree.

CHRISTIAN COMMUNITY CENTER
Rte.1, Box 6-A, Vanceburg, KY 41179. (606) 796-3289; 6448
Contact: Jan Kreher
Mission Area: Rural Appalachia (Eastern Kentucky)
Type of Service: community work, advocacy, counseling, shelters for homeless/abused
Term of Service: 1 year (flexible)
Basic Requirements: M/F; single; 21 years and up.

CHRISTIAN FOUNDATION FOR CHILDREN AND AGING
One Elmwood Ave., Kansas City, KS 66103. (913) 384-6500
Contacts: Robert K. Hentzen; Holly Neff
Mission Areas: Mexico, Guatemala, Honduras, El Salvador, Nicaragua, Costa Rica, the Dominican Republic, Haiti, St. Kitts-Nevis, Colombia, Venezuela, Peru, Bolivia, Brazil, Chile, the Philippines, India, Kenya, Madagascar, Uganda and the United States
Type of Service: community work, education, health care
Term of Service: 1 year or more (flexible)
Basic Requirements: M/F; single/married/religious; Catholic/ecumenical.

CHRISTIAN VOLUNTEER MINISTRIES (CRISPAZ)
1135 Mission Rd., San Antonio, TX 78210. (210) 534-6996
Contact: Jacquie Schoonover-Higgins
Mission Area: El Salvador
Type of Service: pastoral work, community work, education, health care, agronomy, literacy
Term of Service: 1 year
Basic Requirements: Spanish; church or community sponsorship

CLARETIAN VOLUNTEERS AND LAY MISSIONARIES (EAST)
205 W. Monroe St., Chicago, IL 60606. (312) 236-7846
Contacts: Heidi Kuhn, Michelle Scheidt
Mission Areas: Chicago, Missouri, New Jersey, Guatemala
Type of Service: catechetics, community work, education, health care, administration, youth ministry, cross cultural ministry, immigration services, Hispanic ministry, campus ministry
Term of Service: 1 year (renewable) Claretian Volunteers (U.S. only), 2+ years Claretian Lay Missionaries (Guatemala); summer program (U.S.)
Basic Requirements: M/F; single/married w/o dependents/widowed; 21 yrs. and up; Christian.

CLARETIAN VOLUNTEERS (WEST)
5562 Clayton Rd., Concord, CA 94521. (510) 672-6246
Contact: Bro. Larry Moen, CMF
Mission Area: Oakland, California
Type of Service: varied ministries serving the needy

Term of Service: 1 year
Basic Requirements: M/F; single/
married w/o dependents; college
degree or practical work experience.

CND MINISTRY PROGRAM
106 Almy St., Providence, RI 02909.
(401) 621-5347
Contact: Sr. Mary Ann Rossi, CND
Mission Areas: Many areas of US (NY,
RI, CT, FL, SD, AZ)
Type of Service: ministry to poor in
educational setting
Term of Service: Week or weeks -
semester breaks
Basic Requirements: M/F; college
students; 20 to 25.

COLUMBAN FATHERS LAY MISSIONARY PROGRAM
St. Columbans, NE 68056. (402) 291-
1920
Contact: Fr. Mark Mengel
Mission Areas: Asia, Latin America,
West Indies
Type of Service: community work,
catechetics, youth work, workers
apostolate
Term of Service: 3 years
Basic Requirements: M/F; single/
married; 23 to 40 years; practicing
Catholics.

COLUMBIAN HOUSE- CATHOLIC CHARITIES OF ORANGE COUNTY
1506 Brookhollow-Suite 112, Santa
Ana, CA 92705. (714) 662-7500
Contact: Teresa Smith, MSW
Mission Area: Orange Co., California
Type of Service: child care (develop-
mentally disabled)
Term of Service: 6 months minimum
Basic Requirements: F; single; 18 and
up.

COMMISSION ON RELIGION IN APPALACHIA (CORA)
111 Crutcher Pike, Richmond, KY
40475-8606. (606) 623-0429
Contact: John A. Mac Lean
Mission Areas: Appalachian states
Type of Service: community work,
education, health care, office work,
home repair
Term of Service: 3-12 months; work-
camps-1 week (spring, summer); also
summer camp counsellors
Basic Requirements: M/F; single/ mar-
ried/ divorced/separated/religious.

COMMUNITY SERVICE CORPS
1654 West Onondaga St., Syracuse,
NY 13204. (315) 474-7428
Contact: Felicia Castricone
Mission Area: Syracuse (NY)
Type of Service: community work
Term of Service: 1 year
Basic Requirements: M/F; at least 2
years college/experience.

COMPANIONS IN MISSION
Sisters of St. Joseph, St. Joseph
Convent, Baden, PA 15005. (412)
321-0433.
Contact: Betty Adams, C.S.J.
Mission Area: Pittsburgh, PA and
surrounding area
Type of Service: education, child care,
social service, health care
Term of Service: 1 year (renewable up
to 5 years)
Basic Requirements: M/F; 21 and up;
college degree and/or work
experience.

COVENANT HOUSE FAITH COMMUNITY
346 W. 17th St., New York, NY 10011.
(212) 727-4971
Contact: Orientation Director
Mission Areas: New York City, Houston, Ft. Lauderdale, Toronto, New
Orleans, Anchorage, Los Angeles.
Type of Service: street outreach,
crisis-intervention, case management,
long-term residential programs, phone
hotline, education, health care, legal,
and office work
Term of Service: 13 months minimum
Basic Requirements: M/F; single/
married/religious/divorced; between 21
and 65; Catholic (welcomes those of
other Christian traditions).

C.PP.S. VOLUNTEER PROGRAM
204 North Main St., O'Fallon, MO
63366-2299 (314) 240-3420
Contact: Sr. Elaine Lamm, C.PP.S.
Mission Areas: Primarily Missouri,
New Mexico, Texas; Bolivia, South
America
Type of Service: care of elderly,
clerical work, food pantry, shelter,
Head Start, teacher's aide, parish
work, housecleaning, yard work,
teaching religion, crafts
Term of Service: 1 week or longer
Basic Requirements: F; 18-45.

CSJ SHARED MINISTRY
P.O. Box 279, Concordia, KS 66901.
(913) 243-2149
Contact: Christine Doman, CSJ
Mission Areas: Southwest, Midwest,
Southeast (wherever a Sister of St.
Joseph of Concordia serves)
Type of Service: community social/
ministry services, education (non-
conventional), cross-cultural; handi-
capped; rural/nonrural; all ages
Term of Service: 6 weeks summer;
extended to year long
Basic Requirements: M/F; 20+.

CSJ SUMMER MINISTRY PROGRAM
Sisters of St. Joseph of Boston, 21
Milwood St., Dorchester, MA 02124.
(617) 782-1547
Contact: Mary Ann Crowley, C.S.J.
Mission Area: Greater Boston area
Type of Service: ministry with home-
less, youth, people with AIDS, par-
ishes in inner cities
Term of Service: month of July
Basic Requirements: F; college age
and up.

DAMIEN MINISTRIES: PASTORAL CARE FOR PEOPLE LIVING WITH AIDS
P.O. Box 10202, Washington, DC
20018. (202) 387-2926
Contact: Lillian Needham, SSJ
Mission Area: Washington, DC
Type of Service: ministry to people
with AIDS (operate a home for ex-
offenders on medical parole, support
groups, retreats, prison and nursing
home outreach, foodbank for HIV-
infected), education, health care, office
work
Term of Service: 1 full year or more
Basic Requirements: M/F; some
experience with HIV/AIDS; opportunity
for community experience; college
graduate or comparable age or older;
HIV-infected persons invited to apply.

DIOCESE OF TULSA – CATHOLIC CHARITIES
739 N. Denver, P.O. Box 6429, Tulsa,
OK 74148. (918) 585-8167
Contact: Dr. Edward L. Maillet
Mission Area: Eastern Oklahoma
Type of Service: community work
Term of Service: 1 year (renewable)
Basic Requirements: M/F; single/
married/religious; 21 years and up;
Catholic.

DOMINICAN TEACHER RECRUITMENT PROGRAM
St. Catherine's Convent, 211 Essex
Ave., Spring Lake, NJ 07762. (908)
449-6199, ext. 126 (after 4 pm EST)
Contact: Rosalie Prew, O.P.
Mission Areas: Abaco Island,
Bahamas
Type of Service: catechetics, com-
munity work, education, health care,
office work
Term of Service: 1 year (renewable
2nd year)
Basic Requirements: M/F; single/
married/divorced/separated/religious;
20 and up; Christian; teaching certi-
fication

DOWNEY SIDE–FAMILIES FOR YOUTH
P.O. Box 2139, New York, NY 10116-
2139. (212) 714-2230
Contact: Fr. Paul Engel, OFM Cap.
Mission Areas: New York City,
Springfield (MA), Hartford (CT)
Type of Service: community work,
office work, youth counselor
Term of Service: 1 year (renewable)
Basic Requirements: M/F; single/
married; 23+ years; nondenomin-
ational.

EDMUNDITE MISSIONS CORPS
707 Arsenal Pl., Selma, AL 36701-4628. (205) 874-3798
Contact: Fr. Stephen Hornat
Mission Area: Selma (surrounding rural areas), New Orleans
Type of Service: health clinics, youth work, aged, community work, tutoring, social work
Term of Service: 1 year
Basic Requirements: M/F; single/married; 21 and up; practicing Catholic.

EMMAUS HOUSE/HARLEM
P.O. Box 1177, New York, NY 10035. (212) 410-6006
Contacts: Steven Delk; Fr. Justin
Mission Area: Harlem (N.Y.C.)
Type of Service: community work, office work, poor, homeless ministry
Term of Service: 1 year; summer program (limited)
Basic Requirements: M/F; single/married.

EXODUS HOUSE/SOME (SO OTHERS MIGHT EAT)
Rt. 1, Box 602, Highview, WV 26808. (304) 856-3417
Contact: Judith McDaniel
Mission Area: rural West Virginia
Type of Service: counseling, community work, office work
Term of Service: year long (renewable)
Basic Requirements: M/F; single/married/widowed/religious/disabled; 20 and up.

FATHER CARR'S PLACE 2B
1965 Oshkosh Ave., Oshkosh, WI 54901-2600. (414) 231-2378
Contact: Fr. Martin P. Carr
Mission Area: Oshkosh
Type of Service: community work, health care, soup kitchen, food pantry, domestic violence shelter, mission
Term of Service: 3 weeks to 1 year (or more)
Basic Requirements: all accepted.

FRANCIS HOUSE, INC.
2226 Maryland Ave., Baltimore, MD 21218. (410) 235-2588
Contacts: Sr. Kathleen DeLancey, OSF; Sr. Patricia McAlpin, OSF
Mission Area: Baltimore (MD)
Type of Service: direct service to the poor
Term of Service: 11 months
Basic Requirements: M/F; single; 21 and up.

FRANCISCAN COMPANIONS IN MISSION
Our Lady of Angels Convent, 609 S. Convent Rd., Aston, PA 19014. (215) 459-4687
Contact: Sr. Jean Ustasiewski, OSF
Mission Areas: Continental US

Type of Service: education, health care, social and pastoral work
Term of Service: 1 to 2 years (renewable)
Basic Requirements: M/F; single/married/widowed; 21 and up; Christian.

FRANCISCAN COVENANT PROGRAM
P.O. Box 970, San Juan Bautista, CA 95045-1070. (408) 623-2412
Contact: Bob or Ruth Ward, Directors
Mission Areas: Arizona, California
Type of Service: administration, receptionist, bookkeeper, accountant, office work, health care, cook, maintenance, kitchen, housekeeping, gift shop, gardening, grounds
Term of Service: 1-3 years
Basic Requirements: single/married couples w/o dependents/ divorced; Catholic; 20-65.

FRANCISCAN LAY VOLUNTEER PROGRAM
4860 W. 29th St., Cicero, IL 60650. (708) 656-7274
Contact: Carol A. DeFiore, Director
Mission Areas: Midwestern and Southern states
Type of Service: parish work, HIV/AIDS service agencies, educational facilities, outreach to the homeless poor
Term of Service: 1 year – renewable.
Basic Requirements: M/F; 22 and up; college graduate.

FRANCISCAN MISSION SERVICE OF NORTH AMERICA
P.O. Box 29034, Washington, DC 20017-0034. (202) 832-1762
Contact: Sr. Jean Amore, SMIC
Mission Area: Central America, Bolivia, Zambia, Thailand and other Franciscan missions.
Type of Service: health care, teachers, social workers, counselors, community developers, agriculturist
Term of Service: 3 months orientation plus 3 years service
Basic Requirements: M/F; single/married; 23 to 45; Catholic.

FRANCISCAN OUTREACH ASSOCIATION
1645 W. Le Moyne St., Chicago, IL 60622. (312) 278-6724
Contacts: Fr. Albert Merz, O.F.M.; Marianne Flesher
Mission Areas: greater Chicago metropolitan area
Type of Service: overnight shelter, transitional shelter for substance abuse recovery; dining room, showers/laundry, AIDS ministry.
Term of Service: 6 mos - 1 year (renewable), summer, interim/holidays program
Basic Requirements: M/F; single/married w/o dependents; college age and up; preferably Catholic.

FRANCISCAN SERVICE PROGRAM
716 Bakewell St., Covington, KY 41011. (606) 431-3202
Contact: Director
Mission Area: Midwestern U.S.
Type of Service: community work, education, inner-city ministry
Term of Service: 1 year
Basic Requirements: M/F; single/married; 21 and up.

FRANCISCAN VOLUNTEER MINISTRY
1802 E. Hagert St., Philadelphia, PA 19125. (215) 427-3070
Contacts: Stephanie DeBenedetti, Program Director; Fr. Michael Duffy, Executive Director
Mission Areas: Buffalo, NY; Philadelphia, PA; Boston, MA
Type of Service: soup kitchens, food and clothing distribution and shelters
Term of Service: 1 year
Basic Requirements: M/F; single; Christian; 18 and up.

FRATERNITY JEANNE JUGAN
Little Sisters of the Poor, 601 Maiden Choice Lane, 21228. (410) 744-9367
Contact: Sr. Constance Carolyn, l.s.p.
Mission Areas: U.S. and Canada, foreign service possible
Type of Service: caring for needy elderly in Homes for Aged and day centers; community prayer and apostolic initiatives.
Term of Service: 1 year of formation, renewed annually, commitment implies permanency. (Also possible to volunteer in a Home without the commitment of the Fraternity member, for any length of time.)
Basic Requirements: (for Fraternity only): F; single/widowed; Catholic; 20-50.

FREEDOM HOUSE
P.O. Box 12144, Richmond, VA 23241. (804) 649-9791
Contact: Joel Ford, Executive Director
Mission Area: Richmond, VA
Type of Service: catechetics, community work, education, office work
Term of Service: 1 to 2 years
Basic Requirements: M/F; 19 and up.

GLENMARY HOME MISSIONERS
P.O. Box 465618, Cincinnati, OH 45246-5618. (513) 874-8900
Contact: Vocation Director
Mission Areas: 12 states in Appalachia, the South and Southwest
Type of Service: founding Catholic communities & community work.
Term of Service: 1 week; summer & winter programs
Basic Requirements: M; single; 18 to 45 generally; Catholic.

GLENMARY SISTERS' LAY MISSIONERS
405 West Parrish Ave., P.O. Box 22264, Owensboro, KY 42304-2264. (502) 686-8401
Contact: Membership Team: Sr. Mae Koenig, Mrs. Barbara O'Nan
Mission Area: rural areas of Appalachia, the deep South
Type of Service: missionary services with the poor and unchurched: social work, community work, evangelization, ecumenism, counseling, working with issues of injustice, religious education, pastoral associate.
Term of Service: 3 years (renewable); orientation/formation program
Basic Requirements: F; 21 yrs. old and over; Catholic.

GOOD SHEPHERD VOLUNTEERS
12 W. 12th St., New York, NY 10011. (212) 242-3815.
Contact: Maureen McGovern, RGS
Mission Area: New York City, New Jersey, Philadelphia
Type of Service: family and youth services
Term of Service: 1 to 2 years
Basic Requirements: M/F; single; over 21, college or 2 years work experience.

GREY NUNS – PARTNERS IN MINISTRY
10 Pelham Rd., Lexington, MA 02173-5799. (617) 862-4700
Contact: Sr. Marie Mansfield
Mission Areas: New England, Ohio
Type of Service: health care, elderly, homeless, social services, Spanish ministry
Term of Service: 1 year (renewable), summer
Basic Requirements: F; single; 21 and up.

HABITAT FOR HUMANITY INTERNATIONAL
Human Resources Dept., 121 Habitat St., Americus, GA 31709-3498. (912) 924-6935
Contact: Martha Morgan
Mission Areas: U.S., Canada, Latin America, Africa, Asia, Pacific Islands
Type of Service: community work, office work, housing ministry
Term of Service: 3 years (overseas); 3 months to 1 year (North America)
Basic Requirements: M/F; single/married (dependents ok); 18 and up (North America); 21 and up (overseas).

HAND OF HELP – CHRISTIAN SERVICE
2401 Carr St., St. Louis, MO 63106. (314) 231-8870
Contact: Fred Buerman
Mission Area: Colon, Mexico
Type of Service: social work, catechetics, community work

Term of Service: 12 months (renewable)
Basic Requirements: M/F; bilingual (Spanish).

HANDS TOGETHER
P.O. Box 80985, Springfield, MA 01138. (413) 731-7716; (609) 252-0552
Contacts: Douglas Campbell; Fr. Tom Hagan
Mission Areas: U.S., Haiti, Jamaica, Mexico, Venezuela
Type of Service: community work, education, health care, agriculture, technicians, construction, children's services
Term of Service: 1-3 months; 1 year (renewable)
Basic Requirements: M/F; single/married; 21 and older; college graduate or work experience.

HOLY CROSS ASSOCIATES
P.O. Box 668, Moreau Seminary, Notre Dame, IN 46556. (219) 631-5521
Contact: John Pinter
Mission Areas: Portland, OR; Phoenix, AZ; Oakland, CA; Colorado Springs, CO; Brockton, MA; Wilkes-Barre, PA; Santiago, Chile; Pocuro, Chile
Type of Service: teaching, social work, outreach
Term of Service: August through following July (US), 2-1/2 years (Chile)
Basic Requirements: M/F; single; 21 and up; Christian.

HOPE (HOLY OUTREACH TO THE POOR THROUGH EVANGELIZATION)
5058 S. Ashland, P.O. Box 09168, Chicago, IL 60609-0168. (312) 778-5955
Contact: Fr. Augustin Milon, OFM
Mission Area: Chicago, IL
Type of Service: 1 year (renewable)
Basic Requirements: M/F; single/married w/o dependents/widowed; Christian; functional Spanish and Polish helpful.

HUMILITY OF MARY SERVICE
19220 Lorain Rd., Fairview Park, OH 44126.
Contact: Sr. Kathleen King, HM
Mission Areas: FL, WV, AZ, IL, OH, El Salvador
Type of Service: social work, community work, nursing, parish outreach
Term of Service: 1 year (long term); short term varies
Basic Requirements: M/F; 18 and up.

IDAHO MONASTIC LIVING EXPERIENCE
Monastery of St. Gertrude, HC 3 Box 121, Cottonwood, ID 83522. (208) 962-3224
Contact: Corinne Forsman, O.S.B.
Mission Areas: rural Idaho

Type of Service: join in monastic life, particularly in aspects of community, prayer and outside work.
Term of Service: 2 weeks in July
Basic Requirements: Female, single, 18-45.

IHM VOLUNTEER PROGRAM
502 West Elm Ave., Monroe, MI 48162. (313) 457-4140
Contact: Evelyn Craig, IHM
Mission Area: varied sites
Type of Service: ministry with Hispanics, migrant workers, refugees, women and children, homeless
Term of Service: summer, 1 full year
Basic Requirements: M/F; single/married w/o dependents; 21 and up; 2 years of college or work experience

INNER-CITY TEACHING CORPS
2648 West Pershing Rd., Chicago, IL 60632. (312) 579-0150
Contact: Rick Swanson
Mission Area: Chicago
Type of Service: teachers, inner-city elementary schools
Term of Service: 2 years
Basic Requirements: M/F; single; 21-30; college degree.

INTERNATIONAL CHRISTIAN YOUTH EXCHANGE (ICYE)
134 W. 26th St., New York, NY 10001. (212) 206-7307
Contact: Heather Hutchens
Mission Areas: Throughout the U.S., Europe, Central America, Scandinavia, Africa and Asia
Type of Service: catechetics, community work, education, farming, health care, office work
Term of Service: year long; 6 months
Basic Requirements: M/F; age requirements vary (18-26 most countries, some countries through 30 yrs.); no religious or marital requirements apply.

JESUIT VOLUNTEER CORPS
EAST: 18th & Thompson Sts., Philadelphia, PA 19121. (215) 232-0300
MIDWEST: P.O. Box 32692, Detroit, MI 48232. (313) 841-4420
NORTHWEST: P.O. Box 3928, Portland, OR 97208-3928. (503) 335-8202
SOUTHWEST: P.O. Box 3266, Berkeley, CA 94703. (510) 653-8564
SOUTH: P.O. Box 3126, Houston, TX 77253. (713) 756-5095
INTERNATIONAL: P.O. Box 25478, Washington, DC 20007. (202) 687-1132
Contact: office nearest the area in which you wish to serve
Mission Areas: Throughout the U.S. and in Micronesia, Nepal, Belize, Peru, Jamaica, Tanzania.
Type of Service: International ministry is primarily in Education (including Science and Math) youth work, legal

issues, AIDS ministry, emergency assistance, education, health care, housing issues, immigration, advocacy, etc.
Term of Service: 1 year (Aug. to Aug. domestic); 2 years (international)
Basic Requirements: M/F; single/married—no dependents; college degree for most positions; over 21; Christian.

JOSEPH HOUSE VOLUNTEERS
P.O. Box 1755, Salisbury, MD 21802-1755. (410) 543-1645
Contacts: Sr. Mary Elizabeth Gintling, Sr. Connie Ladd
Mission Areas: MD, DE, VA, Bolivia (near future)
Type of Service: any gifts and skills are useful
Term of Service: 1 year (renewable)
Basic Requirements: M/F; single/married/widowed/divorced/religious; 21 and up; Christian.

LALMBA ASSOCIATION
7685 Quartz St., Arvada, CO 80007. (303) 420-1810
Contact: Marty Downey
Mission Areas: Sudan and Kenya, East Africa; Mexico
Type of Service: medicine, nursing, health care
Term of Service: 1 to 2 years
Basic Requirements: M/F; single/married/widowed/religious/disabled; Christian.

LAMP MINISTRIES COMMUNITY
2704 Schurz Ave., Bronx, NY 10465. (718) 409-5062
Contacts: Tom and Lyn Scheuring, Ed and Marybeth Greene
Mission Areas: Metropolitan New York, Upper Appalachia
Type of Service: ministries of Catholic evangelization, in materially poor parishes and with the homeless, sick and disabled
Term of Service: 1 year minimum, community living
Basic Requirements: M/F; single/married/religious; over 22; Catholic.

L'ARCHE COMMUNITIES
Contact: Linda Gasparini
L'ARCHE CLEVELAND
P.O. Box 20450, 2630 E. 127th St., Cleveland, OH 44120. (216) 721-5719
L'ARCHE EASTERN U.S. REGION
2122 California St., Apt. 662 N.W., Washington, DC 20008-1803. (202) 387-7529
Contact: Carole Brown
THE ARCH
P.O. Box 0278, Clinton, IA 52732. (319) 243-9035
Contact: JoAnne Horstmann
IRENICON
73 Lamoille Ave., Bradford, MA 01835. (508) 374-6928

Contact: Barbara A. McEndarfer, Director
COMMUNITY OF THE ARK
2474 Ontario Rd., N.W., Washington, DC 20009. (202) 232-4539
Contact: Dennis Calderone
FRIENDS OF L'ARCHE
523 W.8th St., Erie, PA 16502. (814) 452-2065
Contact: Steve Washek
L'ARCHE HEARTLAND
P.O. Box 40493, Overland Park, KS 66204-4493. (913) 341-2265
Contact: Michael Wilks
L'ARCHE HARBOR HOUSE
700 Arlington Rd., Jacksonville, FL 32211. (904) 725-7740
Contact: Dottie Klein
L'ARCHE MOBILE AND CENTRAL U.S. REGION
151 S. Ann St., Mobile, AL 36604-2302. (205) 438-2094
Contact: Marty O'Malley
NOAH SEALTH
816 15th Ave. E., Seattle, WA 98112. (206) 325-9434
Contact: Jennifer Kelly
L'ARCHE SPOKANE
E. 703 Nora, Spokane, WA 99207. (509) 324-8616
Contact: Joe Gaffney-Brown
L'ARCHE SYRACUSE
1232 Teall Ave., Syracuse, NY 13206. (315) 479-8088
Contact: Bob Sackel
L'ARCHE TAHOMA HOPE
Tahoma Hope, 11716 Vickery Rd. E., Tacoma, WA 98446. (206) 535-3178
Contact: Shannon Ronald
L'ARCHE NEHALEM
8501 SE Stephens, Portland, OR 97216. (503) 251-6901
Mission Areas: Alabama, Florida, Iowa, Massachusetts, Oregon, Pennsylvania, Ohio, Washington (DC), New York, Kansas, State of Washington
Type of Service: live-in residence for developmentally disabled adults
Term of Service: 1 year to long term (flexible); some summer programs
Basic Requirements: M/F; single/married/religious; over 18.

LASALLIAN VOLUNTEERS
4351 Garden City Dr., Suite 200, Landover, MD 20785. (800) 433-7593
Contact: John Garry
Mission Areas: many cities in U.S.; limited places overseas
Type of Service: education, cathechetics, community work
Term of Service: 1 year domestic (renewable); 2 years international (renewable)
Basic Requirements: M/F; 21 and up; college degree or comparable work experience.

THE LAY MISSION – HELPERS ASSOCIATION
1531 West 9th St., Los Angeles, CA 90015. (213) 251-3222
Contact: Msgr. Michael Meyers
Mission Areas: Africa, Papua New Guinea, Micronesia, Thailand, Pacific Islands
Type of Service: education, engineering/construction, health care, office/computer work, finance/administration
Term of Service: 2 or 3 years
Basic Requirements: M/F; single/married; over 21.

LAY MISSIONARY APOSTOLATE OF THE HOLY WORD
c/o St. Peter's Parish, 1200 Florida St., San Francisco, CA 94110. (415) 282-1652
Contact: Brother Daniel, H.W.M.
Mission Areas: throughout the U.S.
Type of Service: dedicated to bringing the "Holy Word" to the poor and homeless (Mt. 4:4)
Term of Service: 6 months to 3 years, or more
Basic Requirements: M/F; married couples; Catholic; 18 and up; caring.

LAY VOLUNTEER PROGRAM OF THE ARCHDIOCESE OF BOSTON
c/o Office for Pastoral Ministries, Tribunal Building, 1 Lake St., Brighton, MA 02135. (617) 782-6675
Contact: Barbara Shine
Mission Area: Archdiocese of Boston: inner city, suburbs
Type of Service: community work, parish ministry, teaching, youth ministry
Term of Service: 1 year
Basic Requirements: M/F; single; young adults (20's & 30's) college degree or equivalent experience; Catholic.

THE LAY VOLUNTEERS OF JEAN BAPTISTE
Benilde Hall, 1600 Paseo, Kansas City, MO 64108-1690. (816) 842-5836
Contact: Stephen B. Sullivan, L.V.J.B.
Mission Area: Kansas City (MO)
Type of Service: community work, education, drug & alcohol residental program
Term of Service: 1 year (renewable)
Basic Requirements: M; single/divorced/separated; over 18; Catholic preferred.

LSAV (LITTLE SISTERS OF THE ASSUMPTION VOLUNTEERS)
214 E. 30th St., New York, NY 10016. (212) 889-4310
Contact: Coordinator
Mission Areas: Massachusetts, New York, Pennsylvania
Type of Service: child care and youth workers, social workers, van drivers, community health nurses, shelter staff, advocate and counselors, teachers, ESL and GED tutors, computer data

entry, clerical, thrift shop workers, organizers for food banks, etc.; summer youth programs seek recreational, organizational, creative talents
Term of Service: 2 months to 2 years (preferably 1 year); summer program
Basic Requirements: M/F; 20 and up; any religion.

LIVING WORD VOLUNTEER PROGRAM
800 N. Fernandez-B, Arlington Heights, IL 60004. (708) 577-5972
Contact: Donna M. Williams, SLW
Mission Areas: Midwest & southern U.S.
Type of Service: varies
Term of Service: One year
Basic Requirements: F; single/married; 20 or older, able to live/ work well with others.

LONG TERM MISSION PROGRAM OF THE DIOCESE OF ORLANDO
Mission Office, P.O. Box 1800, Orlando, FL 32802-1800. (407) 425-3556
Contact: Sr. Bernadette Mackay, O.S.U.
Mission Area: Dominican Republic
Type of Service: assignments vary
Term of Service: 1 year, 3 years
Basic Requirements: M/F; single/married/widowed/religious; college graduate.

LORETTO VOLUNTEERS
Sisters of Loretto and Loretto Co-Members, c/o 16 Hillcrest Ct., San Anselmo, CA 94960.
Contact: Therese Stawowy .
Mission Areas: mainly in the Midwest: Denver, CO; St. Louis, MO; some locales in the Southwest and East (Washington, DC)
Type of Service: community work, education, tutoring, office work, recreation, shelter for abused women, emergency assistance centers, work with elderly
Term of Service: short term: 3 months; long term: 6 months-1 year
Basic Requirements: M/F; single; 20 or older.

LOS ANGELES CATHOLIC WORKER
632 N. Britannia St., Los Angeles, CA 90033. (213) 267-8789
Contact: Jeff Dietrich
Mission Area: Los Angeles and environs
Type of Service: community work, health care
Term of Service: 1 year; summer program-8 weeks
Basic Requirements: M/F; single/married, dependents negotiable; Spanish speaking helpful; 19 years and up.

MARIANIST VOLUNTARY SERVICE COMMUNITIES (MVSC)
P.O. Box 9224, Wright Brothers Branch, Dayton, OH 45409. (513) 229-4630 or (513) 229-3287
Contact: Laura Libertore
Mission Areas: Dayton, Cleveland, Cincinnati, OH; Covington, KY; Rockaway, NY
Type of Service: social work, education, community work, legal, office work
Term of Service: 1 year (renewable); summer program
Basic Requirements: M/F; single/married/divorced (without dependents); 20 and up; Christian.

MARIST VOLUNTEER PROGRAM
26 First Ave., Pelham, NY 10803. (914) 738-8640
Contact: Br. Frank Kelly, FMS
Mission Areas: US and Mexico
Type of Service: education, counseling, community work, shelter, soup kitchen, etc.
Term of Service: 1 year (renewable)
Basic Requirements: M/F; single; 21 and up; Christian.

MARY HOUSE OF HOSPITALITY
3359 Hwy. G, Wisconsin Dells, WI 53965. (608) 586-4447
Contact: Cassandra Dixon
Mission Area: Wisconsin
Type of Service: domestic work, gardening, food pantry, shelter, drivers to assist guests visiting prison
Term of Service: summer: 2 week minimum; year round: 1 month minimum
Basic Requirements: 21 and over.

MARYKNOLL MISSION ASSOCIATION OF THE FAITHFUL (MMAF)
Box 307, Maryknoll, NY 10545-0307. (914) 762-6364
Contact: Kathy Wright
Mission Areas: Bolivia, Brazil, Cambodia, Chile, Japan, Kenya, Mexico, Nicaragua, Peru, Salvador, Tanzania, Thailand, Venezuela, Vietnam
Type of Service: agriculture, communications, catechetics, education, health care, community work, pastoral, leadership training
Term of Service: 3-1/2 years
Basic Requirements: M/F; 24 to 45 (generally); single/married with/ without dependents, families with no more than 2 children no older than 8 yrs.

MENNONITE VOLUNTARY SERVICE
Box 347, Newton, KS 67114. (316) 283-5100
Contact: Kristen Mayhue
Mission Areas: Colorado, Ohio, Texas, California, Kansas, Arizona, Illinois,

Missouri, Minnesota, Washington; Canada (Ontario, Manitoba, Saskatchewan)
Type of Service: community work, education, health care, office work, housing rehabilitation, peace and justice, social service, child care
Term of Service: 1-3 years; short-term 1-11 months
Basic Requirements: M/F; single/married; 18 years and up; Christian.

MERCY CORPS
Gwynedd-Mercy College, Gwynedd Valley, PA 19437. (215) 641-5535
Contact: Sr. Eileen Campbell, R.S.M.
Mission Areas: different areas in U.S.
Type of Service: education, health care, social services, community work
Term of Service: 1 to 2 years (renewable)
Basic Requirements: M/F; single/married w/o dependents; 21 and over; ecumenical.

MILFORD SPIRITUAL CENTER YOUTH MINISTRY INTERNSHIP
5361 S. Milford Rd., Milford, OH 45150-9744. (513) 248-3500
Contact: Thomas J. Sheibley
Mission Area: Milford, OH (Cincinnati area)
Type of Service: youth retreat team
Term of Service: 9 months (school year)
Basic Requirements: M/F; single/married/religious.

MILWAUKEE GROVE HOUSE
753 Scotland St., Dunedin, FL 34698. (813) 736-6632
Contact: Jack Bray
Mission Area: Dunedin, FL
Type of Service: work with the elderly in small group home
Term of Service: 1 year (renewable)
Basic Requirements: M/F; single/married no dependents/widowed/religious; 30 to 80.

MISERICORDIA HOME
6300 North Ridge, Chicago,IL 60660. (312) 973-6300
Contact: Kathleen Ludwig
Mission Area: Chicago (IL)
Type of Service: working with people with mental and/or physical disability in residential, vocational and recreational environments
Term of Service: minimum 2 to 3 hours per week
Basic Requirements: at least 16; desire to work with people with mental disability.

MISSION DOCTORS ASSOCIATION
1531 W. Ninth St., Los Angeles, CA 90015. (818) 285-8868
Contact: Elise Frederick
Mission Area: Africa, Papua (New

Guinea)
Type of Service: health care
Term of Service: 2 to 3 years plus training period
Basic Requirements: Doctors and their families.

MISSION HELPERS OF THE SACRED HEART

1001 W. Joppa Rd., Baltimore, MD 21204. (410) 823-8585, ext. 246
Contact: Sr. Judy Waldt, MHSH
Mission Areas: 17 states throughout the U.S., Puerto Rico, Venezuela
Type of Service: religious education (adults, youth and children), advocates for handicapped and hearing impaired, Hispanic ministry, youth and campus ministries, pastoral care and comfort to hospital patients and families of the terminally ill, family counseling, developing leadership among African-American Catholics.
Term of Service: 1 year (renewable)
Basic Requirements: F; single; 20's-30's; Catholic.

MISSIONARY CENACLE VOLUNTEERS

107 Holy Trinity Rd., Holy Trinity, AL 36859. (205) 855-4473
Contact: Dr. Harold Grant
Mission Areas: Throughout the U.S.; Mexico; Puerto Rico; Costa Rica
Type of Service: catechetics, community work, education, health care, office work
Term of Service: 1 year or summer (1-2 months)
Basic Requirements: M/F; fluency in Spanish for Hispanic ministry.

MISSIONARY OBLATES OF MARY IMMACULATE LAY MISSIONARY PROGRAM

Southern US Provinces, 7711 Madonna Dr., San Antonio, TX 78216. (210) 349-1475
Contact: Director of Oblate Lay Missionary Program
Mission Area: Zambia
Type of Service: community work
Term of Service: 3 years
Basic Requirements: M; single/married; over 21 and under 55.

MOUNT ST. BENEDICT MONASTERY LIVE-IN VOLUNTEER PROGRAM

Mount St. Benedict Monastery, 620 E. Summit Ave., Crookston, MN 56716-2799. (218) 281-3441
Contact: Sr. Kathleen McGeary
Mission Area: Crookston, MN
Type of Service: community work, education, health care, homeless
Term of Service: 1 month to 1 year (renewable)
Basic Requirements: F; single/divorced/separated/widowed; 25 to 60.

NAZARETH FARM

Rt. 2, Box 194-3, Salem, WV 26426. (304) 782-2742
Contact: Executive Director
Mission Area: Doddridge County, West Virginia
Type of Service: community work, construction, housing rehabilitation
Term of Service: 3 to 6 months possible; 1 to 2 years preferred
Basic Requirements: M/F; single/married/widowed/ divorced/separated/religious; 21 years and up; Catholic.

NEW ORLEANS VOLUNTEER SERVICE COMMUNITY

Brothers of the Sacred Heart, 4671 Painters St., New Orleans, LA 70122-3938. (504) 282-7456; 2228
Contact: Br. Henry Gaither
Mission Areas: LA, MS, AL (England and Africa possible - 2nd year)
Type of Service: work with young people (tutoring, coach, etc.)
Term of Service: Aug. 12 to June 1
Basic Requirements: M; single; 20 to 35; Catholic.

NOTRE DAME MISSION VOLUNTEER PROGRAM

403 Markland Ave., Baltimore, MD 21212. (410) 532-6864
Contact: Sr. Katherine Corr, SND, Director
Mission Area: rural, urban U.S.
Type of Service: AIDS ministry, community organizing, counseling, literacy education, elderly outreach, fundraising, administration, group home/shelter staff, health care, Hispanic ministry, refugee services, lawyer, legal aide, migrant worker ministry, Native American ministry, nurse, parish ministry, peace & justice advocacy, prison ministry, social services, volunteer coordinator and teachers: K-12, ESL, GED.
Term of Service: 1 year renewable.
Basic Requirements: M/F; single/married w/o dependents; 21 and up; work experience and/or college education.

OFFICE OF LAY VOLUNTEERS
(Referral Agency)

Diocese of Youngstown, 144 W. Wood St., Youngstown, OH 44503. (216) 744-8451, ext. 230
Contact: Diocesan Mission Office.

OUR LITTLE BROTHERS AND SISTERS (NUESTROS PEQUENOS HERMANOS)

1210 Hillside Terrace, Alexandria, VA 22302. (703) 836-1233
Contact: Frank Krafft
Mission Areas: Mexico, Honduras, Haiti, Nicaraqua
Type of Service: catechetics, education, health care, office work, house parents
Term of Service: 1 year

Basic Requirements: M/F; single/married/divorced/separated/religious; 21 and up.

PALLOTTINE APOSTOLIC ASSOCIATES

5424 W. Bluemound Rd., Milwaukee, WI 53208. (414) 258-3633
Contact: Michael L. Hess
Mission Areas: Wisconsin, North Dakota, Germany
Type of Service: education, social work, community organizing, employment, social service, pastoral ministry
Term of Service: 1 year (renewable)
Basic Requirements: M/F; single/married without dependents; 21 or older; sense of humor.

PARACLETE CATHOLIC WORKER

411 South St., Utica, NY 13501. (315) 724-5499
Contact: John Martin
Mission Areas: Utica, Rome, NY
Type of Service: prison ministry, hospital, death and dying ministry
Term of Service: minimum of 6 months
Basic Requirements: 21 and older.

PASSIONIST LAY MISSIONERS

Western Province: 5700 N. Harlem Ave., Chicago, IL 60631-2342. (312) 631-6336
Contacts: Anne Avellone; Kris Funk
Mission Areas: Chicago, Detroit, Cincinnati
Type of Service: education, community organizing, social work, legal advocacy, youth work, housing and homelessness issues, outreach to elderly and more
Term of Service: 1 year (renewable–begins mid-August)
Basic Requirements: M/F; single/married w/o dependents; 21 and up; Christian commitment.

PASSIONIST VOLUNTEERS

Short-Term Experience: 80 David St., South River, NJ 08882. (908) 257-7177
Contact: Katie LaCarrubba
Mission Areas: Appalachian Mountains of West Virginia (other sites pending)
Type of Service: Recreation/community outreach/home repair with youth and elderly
Term of Service: 2 to 12 weeks; summer
Basic Requirements: M/F; single/married/families with children/ retirees; 18 and up, out of high school for at least one year; flexibility, sense of humor.

PROVIDENCE HOUSE

703 Lexington Ave., P.O. Box 210529, Brooklyn, NY 11221. (718) 455-0197

Contact: S. Marie Lenihan
Mission Areas: Brooklyn, Queens, Westchester County in New York
Type of Service: being present to the needs of homeless women and children
Term of Service: 1 week to 1 year
Basic Requirements: F; single/ married; 21 or older.

PROVIDENCE MINISTRIES FOR THE NEEDY, INC.
476 Appleton St., P.O. Box 6269, Holyoke, MA 01041. (413) 536-9109
Contact: Robin L. Goshea
Mission Area: Holyoke, MA (inner city)
Type of Service: community work, housekeeping services, kitchen chores, transportation of goods, pantry and clothing center coordinators
Term of Service: 1 year (renewable)
Basic Requirements: M/F; 21 and up; single/married without dependents; ability to live in Christian community.

PROVIDENCE MINISTRY VOLUNTEERS
341 Bishops Hwy., Kingston, MA 02364-2035. (617) 585-7724
Contact: Sr. Mary Francis Fletcher
Mission Areas: small towns south of Boston
Type of Service: education, pastoral care of sick, handicapped, elderly; outreach to homeless and poor as instructor, visitor, musician, caretaker, aide
Term of Service: 3 months to 1 year (renewable); up to three weeks in summer
Basic Requirements: F; single, Catholic; 18 and up (summer); F; single/ married w/o dependents; Christian; 20 and up.

PROVIDENCE SUMMER MINISTRY OUTREACH
9000 Babcock Blvd., Allison Park, PA 15101-2793. (412) 931-5241
Contact: Sr. Sharon Geibel
Mission Area: Pittsburgh
Type of Service: community work, education, health care
Term of Service: summer - 3 weeks in July; 3 months to 2 years
Basic Requirements: F; Christian; 18 and older, 21 and up - longer program; some education or work experience.

PROVIDENCE VOLUNTEER MINISTRY
Owens Hall, St. Mary of-the-Woods, IN 47876-1089. (812) 535-4193 (day); (812) 466-5897 (eve.)
Contact: Sr. Donna Butler, S.P.
Mission Areas: DC, CA, IN, IL
Type of Service: education, community services, trades, office work, parish ministries
Term of Service: short term (8 wks. minimum); long term (1-2 yrs).

Basic Requirements: M/F; single/ married; 20 and up (long term), 18 and up (short term).

QUEST
3706 Rhode Island Ave., Mt. Rainier, MD 20712-2009. (301) 277-3594
Contact: Ellen Cumming
Mission Areas: Throughout the U.S. & Tijuana, Mexico
Type of Service: education, child care, community work
Term of Service: 6 weeks (summer); 1 year (renewable; Sept. to Aug.)
Basic Requirements: M/F; single/ married/religious/disabled; 21 and older (yearlong), 18 and older (summer).

RED CLOUD VOLUNTEERS
Holy Rosary Mission, Pine Ridge, SD 57770. (605) 867-5888
Contact: Volunteer Coordinator
Mission Area: Pine Ridge Indian Reservation, SD
Type of Service: elementary & secondary education
Term of Service: 1 school year (renewable)
Basic Requirements: M/F; single/married/religious; college degree; Christian.

REDEEMER MINISTRY CORPS
521 Moredon Rd., Huntingdon Valley, PA 19006. (215) 938-0540
Contact: Maleita Gousie
Mission Areas: Philadelphia and suburbs, South Jersey
Type of Service: health care and social services, including nursing, therapies, social work, child day care, pastoral counseling, clerical work; also homeless mothers, geriatric care, hospice care
Term of Service: 1 year (renewable), one week summer
Basic Requirements: M/F; single; 20 and over (yearlong); Christian.

RESPONSIBILITY
P.O. Box 433199, San Ysidro, CA 92143-3199. (619) 428-8225
Contact: David Lynch
Mission Area: Tijuana, Mexico
Type of Service: teachers
Term of Service: summer: July; year: Sept. – June
Basic Requirements: M/F; single/ married w/o dependents; 18 and up.

RESPONSE-ABILITY
Rosemont College, Rosemont, PA 19010-1900. (610) 525-2186
Contact: Jackie Wojtusik
Mission Areas: U.S.; Dominican Republic
Type of Service: catechetics, education, community work, counseling, crafts; other opportunities in Dominican Republic

Term of Service: summer; 1 or 2 year programs
Basic Requirements: M/F; single/ married; 18 and up; ecumenical.

SACRED HEART LAY MISSIONERS
P.O. Box 222, Hales Corners, WI 53130. (414) 425-6910
Contact: Director
Mission Areas: Texas, South Dakota, Mississippi, Wisconsin
Type of Service: Various aspects of ministry among the poor: social service, child care, elderly care, abuse shelters, poverty relief services, education, catechetics, counseling.
Term of Service: 3 years
Basic Requirements: M/F; single/ married (dependents possible); 21 and older; Catholic (active in the Church).

ST. BONAVENTURE INDIAN MISSION AND SCHOOL
P.O. Box 610, Thoreau, NM 87323-0610. (505) 862-7847
Contact: Personnel Director
Mission Area: Navajo reservation (northwest NM)
Type of Service: elementary and secondary education, catechetics, community work, health care, communications, office work and counseling
Term of Service: 1 to 3 years
Basic Requirements: M/F; single/ married/divorced/separated/religious/ families with small children; over 21; Christian.

ST. FRANCIS CATHOLIC MISSION SCHOOL
P.O. Box 26, Lumberton, NM 87547. (505) 759-3252
Contact: Fr. Thomas Maikowski
Mission Area: northern New Mexico
Type of Service: primary teachers
Term of Service: 9 months
Basic Requirements: M/F; single; 21 and up; Catholic (preferred).

ST. GERARD HOUSE
P.O. Box 4382, St. Augustine, FL 32085. (904) 829-5516
Contact: Caroline A. Wolff
Mission Areas: St. Augustine, FL
Type of Service: teaching, counseling, house parent to unwed, pregnant teenagers and women
Term of Service: 1 year (minimum)
Basic Requirements: College degree, teaching certificate (for teacher), willingness to understand trauma of unwanted pregnancies and uphold Christian morality.

ST. JOSEPH'S CATHOLIC WORKER HOUSE
P.O. Box 1062, Rochester, NY 14603. (716) 232-3262
Contact: Volunteer Coordinator

Mission Area: Rochester
Type of Service: work with poor and homeless of Rochester, NY in soup kitchen, shelter and outreach
Term of Service: 6 months to 1 year
Basic Requirements: M/F; ability to get along with others in a diverse Catholic worker community setting.

ST. JOSEPH'S INDIAN SCHOOL
P.O. Box 89, Chamberlain, SD 57325. (605) 734-6021
Contact: Kimberley Tyrell
Mission Area: Chamberlain
Type of Service: Native American ministry: child care, houseparent, nursing, teaching
Term of Service: 1 year
Basic Requirements: M/F; single/ married/disabled; 21 and up (preferred).

ST. KEVIN VICTORY CORPS
35 Virginia St., Dorchester, MA 02125. (617) 436-2771
Contact: Rev. Joseph J. Kierce
Mission Area: Inner-city Boston (MA)
Type of Service: education, health, catechetics, community work, music, house staff, carpenter, maintenance
Term of Service: 1, 2, or 3 years
Basic Requirements: M/F; single/ married; over 18.

ST. VINCENT PALLOTTI CENTER FOR APOSTOLIC DEVELOPMENT
(Clearinghouse/long-term volunteer - Referral agency).
National Office: P.O. Box 893-Cardinal Station, Washington, DC 20064. (202) 529-3330
Contacts: Andrew Thompson, National Director; Susan Marble, Program Director; Susie Mullaney, Volunteer Contact
REGIONAL OFFICES:
Boston, MA
St. Vincent Pallotti Center, 159 Washington St., Brighton, MA 02135. (617) 783-3924
Contact: Patrick Marcham, Director
Memphis, TN
St. Vincent Pallotti Center, 85 N. Cleveland, Box 41679, Memphis, TN 38174-1679. (901) 722-4758
Contact: Betty Wallin, Director
Paterson, NJ
St. Vincent Pallotti Center, 44 Ward St., Paterson, NJ 07505. (201) 523-1544
Contact: Linda Ferriero, Director
St. Louis, MO
St. Vincent Pallotti Center, 4532 Lindell Blvd., St. Louis, MO 63108. (314) 367-5500
Contact: Joan Smith, Director
Northern California
St. Vincent Pallotti Center, 5890 Newman Court, Rm. 14, Sacramento, CA 95819. (916) 454-4320
Contact: Wendy Borchers, Director

SALESIAN LAY MISSIONERS
148 Main St., New Rochelle, NY 10802. (914) 636-4225
Contact: Rev. Gennaro Sesto
Mission Areas: Dominican Republic, Mexico, Bolivia, Brazil, Colombia, Ecuador, Liberia, Sierra Leone, Ethiopia, Papua New Guinea, Alabama, Florida, Massachusetts, New York, New Jersey.
Type of Service: youth minister, religious education, staff for recreation/ camp services, rural life ministry, counselor, pastoral/parish minister, maintenance worker, nurse, nurse's aide, physical therapist, agriculture/ animal husbandry worker, building tradesman, Hispanic ministry
Term of Service: 2 years ordinarily; 1 year by arrangement; summer programs
Basic Requirements: M/F; single/ married; 20 and over; Christian commitment.

S.A.L.T.
(Serve and Learn Together)
402 S. Independence Blvd., Romeoville, IL 60441-2238. (815) 834-4028
Contact: Thomas L. Garlitz
Mission Area: Diocese of Joliet, IL
Type of Service: parish ministry, community work, social work, peace and justice advocacy
Term of Service: 1 year
Basic Requirements: M/F; single; Christian; 2 years college or work experience; 20 and up.

SCALABRINIAN MISSION EXPERIENCE
St. Charles House of Studies, 168-41 84th Ave., Jamaica, NY 11432. (718) 526-3917 or (718) 291-1678
Contact: Rev. Mariano Cisco, C.S.
Mission Areas: Immokalee, FL; Tijuana, Mexico
Type of Service: migrant worker ministry, immigration/refugee services
Term of Service: summer or winter; 3 months to 1 year
Basic Requirements: M; single; between 17 and 35 years; Catholic.

SCHOOL SISTERS OF NOTRE DAME LAY VOLUNTEERS: NATIONAL & INTERNATIONAL
Baltimore, MD: 6401 N. Charles, Baltimore, MD 21212. (410) 377-5179
Contact: Marguerite Weiler, SSND
Mankato, MN/Milwaukee, WI: 1233 N. Marshall St., Milwaukee, WI 53202. (414) 278-7300
Contact: Kay Jarema, SSND
St. Louis, MO: 320 E. Ripa St., St. Louis, MO 63125. (314) 544-0455.
Contact: Patricia Murphy, SSND
Contact the office nearest the area you wish to serve.
Mission Areas: Baltimore, Philadelphia, Midwest, Central America and other developing areas

Type of Service: education, health care, pastoral, social service, business
Term of Service: varies with sites: one month to one year with some option to renew
Basic Requirements: M/F single/ married w/o dependents; age varies (high school and up) Gospel motivated; respects/ accepts cultural differences; physical/psychological health; screening process; relates well in work/living; willingness to work in variety of situations.

SERVICE IN THE CITY
5440 S. Talman Ave., Chicago, IL 60632. (312) 737-2081
Contact: Sr. Mary Ellen Dow, SND
Type of Service: Work with poor, youth, homebound, homeless
Term of Service: 1 full week - summer
Basic Requirements: F; in good health; 16 or older.

SETON VOLUNTEER PROGRAM
Sisters of Charity, Seton House #2, Box 476, Convent Station, NJ 07961-0476. (201) 292-6761
Contact: Sr. Julie Scanlan, SC
Mission Areas: NJ, CT, MA
Type of Service: inner city schools, residences for the elderly, social services, health care ministries
Term of Service: 1 year (renewable), shorter terms negotiable
Basic Requirements: F; single; 20 and up.

SETON VOLUNTEER PROGRAM
De Paul Center, Mt. Thor Rd., Greensburg, PA 15601. (412) 836-0406, ext. 8
Contact: Sr. Edith Strong, Sisters of Charity of Seton Hill
Mission Areas: throughout U.S., wherever Sisters serve
Type of Service: education, health care, child care, tutoring, pastoral/ social services
Term of Service: 9 months to 1 year (shorter options also available)
Basic Requirements: F w/o dependents, 18 and up (short term); 20 and up (long term).

SIDE BY SIDE LAY VOLUNTEER PROGRAM
5625 Isleta Blvd., SW, Albuquerque, NM 87105. (505) 873-2059
Contact: Sr. Maria Orlandini
Mission Areas: New Mexico, Latin America, Mexico, Africa, Asia
Type of Service: pastoral ministry, health care, education, social work, community work
Term of Service: 18 months; 1 year; summer
Basic Requirements: M/F; single; Catholic.

SISTERS OF THE BLESSED SACRAMENT LAY VOLUNTEERS

1663 Bristol Pike, Bensalem, PA 19020-8502. (215) 244-9900; 639-1262
Contact: Sr. Patricia Suchalski, SBS
Mission Areas: St. Michaels on Navajo Reservation, AZ; Santa Fe, NM; Bensalem, PA
Type of Service: education, house staff, nurse or nurse's aide
Term of Service: 10 months to 1 year (renewable)
Basic Requirements: M/F; single/ married w/o dependents/widowed/ religious; 21 and over; Catholic.

SISTERS OF CHARITY OF CINCINNATI: ASSOCIATES IN VOLUNTEER MINISTRY

5900 Delphi Rd., Mt. St. Joseph, OH 45051. (513) 347-5473
Contact: Sr. Rita Hawk, SC
Mission Areas: Ohio, Kentucky, Texas, New Mexico, Colorado, Michigan and Florida
Type of Service: education, health care, pastoral ministry, social service
Term of Service: 10-12 months
Basic Requirements: M/F; single/ married; no dependents; 20 and older.

SISTERS OF THE DIVINE SAVIOR SALVATORIAN SUMMER SERVICE PROGRAM

4311 North 100 St., Milwaukee, WI 53222-1393. (414) 466-0810
Contact: Sr. Jenada Fanetti
Mission Area: Wisconsin
Type of Service: poverty relief services, elderly outreach, parish/ pastoral ministries
Term of Service: summer: extended weekend; 1 week
Basic Requirements: F; single; Catholic; interested in religious life; 18 and up.

S.M.A. LAY MISSIONARIES

256 North Manor Circle, Takoma Park, MD 20912. (301) 891-2037
Contact: Theresa Hicks, S.M.A.
Mission Areas: Liberia, Ghana, Cote d'Ivoire
Type of Service: education, health, development, agriculture, pastoral ministries, catechetics, social work, etc.
Term of Service: 8 months (Sept.-April) orientation/formation program + 2 years (minimum) (Looking for candidates who are open to longer term commitments.)
Basic Requirements: M/F; single or married w/o dependents; college degree; at least 2 years work experience; 23-50 years; Catholic.

SO OTHERS MIGHT EAT (S.O.M.E.)

71 O St., N.W., Washington, DC 20001. (202) 797-8806

Contact: Fr. John Adams
Mission Area: Washington, DC
Type of Service: health care, community work, office work, cook, house staff, social work, work with the poor, homeless, elderly, as well as housing and alcohol and drug addiction counselor, nurse, cook, maintenance, drivers
Term of Service: 1 year (renewable); 1 week to several months, summer
Basic Requirements: M/F; single/ married/widowed/disabled/religious; 20 and up.

SOCIETY OF OUR LADY OF THE MOST HOLY TRINITY

P.O. Box 152, Robstown, TX 78380-3502. (512) 387-2774; (512) 387-8090
Contacts: Rev. James H. Flanagan; Deacon Wayne Lickteig
Mission Areas: Throughout the U.S.; Belize; Guatemala; Thailand; the Philippines; Mexico, Haiti, New Guinea
Type of Service: catechetics, health care, community work, education, carpenter, mechanic, crafts
Term of Service: 2 years (renewable); lifetime; summer program
Basic Requirements: M/F; single/ married with or w/o dependents/ widowed/disabled; 18 and over; Catholic.

SOCIETY OF OUR MOTHER OF PEACE

Maria Fonte Solitude, P.O. Box 322, High Ridge, MO 63049. (314) 677-3235
Contact: Sister Mary Faith
Mission Areas: St. Louis (MO), Springfield (MO)
Type of Service: person-to-person evangelization within the black community; manual and domestic work at the monastery: cooking, maintenance, carpentry, plumbing, etc.
Term of Service: Negotiable/but at least 1 year for manual and domestic service/long term preferred for evangelization service
Basic Requirements: M/F; single/ married/divorced/separated (w/o dependents); 22 to 55; Catholic.

SOJOURNERS

1323 Girard St., NW, Washington, DC 20009. (202) 387-7000
Contact: Barbara Tamialis
Mission Area: Washington, DC
Type of Service: community work, office work
Term of Service: 1 month to 1 year
Basic Requirements: M/F; Christian; 21 to 75.

SPIRITAN ASSOCIATES

Laval House, Duquesne University, Pittsburgh, PA 15282. (412) 396-1666
Contact: Steve Pearson
Mission Area: Africa, US

Type of Service: education, administration, crafts, tradesman, agriculture, mechanic, pilot, administrator
Term of Service: 3 years
Basic Requirements: M/F; 22 or older; college education plus a few years of professional experience.

STARCROSS COMMUNITY

34500 Annapolis Rd., Annapolis, CA 95412. (707) 886-1919
Contact: Sr. Julie De Rossi
Mission Area: Sonoma County (CA)
Type of Service: homecare for AIDS infected children, office work, housework, farm, maintenance
Term of Service: 6 months to 1 year (renewable)
Basic Requirements: M/F; single/ married/divorced/separated/religious; 21 years and up.

THE PORT – A PLACE OF PRAYER AND HOPE

5058 S. Ashland, Chicago, IL 60609. (312) 778-5955
Contact: Rev. Augustin Milon, OFM
Mission Area: Chicago (inner city)
Type of Service: community work, poor, homeless ministry, family/ children ministry
Term of Service: 1 year (less if area resident)
Basic Requirements: M/F; single/ married/religious; 19 and up; Christian.

URSULINE COMPANIONS IN MISSION

College of New Rochelle, College Center, Rm. 155, New Rochelle, NY 10805. (914) 654-5270
Contact: Sr. Gayle Sims, OSU
Mission Areas: rural and urban NY; St. Louis, MO; Sanford, FL; Youngstown, OH; Cleveland, OH; Owensboro, KY; Louisville, KY; Appalachia, KY; Washington, DC; Zuni, NM; Gallup, NM; Farmington, NM; Cincinnati, OH; Paola, KS.
Type of Service: education, health care, child care, social work, pastoral ministries, youth ministry, poverty relief services, Native American ministry, ministry to the elderly, migrant ministry
Term of Service: academic and calendar year (renewable).
Basic Requirements: Christian men and women, single/married w/o dependents; 21 and up.

VIDA VOLUNTEERS

P.O. Box 984, Alamosa, CO 81101. (719) 589-5192
Contact: Therese O'Grady, osb
Mission Area: southern Colorado
Type of Service: community work, teachers, nurses, advocate
Term of Service: 1 year (renewable)
Basic Requirements: M/F; college degree; ecumenical; 21 and up.

VINCENTIAN SERVICE CORPS (VSC)

VSC: EAST St. John's University-SVH 102, Jamaica, NY 11439. (718) 990-6266

Contact: John D. McElynn, C.M., Director

VSC: CENTRAL 7800 Natural Bridge Rd., St. Louis, MO 63121. (314) 382-2800

Contact: Director

VSC: WEST 650 W. 23rd St., Los Angeles, CA 90007. (213) 741-0105

Contact: George Stevens, C.M., Director

Mission Areas: Urban and rural areas throughout the United States. Contact office nearest the area in which you choose to serve

Type of Service: Adult literacy teachers, advocacy workers, case workers for shelters and/or mentally ill, child care workers, community organizers, computer programmers, volunteer coordinators, crisis counselors, day care workers, fund raisers, health care professionals (RN, LPN, CNA, therapists), immigration/refugee counselors, legal aides, maintenance workers, nursing home assistants, outreach workers to the homebound elderly, parish ministers, pastoral care ministers, skilled laborers, social workers, teachers and teachers' aides (grade and middle schools), youth ministers.

Term of Service: 1 to 2 years (renewable).

Basic Requirements: M/F; single, married/widowed; 20 years and up; college degree or significant life/work experience; persons with disabilities possible; Christian; desire for challenge and ability to be flexible.

VOLUNTEER MISSIONARY MOVEMENT

5980 W. Loomis, Greendale, WI 53129. (414) 423-8660

Contacts: Mary Jo Runnoe, Phil Leonard

Mission Areas: Africa, Central America, central cities in U.S.

Type of Service: health care, agriculture, community work, education, labor, pastoral ministry, social work

Term of Service: 2 years

Basic Requirements: M/F; single/married/widowed; 23 and over; Christian commitment.

VOLUNTEER SERVICE COMMUNITY- BROTHERS OF THE SACRED HEART

800 Logee St., Woonsocket, RI 02895-5599. (401) 769-0313

Contact: Br. John Louis Collignon, SC,

Brothers of the Sacred Heart

Mission Area: New England

Type of Service: tutor, youth ministry, coach, parish religious education, serve disabled, elderly and homeless

Term of Service: Sept. to June

Basic Requirements: M; single; Catholic; 20 to 35.

VOLUNTEERS FOR EDUCATIONAL & SOCIAL SERVICES (VESS)

3001 S. Congress, Austin, TX 78704-6489. (512) 447-6144; 1-800-771-5677

Contact: Barbara Price

Mission Area: Texas

Type of Service: education, human services, parish, campus and youth ministry, immigrant/refugee work, health care, administrative work

Term of Service: 1 year (renewable)

Basic Requirements: 21 and over; most positions require bachelor's degree; appropriate life and work experience considered; Christian orientation.

VOLUNTEERS FOR TAU

2117 S. 33rd St., Omaha, NE 68105-3117. (402) 342-5570

Contact: Joyce Thompson, Coordinator

3545 N. Nora Ave., Chicago, IL 60634. (312) 685-0187

Contact: Sr. Rosemary Reier, SSSF, Director

Mission Areas: U.S. and Central America

Type of Service: catechetics/pastoral ministry, community work, education, health care, office work

Term of Service: 1 week to 1 year (renewable)

Basic Requirements: F; 18 years and up.

VOLUNTEERS IN ACTION

11999 Chalon Rd., Los Angeles, CA 90049-1524. (213) 272-8016, ext. 241

Contact: Director

Mission Areas: California, Arizona, Washington, Idaho

Type of Service: education, community work, health care, parish, prison ministry, religious education, social services, office work, work with elderly, other

Term of Service: 1 year (renewable)

Basic Requirements: F; single; Christian, 20 and older; at least two years of college or work experience.

WASHINGTON TEACHER SERVICE CORPS

Archdiocesan Pastoral Center, 5001 Eastern Ave., P.O. Box 29260, Washington, DC 20017. (301) 853-4569

Contact: Sr. Rose Mary Collins

Mission Area: Washington, DC

Type of Service: elementary, secondary education

Term of Service: 1 year minimum (renewable)

Basic Requirements: M/F; single; college education; Catholic.

WE CARE - IHM VOLUNTEER SERVICES

IHM Center-Marywood, Scranton, PA 18509. (717) 346-5411

Contact: Sr. Katherine Sugrue, IHM

Mission Areas: NY, NJ, PA, DE, MD, MS, NC, CT, WV, and Washington, DC

Type of Service: catechetics, community work, education, health care, office work, migrant ministry, inner city clinic, teen-age shelter, ministry to Native Americans, Hispanics, AIDS victims

Term of Service: 1-2 years; summer

Basic Requirements: F; 21 and older (18 for summer program).

XAVERIAN BROTHERS VOLUNTEER CORPS

10318B Baltimore National Pike, Ellicott City, MD 21042-2191. (410) 750-2850.

Contact: Br. Richard Angarola, CFX

Missions Areas: Baltimore, Bolivia

Type of Service: catechetics, education, health care

Term of Service: Baltimore-1 year; Bolivia-18 months.

Basic Requirements: M/F; college graduates; some Spanish proficiency (for Bolivia).

YOUTH SERVICE OPPORTUNITIES PROJECT (YSOP)

15 Rutherford Place, New York, NY 10003. (212) 598-0973

Contact: Jean Sommerfield

Mission Area: Metropolitan NY

Type of Service: community work, workcamps for high school and college students

Term of Service: Weekend, 1-4 weeks

Basic Requirements: M/F; nondenominational.

Secular Institutes

APOSTOLIC OBLATES
(For Women)
For information contact: Teresa Monaghen, 11002 N. 204th St., Elkhorn, NE 68022. (402) 289-2670; Rene Jarecki, 205 S. Pine Dr., Fullerton, CA 92633. (714) 956-1020; Angela DiPaolo, 730 E. 87th St., Brooklyn, NY 11236. (718) 649-0324.

CARITAS CHRISTI
(For Women)
For information contact: Caritas Christi, P.O. Box 5162, River Forest, IL 60305.

COMPANY OF ST. PAUL
(Lay People and Priests)
For information contact: Rev. Stuart Sandberg, 52 Davis Ave., White Plains, NY 10605. (914) 946-1019.

COMPANY OF ST. URSULA
(For Women)
For information contact: Juline A. Lamb, P.O. Box 101193, Ft. Worth, TX 76185. (817) 924-3955.

DIOCESAN LABORER PRIESTS
For information contact: Rev. Rutilo J. del Riego, 3706 15th St. N.E., Washington, DC 20017. (202) 832-4217.

DON BOSCO VOLUNTEERS
(For Women and Men)
For information contact: Rev. Paul P. Avallone, S.D.B., 202 Union Ave., Paterson, NJ 07502.

FR. KOLBE MISSIONARIES OF THE IMMACULATA
(For Women)
For information contact: Fr. Kolbe Missionaries, 531 E. Merced Ave., West Covina, CA 91790. (818) 917-0040.

FRANCISCAN MISSIONARIES OF JESUS CRUCIFIED
(For Men and Women. Persons with disabilities most welcome.)
For information contact: Louise D. Principe, FMJC, 400 Central Ave., Apt. 3D, Albany, NY 12206-2207 or Fr. Reginald J. Reddy, OFM, Siena College, Loudonville, NY 12211-1462.

HANDMAIDS OF DIVINE MERCY
(For Women)
For information contact: 2410 Hughes Ave., Bronx, NY 10458.

INSTITUTE OF THE HEART OF JESUS
(For Secular Priests and Lay People)
For information contact: Fr. Frank Mann, St. Rose Church, 601 Broadway, Chelsea, MD 20150. (617) 889-2774.

INSTITUTE OF SECULAR MISSIONARIES
(For Women)
For information contact: Evelyn Dilger, 2710 Ruberg, Cincinnati, OH 45211.

LAY MISSIONARIES OF THE PASSION
For information contact: 633 Main St., Dickson City, PA 18519.

LITTLE FRANCISCAN FAMILY
(For Women – U.S. and Canada)
For information contact: Julie Curley, 319 Main St., Cromwell, CT 06416. (203) 635-6384.

MISSION OF OUR LADY OF BETHANY
(For Women)
For information contact: P.O. Box 807, Boston, MA 02130. (617) 522-1961.

MISSIONARIES OF THE KINGSHIP OF CHRIST
(Composed of three institutes: one for women, one for men, one for priests)
For information on the men's group contact: Rev. Dominic Monti, O.F.M.; 10400 Lorain, Silver Springs, MD 10901; for information on the women's group contact: Rev. Geoffrey Bridges, O.F.M., 3215 Army St., San Francisco, CA 94110.

OBLATE MISSIONARIES OF MARY IMMACULATE
For information contact: Men: P.O. Box 303, Manville, RI 02838; Women: P.O. Box 764, Lowell, MA 01853.

OPUS SPIRITUS SANCTI
(For Priests, Sisters, Lay People)
For information contact: Arlene Loesche, Midwest Regional Coordinator, 1812 8 1/2 Ave. N., Ft. Dodge, IA 50501. (515) 955-8725.

PIUS X
(For Men)
For information contact: Lynchville Park, Goffstown, NH 03045. (603) 669-8614.

ST. FRANCIS DE SALES SECULAR INSTITUTE
(Composed of two groups: professed-women; associates-men and women)
For information contact: Joan Bereswill, 3503 Jean St., Fairfax, VA 22030. (703) 591-5196.

SECULAR INSTITUTE OF THE SCHOENSTATT SISTERS OF MARY
(For Women)
Star Route 1, Box 100, Rockport, TX 78382.

SERVITIUM CHRISTI
(For Women)
Secular Institute of the Blessed Sacrament. Origin and Spirituality: St. Peter Julian Eymard.
For information contact: Elaine Kozlowski, 1209 Greenwood Ave., Pueblo, CO 81003.

SOCIETY OF OUR LADY OF THE WAY
(For Women)
2339 N. Catalina St., Los Angeles, CA 90027.

TERESIAN INSTITUTE
For information contact: Poveda Center, 3400 S.W. 99th Ave., Miami, FL 33165. (305) 553-8567. Contact Person: A. Mandiola

VOLUNTAS DEI INSTITUTE
(For Priests and Lay People)
For information contact: Michael Craig, 4257 Tazewell Terrace, Burtonsville, MD 20866.